Oxford Custom Edition

Economics and Finance for Engineers

IEMS 326

Northwestern University

Containing material from:

Newnan: *Engineering Economic Analysis*
ISBN: 9780195335415

Luenberger: *Investment Sciences*
ISBN: 9780195108095

OXFORD
UNIVERSITY PRESS

UNIVERSITY PRESS

Oxford University Press, Inc., publishes works that further Oxford University's
objective of excellence in research, scholarship, and education.

Oxford New York
Auckland   Cape Town   Dar es Salaam   Hong Kong   Karachi
Kuala Lumpur   Madrid   Melbourne   Mexico City   Nairobi
New Delhi   Shanghai   Taipei   Toronto

With offices in
Argentina   Austria   Brazil   Chile   Czech Republic   France   Greece
Guatemala   Hungary   Italy   Japan Poland   Portugal   Singapore
South Korea   Switzerland   Thailand   Turkey   Ukraine   Vietnam

Copyright © 2009 by Oxford University Press, Inc.

Published by Oxford University Press, Inc.
198 Madison Avenue, New York, New York 10016
http://www.oup.com

Oxford is a registered trademark of Oxford University Press

ISBN 978-0-19-973498-6

Printed in the United States of America
on acid-free paper

1 INTRODUCTION

Traditionally, investment is defined as the current commitment of resources in order to achieve later benefits. If resources and benefits take the form of money, investment is the present commitment of money for the purpose of receiving (hopefully more) money later. In some cases, such as the purchase of a bank certificate of deposit, the amount of money to be obtained later is known exactly. However, in most situations the amount of money to be obtained later is uncertain.

There is also a broader viewpoint of investment—based on the idea of flows of expenditures and receipts spanning a period of time. From this viewpoint, the objective of investment is to tailor the pattern of these flows over time to be as desirable as possible. When expenditures and receipts are denominated in cash, the net receipts at any time period are termed **cash flow,** and the series of flows over several periods is termed a **cash flow stream.** The investment objective is that of tailoring this cash flow stream to be more desirable than it would be otherwise. For example, by taking out a loan, it may be possible to exchange a large negative cash flow next month for a series of smaller negative cash flows over several months, and this alternative cash flow stream may be preferred to the original one. Often future cash flows have a degree of uncertainty, and part of the design, or tailoring, of a cash flow stream may be concerned with controlling that uncertainty, perhaps reducing the level of risk. This broader definition of investment, as tailoring a pattern of cash flows, encompasses the wide assortment of financial activities more fully than the traditional view. It is this broader interpretation that guides the presentation of this book.

Investment science is the application of scientific tools to investments. The scientific tools used are primarily mathematical, but only a modest level of mathematics is required to understand the primary concepts discussed in this book. The purpose of this book is to convey both the principles of investment science and an understanding of how these principles can be used in practice to make calculations that lead to good investment decisions.

There is also an art to investment. Part of this art is knowing what to analyze and how to go about it. This part of the art can be enhanced by studying the material in this book. However, there is also an intuitive art of being able to evaluate an investment from an assortment of qualitative information, such as the personality characteristics of the people involved (the principals), whether a proposed new product will sell well, and so forth. This part of the art is not treated explicitly in this book, although the reader will gain some appreciation for just what this art entails.

1.1 CASH FLOWS

According to the broad interpretation, an investment is defined in terms of its resulting cash flow sequence—the amounts of money that will flow to and from an investor over time. Usually these cash flows (either positive or negative) occur at known specific dates, such as at the end of each quarter of a year or at the end of each year. The stream can then be described by listing the flow at each of these times. This is simplest if the flows are known deterministically, as in bank interest receipts or mortgage payments. In such cases the stream can be described by a series of numbers. For example, if the basic time period is taken as one year, one possible stream over a year, from beginning to end, is $(-1, 1.2)$, corresponding to an initial payment (the investment) of $1 at the beginning of the year and the receipt of $1.20 a year later. An investment over four years might be $(-1, .10, .10, .10, 1.10)$, where an initial investment of $1 leads to payment of $.10 at the end of each year for three years and then a final payment of $1.10. Note that for a span of one year, two cash flow numbers are specified—one at the beginning and one at the end. Likewise, the four-year example involves five cash flow numbers.

Cash flow streams can also be represented in diagram form, as illustrated in Figure 1.1. In such a figure a time axis is drawn and a cash flow at a particular time is indicated by a vertical line at that time, the length of the line being proportional to the magnitude of the flow.

If the magnitudes of some future cash flows are uncertain (as is frequently the case), a more complex representation of a cash flow stream must be employed. There are a few different techniques for doing this, and they are presented later in the book. But whether or not uncertainty is present, investments are described in terms of cash flow streams.

A diversity of investment issues can be stated in terms of cash flow streams, such as the following: Which of two cash flow streams is most preferable? How much would I be willing to pay to own a given stream? Are two streams together worth more to me than the sum of their individual values? If I can purchase a share of a stream, how much should I purchase? Given a collection of available cash flow streams, what is the most favorable combination of them?

Time

FIGURE 1.1   Cash flow stream. The cash flow stream of an investment can be represented by a diagram. In the example shown, the cash flows occur periodically. The first of these flows is negative, representing a cash outlay, and the subsequent flows are all positive.

Other more complex questions also arise. For example, sometimes the timing of all cash flows is not fixed, but can be influenced by the investor. If I purchase stock in a company, I have a negative cash flow initially, corresponding to my purchase payment; while I hold the stock, I perhaps receive dividends (relatively small positive cash flows) on a regular basis; finally, when I sell the stock, I obtain a major cash flow. However, the time of the last cash flow is not predetermined; I am free to choose it. Indeed, investments sometimes can be actively managed to influence both the amounts and the timing of all cash flows. For example, if I purchase a gold mine as an investment, I can decide how to mine it and thereby influence the cash flow every year. Determination of suitable management strategies is also part of investment science.

The view of investment science as the tailoring of cash flow streams gives the subject wide application. For individuals it applies to personal investment decisions, such as deciding on a home mortgage or planning for retirement. It also applies to business decisions, such as whether to invest in product development, whether to build a new manufacturing plant, and how to manage cash resources. Finally, it applies to government decisions, such as whether to build a dam or change the tax rate. Investment science guides us in the process of combining stocks, bonds, and other investment products into an overall package that has desirable properties. This process enhances total productivity by converting projects that in isolation may be too risky into members of attractive combinations.

1.2 INVESTMENTS AND MARKETS

At its root, investment analysis is a process of examining alternatives and deciding which alternative is most preferable. In this respect investment analysis is similar to the analysis of other decisions—operating a production facility, designing a building, planning a trip, or formulating an advertising campaign. Indeed, much of investment science relies on the same general tools used for analysis of these other decisions.

Investment problems differ from other decision problems in an important respect, however: most investments are carried out within the framework of a financial market, and these markets provide alternatives not found in other decision situations. This structure is what makes investment analysis unique and unusually powerful.

The Comparison Principle

Financial markets simplify decision making through a concept that we term the **comparison principle.** To introduce this principle, consider the following hypothetical situation.

Your uncle offers you a special investment. If you give him $100 now, he will repay you $110 in one year. His repayment is fully guaranteed by a trust fund of U.S. Treasury securities, and hence there is virtually no risk to the investment. Also, there is no moral or personal obligation to make this investment. You can either accept the offer or not. What should you do?

To analyze this situation, you would certainly note that the investment offers 10% interest, and you could compare this rate with the prevailing rate of interest that can be obtained elsewhere, say, at your local bank or from the U.S. Government through, for example, a Treasury bill. If the prevailing interest rate were only 7%, you would probably invest in this special offer by your uncle (assuming you have the cash to invest). If on the other hand the prevailing interest rate were 12%, you would surely decline the offer. From a pure investment viewpoint you can evaluate this opportunity very easily without engaging in deep reflection or mathematical analysis. If the investment offers a rate above normal, you accept; if it offers a rate below normal, you decline.

This analysis is an example of the comparison principle. You evaluate the investment by comparing it with other investments available in the financial market. The financial market provides a basis for comparison.

If, on the other hand, your uncle offers to sell you a family portrait whose value is largely sentimental, an outside comparison is not available. You must decide whether, to you, the portrait is worth his asking price.

Arbitrage

When two similar investment alternatives are both available in the market, conclusions stronger than the comparison principle hold. For example, consider (idealized) banks that offer to loan money or accept deposits at the same rate of interest. Suppose that the rate used at one bank for loans and deposits is 10% and at another bank the rate is 12%. You could go to the first bank and borrow, say, $10,000 at 10% and then deposit that $10,000 in the second bank at 12%. In one year you would earn 2% of $10,000, which is $200, without investing any cash of your own. This is a form of **arbitrage**—earning money without investing anything. Presumably, you could even make more money by running your scheme at a higher level. It should be clear that this kind of thing does not occur—at least not very often. The interest rates in the two banks would soon equalize.

The example of the two banks assumed that the interest rate for loans and the interest rate paid for deposits were equal within any one bank. Generally, of course, there is a difference in these rates. However, in markets of high volume, such as the markets for U.S. Treasury securities, the difference between the buying price and the selling price is small. Therefore two different securities with identical properties must have approximately the same price—otherwise there would be an arbitrage opportunity.

Often it is assumed, for purposes of analysis, that no arbitrage opportunity exists. This is the **no-arbitrage** assumption.

Ruling out the possibility of arbitrage is a simple idea, but it has profound consequences. We shall find that the principle of no arbitrage implies that pricing relations are linear, that stock prices must satisfy certain relations, and that the prices of derivative securities, such as options and futures, can be determined analytically.

This one principle, based on the existence of well-developed markets, permeates a good portion of modern investment science.

Dynamics

Another important feature of financial markets is that they are dynamic, in the sense that the same or similar financial instruments are traded on a continuing basis. This means that the future price of an asset is not regarded as a single number, but rather as a process moving in time and subject to uncertainty. An important part of the analysis of an investment situation is the characterization of this process.

There are a few standard frameworks that are used to represent price processes. These include binomial lattice models, difference equation models, and differential equation models, all of which are discussed in this text. Typically, a record of the past prices and other information are used to specify the parameters of such a model.

Because markets are dynamic, investment is itself dynamic—the value of an investment changes with time, and the composition of good portfolios may change. Once this dynamic character is understood and formalized, it is possible to structure investments to take advantage of their dynamic nature so that the overall portfolio value increases rapidly.

Risk Aversion

Another principle of investment science is **risk aversion.** Suppose two possible investments have the same cost, and both are expected to return the same amount (somewhat greater than the initial cost), where the term *expected* is defined in a probabilistic sense (explained in Chapter 6). However, the return is certain for one of these investments and uncertain for the other. Individuals seeking investment rather than outright speculation will elect the first (certain) alternative over the second (risky) alternative. This is the risk aversion principle.

Another way to state this principle is in terms of market rates of return. Suppose one investment will pay a fixed return with certainty—say 10%—as obtained perhaps from a government-guaranteed bank certificate of deposit. A second investment, say the stock in a corporation, has an uncertain return. Then the expected rate of return on that stock must be greater than 10%; otherwise investors will not purchase the stock. In general, we accept more risk only if we expect to get greater expected (or average) return.

This risk aversion principle can be formalized (and made analytical) in a few different ways, which are discussed in later chapters. Once a formalism is established, the risk aversion principle can be used to help analyze many investment alternatives.

One way that the risk aversion principle is formalized is through **mean–variance analysis.** In this approach, the uncertainty of the return on an asset is characterized by just two quantities: the mean value of the return and the variance of the return. The risk aversion principle then says that if several investment opportunities have the same mean but different variances, a rational (risk-averse) investor will select the one that has the smallest variance.

This mean–variance method of formalizing risk is the basis for the most well-known method of quantitative portfolio analysis, which was pioneered by Harry Markowitz (who won the Nobel prize in economics for his work). This approach leads to a comprehensive theory of investment and is widely considered to be the foundation for modern portfolio theory. We discuss this important theory in Chapter 6.

A more general way to formalize the risk aversion principle is through the introduction of individual **utility functions.** This approach is presented in Chapter 9.

Later, in Chapter 15, we find that risk aversion takes on a new character when investments are made repeatedly over time. In fact, short-term variance will be found to be *good,* not bad. This is one of the surprising conclusions of the comprehensive view of investment represented by investment science.

1.3 TYPICAL INVESTMENT PROBLEMS

Every investment problem has unique features, but many fit into a few broad categories or types. We briefly outline some of the most important problem types here. Fuller descriptions of these general types and more specific examples appear in the relevant chapters.

Pricing

Let us go back to our very first example of an investment situation, the first offer from your uncle, but now let us turn it around. Imagine that there is an investment opportunity that will pay exactly $110 at the end of one year. We ask: How much is this investment worth today? In other words, what is the appropriate price of this investment, given the overall financial environment?

If the current interest rate for one-year investments is 10%, then this investment should have a price of exactly $100. In that case, the $110 paid at the end of the year would correspond to a rate of return of 10%. If the current interest rate for one-year investments is less than 10%, then the price of this investment would be somewhat greater than $100. In general, if the interest rate is r (expressed as a decimal, such as $r = .10$), then the price of an investment that pays X after one year should be $X/(1 + r)$.

We determined the price by a simple application of the comparison principle. This investment can be directly compared with one of investing money in a one-year certificate of deposit (or one-year Treasury bill), and hence it must bear the same effective interest rate.

This interest rate example is a simple example of the general pricing problem: Given an investment with known payoff characteristics (which may be random), what is the reasonable price; or, equivalently, what price is consistent with the other securities that are available? We shall encounter this problem in many contexts. For example, early in our study we shall determine the appropriate price of a bond. Later we shall compute the appropriate price of a share of stock with random return characteristics. Still later we shall compute suitable prices of more complicated securities, such as futures and options. Indeed, the pricing problem is one of the basic problems of modern investment science and has obvious practical applications.

As in the simple interest rate example, the pricing problem is usually solved by use of the comparison principle. In most instances, however, the application of that principle is not as simple and obvious as in this example. Clever arguments have been devised to show how a complex investment can be separated into parts, each of which can be compared with other investments whose prices are known. Nevertheless, whether by a simple or a complex argument, comparison is the basis for the solution of many pricing problems.

Hedging

Hedging is the process of reducing the financial risks that either arise in the course of normal business operations or are associated with investments. Hedging is one of the most important uses of financial markets, and is an essential part of modern industrial activity. One form of hedging is **insurance** where, by paying a fixed amount (a **premium**), you can protect yourself against certain specified possible losses—such as losses due to fire, theft, or even adverse price changes—by arranging to be paid compensation for the losses you incur. More general hedging can arise in the following way. Imagine a large bakery. This bakery will purchase flour (made from wheat) and other ingredients and transform these ingredients into baked goods, such as bread. Suppose the bakery wins a contract to supply a large quantity of bread to another company over the next year at a fixed price. The bakery is happy to win the contract, but now faces risk with respect to flour prices. The bakery will not immediately purchase all the flour needed to satisfy the contract, but will instead purchase flour as needed during the year. Therefore, if the price of flour should increase part way during the year, the bakery will be forced to pay more to satisfy the needs of the contract and, hence, will have a lower profit. In a sense the bakery is at the mercy of the flour market. If the flour price goes up, the bakery will make less profit, perhaps even losing money on the contract. If the flour price goes down, the bakery will make even more money than anticipated.

The bakery is in the baking business, not in the flour speculation business. It wants to eliminate the risk associated with flour costs and concentrate on baking. It can do this by obtaining an appropriate number of wheat futures contracts in the futures market. Such a contract has small initial cash outlay and at a set future date gives a profit (or loss) equal to the amount that wheat prices have changed since entering the contract. The price of flour is closely tied to the price of wheat, so if the price of flour should go up, the value of a wheat futures contract will go up by a somewhat comparable amount. Hence the net effect to the bakery—the profit from the wheat futures contracts together with the change in the cost of flour—is nearly zero.

There are many other examples of business risks that can be reduced by hedging. And there are many ways that hedging can be carried out: through futures contracts, options, and other special arrangements. Indeed, the major use, by far, of these financial instruments is for hedging—not for speculation.

Pure Investment

Pure investment refers to the objective of obtaining increased future return for present allocation of capital. This is the motivation underlying most individual investments in the stock market, for example. The investment problem arising from this motivation is referred to as the **portfolio selection problem,** since the real issue is to determine where to invest available capital.

Most approaches to the pure investment problem rely on the risk aversion principle, for in this problem one must carefully assess one's preferences, deciding how to balance risk and expected reward. There is not a unique solution. Judgment and taste are important, which is evidenced by the vast amount of literature and advice directed each year to helping individuals find solutions to this problem.

The pure investment problem also characterizes the activities of a profit-seeking firm which, after all, takes existing capital and transforms it, through investment—in equipment, people, and operations—into profit. Hence the methods developed for analyzing pure investment problems can be used to analyze potential projects within firms, the overall financial structure of a firm, and even mergers of firms.

Other Problems

Investment problems do not always take the special shapes outlined in the preceding categories. A hedging problem may contain an element of pure investment, and conversely an investment may be tempered with a degree of hedging. Fortunately, the same principles of analysis are applicable to such combinations.

One type of problem that occurs frequently is a combined consumption–investment problem. For example, a married couple at retirement, living off the income from their investments, will most likely invest differently than a young couple investing for growth of capital. The requirement for income changes the nature of the investment problem. Likewise, the management of an endowment for a public enterprise, such as a university must consider growth objectives as well as consumptionlike objectives associated with the current operations of the enterprise.

We shall also find that the framework of an investment problem is shaped by the formal methods used to treat it. Once we have logical methods for representing investment issues, new problems suggest themselves. As we progress through the book we shall uncover additional problems and obtain a deeper appreciation for the simple outlines given here.

1.4 ORGANIZATION OF THE BOOK

The organization of this book reflects the notion that investment science is the study of how to tailor cash flow streams. Indeed, the cash flow viewpoint leads to a natural partition of the subject into four main parts, as follows.

Deterministic Cash Flow Streams

The simplest cash flow streams are those that are deterministic (that is, not random, but definite). The first part of the book treats these. Such cash flows can be represented by sequences such as $(-1, 0, 3)$, as discussed earlier. Investments of this type, either with one or with several periods, are analyzed mainly with various concepts of interest rate. Accordingly, interest rate theory is emphasized in this first part of the book. This theory provides a basis for a fairly deep understanding of investment and a framework for addressing a wide variety of important and interesting problems.

Single-Period Random Cash Flow Streams

The second level of complexity in cash flow streams is associated with streams having only a single period, with beginning and ending flows, but with the magnitude of the second flow being uncertain. Such a situation occurs when a stock is purchased at the beginning of the year and sold at the end of the year. The amount received at the end of the year is not known in advance and, hence, must be considered uncertain. This level of complexity captures the essence of many investment situations.

In order to analyze cash flows of this kind, one must have a formal description of **uncertain returns.** There are several such descriptions (all based on probability theory), and we shall study the main ones, the simplest being the **mean–variance** description. One must also have a formal description of how individuals assess uncertain returns. We shall consider such assessment methods, starting with mean–variance analysis. These single-period uncertain cash flow situations are the subject of the second part of the book.

Derivative Assets

The third level of complexity in cash flow streams involves streams that have random flows at each of several time points, but where the asset producing a stream is functionally related to another asset whose price characteristics are known.

An asset whose cash flow values depend functionally on another asset is termed a **derivative asset.** A good example is a stock option. To describe such an option, suppose that I own 100 shares of stock in company A. This asset, the 100 shares, is a **basic asset.** Now suppose that I have granted you the right (but not the obligation) to buy, at say $54 per share, all 100 of my shares in three months. This right is a call option on 100 shares of stock in company A. This option is an asset; it has value, and that value may change with time. It is, however, a derivative of the stock of company A because the value of the option depends on the price of the stock. If the stock price goes up, the option value also goes up. Other derivative assets include futures contracts, other kinds of options, and various other financial contracts. One example seen by many home buyers is the adjustable-rate mortgage, which periodically adjusts interest payments according to an interest rate index. Such a mortgage is a derivative of the securities that determine the interest rate index.

The third part of the book is devoted to these derivative assets. Analysis of these assets is often simpler than that for assets with general multiperiod uncertain cash flows because properties of a derivative can be traced back to the underlying basic asset. The study of derivative assets, however, is an important and lively aspect of investment science, one for which strong theoretical results can be derived and important numerical quantities, such as implied prices, can be obtained.

General Cash Flow Streams

Finally, the fourth part of the book is devoted to cash flow streams with uncertain cash flows at many different times—flows that are not functionally related to other assets. As can be expected, this final level of complexity is the most difficult part of the subject, but also the one that is the most important. The cash flow streams encountered in most investments have this general form.

The methods of this part of the book build on those of earlier parts, but new concepts are added. The fact that the mix of investments—the portfolio structure—can be changed as time progresses, depending on what has happened to that point, leads to new phenomena and new opportunities. For example, the growth rate of a portfolio can be enhanced by employing suitable reinvestment strategies. This part of the book represents some of the newest aspects of the field.

Investment science is a practical science; and because its main core is built on a few simple principles, it can be easily learned and fruitfully applied to interesting and important problems. It is also an evolving science, which is expanding rapidly. Perhaps the reader, armed with a basic understanding of the field, will contribute to this evolution through either theory or application.

PART I

DETERMINISTIC CASH FLOW STREAMS

2 THE BASIC THEORY OF INTEREST

Interest is frequently called *the time value of money,* and the next few chapters explore the structure and implications of this value. In this first chapter on the subject, we outline the basic elements of interest rate theory, showing that the theory can be translated into analytic form and thus used as a basis for making intelligent investment decisions.

2.1 PRINCIPAL AND INTEREST

The basic idea of interest is quite familiar. If you invest $1.00 in a bank account that pays 8% interest per year, then at the end of 1 year you will have in your account the **principal** (your original amount) of $1.00 plus **interest** of $.08 for a total of $1.08. If you invest a larger amount, say A dollars, then at the end of the year your account will have grown to $A \times 1.08$ dollars. In general, if the interest rate is r, expressed as a decimal, then your initial investment would be multiplied by $(1 + r)$ after 1 year.

Simple Interest

Under a **simple interest** rule, money invested for a period different from 1 year accumulates interest proportional to the total time of the investment. So after 2 years, the total interest due is $2r$ times the original investment, and so forth. In other words, the investment produces interest equal to r times the original investment every year. Usually partial years are treated in a proportional manner; that is, after a fraction f of 1 year, interest of rf times the original investment is earned.

The general rule for simple interest is that if an amount A is left in an account at simple interest r, the total value after n years is

$$V = (1 + rn)A.$$

If the proportional rule holds for fractional years, then after any time t (measured in years), the account value is

$$V = (1 + rt)A.$$

The account grows **linearly** with time. As shown in the preceding formula, the account value at any time is just the sum of the original amount (the principal) and the accumulated interest, which is proportional to time.

Compound Interest

Most bank accounts and loans employ some form of compounding—producing compound interest. Again, consider an account that pays interest at a rate of r per year. If interest is compounded yearly, then after 1 year, the first year's interest is added to the original principal to define a larger principal base for the second year. Thus during the second year, the account earns *interest on interest*. This is the compounding effect, which is continued year after year.

Under yearly compounding, money left in an account is multiplied by $(1 + r)$ after 1 year. After the second year, it grows by another factor of $(1 + r)$ to $(1 + r)^2$. After n years, such an account will grow to $(1 + r)^n$ times its original value, and this is the analytic expression for the account growth under **compound interest.** This expression is said to exhibit **geometric growth** because of its nth-power form.

As n increases, the growth due to compounding can be substantial. For example, Figure 2.1 shows a graph of a \$100 investment over time when it earns 10% interest under simple and compound interest rules. The figure shows the characteristic shapes of linear growth for simple interest and of accelerated upward growth for compound interest. Note that under compounding, the value doubles in about 7 years.

There is a cute little rule that can be used to estimate the effect of interest compounding.

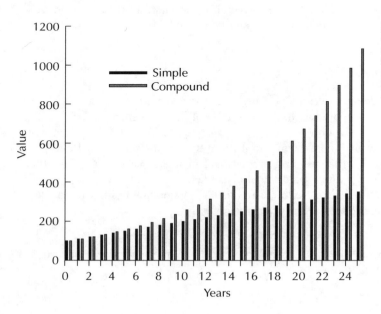

FIGURE 2.1 Simple and compound interest. Simple interest leads to linear growth over time, whereas compound interest leads to an accelerated increase defined by geometric growth. The figure shows both cases for an interest rate of 10%.

The seven–ten rule   *Money invested at 7% per year doubles in approximately 10 years. Also, money invested at 10% per year doubles in approximately 7 years.*

(More exactly, at 7% and 10 years, an account increases by a factor of 1.97, whereas at 10% and 7 years it increases by a factor of 1.95.) The rule can be generalized, and slightly improved, to state that, for interest rates less than about 20%, the doubling time is approximately $72/i$, where i is the interest rate expressed as a percentage (that is, 10% interest corresponds to $i = 10$). (See Exercise 2.)

Compounding at Various Intervals

In the preceding discussion, interest was calculated at the end of each year and paid to the account at that time. Most banks now calculate and pay interest more frequently—quarterly, monthly, or in some cases daily. This more frequent compounding raises the effective yearly rate. In this situation, it is traditional to still quote the interest rate on a yearly basis, but then apply the appropriate proportion of that interest rate over each compounding period. For example, consider quarterly compounding. Quarterly compounding at an interest rate of r per year means that an interest rate of $r/4$ is applied every quarter. Hence money left in the bank for 1 quarter will grow by a factor of $1 + (r/4)$ during that quarter. If the money is left in for another quarter, then that new amount will grow by another factor of $1 + (r/4)$. After 1 year the account will have grown by the compound factor of $[1 + (r/4)]^4$. For any $r > 0$, it holds that $[1 + (r/4)]^4 > 1 + r$. Hence at the same annual rate, the amount in the bank account after 4 quarters of compounding is greater than the amount after 1 year without compounding.

The effect of compounding on yearly growth is highlighted by stating an **effective interest rate,** which is the equivalent yearly interest rate that would produce the same result after 1 year without compounding. For example, an annual rate of 8% compounded quarterly will produce an increase of $(1.02)^4 = 1.0824$; hence the effective interest rate is 8.24%. The basic yearly rate (8% in this example) is termed the **nominal rate.**

Compounding can be carried out with any frequency. The general method is that a year is divided into a fixed number of equally spaced periods—say m periods. (In the case of monthly compounding the periods are not quite equal, but we shall ignore that here and regard monthly compounding as simply setting $m = 12$.) The interest rate for each of the m periods is thus r/m, where r is the nominal annual rate. The account grows by $1 + (r/m)$ during 1 period. After k periods, the growth is $[1 + (r/m)]^k$, and hence after a full year of m periods it is $[1 + (r/m)]^m$. The effective interest rate is the number r' that satisfies $1 + r' = [1 + (r/m)]^m$.

Continuous Compounding

We can imagine dividing the year into smaller and smaller periods, and thereby apply compounding monthly, weekly, daily, or even every minute or second. This leads

TABLE 2.1
Continuous Compounding

	Interest rate (%)							
Nominal	1.00	5.00	10.00	20.00	30.00	50.00	75.00	100.00
Effective	1.01	5.13	10.52	22.14	34.99	64.87	111.70	171.83

The nominal interest rates in the top row correspond, under continuous compounding, to the effective rates shown in the second row. The increase due to compounding is quite dramatic at large nominal rates.

to the idea of continuous compounding. We can determine the effect of continuous compounding by considering the limit of ordinary compounding as the number m of periods in a year goes to infinity. To determine the yearly effect of this continuous compounding we use the fact that

$$\lim_{m \to \infty} [1 + (r/m)]^m = e^r$$

where $e = 2.7818...$ is the base of the natural logarithm. The effective rate of interest r' is the value satisfying $1 + r' = e^r$. If the nominal interest rate is 8% per year, then with continuous compounding the growth would be $e^{.08} = 1.0833$, and hence the effective interest rate is 8.33%. (Recall that quarterly compounding produces an effective rate of 8.24%.) Table 2.1 shows the effect of continuous compounding for various nominal rates. Note that as the nominal rate increases, the compounding effect becomes more dramatic.

We can also calculate how much an account will have grown after any arbitrary length of time. We denote time by the variable t, measured in years. Thus $t = 1$ corresponds to 1 year, and $t = .25$ corresponds to 3 months. Select a time t and divide the year into a (large) number m of small periods, each of length $1/m$. Then $t \simeq k/m$ for some k, meaning that k periods approximately coincides with the time t. If m is very large, this approximation can be made very accurate. Therefore $k \approx mt$. Using the general formula for compounding, we know that the growth factor for k periods is

$$[1 + (r/m)]^k = [1 + (r/m)]^{mt} = \left\{ [1 + (r/m)]^m \right\}^t \to e^{rt}$$

where that last expression is valid in the limit as m goes to infinity, corresponding to continuous compounding. Hence continuous compounding leads to the familiar **exponential growth** curve. Such a curve is shown in Figure 2.2 for a 10% nominal interest rate.

Debt

We have examined how a single investment (say a bank deposit) grows over time due to interest compounding. It should be clear that exactly the same thing happens to debt. If I *borrow* money from the bank at an interest rate r and make no payments to the bank, then my debt increases according to the same formulas. Specifically, if my debt is compounded monthly, then after k months my debt will have grown by a factor of $[1 + (r/12)]^k$.

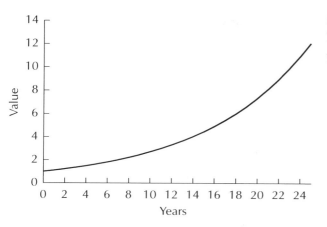

FIGURE 2.2 Exponential growth curve; continuous compound growth. Under continuous compounding at 10%, the value of $1 doubles in about 7 years. In 20 years it grows by a factor of about 8.

Money Markets

Although we have treated interest as a given known value, in reality there are many different rates each day. Different rates apply to different circumstances, different user classes, and different periods. Most rates are established by the forces of supply and demand in broad markets to which they apply. These rates are published widely; a sampling for one day is shown in Table 2.2. Many of these market rates are discussed

TABLE 2.2
Market Interest Rates

Interest rates (August 9, 1995)	
U.S. Treasury bills and notes	
3-month bill	5.39
6-month bill	5.39
1-year bill	5.36
3-year note (% yield)	6.05
10-year note (% yield)	6.49
30-year bond (% yield)	6.92
Fed funds rate	5.6875
Discount rate	5.26
Prime rate	8.75
Commercial paper	5.84
Certificates of deposit	
1 month	5.17
2 months	5.24
1 year	5.28
Banker's acceptances (30 days)	5.68
London late Eurodollars (1 month)	5.75
London Interbank offered rate (1 month)	5.88
Federal Home Loan Mortgage Corp. (Freddie Mae) (30 years)	7.94

Many different rates apply on any given day. This is a sampling.

more fully in Chapters 3 and 4. Not all interest rates are broad market rates. There may be private rates negotiated by two private parties. Or in the context of a firm, special rates may be established for internal transactions or for the purpose of evaluating projects, as discussed later in this chapter.

2.2 PRESENT VALUE

The theme of the previous section is that money invested today leads to increased value in the future as a result of interest. The formulas of the previous section show how to determine this future value.

That whole set of concepts and formulas can be reversed in time to calculate the value that should be assigned now, in the present, to money that is to be received at a later time. This reversal is the essence of the extremely important concept of **present value.**

To introduce this concept, consider two situations: (1) you will receive $110 in 1 year, (2) you receive $100 now and deposit it in a bank account for 1 year at 10% interest. Clearly these situations are identical after 1 year—you will receive $110. We can restate this equivalence by saying that $110 received in 1 year is equivalent to the receipt of $100 now when the interest rate is 10%. Or we say that the $110 to be received in 1 year has a **present value** of $100. In general, $1 to be received a year in the future has a present value of $1/(1 + r)$, where r is the interest rate.

A similar transformation applies to future obligations such as the repayment of debt. Suppose that, for some reason, you have an obligation to pay someone $100 in exactly 1 year. This obligation can be regarded as a negative cash flow that occurs at the end of the year. To calculate the present value of this obligation, you determine how much money you would need *now* in order to cover the obligation. This is easy to determine. If the current yearly interest rate is r, you need $100/(1 + r)$. If that amount of money is deposited in the bank now, it will grow to $100 at the end of the year. You can then fully meet the obligation. The present value of the obligation is therefore $100/(1 + r)$.

The process of evaluating future obligations as an equivalent present value is alternatively referred to as **discounting.** The present value of a future monetary amount is less than the face value of that amount, so the future value must be discounted to obtain the present value. The factor by which the future value must be discounted is called the **discount factor.** The 1-year discount factor is $d_1 = 1/(1 + r)$, where r is the 1-year interest rate. So if an amount A is to be received in 1 year, the present value is the discounted amount $d_1 A$.

The formula for present value depends on the interest rate that is available from a bank or other source. If that source quotes rates with compounding, then such a compound interest rate should be used in the calculation of present value. As an example, suppose that the annual interest rate r is compounded at the end of each of m equal periods each year; and suppose that a cash payment of amount A will be received at the end of the kth period. Then the appropriate discount factor is

$$d_k = \frac{1}{[1 + (r/m)]^k} \; .$$

The present value of a payment of A to be received k periods in the future is $d_k A$.

2.3 PRESENT AND FUTURE VALUES OF STREAMS

The previous section studied the impact of interest on a single cash deposit or loan; that is, on a single cash flow. We now extend that discussion to the case where cash flows occur at several time periods, and hence constitute a cash flow stream or sequence. First we require a new concept.

The Ideal Bank

When discussing cash flow streams, it is useful to define the notion of an **ideal bank.** An ideal bank applies the same rate of interest to both deposits and loans, and it has no service charges or transactions fees. Its interest rate applies equally to any size of principal, from 1 cent (or fraction thereof) to $1 million (or even more). Furthermore, separate transactions in an account are completely additive in their effect on future balances.

Note that the definition of an ideal bank does *not* imply that interest rates for all transactions are identical. For example, a 2-year certificate of deposit (CD) might offer a higher rate than a 1-year CD. However, the 2-year CD must offer the same rate as a loan that is payable in 2 years.

If an ideal bank has an interest rate that is independent of the length of time for which it applies, and that interest is compounded according to normal rules, it is said to be a **constant ideal bank.** In the rest of this chapter, we always assume that interest rates are indeed constant.

The constant ideal bank is the reference point used to describe the outside financial market—the public market for money.

Future Value

Now we return to the study of cash flow streams. Let us decide on a fixed time cycle for compounding (for example, yearly) and let a period be the length of this cycle. We assume that cash flows occur at the end of each period (although some flows might be zero). We shall take each cash flow and deposit it in a constant ideal bank as it arrives. (If the flow is negative, we cover it by taking out a loan.) Under the terms of a constant ideal bank, the final balance in our account can be found by combining the results of the individual flows. Explicitly, consider the cash flow stream $(x_0, x_1, \ldots, x_n)$. At the end of n periods the initial cash flow x_0 will have grown to $x_0(1 + r)^n$, where r is the interest rate *per period* (which is the yearly rate divided by the number of periods per year). The next cash flow, x_1, received after the first period, will at the final time have been in the account for only $n-1$ periods, and hence it will have a value of $x_1(1+r)^{n-1}$. Likewise, the next flow x_2 will collect interest during $n-2$ periods and have value $x_2(1+r)^{n-2}$. The final flow x_n will not collect any interest, so will remain x_n. The total value at the end of n periods is therefore $FV = x_0(1+r)^n + x_1(1+r)^{n-1} + \cdots + x_n$. To summarize:

Future value of a stream   *Given a cash flow stream $(x_0, x_1, \ldots, x_n)$ and interest rate r each period, the future value of the stream is*

$$FV = x_0(1+r)^n + x_1(1+r)^{n-1} + \cdots + x_n.$$

Example 2.1 (A short stream)   Consider the cash flow stream $(-2, 1, 1, 1)$ when the periods are years and the interest rate is 10%. The future value is

$$FV = -2 \times (1.1)^3 + 1 \times (1.1)^2 + 1 \times 1.1 + 1 = .648. \tag{2.1}$$

This formula for future value always uses the interest rate per period and assumes that interest rates are compounded each period.

Present Value

The present value of a general cash flow stream—like the future value—can also be calculated by considering each flow element separately. Again consider the stream $(x_0, x_1, \ldots, x_n)$. The present value of the first element x_0 is just that value itself since no discounting is necessary. The present value of the flow x_1 is $x_1/(1+r)$, because that flow must be discounted by one period. (Again the interest rate r is the per-period rate.) Continuing in this way, we find that the present value of the entire stream is $PV = x_0 + x_1/(1+r) + x_2/(1+r)^2 + \cdots + x_n/(1+r)^n$. We summarize this important result as follows.

Present value of a stream   *Given a cash flow stream $(x_0, x_1, \ldots, x_n)$ and an interest rate r per period, the present value of this cash flow stream is*

$$PV = x_0 + \frac{x_1}{1+r} + \frac{x_2}{(1+r)^2} + \cdots + \frac{x_n}{(1+r)^n}. \tag{2.2}$$

Example 2.2   Again consider the cash flow stream $(-2, 1, 1, 1)$. Using an interest rate of 10% we have

$$PV = -2 + \frac{1}{1.1} + \frac{1}{(1.1)^2} + \frac{1}{(1.1)^3} = .487.$$

The present value of a cash flow stream can be regarded as the present payment amount that is equivalent to the entire stream. Thus we can think of the entire stream as being replaced by a single flow at the initial time.

There is another way to interpret the formula for present value that is based on transforming the formula for future value. Future value is the amount of future payment that is equivalent to the entire stream. We can think of the stream as being transformed into that single cash flow at period n. The present value of this single equivalent flow is obtained by discounting it by $(1 + r)^n$. That is, the present value and the future value are related by

$$PV = \frac{FV}{(1 + r)^n}.$$

In the previous examples for the cash flow stream $(-2, 1, 1, 1)$ we have $.487 = PV = FV/(1.1)^3 = .648/1.331 = .487$.

Frequent and Continuous Compounding

Suppose that r is the nominal annual interest rate and interest is compounded at m equally spaced periods per year. Suppose that cash flows occur initially and at the end of each period for a total of n periods, forming a stream $(x_0, x_1, \ldots, x_n)$. Then according to the preceding we have

$$PV = \sum_{k=0}^{n} \frac{x_k}{[1 + (r/m)]^k}.$$

Suppose now that the nominal interest rate r is compounded continuously and cash flows occur at times $t_0, t_1, \ldots, t_n$. (We have $t_k = k/m$ for the stream in the previous paragraph; but the more general situation is allowed here.) We denote the cash flow at time t_k by $x(t_k)$. In that case,

$$PV = \sum_{k=0}^{n} x(t_k)e^{-rt_k}.$$

This is the continuous compounding formula for present value.

Present Value and an Ideal Bank

We know that an ideal bank can be used to change the pattern of a cash flow stream. For example, a 10% bank can change the stream $(1, 0, 0)$ into the stream $(0, 0, 1.21)$ by receiving a deposit of $1 now and paying principal and interest of $1.21 in 2 years. The bank can also work in a reverse fashion and transform the second stream into the first by issuing a loan for $1 now.

In general, if an ideal bank can transform the stream $(x_0, x_1, \ldots, x_n)$ into the stream $(y_0, y_1, \ldots, y_n)$, it can also transform in the reverse direction. Two streams that can be transformed into each other are said to be **equivalent streams.**

How can we tell whether two given streams are equivalent? The answer to this is the main theorem on present value.

Main theorem on present value *The cash flow streams* $\mathbf{x} = (x_0, x_1, \ldots, x_n)$ *and* $\mathbf{y} = (y_0, y_1, \ldots, y_n)$ *are equivalent for a constant ideal bank with interest rate r if and only if the present values of the two streams, evaluated at the bank's interest rate, are equal.*

Proof: Let $v_\mathbf{x}$ and $v_\mathbf{y}$ be the present values of the $\mathbf{x}$ and $\mathbf{y}$ streams, respectively. Then the $\mathbf{x}$ stream is equivalent to the stream $(v_\mathbf{x}, 0, 0, \ldots, 0)$ and the $\mathbf{y}$ stream is equivalent to the stream $(v_\mathbf{y}, 0, 0, \ldots, 0)$.

It is clear that these two streams are equivalent if and only if $v_\mathbf{x} = v_\mathbf{y}$. Hence the original streams are equivalent if and only if $v_\mathbf{x} = v_\mathbf{y}$. ∎

This result is important because it implies that present value is the only number needed to characterize a cash flow stream when an ideal bank is available. The stream can be transformed in a variety of ways by the bank, but the present value remains the same. So if someone offers you a cash flow stream, you only need to evaluate its corresponding present value, because you can then use the bank to tailor the stream with that present value to any shape you desire.

2.4 INTERNAL RATE OF RETURN

Internal rate of return is another important concept of cash flow analysis. It pertains specifically to the entire cash flow stream associated with an investment, not to a partial stream such as a cash flow at a single period. The streams to which this concept is applied typically have both negative and positive elements: the negative flows correspond to the payments that must be made; the positive flows to payments received. A simple example is the process of investing in a certificate of deposit for a fixed period of 1 year. Here there are two cash flow elements: the initial deposit or payment (a negative flow) and the final redemption (a positive flow).

Given a cash flow stream $(x_0, x_1, \ldots, x_n)$ associated with an investment, we write the present value formula

$$\text{PV} = \sum_{k=0}^{n} \frac{x_k}{(1+r)^k}.$$

If the investment that corresponds to this stream is constructed from a series of deposits and withdrawals from a constant ideal bank at interest rate r, then from the main theorem on present value of the previous section, PV would be zero. The idea behind internal rate of return is to turn the procedure around. Given a cash flow stream, we write the expression for present value and then find the value of r that renders this present value equal to zero. That value is called the internal rate of return because it is the interest rate implied by the internal structure of the cash flow stream. The idea can be applied to any series of cash flows.

The preliminary formal definition of the internal rate of return (IRR) is as follows:

Internal rate of return   *Let* $(x_0, x_1, x_2, \ldots, x_n)$ *be a cash flow stream. Then the internal rate of return of this stream is a number r satisfying the equation*

$$0 = x_0 + \frac{x_1}{1+r} + \frac{x_2}{(1+r)^2} + \cdots + \frac{x_n}{(1+r)^n}. \tag{2.3}$$

Equivalently, it is a number r satisfying $1/(1+r) = c$ [that is, $r = (1/c) - 1$], where c satisfies the polynomial equation

$$0 = x_0 + x_1 c + x_2 c^2 + \cdots + x_n c^n. \tag{2.4}$$

We call this a preliminary definition because there may be ambiguity in the solution of the polynomial equation of degree n. We discuss this point shortly. First, however, let us illustrate the computation of the internal rate of return.

Example 2.3 (The old stream)   Consider again the cash flow sequence $(-2, 1, 1, 1)$ discussed earlier. The internal rate of return is found by solving the equation

$$0 = -2 + c + c^2 + c^3.$$

The solution can be found (by trial and error) to be $c = .81$, and thus IRR $= (1/c) - 1 = .23$.

Notice that the internal rate of return is defined without reference to a prevailing interest rate. It is determined entirely by the cash flows of the stream. This is the reason why it is called the *internal* rate of return; it is defined internally without reference to the external financial world. It is the rate that an ideal bank would have to apply to generate the given stream from an initial balance of zero.

As pointed out, equation (2.4) for the internal rate of return is a polynomial equation in c of degree n, which does not, in general, have an analytic solution. However, it is almost always easy to solve the equation with a computer. From algebraic theory it is known that such an equation always has at least one root, and may have as many as n roots, but some or all of these roots may be complex numbers. Fortunately the most common form of investment, where there is an initial cash outlay followed by several positive flows, leads to a unique positive solution. Hence the internal rate of return is then well defined and relatively easy to calculate. (See Exercise 4.) The formal statement of the existence of the positive root embodies the main result concerning the internal rate of return.

Main theorem of internal rate of return   *Suppose the cash flow stream $(x_0, x_1, \ldots, x_n)$ has $x_0 < 0$ and $x_k \geq 0$ for all k, $k = 1, 2, \ldots, n$, with at least one term being*

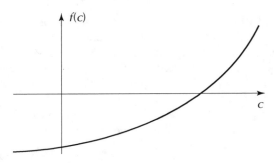

FIGURE 2.3   Function for proof. If $x_0 < 0$ and $x_k \geq 0$ for all k, $1 \leq k \leq n$, with at least one term being strictly positive, then the function $f(c)$ will start below the horizontal axis and increase monotonically as c increases. Therefore there must be a unique positive solution c satisfying $f(c) = 0$.

strictly positive. Then there is a unique positive root to the equation

$$0 = x_0 + x_1 c + x_2 c^2 + \cdots + x_n c^n .$$

Furthermore, if $\sum_{k=0}^{n} x_k > 0$ (meaning that the total amount returned exceeds the initial investment), then the corresponding internal rate of return $r = (1/c) - 1$ is positive.

> **Proof:** We plot the function $f(c) = x_0 + x_1 c + x_2 c^2 + \cdots + x_n c^n$, as shown in Figure 2.3. Note that $f(0) < 0$. However, as c increases, the value of $f(c)$ also increases, since at least one of the cash flow terms is strictly positive. Indeed, it increases without limit as c increases to infinity. Since the function is continuous, it must cross the axis at some value of c. It cannot cross more than once, because it is strictly increasing. Hence there is a unique real value c_0, which is positive, for which $f(c_0) = 0$.
>
> If $\sum_{k=0}^{n} x_k > 0$, which means that there is a net positive (nondiscounted) cash flow, then $f(1) > 0$. This means that the solution c_0 satisfying $f(c_0) = 0$ must be less than 1. Therefore $r_0 = (1/c_0) - 1 > 0$, where r_0 is the internal rate of return. ∎

If some (or all) solutions to the equation for internal rate of return are complex, the interpretation of these values is not simple. In general it is reasonable to select the solution that has the largest real part and use that real part to determine the internal rate of return. In practice, however, this is not often a serious issue, since suitable real roots typically exist.

2.5 EVALUATION CRITERIA

The essence of investment is selection from a number of alternative cash flow streams. In order to do this intelligently, the alternative cash flow streams must be evaluated according to a logical and standard criterion. Several different criteria are used in practice, but the two most important methods are those based on present value and on internal rate of return.

Net Present Value

Present value evaluates alternatives by simply ranking them according to their present values—the higher the present value, the more desirable the alternative. When one uses present value this way, one must include *all* cash flows associated with the investment, both positive and negative. To emphasize that, the expression **net present value** (NPV) is frequently used. Net present value is the present value of the benefits minus the present value of the costs. Often, to emphasize this partition of benefits and costs, the terms **present worth of benefits** and **present worth of costs** are used, both of which are just present values. Net present value is the difference between these two terms. To be worthy of consideration, the cash flow stream associated with an investment must have a positive net present value.

Example 2.4 (When to cut a tree)   Suppose that you have the opportunity to plant trees that later can be sold for lumber. This project requires an initial outlay of money in order to purchase and plant the seedlings. No other cash flow occurs until the trees are harvested. However, you have a choice as to when to harvest: after 1 year or after 2 years. If you harvest after 1 year, you get your return quickly; but if you wait an additional year, the trees will have additional growth and the revenue generated from the sale of the trees will be greater.

We assume that the cash flow streams associated with these two alternatives are

(*a*) $(-1, 2)$ cut early

(*b*) $(-1, 0, 3)$ cut later.

We also assume that the prevailing interest rate is 10%. Then the associated net present values are

(*a*) $\text{NPV} = -1 + 2/1.1 = .82$

(*b*) $\text{NPV} = -1 + 3/(1.1)^2 = 1.48.$

Hence according to the net present value criterion, it is best to cut later.

The net present value criterion is quite compelling, and indeed it is generally regarded as the single best measure of an investment's merit. It has the special advantage that the present values of different investments can be added together to obtain a meaningful composite. This is because the present value of a sum of cash flow streams is equal to the sum of the present values of the corresponding cash flows. Note, for example, that we were able to compare the two investment alternatives associated with tree farming even though the cash flows were at different times. In general, an investor can compute the present value of individual investments and also the present value of an entire portfolio.

Internal Rate of Return

Internal rate of return can also be used to rank alternative cash flow streams. The rule is simply this: the higher the internal rate of return, the more desirable the investment. However, a potential investment, or project, is presumably not worth considering unless its internal rate of return is greater than the prevailing interest rate. If the internal rate of return is greater than the prevailing interest rate, the investment is considered better than what is available externally in the financial market.

Example 2.5 (When to cut a tree, continued)   Let us use the internal rate of return method to evaluate the two tree harvesting proposals considered in Example 2.4. The equations for the internal rate of return in the two cases are

(a) $-1 + 2c = 0$

(b) $-1 + 3c^2 = 0.$

As usual, $c = 1/(1 + r)$. These have the following solutions:

(a) $c = \dfrac{1}{2} = \dfrac{1}{1 + r};$ $r = 1.0$

(b) $c = \dfrac{\sqrt{3}}{3} = \dfrac{1}{1 + r};$ $r = \sqrt{3} - 1 \approx .7.$

In other words, for (a), cut early, the internal rate of return is 100%, whereas for (b) it is about 70%. Hence under the internal rate of return criterion, the best alternative is (a). Note that this is opposite to the conclusion obtained from the net present value criterion.

Discussion of the Criteria

There is considerable debate as to which of the two criteria, net present value or internal rate of return, is the most appropriate for investment evaluation. Both have attractive features, and both have limitations. (As shown, they can even give conflicting recommendations.) Net present value is simplest to compute; it does not have the ambiguity associated with the several possible roots of the internal rate of return equation. Also net present value can be broken into component pieces, unlike internal rate of return. However, internal rate of return has the advantage that it depends only on the properties of the cash flow stream, and not on the prevailing interest rate (which in practice may not be easily defined). In fact, the two methods both have appropriate roles, but in different situations.

The primary difference between the two criteria can be explained in terms of the "when to cut a tree" example. We must look beyond the single cycle of tree farming to a series of cycles. Suppose that the proceeds of the first harvest are used to plant additional trees, starting a long series of expansion in the tree farming business. Under plan (a), cut early, the business can be doubled every year because the revenue received at the end of the year is twice that required at the beginning. In plan (b), cut later, the business can be tripled every 2 years by the same reasoning. Tripling every 2 years is equivalent, in the long run, to increasing by a factor of $\sqrt{3}$ every year. The yearly growth rates of these two plans, factors of 2 and $\sqrt{3}$, respectively, are each equal to 1 plus the internal rates of return of the plans—and this equality is true in general. So in this kind of situation, where the proceeds of the investment can be repeatedly reinvested in the same type of project but scaled in size, it makes sense to select the project with the largest internal rate of return—in order to get the greatest growth of capital.

On the other hand, suppose that this investment is a one-time opportunity and cannot be repeated. Here the net present value method is the appropriate criterion, since it compares the investment with what could be obtained through normal channels (which offer the prevailing rate of interest).

It is widely agreed (by theorists, but not necessarily by practitioners) that, overall, the best criterion is that based on net present value. If used intelligently, it will provide consistency and rationality. In the case of cutting the trees, for example, an enlightened present value analysis will agree with the result obtained by the internal rate of return criterion. If the two possible futures are developed fully, corresponding to the two cutting policies, the present value criterion, applied to the long series of expanding cash flows, would also direct that plan (a) be adopted.

There are many other factors that influence a good present value analysis—and perhaps make such an analysis more complex than suggested by the direct formal statement of the criterion. One significant issue is the selection of the interest rate to be used in the calculation. In practice, there are several different "risk-free" rates of interest in the financial market: the rate paid by bank certificates of deposit, the 3-month U.S. Treasury bill rate, and the rate paid by the highest grade commercial bonds are examples. Furthermore, the rates for borrowing are typically slightly higher than those for lending. The difference between all these choices can be several percentage points. In business decisions it is common to use a figure called the **cost of capital** as the baseline rate. This figure is the rate of return that the company must offer to potential investors in the company; that is, it is the cost the company must pay to get additional funds. Or sometimes it is taken to be the rate of return expected on alternative desirable projects. However, some of these cost of capital figures are derived from uncertain cash flow streams and are not really appropriate measures of a risk-free interest rate. For present value calculations it is best to use rates that represent true interest rates, since we assume that the cash flows are certain. Some of the apparent differences in these rates are explained and justified in Chapter 4, but still there is room for judgment.

Another factor to consider is that present value by itself does not reveal much about the rate of return. Two alternative investments might each have a net present value of $100, but one might require an investment of $100 whereas the other requires $1,000,000. Clearly these two alternatives should be viewed differently. Net present value is not the whole story (but we never said it was). It forms a solid starting point, but one must supplement its use with additional structure.

2.6 APPLICATIONS AND EXTENSIONS*

This section illustrates how the concepts of this chapter can be used to evaluate real investment opportunities and projects. Often creative thinking is required to capture the essence of a situation in a form that is suitable for analysis.

Not all of these applications need be read during the first pass through this chapter; but as one returns to the chapter, these examples should help clarify the underlying concepts.

Net Flows

In conducting a cash flow analysis using either net present value or internal rate of return, it is essential that the net of income minus expense (that is, net profit) be used as the cash flow each period. The net profit usually can be found in a straightforward manner, but the process can be subtle in complex situations. In particular, taxes often introduce complexity because certain tax-accounting costs and profits are not always equal to actual cash outflows or inflows. Taxes are considered in a later subsection.

Here we use a relatively simple example involving a gold mine to illustrate net present value analysis. Various gold mine examples are used throughout the book to illustrate how, as we extend our conceptual understanding, we can develop deeper analyses of the same kind of investment. The Simplico gold mine is the simplest of the series.

Example 2.6 (Simplico gold mine)   The Simplico gold mine has a great deal of remaining gold deposits, and you are part of a team that is considering leasing the mine from its owners for a period of 10 years. Gold can be extracted from this mine at a rate of up to 10,000 ounces per year at a cost of $200 per ounce. This cost is the total operating cost of mining and refining, exclusive of the cost of the lease. Currently the market price of gold is $400 per ounce. The interest rate is 10%. Assuming that the price of gold, the operating cost, and the interest rate remain constant over the 10-year period, what is the present value of the lease?

This is fairly straightforward. We ignore the lease expense and just find the present value of the operating profits. It is clear that the mine should be operated at full capacity every year, giving a profit of $10,000 \times (\$400 - \$200) = \$2$ million per year. We assume that these cash flows occur at the end of each year.

The cash flow stream therefore consists of 10 individual flows of $2M (that is, $2 million) at the end of each year. The present value is accordingly

$$PV = \sum_{k=1}^{10} \frac{\$2M}{(1.1)^k} .$$

---

*Sections marked by stars may be skipped at first reading.

This can be evaluated either by direct summation or by using the formula for the sum of a geometric series. The result is

$$PV = \$2M\left[1 - \left(\frac{1}{1.1}\right)^{10}\right] \times 10 = \$12.29M$$

and this is the value of the lease.

Cycle Problems

When using interest rate theory to evaluate ongoing (repeatable) activities, it is essential that alternatives be compared over the same time horizon. The difficulties that can arise from not doing this are illustrated in the tree cutting example. The two alternatives in that example have different cycle lengths, but the nature of the possible repetition of the cycles was not clearly spelled out originally.

We illustrate here two ways to account properly for different cycle lengths. The first is to repeat each alternative until both terminate at the same time. For example, if a first alternative lasts 2 years and a second lasts 4 years, then two cycles of the first alternative are comparable to one of the second. The other method for comparing alternatives with different cycle lengths is to assume that an alternative will be repeated indefinitely. Then a simple equation can be written for the value of the entire infinite-length stream.

Example 2.7 (Automobile purchase) You are contemplating the purchase of an automobile and have narrowed the field down to two choices. Car A costs $20,000, is expected to have a low maintenance cost of $1,000 per year (payable at the beginning of each year after the first year), but has a useful mileage life that for you translates into 4 years. Car B costs $30,000 and has an expected maintenance cost of $2,000 per year (after the first year) and a useful life of 6 years. Neither car has a salvage value. The interest rate is 10%. Which car should you buy?

We analyze this choice by assuming that similar alternatives will be available in the future—we are ignoring inflation—so this purchase is one of a sequence of car purchases. To equalize the time horizon, we assume a planning period of 12 years, corresponding to three cycles of car A and two of car B.

We analyze simple cycles and combined cycles as follows.
Car A:

$$\text{One cycle} \qquad PV_A = 20,000 + 1,000\sum_{k=1}^{3}\frac{1}{(1.1)^k}$$
$$= \$22,487$$
$$\text{Three cycles} \qquad PV_{A3} = PV_A\left[1 + \frac{1}{(1.1)^4} + \frac{1}{(1.1)^8}\right]$$
$$= \$48,336$$

Car B:

$$\text{One cycle} \quad PV_B = 30,000 + 2,000 \sum_{k=1}^{5} \frac{1}{(1.1)^k}$$
$$= \$37,582$$
$$\text{Two cycles} \quad PV_{B2} = PV_B \left[1 + \frac{1}{(1.1)^6} \right]$$
$$= \$58,795.$$

Hence car A should be selected because its cost has the lower present value over the common time horizon.

Example 2.8 (Machine replacement) A specialized machine essential for a company's operations costs \$10,000 and has operating costs of \$2,000 the first year. The operating cost increases by \$1,000 each year thereafter. We assume that these operating costs occur at the end of each year. The interest rate is 10%. How long should the machine be kept until it is replaced by a new identical machine? Assume that due to its specialized nature the machine has no salvage value.

This is an example where the cash flow stream is not fixed in advance because of the unknown replacement time. We must also account for the cash flows of the replacement machines. This can be done by writing an equation having PV on *both* sides. For example, suppose that the machine is replaced every year. Then the cash flow (in thousands) is $(-10, -2)$ followed by $(0, -10, -2)$ and then $(0, 0, -10, -2)$, and so forth. However, we can write the total PV of the costs compactly as

$$PV = 10 + 2/1.1 + PV/1.1$$

because after the first machine is replaced, the stream from that point looks identical to the original one, except that this continuing stream starts 1 year later and hence must be discounted by the effect of 1 year's interest. The solution to this equation is $PV = 130$ or, in our original units, \$130,000.

We may do the same thing assuming 2-year replacement, then 3 years, and so forth. The general approach is based on the equation

$$PV_{\text{total}} = PV_{1\text{ cycle}} + \left(\frac{1}{1.1} \right)^k PV_{\text{total}}$$

where k is the length of the basic cycle. This leads easily to Table 2.3.

From the table we see that the smallest present value of cost occurs when the machine is replaced after 5 years. Hence that is the best replacement policy.

Taxes

Taxes can complicate a cash flow value analysis. No new conceptual issues arise; it is just that taxes can obscure the true definition of cash flow. If a uniform tax rate were applied to all revenues and expenses as taxes and credits, respectively, then recommendations from before-tax and after-tax analyses would be identical. The

TABLE 2.3
Machine Replacement

Replacement year	Present value
1	130,000
2	82,381
3	69,577
4	65,358
5	64,481
6	65,196

The total present value is found for various replacement frequencies. The best policy corresponds to the frequency having the smallest total present value.

present value figures from the latter analysis would merely all be scaled by the same factor; that is, all would be multiplied by 1 minus the tax rate. The internal rate of return figures would be identical. Hence rankings using either net present value or internal rate of return would remain the same as those without taxes. For this reason taxes are ignored in many of our examples. Sometimes, however, the cash flows required to be reported to the government on tax forms are *not* true cash flows. This is why firms often must keep two sets of accounts—one for tax purposes and one for decision-making purposes. There is nothing illegal about this practice; it is a reality introduced by the tax code.

A tax-induced distortion of cash flows frequently accompanies the treatment of property depreciation. Depreciation is treated as a negative cash flow by the government, but the timing of these flows, as reported for tax purposes, rarely coincides with actual cash outlays. The following is a simple example illustrating this discrepancy.

Example 2.9 (Depreciation)   Suppose a firm purchases a machine for $10,000. This machine has a useful life of 4 years and its use generates a cash flow of $3,000 each year. The machine has a salvage value of $2,000 at the end of 4 years.

The government does not allow the full cost of the machine to be reported as an expense the first year, but instead requires that the cost of the machine be depreciated over its useful life. There are several depreciation methods, each applicable under various circumstances, but for simplicity we shall assume the straight-line method. In this method a fixed portion of the cost is reported as depreciation each year. Hence corresponding to a 4-year life, one-fourth of the cost (minus the estimated salvage value) is reported as an expense deductible from revenue each year.

If we assume a combined federal and state tax rate of 43%, we obtain the cash flows, before and after tax, shown in Table 2.4. The salvage value is not taxed (since it was not depreciated). The present values for the two cash flows (at 10%) are also shown. Note that in this example tax rules convert an otherwise profitable operation into an unprofitable one.

TABLE 2.4
Cash Flows Before and After Tax

Year	Before-tax cash flow	Depreciation	Taxable income	Tax	After-tax cash flow
0	−10,000				−10,000
1	3,000	2,000	1,000	430	2,570
2	3,000	2,000	1,000	430	2,570
3	3,000	2,000	1,000	430	2,570
4	5,000	2,000	1,000	430	4,570
PV	876				−487

From a present value viewpoint, tax rules for treatment of depreciation can convert a potentially profitable venture into an unprofitable one.

Inflation

Inflation is another factor that often causes confusion, arising from the choice between using actual dollar values to describe cash flows and using values expressed in purchasing power, determined by reducing inflated future dollar values back to a nominal level.

Inflation is characterized by an increase in general prices with time. Inflation can be described quantitatively in terms of an **inflation rate** f. Prices 1 year from now will on average be equal to today's prices multiplied by $(1 + f)$. Inflation compounds much like interest does, so after k years of inflation at rate f, prices will be $(1 + f)^k$ times their original values. Of course, inflation rates do not remain constant, but in planning studies future rates are usually estimated as constant.

Another way to look at inflation is that it erodes the purchasing power of money. A dollar today does not purchase as much bread or milk, for example, as a dollar did 10 years ago. In other words, we can think of prices increasing or, alternatively, of the value of money decreasing. If the inflation rate is f, then the value of a dollar next year in terms of the purchasing power of today's dollar is $1/(1 + f)$.

It is sometimes useful to think explicitly in terms of the same kind of dollars, eliminating the influence of inflation. Thus we consider **constant dollars** or, alternatively, **real dollars,** defined relative to a given reference year. These are the (hypothetical) dollars that continue to have the same purchasing power as dollars did in the reference year. These dollars are defined in contrast to the **actual** or **nominal dollars** that we really use in transactions.

This leads us to define a new interest rate, termed the **real interest rate,** which is the rate at which real dollars increase if left in a bank that pays the nominal rate. To understand the meaning of the real interest rate, imagine depositing money in the bank at time zero, then withdrawing it 1 year later. The purchasing power of the bank balance has probably increased in spite of inflation, and this increase measures the real rate of interest.

If one goes through that thinking, when r is the nominal interest rate and f is the inflation rate, it is easy to see that

$$1 + r_0 = \frac{1 + r}{1 + f}$$

where r_0 denotes the real rate of interest. This equation expresses the fact that money in the bank increases (nominally) by $1 + r$, but its purchasing power is deflated by $1/(1 + f)$. We can solve for r_0 as

$$r_0 = \frac{r - f}{1 + f}. \tag{2.5}$$

Note that for small levels of inflation the real rate of interest is approximately equal to the nominal rate of interest minus the inflation rate.

A cash flow analysis can be carried out using either actual (nominal) dollars or real dollars, but the danger is that a mixture of the two might be used inadvertently. Such a mixture sometimes occurs in the planning studies in large corporations. The operating divisions, which are primarily concerned with physical inputs and outputs, may extrapolate real cash flows into the future. But corporate headquarters, being primarily concerned with the financial market and tax rules, may find the use of nominal (that is, actual) cash flows more convenient and hence may discount at the nominal rate. The result can be an undervaluation by headquarters of project proposals submitted by the divisions relative to valuations that would be obtained if inflation were treated consistently.

We illustrate now how an analysis can be carried out consistently by using either real or nominal cash flows.

Example 2.10 (Inflation)   Suppose that inflation is 4%, the nominal interest rate is 10%, and we have a cash flow of real (or constant) dollars as shown in the second column of Table 2.5. (It is common to estimate cash flows in constant dollars, relative to the present, because "ordinary" price increases can then be neglected in a simple estimation of cash flows.) To determine the present value in real terms we must use the real rate of interest, which from (2.5) is $r_0 = (.10 - .04)/1.04 = 5.77\%$.

TABLE 2.5
Inflation

Year	Real cash flow	PV @5.77%	Nominal cash flow	PV @10%
0	−10,000	−10,000	−10,000	−10,000
1	5,000	4,727	5,200	4,727
2	5,000	4,469	5,408	4,469
3	5,000	4,226	5,624	4,226
4	3,000	2,397	3,510	2,397
Total		5,819		5,819

The projected real cash flows of the second column have the present values, at the real rate of interest, shown in the third column. The fourth column lists the cash flows that would occur under 4% inflation, and their present values at the 10% nominal rate of interest are given in the fifth column.

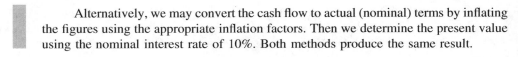

Alternatively, we may convert the cash flow to actual (nominal) terms by inflating the figures using the appropriate inflation factors. Then we determine the present value using the nominal interest rate of 10%. Both methods produce the same result.

2.7 SUMMARY

The time value of money is expressed concretely as an interest rate. The 1-year interest rate is the price paid (expressed as a percentage of principal) for borrowing money for 1 year. In simple interest, the interest payment when borrowing money in subsequent years is identical in magnitude to that of the first year. Hence, for example, the bank balance resulting from a single deposit would grow linearly year by year. In compound interest, the interest payment in subsequent years is based on the balance at the beginning of that year. Hence the bank balance resulting from a single deposit would grow geometrically year by year.

A useful approximation is that the number of years required for a deposit to double in value when compounded yearly is $72/i$, where i is the interest rate expressed as a percentage. For example, at 10%, money doubles in about 7 years.

Interest can be compounded at any frequency, not just yearly. It is even possible to compound continuously, which leads to bank balances that grow exponentially with time. When interest is compounded more frequently than yearly, it is useful to define both a nominal rate and an effective annual rate of interest. The nominal rate is the rate used for a single period divided by the length (in years) of a period. The effective rate is the rate that, if applied without compounding, would give the same total balance for money deposited for one full year. The effective rate is larger than the nominal rate. For example, an 8% nominal annual rate corresponds to an 8.24% effective annual rate under quarterly compounding.

Money received in the future is worth less than the same amount of money received in the present because money received in the present can be loaned out to earn interest. Money to be received at a future date must be discounted by dividing its magnitude by the factor by which present money would grow if loaned out to that future date. There is, accordingly, a discount factor for each future date.

The present value of a cash flow stream is the sum of the discounted magnitudes of the individual cash flows of the stream. An ideal bank can transform a cash flow stream into any other with the same present value.

The internal rate of return of a cash flow stream is an interest rate that, if used to evaluate the present value of the stream, would cause that present value to be zero. In general, this rate is not well defined. However, when the cash flow stream has an initial negative flow followed by positive flows, the internal rate of return is well defined.

Present value and internal rate of return are the two main methods used to evaluate proposed investment projects that generate deterministic cash flow streams. Under the present value framework, if there are several competing alternatives, then the one with the highest present value should be selected. Under the internal rate of return criterion, the alternative with the largest internal rate of return should be selected.

Analyses using these methods are not always straightforward. In particular, consideration of various cycle lengths, taxes, and inflation each require careful attention.

EXERCISES

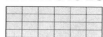

1. (A nice inheritance)   Suppose \$1 were invested in 1776 at 3.3% interest compounded yearly.

    (a) Approximately how much would that investment be worth today: \$1,000, \$10,000, \$100,000, or \$1,000,000?
    (b) What if the interest rate were 6.6%?

2. (The 72 rule)   The number of years n required for an investment at interest rate r to double in value must satisfy $(1 + r)^n = 2$. Using $\ln 2 = .69$ and the approximation $\ln(1 + r) \approx r$ valid for small r, show that $n \approx 69/i$, where i is the interest rate percentage (that is, $i = 100r$). Using the better approximation $\ln(1 + r) \approx r - \frac{1}{2}r^2$, show that for $r \approx .08$ there holds $n \approx 72/i$.

3. (Effective rates)   Find the corresponding effective rates for:

    (a) 3% compounded monthly.
    (b) 18% compounded monthly.
    (c) 18% compounded quarterly.

4. (Newton's method $\diamond$)   The IRR is generally calculated using an iterative procedure. Suppose that we define $f(\lambda) = -a_0 + a_1\lambda + a_2\lambda^2 + \cdots + a_n\lambda^n$, where all a_i's are positive and $n > 1$. Here is an iterative technique that generates a sequence $\lambda_0, \lambda_1, \lambda_2, \ldots, \lambda_k, \ldots$ of estimates that converges to the root $\overline{\lambda} > 0$, solving $f(\overline{\lambda}) = 0$. Start with any $\lambda_0 > 0$ close to the solution. Assuming λ_k has been calculated, evaluate

$$f'(\lambda_k) = a_1 + 2a_2\lambda_k + 3a_3\lambda_k^2 + \cdots + na_n\lambda_k^{n-1}$$

and define

$$\lambda_{k+1} = \lambda_k - \frac{f(\lambda_k)}{f'(\lambda_k)}.$$

This is Newton's method. It is based on approximating the function f by a line tangent to its graph at λ_k, as shown in Figure 2.4. Try the procedure on $f(\lambda) = -1 + \lambda + \lambda^2$. Start with $\lambda_0 = 1$ and compute four additional estimates.

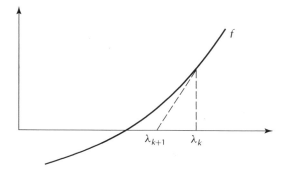

FIGURE 2.4   Newton's method.

$\diamond$Exercises followed by $\diamond$ are mathematically more difficult than average.

5. (A prize)   A major lottery advertises that it pays the winner $10 million. However, this prize money is paid at the rate of $500,000 each year (with the first payment being immediate) for a total of 20 payments. What is the present value of this prize at 10% interest?

6. (Sunk costs)   A young couple has made a nonrefundable deposit of the first month's rent (equal to $1,000) on a 6-month apartment lease. The next day they find a different apartment that they like just as well, but its monthly rent is only $900. They plan to be in the apartment only 6 months. Should they switch to the new apartment? What if they plan to stay 1 year? Assume an interest rate of 12%.

7. (Shortcut)   Gavin Jones is inquisitive and determined to learn both the theory and the application of investment theory. He pressed the tree farmer for additional information and learned that it was possible to delay cutting the trees of Example 2.4 for another year. The farmer said that, from a present value perspective, it was not worthwhile to do so. Gavin instantly deduced that the revenue obtained must be less than x. What is x?

8. (Copy machines ⊕)   Two copy machines are available. Both have useful lives of 5 years. One machine can be either leased or purchased outright; the other must be purchased. Hence there are a total of three options: A, B, and C. The details are shown in Table 2.6. (The first year's maintenance is included in the initial cost. There are then four additional maintenance payments, occurring at the beginning of each year, followed by revenues from resale.) The present values of the expenses of these three options using a 10% interest rate are also indicated in the table. According to a present value analysis, the machine of least cost, as measured by the present value, should be selected; that is, option B.

TABLE 2.6
Copy Machine Options

	Option		
	A	B	C
Initial outlay	6,000	30,000	35,000
Yearly expense	8,000	2,000	1,600
Resale value	0	10,000	12,000
Present value (@10%)	31,359	30,131	32,621

Option A is a lease; options B and C are purchases of two alternative machines. All have 5-year lives.

It is not possible to compute the IRR for any of these alternatives, because all cash flows are negative (except for the resale values). However, it is possible to calculate the IRR on an incremental basis. Find the IRR corresponding to a change from A to B. Is a change from A to B justified on the basis of the IRR?

9. (An appraisal)   You are considering the purchase of a nice home. It is in every way perfect for you and in excellent condition, except for the roof. The roof has only 5 years of life

---

⊕Exercises followed by ⊕ require numerical computation.

remaining. A new roof would last 20 years, but would cost $20,000. The house is expected to last forever. Assuming that costs will remain constant and that the interest rate is 5%, what value would you assign to the existing roof?

10. (Oil depletion allowance ⊕)   A wealthy investor spends $1 million to drill and develop an oil well that has estimated reserves of 200,000 barrels. The well is to be operated over 5 years, producing the estimated quantities shown in the second column of Table 2.7. It is estimated that the oil will be sold for $20 per barrel. The net income is also shown.

TABLE 2.7
Oil Investment Details

Year	Barrels produced	Gross revenue	Net income	Option 1	Option 2	Depletion allowance	Taxable income	Tax	After-tax income
1	80,000	1,600,000	1,200,000	352,000	400,000	400,000	800,000	360,000	840,000
2	70,000	1,400,000	1,000,000						
3	50,000	1,000,000	500,000						
4	30,000	600,000	200,000						
5	10,000	200,000	50,000						

A depletion allowance, for tax purposes, can be computed in either of two ways each year: 22% of gross revenue up to 50% of net income before such deduction (option 1), or the investment cost of the product, equal in this case to the unit cost of the reserves, $5 per barrel (option 2). The allowance is deducted from the net income to determine the taxable income. The investor is in the 45% tax bracket.

(a) Complete Table 2.7 and show that the total depletion allowance exceeds the original investment.

(b) Calculate the PV and the IRR for this investment. Assume an interest rate of 20%.

11. (Conflicting recommendations ⊕)   Consider the two projects whose cash flows are shown in Table 2.8. Find the IRRs of the two projects and the NPVs at 5%. Show that the IRR and NPV figures yield different recommendations. Can you explain this?

TABLE 2.8

	Years					
	0	1	2	3	4	5
Project 1	−100	30	30	30	30	30
Project 2	−150	42	42	42	42	42

12. (Domination)   Suppose two competing projects have cash flows of the form $(-A_1, B_1, B_1, \ldots, B_1)$ and $(-A_2, B_2, B_2, \ldots, B_2)$, both with the same length and A_1, A_2, B_1, B_2 all positive. Suppose $B_1/A_1 > B_2/A_2$. Show that project 1 will have a higher IRR than project 2.

13. (Crossing ◇)   In general, we say that two projects with cash flows x_i and y_i, $i = 0, 1, 2, \ldots,$ n, *cross* if $x_0 < y_0$ and $\sum_{i=0}^{n} x_i > \sum_{i=0}^{n} y_i$. Let $P_x(d)$ and $P_y(d)$ denote the present values of these two projects when the discount factor is d.

(a) Show that there is a crossover value $c > 0$ such that $P_x(c) = P_y(c)$.

(b) For Exercise 11, calculate the crossover value c.

14. (Depreciation choice)   In the United States the accelerated cost recovery system (ACRS) must be used for depreciation of assets placed into service after December 1980. In this system, assets are classified into categories specifying the effective tax life. The classification of "3-year property," for example, includes automobiles, tractors for hauling highway trailers, light trucks, and certain manufacturing tools. The percentages of the cost for 3-year property that can be deducted for each of the first 3 years after purchase (including the year of purchase) are 25%, 38%, and 37%, respectively. The tax code also allows the alternate ACRS method, which for 3-year property means that the straight-line percentage of $33\frac{1}{3}\%$ can be used for 3 years.

   Which of these methods is preferred by an individual who wishes to maximize the present value of depreciation? How does the choice depend on the assumed rate of interest?

15. (An erroneous analysis)   A division of ABBOX Corporation has developed the concept of a new product. Production of the product would require $10 million in initial capital expenditure. It is anticipated that 1 million units would be sold each year for 5 years, and then the product would be obsolete and production would cease. Each year's production would require 10,000 hours of labor and 100 tons of raw material. Currently the average wage rate is $30 per hour and the cost of the raw material is $100 per ton. The product would sell for $3.30 per unit, and this price is expected to be maintained (in real terms). ABBOX management likes to use a 12% discount rate for projects of this type and faces a 34% tax rate on profit. The initial capital expenditure can be depreciated in a straight-line fashion over 5 years. In its first analysis of this project, management did not apply inflation factors to the extrapolated revenues and operating costs. What present value did they obtain? How would the answer change if an inflation rate of 4% were applied?

REFERENCES

The theory of interest, compounding, present value, and internal rate of return is covered extensively in many excellent textbooks. A few investment-oriented texts which discuss general notions of interest are [1–5]. The use of the concepts of NPV and IRR for ranking investment alternatives is developed in detail in the field of engineering economy. Excellent texts in that field include [6–9]. A more advanced study of interest is [10], which contains a continuous-time version of the "when to cut a tree" example, which inspired the example given in Section 2.5. Exercise 10 is a modification of an example in [6].

1. Alexander, G. J., W. F. Sharpe, and V. J. Bailey (1993), *Fundamentals of Investment*, 2nd ed., Prentice Hall, Englewood Cliffs, NJ.

2. Bodie, H. M., A. Kane, and A. J. Marcus (1993), *Investments*, 2nd ed., Irwin, Homewood, IL.

3. Brealey, R., and S. Meyers (1981), *Principles of Corporate Finance,* McGraw-Hill, New York.

4. Francis, J. C. (1991), *Investments: Analysis and Management*, 5th ed., McGraw-Hill, New York.
5. Haugen, R. A. (1993), *Modern Investment Theory*, 3rd ed., Prentice Hall, Englewood Cliffs, NJ.
6. DeGarmo, E. P., W. G. Sullivan, and J. A. Bontadelli (1988), *Engineering Economy*, 8th ed., Macmillan, New York.
7. Grant, E. L., W. G. Ireson, and R. S. Leavensworth (1982), *Principles of Engineering Economy*, 7th ed., Wiley, New York.
8. Steiner, H. M. (1992), *Engineering Economy,* McGraw-Hill, New York.
9. Thuesen, G. J., and W. J. Fabrycky (1989), *Engineering Economy*, 7th ed., Prentice Hall, Englewood Cliffs, NJ.
10. Hirshleifer, J. (1970), *Investment, Interest, and Capital,* Prentice Hall, Englewood Cliffs.

3 FIXED-INCOME SECURITIES

An interest rate is a price, or rent, for the most popular of all traded commodities—money. The one-year interest rate, for example, is just the price that must be paid for borrowing money for one year. Markets for money are well developed, and the corresponding basic market price—interest—is monitored by everyone who has a serious concern about financial activity.

As shown in the previous chapter, the market interest rate provides a ready comparison for investment alternatives that produce cash flows. This comparison can be used to evaluate any cash flow stream: whether arising from transactions between individuals, associated with business projects, or generated by investments in securities.

However, the overall market associated with interest rates is more complex than the simple bank accounts discussed in the last chapter. Vast assortments of bills, notes, bonds, annuities, futures contracts, and mortgages are part of the well-developed markets for money. These market items are not real goods (or hard assets) in the sense of having intrinsic value—such as potatoes or gold—but instead are traded only as pieces of paper, or as entries in a computer database. These items, in general, are referred to as **financial instruments.** Their values are derived from the promises they represent. If there is a well-developed market for an instrument, so that it can be traded freely and easily, then that instrument is termed a **security.** There are many financial instruments and securities that are directly related to interest rates and, therefore, provide access to income—at a price defined by the appropriate interest rate or rates.

Fixed-income securities are financial instruments that are traded in well-developed markets and promise a fixed (that is, definite) income to the holder over a span of time. In our terminology, they represent the ownership of a definite cash flow stream.

Fixed-income securities are important to an investor because they define the market for money, and most investors participate in this market. These securities are also important as additional comparison points when conducting analyses of investment opportunities that are not traded in markets, such as a firm's research projects, oil leases, and royalty rights. A comprehensive study of financial instruments most naturally starts with a study of fixed-income securities.

3.1 THE MARKET FOR FUTURE CASH

The classification of a security as being a fixed-income security is actually a bit vague. Originally this classification meant, as previously stated, that the security pays a fixed, well-defined cash flow stream to the owner. The only uncertainties about the promised stream were associated with whether the issuer of the security might **default** (by, say, going bankrupt), in which case the income would be discontinued or delayed. Now, however, some "fixed-income" securities promise cash flows whose magnitudes are tied to various contingencies or fluctuating indices. For example, payment levels on an adjustable-rate mortgage may be tied to an interest rate index, or corporate bond payments may in part be governed by a stock price. But in common parlance, such variations are allowed within a broader definition of fixed-income securities. The general idea is that a fixed-income security has a cash flow stream that is fixed except for variations due to well-defined contingent circumstances.

There are many different kinds of fixed-income securities, and we cannot provide a comprehensive survey of them here. However, we shall mention some of the principal types of fixed-income securities in order to indicate the general scope of such securities.

Savings Deposits

Probably the most familiar fixed-income instrument is an interest-bearing bank deposit. These are offered by commercial banks, savings and loan institutions, and credit unions. In the United States most such deposits are guaranteed by agencies of the federal government. The simplest **demand deposit** pays a rate of interest that varies with market conditions. Over an extended period of time, such a deposit is not strictly of a fixed-income type; nevertheless, we place it in the fixed-income category. The interest *is* guaranteed in a **time deposit account,** where the deposit must be maintained for a given length of time (such as 6 months), or else a penalty for early withdrawal is assessed. A similar instrument is a **certificate of deposit** (CD), which is issued in standard denominations such as $10,000. Large-denomination CDs can be sold in a market, and hence they qualify as securities.

Money Market Instruments

The term **money market** refers to the market for short-term (1 year or less) loans by corporations and financial intermediaries, including, for example, banks. It is a well-organized market designed for large amounts of money, but it is not of great importance to long-term investors because of its short-term and specialized nature. Within this market **commercial paper** is the term used to describe unsecured loans (that is, loans without collateral) to corporations. The larger denominations of CDs mentioned earlier are also part of this market.

A **banker's acceptance** is a more involved money market instrument. If company A sells goods to company B, company B might send a written promise to company A that it will pay for the goods within a fixed time, such as 3 months. Some bank *accepts* the promise by promising to pay the bill on behalf of company B. Company A can then sell the banker's acceptance to someone else at a discount before the time has expired.

Eurodollar deposits are deposits denominated in dollars but held in a bank outside the United States. Likewise **Eurodollar CDs** are CDs denominated in dollars and issued by banks outside the United States. A distinction between these Eurodollars and regular dollars is due to differences in banking regulations and insurance.

U.S. Government Securities

The U.S. Government obtains loans by issuing various types of fixed-income securities. These securities are considered to be of the highest credit quality since they are backed by the government itself. The most important government securities are sketched here.

U.S. Treasury bills are issued in denominations of $10,000 or more with fixed terms to maturity of 13, 26, and 52 weeks. They are sold on a discount basis. Thus a bill with a face value of $10,000 may sell for $9,500, the difference between the price and the face value providing the interest. A bill can be redeemed for the full face value at the maturity date. New bills are offered each week and are sold at auction. They are highly **liquid** (that is, there is a ready market for them); hence they can be easily sold prior to the maturity date.

U.S. Treasury notes have maturities of 1 to 10 years and are sold in denominations as small as $1,000. The owner of such a note receives a **coupon payment** every 6 months until maturity. This coupon payment represents an interest payment and its magnitude is fixed throughout the life of the note. At maturity the note holder receives the last coupon payment and the face value of the note. Like Treasury bills, these notes are sold at auction.

U.S. Treasury bonds are issued with maturities of more than 10 years. They are similar to Treasury notes in that they make coupon payments. However, some Treasury bonds are **callable,** meaning that at some scheduled coupon payment date the Treasury can force the bond holder to redeem the bond at that time for its face (par) value.

U.S. Treasury strips are bonds that the U.S. Treasury issues in stripped form. Here each of the coupons is issued separately, as is the principal. So a 10-year bond when stripped will consist of 20 semiannual coupon securities (each with a separate CUSIP[1]) and an additional principal security. Each of these securities generates a

---

[1] The Committee on Uniform Securities Identification Procedures (CUSIP) assigns identifying CUSIP numbers and codes to all securities.

single cash flow, with no intermediate coupon payments. Such a security is termed a **zero-coupon bond.**

Other Bonds

Bonds are issued by agencies of the federal government, by state and local governments, and by corporations.

Municipal bonds are issued by agencies of state and local governments. There are two main types: **general obligation bonds,** which are backed by a governing body such as the state; and **revenue bonds,** which are backed either by the revenue to be generated by the project that will initially be funded by the bond issue or by the agency responsible for the project.

The interest income associated with municipal bonds is exempt from federal income tax and from state and local taxes in the issuing state. This feature means that investors are willing to accept lower interest rates on these bonds compared to other securities of similar quality.

Corporate bonds are issued by corporations for the purpose of raising capital for operations and new ventures. They vary in quality depending on the strength of the issuing corporation and on certain features of the bond itself.

Some corporate bonds are traded on an exchange, but most are traded over-the-counter in a network of bond dealers. These over-the-counter bonds are less liquid in the sense that there may be only a few trades per day of a particular issue.

A bond carries with it an **indenture,** which is a contract of terms. Some features that might be included are:

Callable bonds   A bond is callable if the issuer has the right to repurchase the bond at a specified price. Usually this call price falls with time, and often there is an initial call protection period wherein the bond cannot be called.

Sinking funds   Rather than incur the obligation to pay the entire face value of a bond issue at maturity, the issuer may establish a sinking fund to spread this obligation out over time. Under such an arrangement the issuer may repurchase a certain fraction of the outstanding bonds each year at a specified price.

Debt Subordination   To protect bond holders, limits may be set on the amount of additional borrowing by the issuer. Also the bondholders may be guaranteed that in the event of bankruptcy, payment to them takes priority over payments of other debt—the other debt being subordinated.

Mortgages

To a typical homeowner, a mortgage looks like the opposite of a bond. A future homeowner usually will *sell* a home mortgage to generate immediate cash to pay for a home, obligating him- or herself to make periodic payments to the mortgage holder. The standard mortgage is structured so that equal monthly payments are made throughout its term, which contrasts to most bonds, which have a final payment equal to the face value at maturity. Most standard mortgages allow for early repayment of the balance. Hence from the mortgage holder's viewpoint the income stream generated is not completely fixed, since it may be terminated with an appropriate lump-sum payment at the discretion of the homeowner.

There are many variations on the standard mortgage. There may be modest-sized periodic payments for several years followed by a final **balloon payment** that completes the contract. **Adjustable-rate mortgages** adjust the effective interest rate periodically according to an interest rate index, and hence these mortgages do not really generate fixed income in the strict sense.

Mortgages are not usually thought of as securities, since they are written as contracts between two parties, for example, a homeowner and a bank. However, mortgages are typically "bundled" into large packages and traded among financial institutions. These **mortgage-backed securities** are quite liquid.

Annuities

An **annuity** is a contract that pays the holder (the **annuitant**) money periodically, according to a predetermined schedule or formula, over a period of time. Pension benefits often take the form of annuities. Sometimes annuities are structured to provide a fixed payment every year for as long as the annuitant is alive, in which case the price of the annuity is based on the age of the annuitant when the annuity is purchased and on the number of years until payments are initiated.

There are numerous variations. Sometimes the level of the annuity payments is tied to the earnings of a large pool of funds from which the annuity is paid, sometimes the payments vary with time, and so forth.

Annuities are not really securities, since they are not traded. (The issuer certainly would not allow a change in annuitant if payments are tied to the life of the owner; likewise, an annuitant would not allow the annuity company to transfer their obligation to another company which might be less solvent.) Annuities are, however, considered to be investment opportunities that are available at standardized rates. Hence from an investor's viewpoint, they serve the same role as other fixed-income instruments.

3.2 VALUE FORMULAS

Many fixed-income instruments include an obligation to pay a stream of equal periodic cash flows. This is characteristic of standard coupon bonds that pay the holder a fixed sum on a regular basis; it also is characteristic of standard mortgages, of many annuities, of standard automobile loans, and of other consumer loans. It is therefore useful to recognize that the present value of such a constant stream can be determined by a compact formula. This formula is difficult to evaluate by hand, and hence professionals working each day with such financial instruments typically have available appropriate tables, handheld calculators, or computer programs that relate present value to the magnitude and term of periodic payments. There are, for example, extensive sets of mortgage tables, bond tables, annuity rate tables, and so forth. We shall develop the basic formula here and illustrate its use.

Perpetual Annuities

As a step toward the development of the formula we consider an interesting and conceptually useful fixed-income instrument termed a **perpetual annuity,** or **perpetuity,** which pays a fixed sum periodically *forever.* For example, it might pay $1,000 every January 1 forever. Such annuities are quite rare (although such instruments actually do exist in Great Britain, where they are called **consols**).

The present value of a perpetual annuity can be easily derived. Suppose an amount A is paid at the end of each period, starting at the end of the first period, and suppose the *per-period* interest rate is r. Then the present value is

$$P = \sum_{k=1}^{\infty} \frac{A}{(1+r)^k}.$$

The terms in the summand represent a geometric series, and this series can be summed easily using a standard formula. Alternatively, if you have forgotten the standard formula, we can derive it by noting that

$$P = \sum_{k=1}^{\infty} \frac{A}{(1+r)^k} = \frac{A}{1+r} + \sum_{k=2}^{\infty} \frac{A}{(1+r)^k} = \frac{A}{1+r} + \frac{P}{1+r}.$$

We can solve this equation to find $P = A/r$. Hence we have the following basic result:

Perpetual annuity formula   *The present value P of a perpetual annuity that pays an amount A every period, beginning one period from the present, is*

$$P = \frac{A}{r}$$

where r is the one-period interest rate.

Example 3.1 (Perpetual annuity)   Consider a perpetual annuity of $1,000 each year. At 10% interest its present value is

$$P = \frac{1,000}{.10} = \$10,000.$$

Finite-Life Streams

Of more practical importance is the case where the payment stream has a finite lifetime. Suppose that the stream consists of n periodic payments of amount A, starting at the end of the current period and ending at period n. The pattern of periodic cash flows together with the time indexing system is shown in Figure 3.1.

The present value of the finite stream relative to the interest rate r per period is

$$P = \sum_{k=1}^{n} \frac{A}{(1+r)^k}.$$

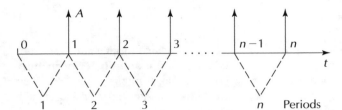

FIGURE 3.1   Time indexing. Time is indexed from 0 to n. A period is a span between time points, with the first period being the time from 0 to 1. A standard annuity has a constant cash flow at the end of each period.

This is the sum of a finite geometric series. If you do not recall the formula for this sum, we can derive it easily by a simple trick. The value can be found by considering two perpetual annuities. Both pay an amount A each year, but one starts at time 1 and the other starts at time $n + 1$. We *subtract* the second from the first. The result is the same as the original stream of finite life. This combination is illustrated in Figure 3.2 for the case of a stream of length 3.

The value of the delayed annuity is found by discounting that annuity by the factor $(1 + r)^{-n}$ because it is delayed n periods. Hence we may write

$$P = \frac{A}{r} - \frac{A}{r(1+r)^n} = \frac{A}{r}\left[1 - \frac{1}{(1+r)^n}\right].$$

We now highlight this important result:

Annuity formulas   *Consider an annuity that begins payment one period from the present, paying an amount A each period for a total of n periods. The present value P, the one-period annuity amount A, the one-period interest rate r, and the number of periods n of the annuity are related by*

$$P = \frac{A}{r}\left[1 - \frac{1}{(1+r)^n}\right]$$

or, equivalently,

$$A = \frac{r(1+r)^n P}{(1+r)^n - 1}.$$

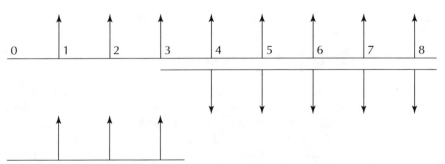

FIGURE 3.2   Finite stream from two perpetual annuities. The top line shows a perpetuity starting at time 1, the second a negative perpetuity starting at time 4. The sum of these two is a finite-life annuity with payments starting at time 1 and ending at time 3.

Although these formulas are simple in concept and quite easy to derive, they are sufficiently complex that they cannot be evaluated easily by hand. It is for this reason that financial tables and financial calculators are commonly available. Professional tables of this type occupy several pages and typically give P/A as a function of r and n. For some purposes A/P (just the reciprocal) is more convenient, and there are tables written both ways.

It is important to note that in the formulas of this section, r is expressed as a per-period interest rate. If the period length is not equal to 1 year, this r will *not* be equal to the yearly rate; so care must be exercised.

The annuity formula is frequently used in the reverse direction; that is, A as a function of P. This determines the periodic payment that is equivalent (under the assumed interest rate) to an initial payment of P. This process of substituting periodic payments for a current obligation is referred to as **amortization.** Hence one may **amortize** the cost of an automobile over 5 years by taking out a 5-year loan.

Example 3.2 (Loan calculation) Suppose you have borrowed $1,000 from a credit union. The terms of the loan are that the yearly interest is 12% compounded monthly. You are to make equal monthly payments of such magnitude as to repay (amortize) this loan over 5 years. How much are the monthly payments?

Five years is 60 months, and 12% a year compounded monthly is 1% per month. Hence we use the formula for $n = 60$, $r = 1\%$, and $P = \$1,000$. We find that the payments A are $22.20 per month.

Example 3.3 (APR) A typical advertisement from a mortgage broker is shown in Table 3.1. In addition to the interest rate, term of the loan, and maximum amount, there are listed points and the annual percentage rate (APR), which describe fees and expenses. **Points** is the percentage of the loan amount that is charged for providing the mortgage. Typically, there are additional expenses as well. All of these fees and

TABLE 3.1
Mortgage Broker Advertisement

Rate	Pts	Term	Max amt	APR
7.625	1.00	30 yr	$203,150	7.883
7.875	.50	30 yr	$203,150	8.083
8.125	2.25	30 yr	$600,000	8.399
7.000	1.00	15 yr	$203,150	7.429
7.500	1.00	15 yr	$600,000	7.859

Call 555-1213
Real Estate Broker, CA Dept. of Real Estate,
Mortgage Masters, Inc.
Current Fixed Rates

APR is the rate of interest that implicitly includes the fees associated with a mortgage.

expenses are added to the loan balance, and the sum is amortized at the stated rate over the stated period. This results in a fixed monthly payment amount A.

The **APR** is the rate of interest that, if applied to the loan amount without fees and expenses, would result in a monthly payment of A, exactly as before.

As a concrete example, suppose you took out a mortgage corresponding to the first listing in Table 3.1. Let us calculate the total fees and expenses. Using the APR of 7.883%, a loan amount of $203,150, and a 30-year term, we find a monthly payment of $A = \$1,474$.

Now using an interest rate of 7.625% and the monthly payment calculated, we find a total initial balance of $208,267. The total of fees and expenses is therefore $208,267 − $203,150 = $5,117. The loan fee itself is 1 point, or $2,032. Hence other expenses are $5,117 − $2,032 = $3,085.

Running Amortization*

The formulas for amortization can be looked at in another way, linked directly to common accounting practice. Consider the loan of $1,000 discussed in Example 3.2, which you will repay over 5 years at 12% interest (compounded monthly). Suppose you took out the loan on January 1, and the first payment is due February 1. The repayment process can be viewed as credits to a running monthly account. The account has an initial balance equal to the value of the loan—the original principal. Each month this balance is increased by an interest charge of 1% and then reduced by the payment amount. Assuming that you make payments as scheduled, the balance will decrease each month, reaching zero after 60 months. On July 1 you might receive a 6-month accounting such as that shown in Table 3.2, which illustrates how the balance decreases as payments are made.

It is common to regard each payment as consisting of two parts. The first part is the current interest; the second is a partial repayment of the principal. The running balance account procedure is consistent with reamortizing the loan each month. Specifically, assuming all payments to date were made on schedule and of the proper amount, the payment level predicted by the formula to amortize the current balance over the months remaining in the original contract will always be $22.20. For exam-

TABLE 3.2
Statement of Account Transactions

	Previous balance	Current interest	Payment received	New balance
January 1				1,000.00
February 1	1,000.00	10.00	22.20	987.80
March 1	987.80	9.88	22.20	975.48
April 1	975.48	9.75	22.20	963.03
May 1	963.03	9.63	22.20	950.46
June 1	950.46	9.50	22.20	937.76

Each month the previous balance accumulates interest and is reduced by the current payment. The balance will be zero at the end of the loan term.

ple, based on the July statement, one can amortize the balance of $937.76 at 12% on June 1 (after making the June 1 payment) over a period of 55 months. The monthly payment required by this amortization would be $22.20.

Annual Worth*

The annuity framework provides an alternative method for expressing a net present value analysis. This **annual worth** method has the advantage that it expresses its results in terms of a constant level of cash flow and thus is easily understood.

Suppose a project has an associated cash flow stream $(x_0, x_1, \ldots, x_n)$ over n years. A present value analysis uses a (fictitious) constant ideal bank with interest rate r to transform this stream hypothetically into an equivalent one of the form $(v, 0, 0, \ldots, 0)$, where v is the net present value of the stream.

An annual worth analysis uses the same ideal bank to hypothetically transform the sequence to one of the form $(0, A, A, A, \ldots, A)$. The value A is the annual worth (over n years) of the project. It is the equivalent net amount that is generated by the project if all amounts are converted to a fixed n-year annuity starting the first year.

Clearly $A > 0$ exactly when $v > 0$, so the condition for acceptance of the project based on whether $A > 0$ coincides with the net present value criterion.

Example 3.4 (A capital cost)   The purchase of a new machine for $100,000 (at time zero) is expected to generate additional revenues of $25,000 for the next 10 years starting at year 1. If the discount rate is 16%, is this a profitable investment?

We simply need to determine how to amortize the initial cost uniformly over 10 years; that is, we need to find the annual payments at 16% that are equivalent to the original cost. Using the annuity formula, we find that this corresponds to $20,690 per year. Hence the annual worth of the project is $25,000 − $20,690 = $4,310, which is positive; thus the investment is profitable. Note that if the purchase of the machine were financed at 16% over 10 years, the *actual* yearly net cash flows would correspond exactly to the annual worth.

3.3 BOND DETAILS

Bonds represent by far the greatest monetary value of fixed-income securities and are, as a class, the most liquid of these securities. We devote special attention to bonds, both because of their practical importance as investment vehicles and because of their theoretical value, which will be exploited heavily in Chapter 4. We describe the general structure and trading mechanics of bonds in this section and then discuss in the following few sections some methods by which bonds are analyzed. Our description is intended to be an overview. Specific details are quite involved, and one must refer to specialized literature or to a brokerage firm for the exact features of any particular bond issue.

A **bond** is an obligation by the bond issuer to pay money to the bond holder according to rules specified at the time the bond is issued. Generally, a bond pays a specific amount, its **face value** or, equivalently, its **par value** at the date of maturity. Bonds generally have par values of even amounts, such as $1,000 or $10,000. In addition, most bonds pay periodic **coupon payments.** The term *coupon* is due to the fact that in the past actual coupons were attached to bond certificates. The bond holder would mail these to the agent of the issuer (usually a bank) one at a time, at specified dates, and the appropriate coupon payment would then be sent by return mail. These physical coupons are rare today, but the name remains. The last coupon date corresponds to the maturity date, so the last payment is equal to the face value plus the coupon value.

The coupon amount is described as a percentage of the face value. For example, a 9% coupon bond with a face value of $1,000 will have a coupon of $90 per year. However, the period between coupons may be less than a year. In the United States, coupon payments are generally made every 6 months, paying one-half of the coupon amount. This would be $45 in our example.

The issuer of a bond initially sells the bonds to raise capital immediately, and then is obligated to make the prescribed payments. Usually bonds are issued with coupon rates close to the prevailing general rate of interest so that they will sell at close to their face value. However, as time passes, bonds frequently trade at prices different from their face values. While any two parties can agree on a price and execute a trade, the vast majority of bonds are sold either at auction (when originally issued) or through an exchange organization. The price is therefore determined by a market and thus may vary minute by minute.

An example of publicly available bond quotes (for U.S. Treasury bonds and notes) is shown in Table 3.3. Here the indicated coupon rate is the annual rate (one-

TABLE 3.3
U.S. Treasury Bills, Notes, and Bonds

GOVT. BONDS & NOTES											
Rate	Maturity Mo/Yr	Bid	Asked	Chg.	Ask Yld.	Rate	Maturity Mo/Yr	Bid	Asked	Chg.	Ask Yld.
						5⅞	Feb 04n	97:28	97:29	+ 9	6.25
4¾	Feb 97n	99:31	100:00	.....	4.64	7¼	May 04n	105:20	105:22	+11	6.26
6¾	Feb 97n	100:00	100:02	− 1	4.98	12⅜	May 04	135:03	135:09	+18	6.24
6⅞	Feb 97n	100:00	100:02	− 1	5.09	7¼	Aug 04n	105:21	105:25	+13	6.27
6⅝	Mar 97n	100:04	100:06	.....	4.97	13¾	Aug 04	144:04	144:10	+20	6.26
6⅞	Mar 97n	100:05	100:07	.....	4.97	7⅞	Nov 04n	109:20	109:22	+16	6.27
8½	Apr 97n	100:15	100:17	− 1	5.10	11⅝	Nov 04	132:08	132:14	+19	6.27
6½	Apr 97n	100:07	100:09	.....	5.03	7½	Feb 05n	107:09	107:12	+11	6.31
6⅞	Apr 97n	100:09	100:11	.....	5.10	6½	May 05n	101:08	101:10	+17	6.29
6½	May 97n	100:08	100:10	.....	5.14	8¼	May 00-05	105:24	105:26	+ 6	6.24
8½	May 97n	100:24	100:26	.....	5.08	12	May 05	136:00	136:06	+20	6.30
6⅛	May 97n	100:06	100:08	+ 1	5.19	6½	Aug 05n	101:08	101:10	+18	6.30
6¾	May 97n	100:11	100:13	.....	5.26	10¾	Aug 05	128:20	128:26	+20	6.32
5⅝	Jun 97n	100:03	100:05	.....	5.16	5⅞	Nov 05n	97:01	97:03	+18	6.31
6⅜	Jun 97n	100:12	100:14	.....	5.15	5⅝	Feb 06n	95:08	95:10	+18	6.32
8½	Jul 97n	101:09	101:11	.....	5.17	9⅜	Feb 06	120:25	120:31	+21	6.29
5½	Jul 97n	100:02	100:04	+ 1	5.21	6⅞	May 06n	103:21	103:23	+19	6.34

Price

Coupon rate   Maturity date   Denotes note   Change in asked price   Yield to maturity

Prices are quoted as a percentage of face value, with the fractional part expressed in 32nd's. Accrued interest must be added to the quoted price.
Source: *The Wall Street Journal,* February 14, 1997.

half being paid every 6 months in this case). The maturity month is given; the precise maturity date varies with the issue, but it is often the fifteenth of the month of maturity for U.S. Treasury bonds and notes. Prices are quoted as a percentage of face value, so if the face value is $1,000, a price of 100 is equivalent to $1,000. The **bid price** is the price dealers are willing to pay for the bond, and hence the price at which the bond can be sold immediately; whereas the **ask price** is the price at which dealers are willing to sell the bond, and hence the price at which it can be bought immediately. A special and cumbersome feature is that prices are quoted in 32nd's of a point. The bid price for the last bond shown in Table 3.3 is 103 30/32, which for a $1,000 face value translates into $1,039.38. The yield shown is based on the ask price in a manner described in the following section.

Bond quotations ignore **accrued interest,** which must be added to the price quoted in order to obtain the actual amount that must be paid for the bond. Suppose that a bond makes coupon payments every 6 months. If you purchase the bond midway through the coupon period, you will receive your first coupon payment after only 3 months. You are getting extra interest—interest that was, in theory, earned by the previous owner. So you must pay the first 3 months' interest to the previous owner. This interest payment is made at the time of the sale, not when the next coupon payment is made, so this extra payment acts like an addition to the price. The accrued interest that must be paid to the previous owner is determined by a straight-line interpolation based on days. Specifically, the accrued interest (AI) is

$$AI = \frac{\text{number of days since last coupon}}{\text{number of days in current coupon period}} \times \text{coupon amount} .$$

Example 3.5 (Accrued interest calculation)   Suppose we purchase on May 8 a U.S. Treasury bond that matures on August 15 in some distant year. The coupon rate is 9%. Coupon payments are made every February 15 and August 15. The accrued interest is computed by noting that there have been 83 days since the last coupon (in a leap year) and 99 days until the next coupon payment. Hence,

$$AI = \frac{83}{83 + 99} \times 4.50 = 2.05 .$$

This 2.05 would be added to the quoted price, expressed as a percentage of the face value. For example, $20.50 would be added to the bond if its face value were $1,000.

Quality Ratings

Although bonds offer a supposedly fixed-income stream, they are subject to default if the issuer has financial difficulties or falls into bankruptcy. To characterize the nature of this risk, bonds are rated by rating organizations. The two primary rating classifications are issued and published by Moody's and Standard & Poor's. Their classification schemes are shown in Table 3.4. U.S. Treasury securities are not rated, since they are considered to be essentially free of default risk.

TABLE 3.4
Rating Classifications

	Moody's	Standard & Poor's
High grade	Aaa	AAA
	Aa	AA
Medium grade	A	A
	Baa	BBB
Speculative grade	Ba	BB
	B	B
Default danger	Caa	CCC
	Ca	CC
	C	C
		D

Ratings reflect a judgment of the likelihood that bond pay-ments will be made as scheduled. Bonds with low ratings usually sell at lower prices than comparable bonds with high ratings.

Bonds that are either high or medium grade are considered to be **investment grade.** Bonds that are in or below the speculative category are often termed **junk bonds.** Historically, the frequency of default has correlated well with the assigned ratings.

The assignment of a rating class by a rating organization is largely based on the issuer's financial status as measured by various financial ratios. For example, the ratio of debt to equity, the ratio of current assets to current liabilities, the ratio of cash flow to outstanding debt, as well as several others are used. The trend in these ratios is also considered important.

A bond with a low rating will have a lower price than a comparable bond with a high rating. Hence some people have argued that junk bonds may occasionally offer good value if the default risk can be diversified. A careful analysis of this approach requires explicit consideration of uncertainty, however.

3.4 YIELD

A bond's yield is the interest rate implied by the payment structure. Specifically, it is the interest rate at which the present value of the stream of payments (consisting of the coupon payments and the final face-value redemption payment) is exactly equal to the current price. This value is termed more properly the **yield to maturity** (YTM) to distinguish it from other yield numbers that are sometimes used. Yields are always quoted on an annual basis.

It should be clear that the yield to maturity is just the internal rate of return of the bond at the current price. But when discussing bonds, the term *yield* is generally used instead.

Suppose that a bond with face value F makes m coupon payments of C/m each year and there are n periods remaining. The coupon payments sum to C within a year;

the face value of the bond is F. Suppose also that the current price of the bond is P. Then the yield to maturity is the value of λ such that

$$P = \frac{F}{[1 + (\lambda/m)]^n} + \sum_{k=1}^{n} \frac{C/m}{[1 + (\lambda/m)]^k} . \tag{3.1}$$

This value of λ, the yield to maturity, is the interest rate implied by the bond when interest is compounded m times per year. Note that the first term in (3.1) is the present value of the face-value payment. The kth term in the summation is the present value of the kth coupon payment C/m. The sum of the present values, based on a nominal interest rate of λ, is set equal to the bond's price.

The summation in (3.1) can be collapsed by use of the general value formula for annuities in the previous section, since this sum represents the present value of the equal coupon payments of C/m. The collapsed form is highlighted here:

Bond price formula   *The price of a bond, having exactly n coupon periods remaining to maturity and a yield to maturity of λ, satisfies*

$$P = \frac{F}{[1 + (\lambda/m)]^n} + \frac{C}{\lambda} \left\{ 1 - \frac{1}{[1 + (\lambda/m)]^n} \right\} \tag{3.2}$$

where F is the face value of the bond, C is the yearly coupon payment, and m is the number of coupon payments per year.

Equation (3.2) must be solved for λ to determine the yield. This cannot be done by hand except for very simple cases. It should be clear that the terms in (3.2) are the familiar terms giving the present value of a single future payment and of an annuity. However, to determine λ one must do more than just evaluate these expressions. One must adjust λ so that (3.2) is satisfied. As in any calculation of internal rate of return, this generally requires an iterative procedure, easily carried out by a computer. There are, however, specialized calculators and bond tables devised for this purpose, which are used by bond dealers and other professionals. Spreadsheet packages also typically have built-in bond formulas.

The formulas discussed here assume that there is an exact number of coupon periods remaining to the maturity date. The price–yield formula requires adjustment for dates between coupon payment dates.

Qualitative Nature of Price–Yield Curves

Although the bond equation is complex, it is easy to obtain a qualitative understanding of the relationship between price, yield, coupon, and time to maturity. This qualitative understanding helps motivate the ideas underlying bond portfolio construction and, specifically, leads to an understanding of the interest rate risk properties of bonds. The following examples should be studied with an eye toward obtaining this kind of understanding.

As a general rule, the yields of various bonds track one another and the prevailing interest rates of other fixed-income securities quite closely. After all, most people would not buy a bond with a yield of 6% when bank CDs are offering 10%. The general interest rate environment exerts a force on every bond, urging its yield to conform to that of other bonds. However, the only way that the yield of a bond can change is for the bond's price to change. So as yields move, prices move correspondingly. But the price change required to match a yield change varies with the structure of the bond (its coupon rate and its maturity). So as the yields of various bonds move more or less in harmony, their prices move by different amounts. To understand bonds, it is important to understand this relation between the price and the yield. For a given bond, this relationship is shown pictorially by the **price–yield curve.**

Examples of price–yield curves are shown in Figure 3.3. Here the price, as a percentage of par, is shown as a function of YTM expressed in percentage terms. Let us focus on the bond labeled 10%. This bond has a 10% coupon (which means 10% of the face value is paid each year, or 5% every 6 months), and it has 30 years to maturity. The price–yield curve shows how yield and price are related.

The first obvious feature of the curve is that it has negative slope; that is, price and yield have an inverse relation. If yield goes up, price goes down. If I am to obtain a higher yield on a fixed stream of received payments, the price I pay for this stream must be lower. This is a fundamental feature of bond markets. When people say "the bond market went down," they mean that interest rates went up.

Some points on the curve can be calculated by inspection. First, suppose that YTM = 0. This means that the bond is priced as if it offered no interest. Within the framework of this bond, money in the future is not discounted. In that case, the present value of the bond is just equal to the sum of all payments: here coupon payments of 10 points each year for 30 years, giving 300, plus the 100% of par value received at maturity, for a total of 400. This is the value of the bond at zero yield. Second, suppose that YTM = 10%. Then the value of the bond is equal to the par value. The reason for this is that each year the coupon payment just equals the 10% yield expected on the

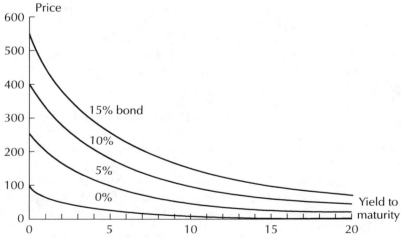

FIGURE 3.3   Price–yield curves and coupon rate. All bonds shown have a maturity of 30 years and the coupon rates indicated on the respective curves. Prices are expressed as a percentage of par.

investment. The value remains at 100 every year. The bond is like a loan where the interest on the principal is paid each year and hence the principal remains constant. In this situation, where the yield is exactly equal to the coupon rate, the bond is termed a **par bond.** In addition to these two specific points on the price–yield curve, we can deduce that the price of the bond must tend toward zero as the yield increases—large yields imply heavy discounting, so even the nearest coupon payment has little present value. Overall, the shape of the curve is **convex** since it bends toward the origin and out toward the horizontal axis. Just given the two points and this rough knowledge of shape, it is possible to sketch a reasonable approximation to the true curve.

Let us briefly examine another one of the curves, say, the 15% bond. The price at YTM = 0 is $15 \times 30 + 100 = 550$, and the par point of 100 is at 15%. We see that with a fixed maturity date, the price–yield curve rises as the coupon rate increases.

Now let us consider the influence of the time to maturity. Figure 3.4 shows the price–yield curves for three different bonds. Each of these bonds has a 10% coupon rate, but they have different maturities: 30 years, 10 years, and 3 years. All of these bonds are at par when the yield is 10%; hence the three curves all pass through the common par point. However, the curves pivot upward around that point by various amounts, depending on the maturity. The values at YTM = 0 can be found easily, as before, by simply summing the total payments. The main feature is that as the maturity is increased, the price–yield curve becomes steeper, essentially pivoting about the par point. This increased steepness is an indication that longer maturities imply greater sensitivity of price to yield.

The price–yield curve is important because it describes the interest rate risk associated with a bond. For example, suppose that you purchased the 10% bond illustrated in Figure 3.3 at par (when the yield was 10%). It is likely that all bonds of maturity approximately equal to 30 years would have yields of 10%, even though some might not be at par. Then 10% would represent the market rate for such bonds.

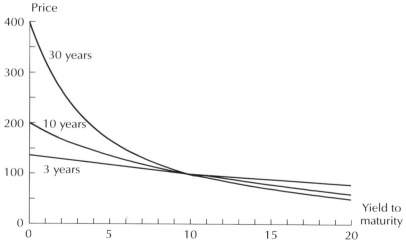

FIGURE 3.4 Price–yield curves and maturity. The price–yield curve is shown for three maturities. All bonds have a 10% coupon.

TABLE 3.5
Prices of 9% Coupon Bonds

Time to maturity	Yield				
	5%	8%	9%	10%	15%
1 year	103.85	100.94	100.00	99.07	94.61
5 years	117.50	104.06	100.00	96.14	79.41
10 years	131.18	106.80	100.00	93.77	69.42
20 years	150.21	109.90	100.00	91.42	62.22
30 years	161.82	111.31	100.00	90.54	60.52

The prices of long-maturity bonds are more sensitive to yield changes than are the prices of bonds of short maturity.

Now suppose that market conditions change and the yield on your bond increases to 11%. The price of your bond will drop to 91.28. This represents an 8.72% change in the value of your bond. It is good to consider the possibility of such a change when purchasing this bond. For example, with a 3-year 10% par bond, if the yield rose to 11%, the price would drop only to 97.50, and hence the interest rate risk is lower with this bond. Of course if yields *decreased*, you would *profit* by similar amounts.

Bond holders are subject to yield risk in the sense described: if yields change, bond prices also change. This is an immediate risk, affecting the near-term value of the bond. You may, of course, continue to hold the bond and thereby continue to receive the promised coupon payments and the face value at maturity. This cash flow stream is not affected by interest rates. (That is after all why the bond is classified as a fixed-income security.) But if you plan to sell the bond before maturity, the price will be governed by the price–yield curve.

Table 3.5 displays the price–yield relation in tabular form for bonds with a 9% coupon rate. It is easy to see that the bond with 30-year maturity is much more sensitive to yield changes than the bond with 1-year maturity.

It is the quantification of this risk that underlies the importance of the price–yield relation. Our rough qualitative understanding is important. The next sections develop additional tools for studying this risk.

Other Yield Measures

Other measures of yield, aside from yield to maturity, are used to gain additional insight into a bond's properties. For example, one important yield measure is **current yield** (CY), which is defined as

$$CY = \frac{\text{annual coupon payment}}{\text{bond price}} \times 100.$$

The current yield gives a measure of the annual return of the bond. For instance, consider a 10%, 30-year bond. If it is selling at par (that is, at 100), then the current yield is 10, which is identical to the coupon rate and to the yield to maturity. If the same bond were selling for 90, then CY = 10/90 = 11.11 while YTM = 11.16.

Another measure, used if the bond is callable after some number of years, is the **yield to call** (YTC), which is defined as the internal rate of return calculated assuming that the bond is in fact called at the earliest possible date.

There are several other yield measures that account for sinking funds, principal payments, and other features.

3.5 DURATION

Everything else being equal, bonds with long maturities have steeper price–yield curves than bonds with short maturities. Hence the prices of **long bonds** are more sensitive to interest rate changes than those of **short bonds.** This is shown clearly in Table 3.5. However, this is only a rough rule of thumb. Maturity itself does not give a complete quantitative measure of interest rate sensitivity.

Another measure of time length termed **duration** *does* give a direct measure of interest rate sensitivity. This section describes this measure.

The duration of a fixed-income instrument is a weighted average of the times that payments (cash flows) are made. The weighting coefficients are the present values of the individual cash flows.

We can write out this definition more explicitly. Suppose that cash flows are received at times $t_0, t_1, t_2, \ldots, t_n$. Then the duration of this stream is

$$D = \frac{\mathrm{PV}(t_0)t_0 + \mathrm{PV}(t_1)t_1 + \mathrm{PV}(t_2)t_2 + \cdots + \mathrm{PV}(t_n)t_n}{\mathrm{PV}}.$$

In this formula the expression $\mathrm{PV}(t_k)$ denotes the present value of the cash flow that occurs at time t_k. The term PV in the denominator is the total present value, which is the sum of the individual $\mathrm{PV}(t_k)$ values.

The expression for D is indeed a weighted average of the cash flow times. Hence D itself has units of time. When the cash flows are all nonnegative, as they are for a bond already owned (so that the purchase is not included in the cash flow), then it is clear that $t_0 \leq D \leq t_n$. Duration is a time intermediate between the first and last cash flows.

Clearly, a zero-coupon bond, which makes only a final payment at maturity, has a duration equal to its maturity date. Nonzero-coupon bonds have durations strictly less than their maturity dates. This shows that duration can be viewed as a generalized maturity measure. It is an average of the maturities of all the individual payments.

Macaulay Duration

The preceding definition is (intentionally) a bit vague about how the present value is calculated; that is, what interest rate to use. For a bond it is natural to base those calculations on the bond's yield. If indeed the yield is used, the general duration formula becomes the Macaulay duration.

Specifically, suppose a financial instrument makes payments m times per year, with the payment in period k being c_k, and there are n periods remaining. The

A	B	C	D	E	F	
		Discount factor	Present value of payment	Weight		
Year	Payment	(@ 8%)	($B \times C$)	(D/Price)	A	E
.5	3.5	.962	3.365	.035		.017
1	3.5	.925	3.236	.033		.033
1.5	3.5	.889	3.111	.032		.048
2	3.5	.855	2.992	.031		.061
2.5	3.5	.822	2.877	.030		.074
3	103.5	.790	81.798	.840		2.520
Sum			97.379	1.000		2.753
			Price			Duration

FIGURE 3.5 Layout for calculating duration. Present values of payments are calculated in column D. Dividing these by the total present value gives the weights shown in column E. The duration is obtained using this weighted average of the payment times.

Macaulay duration D is defined as

$$D = \frac{\sum_{k=1}^{n} (k/m)c_k/[1 + (\lambda/m)]^k}{\text{PV}}$$

where λ is the yield to maturity and

$$\text{PV} = \sum_{k=1}^{n} \frac{c_k}{[1 + (\lambda/m)]^k}.$$

Note that the factor k/m in the numerator of the formula for D is time, measured in years. In this chapter we always use the Macaulay duration (or a slight modification of it), and hence we do not give it a special symbol, but denote it by D, the same as in the general definition of duration.

Example 3.6 (A short bond) Consider a 7% bond with 3 years to maturity. Assume that the bond is selling at 8% yield. We can find the value and the Macaulay duration by the simple spreadsheet layout shown in Figure 3.5. The duration is 2.753 years.

Explicit Formula*

In the case where all coupon payments are identical (which is the normal case for bonds) there is an explicit formula for the sum of the series that appears in the numerator of the expression for the Macaulay duration. We skip the algebra here and just give the result.

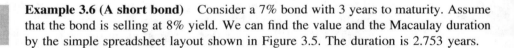

Macaulay duration formula *The Macaulay duration for a bond with a coupon rate c per period, yield y per period, m periods per year, and exactly n periods remaining, is*

$$D = \frac{1+y}{my} - \frac{1 + y + n(c - y)}{mc[(1 + y)^n - 1] + my}. \tag{3.3}$$

Example 3.7 (Duration of a 30-year par bond) Consider the 10%, 30-year bond represented in Figure 3.3. Let us assume that it is at par; that is, the yield is 10%. At par, $c = y$, and (3.3) reduces to

$$D = \frac{1+y}{my}\left[1 - \frac{1}{(1+y)^n}\right].$$

Hence,

$$D = \frac{1.05}{.1}\left[1 - \frac{1}{(1.05)^{60}}\right] = 9.938.$$

Qualitative Properties of Duration*

The duration of a coupon-paying bond is always less than its maturity, but often it is surprisingly short. An appreciation for the relation between a bond's duration and other parameters of the bond can be obtained by examination of Table 3.6. In this table the yield is held fixed at 5%, but various maturities and coupon rates are considered. This procedure approximates the situation of looking through a list of available bonds at a time when all yields hover near 5%. Within a given class (say, government securities) the available bonds then differ mainly by these two parameters.

One striking feature of this table is that as the time to maturity increases to infinity, the durations do *not* also increase to infinity, but instead tend to a finite limit that is independent of the coupon rate. (See Exercise 14.) Another feature of the table is that the durations do not vary rapidly with respect to the coupon rate. The fact that the yield is held constant tends to cancel out the influence of the coupons.

A general conclusion is that very long durations (of, say, 20 years or more) are achieved only by bonds that have both very long maturities and very low coupon rates.

TABLE 3.6
Duration of a Bond Yielding 5%
as Function of Maturity and Coupon Rate

Years to maturity	Coupon rate			
	1%	2%	5%	10%
1	.997	.995	.988	.977
2	1.984	1.969	1.928	1.868
5	4.875	4.763	4.485	4.156
10	9.416	8.950	7.989	7.107
25	20.164	17.715	14.536	12.754
50	26.666	22.284	18.765	17.384
100	22.572	21.200	20.363	20.067
∞	20.500	20.500	20.500	20.500

Duration does not increase appreciably with maturity. In fact, with fixed yield, duration increases only to a finite limit as maturity is increased.

Duration and Sensitivity

Duration is useful because it measures directly the sensitivity of price to changes in yield. This follows from a simple expression for the derivative of the present value expression.

In the case where payments are made m times per year and yield is based on those same periods, we have

$$PV_k = \frac{c_k}{[1 + (\lambda/m)]^k} .$$

The derivative with respect to λ is

$$\frac{d\,PV_k}{d\lambda} = \frac{-(k/m)c_k}{[1 + (\lambda/m)]^{k+1}} = -\frac{k/m}{1 + (\lambda/m)}PV_k .$$

We now apply this to the expression for price,

$$P = \sum_{k=1}^{n} PV_k .$$

Here we have used the fact that the price is equal to the total present value at the yield (by definition of yield). We find that

$$\frac{dP}{d\lambda} = \sum_{k=1}^{n} \frac{d\,PV_k}{d\lambda} = -\sum_{k=1}^{n} \frac{(k/m)PV_k}{1 + (\lambda/m)} = -\frac{1}{1 + (\lambda/m)}DP \equiv -D_M P . \tag{3.4}$$

The value D_M is called the **modified duration.** It is the usual duration modified by the extra term in the denominator. Note that $D_M \approx D$ for large values of m or small values of λ. We highlight this important sensitivity relation:

Price sensitivity formula   *The derivative of price P with respect to yield λ of a fixed-income security is*

$$\frac{dP}{d\lambda} = -D_M P \tag{3.5}$$

where $D_M = D/[1 + (\lambda/m)]$ is the modified duration.

It is perhaps most revealing to write (3.5) as

$$\frac{1}{P}\frac{dP}{d\lambda} = -D_M.$$

The left side is then the relative change in price (or the fractional change). Hence D_M measures the relative change in a bond's price directly as λ changes.

By using the approximation $dP/d\lambda \approx \Delta P/\Delta\lambda$, Equation (3.5) can be used to estimate the change in price due to a small change in yield (or vice versa). Specifically, we would write

$$\Delta P \approx -D_M P \,\Delta\lambda .$$

This gives explicit values for the impact of yield variations.

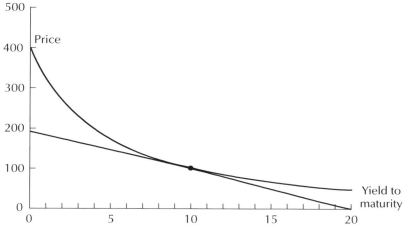

FIGURE 3.6   Price–yield curve and slope. The slope of the line tangent to the curve at P is $-D_M P$.

Example 3.8 (A 10% bond)   The price–yield curve for a 30-year, 10% coupon bond is shown in Figure 3.6. As computed earlier, the duration of this bond at the par point (where price $= 100$) is $D = 9.94$. Hence $D_M = 9.94/1.05 = 9.47$. The slope of the price–yield curve at that point is, according to (3.3), equal to $dP/d\lambda = -947$. A line with this slope can be placed tangent to the price–yield curve at the point where the duration was calculated, as shown in Figure 3.6. This line provides a straight-line approximation to the curve for nearby points. For example, if the yield changes to 11%, we can estimate the change in price as

$$\Delta P = -D_M 100\, \Delta\lambda = -947 \times .01 = -9.47 \,.$$

Hence $P \approx 90.53$.

Example 3.9 (A zero-coupon bond)   Consider a 30-year zero-coupon bond. Suppose its current yield is 10%. Then we have $D = 30$ and $D_M \approx 27$. Suppose that yields increase to 11%. According to (3.2), the relative price change is approximately equal to 27%. This is a very large loss in value. Because of their long durations, zero-coupon bonds have very high interest rate risk.

Duration of a Portfolio

Suppose that a portfolio of several bonds of different maturities is assembled. This portfolio acts like a master fixed-income security: it receives periodic payments, but due to the different maturities, the payments may not be of equal magnitude. What can we say about the duration of this portfolio?

First, suppose that all the bonds have the same yield. (This is usually approximately true, since yields tend to track each other closely, if not exactly.) The duration of the portfolio is then just a weighted sum of the durations of the individual bonds—with weighting coefficients proportional to individual bond prices. We can easily verify this for a portfolio that is the sum of two bonds A and B. The durations are

$$D^A = \frac{\sum_{k=0}^{n} t_k PV_k^A}{P^A}$$

$$D^B = \frac{\sum_{k=0}^{n} t_k PV_k^B}{P^B}.$$

Hence,

$$P^A D^A + P^B D^B = \sum_{k=0}^{n} t_k \left(PV_k^A + PV_k^B \right)$$

which gives, upon division by $P = P^A + P^B$,

$$D = \frac{P^A D^A}{P} + \frac{P^B D^B}{P}$$

as the duration of the portfolio. Therefore D is a weighted average of the durations of the individual bonds, with the weight of a bond's duration being proportional to that bond's price. The result easily extends to a portfolio containing several bonds.

Duration of a portfolio   *Suppose there are m fixed-income securities with prices and durations of P_i and D_i, respectively, $i = 1, 2, \ldots, m$, all computed at a common yield. The portfolio consisting of the aggregate of these securities has price P and duration D, given by*

$$P = P_1 + P_2 + \cdots + P_m$$

$$D = w_1 D_1 + w_2 D_2 + \cdots + w_m D_m$$

where $w_i = P_i/P$, $i = 1, 2, \ldots, m$.

The duration of a portfolio measures the interest rate sensitivity of that portfolio, just as normal duration measures it for a single bond. That is, if the yield changes by a small amount, the total value of the portfolio will change approximately by the amount predicted by the equation relating prices to (modified) duration.

If the bonds composing a portfolio have different yields, the composite duration as defined can still be used as an approximation. In this case a single yield must be chosen—perhaps the average. Then present values can be calculated with respect to this single yield value, although these present values will not be exactly equal to the prices of the bonds. The weighted average duration, calculated as shown, will give the sensitivity of the overall present value to a change in the yield figure that is used.

3.6 IMMUNIZATION

We now have the concepts and tools necessary to solve a problem of major practical value, namely, the structuring of a bond portfolio to protect against interest rate risk.

This procedure is termed **immunization** because it "immunizes" the portfolio value against interest rate changes. The procedure, as well as its refinements, is in fact one of the most (if not *the* most) widely used analytical techniques of investment science, shaping portfolios consisting of billions of dollars of fixed-income securities held by pension funds, insurance companies, and other financial institutions.

Before describing the procedure, let us more fully consider its purpose. A portfolio cannot be structured meaningfully without a statement of its purpose. The purpose helps define the character of risk one is willing to assume. For example, suppose that you wish to invest money now that will be used next year for a major household expense. If you invest in 1-year Treasury bills, you know exactly how much money these bills will be worth in a year, and hence there is little risk relative to your purpose. If, on the other hand, you invested in a 10-year zero-coupon bond, the value of this bond a year from now would be quite variable, depending on what happens to interest rates during the year. This investment has high risk relative to your purpose. The situation would be reversed if you were saving the money to pay off an obligation that was due in 10 years. Then the 10-year zero-coupon bond would provide completely predictable results, but the 1-year Treasury bill would impose **reinvestment risk** since the proceeds would have to be reinvested after 1 year at the then prevailing rate (which could be considerably lower than the current rate).

Suppose now that you face a series of cash obligations and you wish to acquire a portfolio that you will use to pay these obligations as they arise. (This is the sort of problem faced by life insurance companies.) One way to do this is to purchase a set of zero-coupon bonds that have maturities and face values exactly matching the separate obligations. However, this simple technique may not be feasible if corporate bonds are used, since there are few corporate zero-coupon bonds. (You may wish to use corporate bonds because they offer higher yields than U.S. Treasury bonds.) If perfect matching is not possible, you may instead acquire a portfolio having a value equal to the present value of the stream of obligations. You can sell some of your portfolio whenever cash is needed to meet a particular obligation; or if your portfolio delivers more cash than needed at a given time (from coupon or face value payments), you can buy more bonds. If the yield does not change, the value of your portfolio will, throughout this process, continue to match the present value of the remaining obligations. Hence you will meet the obligations exactly.

A problem with this present-value-matching technique arises if the yields change. The value of your portfolio and the present value of the obligation stream will both change in response, but probably by amounts that differ from one another. Your portfolio will no longer be matched.

Immunization solves this problem—at least approximately—by matching durations as well as present values. If the duration of the portfolio matches that of the obligation stream, then the cash value of the portfolio and the present value of the obligation stream will respond identically (to first order) to a change in yield. Specifically, if yields increase, the present value of the asset portfolio will decrease, but the present value of the obligation will decrease by approximately the same amount; so the value of the portfolio will still be adequate to cover the obligation. The process is best explained through an example.

Example 3.10 (The X Corporation)   The X Corporation has an obligation to pay $1 million in 10 years. It wishes to invest money now that will be sufficient to meet this obligation.

The purchase of a single zero-coupon bond would provide one solution; but such zeros are not always available in the required maturities. We assume that none are available for this example. Instead the X Corporation is planning to select from the three corporate bonds shown in Table 3.7. (Note that in this table, and throughout this example, prices are expressed in ordinary decimal form, not in 32nd's.)

These bonds all have the same yield of 9%, and this rate is used in all calculations. The X Corporation first considers using bonds 2 and 3 to construct its portfolio. As a first step it calculates the durations and finds $D_2 = 6.54$ and $D_3 = 9.61$, respectively. This is a serious problem! The duration of the obligation is obviously 10 years, and there is no way to attain that with a weighted average of D_2 and D_3 using positive weights. A bond with a longer duration is required. Therefore the X Corporation decides to use bonds 1 and 2. It is found that $D_1 = 11.44$. (Note that, consistent with the discussion on the qualitative nature of durations, it is quite difficult to obtain a long duration when the yield is 9%—a long maturity and a low coupon are required.) Fortunately $D_1 > 10$, and hence bonds 1 and 2 will work.

Next the present value of the obligation is computed at 9% interest. This is PV = $414,643. The immunized portfolio is found by solving the two equations

$$V_1 + V_2 = \text{PV}$$

$$D_1 V_1 + D_2 V_2 = 10\,\text{PV}$$

for the amounts of money V_1 and V_2 to be invested in the two bonds. The first equation states that the total value of the portfolio must equal the total present value of the obligation. The second states that the duration of the portfolio must equal the duration (10 years) of the obligation. (This relation is best seen by dividing through by PV.) The solution to these equations is $V_1 = \$292,788.73$ and $V_2 = \$121,854.27$. The number of bonds to be purchased is then found by dividing each value by the respective bond price. (We assume a face value of $100.) These numbers are then rounded to integers to define the portfolio.

The results are shown in Table 3.8. Note that, except for rounding error, the present value of the portfolio does indeed equal that of the obligation. Furthermore, at different yields (8% and 10% are shown) the value of the portfolio is still approximately equal to that of the obligation. In fact, due to the structure of the price–yield

TABLE 3.7
Bond Choices

	Rate	Maturity	Price	Yield
Bond 1	6%	30 yr	69.04	9.00%
Bond 2	11%	10 yr	113.01	9.00%
Bond 3	9%	20 yr	100.00	9.00%

Three bonds are considered for the X Corporation's immunized portfolio.

TABLE 3.8
Immunization Results

	Percent yield		
	9.0	**8.0**	**10.0**
Bond 1			
Price	69.04	77.38	62.14
Shares	4,241.00	4,241.00	4,241.00
Value	292,798.64	328,168.58	263,535.74
Bond 2			
Price	113.01	120.39	106.23
Shares	1,078.00	1,078.00	1,078.00
Value	121,824.78	129,780.42	114,515.94
Obligation			
Value	414,642.86	456,386.95	376,889.48
Surplus	−19.44	1,562.05	1,162.20

The net surplus of portfolio value minus obligation value remains approximately equal to zero even if yields change.

curve, the portfolio value will always exceed the value of the obligation in both cases. (See Exercise 16.)

Immunization provides protection against changes in yield. If the yield changes immediately after purchase of the portfolio, the new value of the portfolio will, in theory, still approximately match the new value of the future obligation. However, once the yield does change, the new portfolio will not be immunized at the new rate. It is therefore desirable to **rebalance,** or reimmunize, the portfolio from time to time. Also, in practice more than two bonds would be used, partly to diversify default risk if the bonds included are not U.S. Treasury bonds.

Immunization is a clever idea, but it suffers some shortcomings, at least in this simple form. The method assumes that all yields are equal, whereas in fact they usually are not. Indeed it is quite unrealistic to assume that both long- and short-duration bonds can be found with identical yields. Usually long bonds have somewhat higher yields than short bonds. Furthermore, when yields change, it is unlikely that the yields on all bonds will change by the same amount; hence rebalancing would be difficult. We shall consider some important extensions of immunization in the next chapter, and in Chapter 5 we shall consider other approaches to bond portfolio construction. Overall, however, the technique given here is surprisingly practical.

3.7 CONVEXITY*

Modified duration measures the relative slope of the price–yield curve at a given point. As we have seen, this leads to a straight-line approximation to the price–yield curve that is useful both as a means of assessing risk and as a procedure for controlling it.

An even better approximation can be obtained by including a second-order (or quadratic) term. This second-order term is based on **convexity,** which is the relative curvature at a given point on the price–yield curve. Specifically, convexity is the value of C defined as

$$C = \frac{1}{P} \frac{\mathrm{d}^2 P}{\mathrm{d}\lambda^2}$$

which can be expressed in terms of the cash flow stream as

$$C = \frac{1}{P} \sum_{k=1}^{n} \frac{\mathrm{d}^2 \mathrm{PV}_k}{\mathrm{d}\lambda^2} .$$

Assuming m coupons (and m compounding periods) per year, we have

$$C = \frac{1}{P[1 + (\lambda/m)]^2} \sum_{k=1}^{n} \frac{k(k+1)}{m^2} \frac{c_k}{[1 + (\lambda/m)]^k} .$$

Note that convexity has units of time squared. Convexity is the weighted average of $t_k t_{k+1}$ where, like for duration, the weights are proportional to the present values of the corresponding cash flows. Then the result is *modified* by the factor $1/[1 + (\lambda/m)]^2$. An explicit formula can be derived for the case of equal-valued coupon payments.

Suppose that at a price P and a corresponding yield λ, the modified duration D_M and the convexity C are calculated. Then if $\Delta\lambda$ is a small change in λ and ΔP is the corresponding change in P, we have

$$\Delta P \approx -D_M P \, \Delta\lambda + \frac{PC}{2}(\Delta\lambda)^2.$$

This is the second-order approximation to the price–yield curve. Convexity can be used to improve immunization in the sense that, compared to ordinary immunization, a closer match of asset portfolio value and obligation value is maintained as yields vary. To account for convexity in immunization, one structures a portfolio of bonds such that its present value, its duration, and its convexity match those of the obligation. Generally, at least three bonds are required for this purpose.

3.8 SUMMARY

Fixed-income securities are fundamental investment instruments, which are part of essentially every investment portfolio, and which reflect the market conditions for interest rates directly.

There are numerous kinds of fixed-income securities, designed for various investment and business purposes. However, the vast bulk of money in fixed-income securities is committed to mortgages and bonds.

Many fixed-income securities make periodic payments to the owner of the security. This is true, in particular, for mortgages, loans, annuities, and bonds. In the case of bonds, these payments are usually made every 6 months and are termed coupon payments.

Usually the periodic payments associated with a fixed-income security are of equal magnitude, and there is an important formula relating the payment amount A, the principal value of the security P, the single-period interest rate r, and the number of payment periods n:

$$P = \frac{A}{r}\left[1 - \frac{1}{(1+r)^n}\right].$$

This single formula can be used to evaluate most annuities, mortgages, and bonds, and it can be used to amortize capital expenses over time.

Bonds are the most important type of fixed-income security for general investment purposes. Important reference bonds are U.S. Treasury securities—bills, notes, and bonds—of various maturities and coupon values. These bonds are considered to be default free and thus carry prices that are somewhat higher than corporate securities with similar coupon rates and maturities.

There are many variations to the generic coupon bond—call features, sinking fund bonds, bonds whose coupon rates are tied to economic indices, and so forth. In addition, municipal bonds receive special tax treatment.

A special feature of bonds is that the buyer must usually pay accrued interest in addition to the quoted price. This accrued interest is compensation to the previous owner for the coupon interest that has been earned since the last coupon payment.

Bonds are frequently analyzed by computing the yield to maturity. This is the annual interest rate that is implied by the current price. It is the interest rate that makes the present value of the promised bond payments equal to the current bond price. This calculation of yield can be turned around: the price of a bond can be found as a function of the yield. This is the price–yield relation which, when plotted, produces the price–yield curve.

The slope of the price–yield curve is a measure of the sensitivity of the price to changes in yield. Since yields tend to track the prevailing interest rate, the slope of the price–yield curve is therefore a measure of the interest rate risk associated with a particular bond. As a general rule, long bonds have greater slope than short bonds, and thus long bonds have greater interest rate risk. A normalized version of the slope—the slope divided by the current bond price—is given by the (modified) duration of the bond. Hence duration (or, more exactly, modified duration) is a convenient measure of interest rate risk.

Immunization is the process of constructing a portfolio that has, to first order, no interest rate risk. The process is frequently applied by institutions, such as insurance companies and pension funds, that have large future payment obligations. They wish to prepare for these obligations by making appropriate investments in fixed-income securities. A portfolio is immunized if its present value is equal to that of the stream of obligations and if its duration matches that of the obligation. In other words, the net portfolio, consisting of the obligation stream and the fixed-income assets, has zero present value and zero duration.

EXERCISES

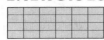

1. (Amortization)   A debt of $25,000 is to be amortized over 7 years at 7% interest. What value of monthly payments will achieve this?

2. (Cycles and annual worth ◇)   Given a cash flow stream $X = (x_0, x_1, x_2, \ldots, x_n)$, a new stream X_∞ of infinite length is made by successively repeating the corresponding finite stream. The interest rate is r. Let P and A be the present value and the annual worth, respectively, of stream X. Finally, let P_∞ be the present value of stream X_∞. Find A in terms of P_∞ and conclude that A can be used as well as P_∞ for evaluation purposes.

3. (Uncertain annuity ◇)   Gavin's grandfather, Mr. Jones, has just turned 90 years old and is applying for a lifetime annuity that will pay $10,000 per year, starting 1 year from now, until he dies. He asks Gavin to analyze it for him. Gavin finds that according to statistical summaries, the chance (probability) that Mr. Jones will die at any particular age is as follows:

age	90	91	92	93	94	95	96	97	98	99	100	101
probability	.07	.08	.09	.10	.10	.10	.10	.10	.10	.07	.05	.04

Then Gavin (and you) answer the following questions:

(a) What is the life expectancy of Mr. Jones?
(b) What is the present value of an annuity at 8% interest that has a lifetime equal to Mr. Jones's life expectancy? (For an annuity of a nonintegral number of years, use an averaging method.)
(c) What is the expected present value of the annuity?

4. (APR)   For the mortgage listed second in Table 3.1 what are the total fees?

5. (Callable bond)   The Z Corporation issues a 10%, 20-year bond at a time when yields are 10%. The bond has a call provision that allows the corporation to force a bond holder to redeem his or her bond at face value plus 5%. After 5 years the corporation finds that exercise of this call provision is advantageous. What can you deduce about the yield at that time? (Assume one coupon payment per year.)

6. (The biweekly mortgage ⊕)   Here is a proposal that has been advanced as a way for homeowners to save thousands of dollars on mortgage payments: pay biweekly instead of monthly. Specifically, if monthly payments are x, it is suggested that one instead pay $x/2$ every two weeks (for a total of 26 payments per year). This will pay down the mortgage faster, saving interest. The savings are surprisingly dramatic for this seemingly minor modification—often cutting the total interest payment by over one-third. Assume a loan amount of $100,000 for 30 years at 10% interest, compounded monthly.

(a) Under a monthly payment program, what are the monthly payments and the total interest paid over the course of the 30 years?
(b) Using the biweekly program, when will the loan be completely repaid, and what are the savings in total interest paid over the monthly program? (You may assume biweekly compounding for this part.)

7. (Annual worth)   One advantage of the annual worth method is that it simplifies the comparison of investment projects that are repetitive but have different cycle times. Consider the automobile purchase problem of Example 2.7. Find the annual worths of the two (single-cycle) options, and determine directly which is preferable.

8. (Variable-rate mortgage ⊕)   The Smith family just took out a variable-rate mortgage on their new home. The mortgage value is $100,000, the term is 30 years, and initially the interest rate is 8%. The interest rate is guaranteed for 5 years, after which time the rate will be adjusted according to prevailing rates. The new rate can be applied to their loan either by changing the payment amount or by changing the length of the mortgage.

(a) What is the original yearly mortgage payment? (Assume payments are yearly.)
(b) What will be the mortgage balance after 5 years?
(c) If the interest rate on the mortgage changes to 9% after 5 years, what will be the new yearly payment that keeps the termination time the same?
(d) Under the interest change in (c), what will be the new term if the payments remain the same?

9. (Bond price)   An 8% bond with 18 years to maturity has a yield of 9%. What is the price of this bond?

10. (Duration)   Find the price and duration of a 10-year, 8% bond that is trading at a yield of 10%.

11. (Annuity duration ◇)   Find the duration D and the modified duration D_M of a perpetual annuity that pays an amount A at the beginning of each year, with the first such payment being 1 year from now. Assume a constant interest rate r compounded yearly. [*Hint:* It is not necessary to evaluate any new summations.]

12. (Bond selection)   Consider the four bonds having annual payments as shown in Table 3.9. They are traded to produce a 15% yield.

(a) Determine the price of each bond.
(b) Determine the duration of each bond (*not* the modified duration).
(c) Which bond is most sensitive to a change in yield?
(d) Suppose you owe $2,000 at the end of 2 years. Concern about interest rate risk suggests that a portfolio consisting of the bonds and the obligation should be immunized. If V_A, V_B, V_C, and V_D are the total values of bonds purchased of types A, B, C, and D, respectively, what are the necessary constraints to implement the immunization? [*Hint:* There are two equations. (Do not solve.)]

TABLE 3.9

End of year payments	Bond A	Bond B	Bond C	Bond D
Year 1	100	50	0	0 + 1000
Year 2	100	50	0	0
Year 3	100 + 1000	50 + 1000	0 + 1000	0

(e) In order to immunize the portfolio, you decide to use bond C and one other bond. Which other bond should you choose? Find the amounts (in total value) of each of these to purchase.

(f) You decided in (e) to use bond C in the immunization. Would other choices, including perhaps a combination of bonds, lead to lower total cost?

13. (Continuous compounding ◇)   Under continuous compounding the Macaulay duration becomes

$$D = \frac{\sum_{k=0}^{n} t_k e^{-\lambda t_k} c_k}{P}$$

where λ is the yield and

$$P = \sum_{k=0}^{n} e^{-\lambda t_k} c_k.$$

Find $dP/d\lambda$ in terms of D and P.

14. (Duration limit)   Show that the limiting value of duration as maturity is increased to infinity is

$$D \to \frac{1 + (\lambda/m)}{\lambda}.$$

For the bonds in Table 3.6 (where $\lambda = .05$ and $m = 2$) we obtain $D \to 20.5$. Note that for large λ this limiting value approaches $1/m$, and hence the duration for large yields tends to be relatively short.

15. (Convexity value)   Find the convexity of a zero-coupon bond maturing at time T under continuous compounding (that is, when $m \to \infty$).

16. (Convexity theorem ◇)   Suppose that an obligation occurring at a single time period is immunized against interest rate changes with bonds that have only nonnegative cash flows (as in the X Corporation example). Let $P(\lambda)$ be the value of the resulting portfolio, including the obligation, when the interest rate is $r + \lambda$ and r is the current interest rate. By construction $P(0) = 0$ and $P'(0) = 0$. In this exercise we show that $P(0)$ is a local minimum; that is, $P''(0) \geq 0$. (This property is exhibited by Example 3.10.)

Assume a yearly compounding convention. The discount factor for time t is $d_t(\lambda) = (1 + r + \lambda)^{-t}$. Let $d_t = d_t(0)$. For convenience assume that the obligation has magnitude 1 and is due at time $\bar{t}$. The conditions for immunization are then

$$P(0) = \sum_t c_t d_t - d_{\bar{t}} = 0$$

$$P'(0)(1 + r) = \sum_t t c_t d_t - \bar{t} d_{\bar{t}} = 0.$$

(a) Show that for all values of α and β there holds

$$P''(0)(1 + r)^2 = \sum_t (t^2 + \alpha t + \beta) c_t d_t - (\bar{t}^2 + \alpha \bar{t} + \beta) d_{\bar{t}}.$$

(b) Show that α and β can be selected so that the function $t^2 + \alpha t + \beta$ has a minimum at $\bar{t}$ and has a value of 1 there. Use these values to conclude that $P''(0) \geq 0$.

REFERENCES

The money market is vast and consists of numerous financial instruments and institutions. Detailed descriptions are available from many sources. Some good starting points are [1–5]. For comprehensive treatments of yield curve analysis, see [5–7]. The concept of duration was invented by Macaulay and by Redington, see [8, 9]. For history and details on the elaboration of this concept into a full methodology for immunization, see [10–13]. The result of Exercise 16 is a version of the Fisher–Weil theorem [13].

1. Cook, T. Q., and T. D. Rowe (1986), *Instruments of the Money Market*, Federal Reserve Bank, Richmond, VA.
2. Fabozzi, F. J., and F. Modigliani (1992), *Capital Markets: Institutions and Instruments*, Prentice Hall, Englewood Cliffs, NJ.
3. *Handbook of U.S. Government and Federal Agency Securities and Related Money Market Instruments, "The Pink Book,"* 34th ed. (1990), The First Boston Corporation, Boston, MA.
4. Wann, P. (1989), *Inside the U$ Treasury Market*, Quorum Books, New York.
5. Livingston, G. D. (1988), *Yield Curve Analysis*, New York Institute of Finance, New York.
6. Fabozzi, F. J., and T. D. Fabozzi (1989), *Bond Markets, Analysis and Strategies*, Prentice Hall, Englewood Cliffs, NJ.
7. Van Horne, J. C. (1990), *Financial Market Rates and Flows*, Prentice Hall, Englewood Cliffs, NJ.
8. Macaulay, F. R. (1938), *Some Theoretical Problems Suggested by the Movement of Interest Rates, Bond Yield, and Stock Prices in the United States since 1856*, National Bureau of Economic Research, New York.
9. Redington, F. M. (October 1971), "Review of the Principles of Life-Office Valuations," *Journal of the Institute of Actuaries*, **78,** no. 3, 286–315.
10. Bierwag, G. O., and G. G. Kaufman (July 1977), "Coping with the Risk of Interest-Rate Fluctuations: A Note," *Journal of Business*, **50,** no. 3, 364–370.
11. Bierwag, G. O., G. G. Kaufman, and A. Toevs (July–August 1983), "Duration: Its Development and Use in Bond Portfolio Management," *Financial Analysts Journal*, **39,** no. 4, 15–35.
12. Bierwag, G. O. (1987), *Duration Analysis*, Ballinger Publishing, Cambridge, MA.
13. Fisher, L., and R. L. Weil (1971), "Coping with the Risk of Interest-Rate Fluctuations: Returns to Bondholders from Naïve and Optimal Strategies," *Journal of Business*, **44,** 408–431.

4 THE TERM STRUCTURE OF INTEREST RATES

A richer theory of interest rates is explored in this chapter, as compared to that in previous chapters. The enriched theory allows for a whole family of interest rates at any one time—a different rate for each maturity time—providing a clearer understanding of the interest rate market and a foundation for more sophisticated investment analysis techniques.

4.1 THE YIELD CURVE

The yield to maturity of any bond is strongly tied to general conditions in the fixed-income securities market. All yields tend to move together in this market. However, all bond yields are not exactly the same.

The variation in yields across bonds is explained in part by the fact that bonds have various quality ratings. A strong AAA-rated bond is likely to cost more (and hence have lower yield) than a bond with an identical promised income stream but having a B-quality rating. It is only natural that high quality is more expensive than low quality. However, quality alone does not fully explain the observed variations in bond yields.

Another factor that partially explains the differences in the yields of various bonds is the time to maturity. As a general rule, "long" bonds (bonds with very distant maturity dates) tend to offer higher yields than "short" bonds of the same quality. The situation is depicted in Figure 4.1. The curve featured in this figure is an example of a **yield curve.** It displays yield as a function of time to maturity. The curve is constructed by plotting the yields of various available bonds of a given quality class. Figure 4.1 shows the yields for various government securities as a function of the maturity date. Note that the yields trace out an essentially smooth curve, which rises gradually as the time to maturity increases. A rising curve is a "normally shaped" yield curve; this shape occurs most often. However, the yield curve undulates around in time, somewhat like a branch in the wind, and can assume various other shapes. If long bonds happen to have *lower* yields than short bonds, the result is said to be an **inverted yield curve.** The inverted shape tends to occur when short-term rates

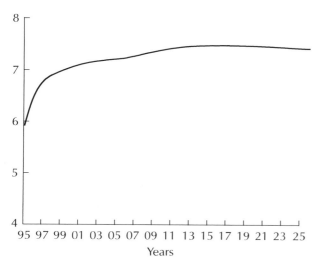

FIGURE 4.1   Yield curve. Yields are plotted as a function of maturity date. The curve shown here is typical and has a normal upward slope.   Source: *Treasury Bulletin,* June 1995.

increase rapidly, and investors believe that the rise is temporary, so that long-term rates remain near their previous levels.

When studying a particular bond, it is useful to determine its yield and maturity date and place it as a point on the yield curve for bonds in its risk class. This will give a general indication of how it is priced relative to the overall market. If it is far from the curve, there is probably a reason, related to special situations or special features (such as call features of the bond or news affecting the potential solvency of the issuer).

The yield curve is helpful, but because it is a bit arbitrary, it does not provide a completely satisfactory explanation of yield differences. Why, for example, should the maturity date be used as the horizontal axis of the curve rather than, say, duration? A more basic theory is required, and such a theory is introduced in the next section.

4.2 THE TERM STRUCTURE

Term structure theory puts aside the notion of yield and instead focuses on pure interest rates. The theory is based on the observation that, in general, the interest rate charged (or paid) for money depends on the length of time that the money is held. Your local bank, for example, is likely to offer you a higher rate of interest for deposits committed for 3 years than for demand deposits (which can be withdrawn at any time). This basic fact, that the interest rate charged depends on the length of time that the funds are held, is the basis of term structure theory. This chapter works out the details and implications of that fact.

Spot Rates

Spot rates are the basic interest rates defining the term structure. The spot rate s_t is the rate of interest, expressed in yearly terms, charged for money held from the present time ($t = 0$) until time t. Both the interest and the original principal are paid at time t. Hence, in particular, s_1 is the 1-year interest rate; that is, it is the rate paid for money held 1 year. Similarly, the rate s_2 represents the rate that is paid for money held 2 years; however, it is expressed on an annualized basis. Thus if your bank promises to pay a rate of s_2 for a 2-year deposit of an amount A compounded yearly, it will actually repay $(1 + s_2)^2 A$ at the end of 2 years; your money grows by a factor of $(1 + s_2)^2$.

The definition of spot rates implicitly assumes a compounding convention, and this convention might vary with the purpose at hand. The preceding discussion assumed a 1-year compounding convention. It is common to use m periods per year, or continuous compounding, as well. In all cases the rates are usually still quoted as yearly rates. For completeness, we list the various possibilities:

(*a*) **Yearly**   Under the yearly compounding convention, the spot rate s_t is defined such that

$$(1 + s_t)^t$$

is the factor by which a deposit held t years will grow. (Here t must be an integer, or an adjustment must be made.)

(*b*) **m periods per year**   Under a convention of compounding m periods per year, the spot rate s_t is defined so that

$$(1 + s_t/m)^{mt}$$

is the corresponding factor. (Here mt must be an integer, so t must be an integral multiple of $1/m$.)

(*c*) **Continuous**   Under a continuous compounding convention, the spot rate s_t is defined so that $e^{s_t t}$ is the corresponding growth factor. This formula applies directly to all values of t.

For theoretical purposes, continuous compounding is "neater" since the formulas apply without change to all values of t. The other methods require an adjustment for values of t between compounding dates. However, the yearly compounding convention is the most convenient, and it is the convention mainly used in this chapter.

Spot rates can, in theory, be measured by recording the yields of zero-coupon bonds. (In order to eliminate the influence of default risk, it would be best to consider only Treasury securities for this purpose.) Since a zero-coupon bond promises to pay a fixed amount at a fixed date in the future, the ratio of the payment amount to the current price defines the spot rate for the maturity date of the bond. By this measurement process we can develop a **spot rate curve,** which is analogous to the yield curve. Such a curve and a chart of the corresponding data are shown in Figure 4.2.

Discount Factors and Present Value

Once the spot rates have been determined, it is natural to define the corresponding **discount factors** d_t for each time point. These are the factors by which future cash flows

Years	Spot Rate
1	5.571
2	6.088
3	6.555
4	6.978
5	7.361
6	7.707
7	8.020
8	8.304
9	8.561
10	8.793
11	9.003
12	9.193
13	9.365
14	9.520
15	9.661
16	9.789
17	9.904
18	10.008
19	10.103
20	10.188

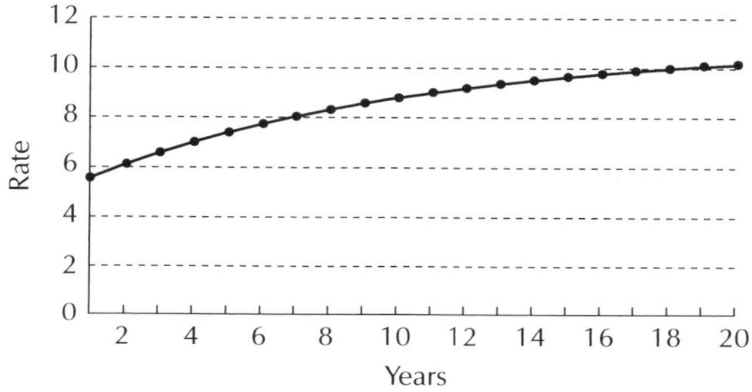

FIGURE 4.2   Spot rate curve. The yearly rate of interest depends on the length of time funds are held.

must be multiplied to obtain an equivalent present value. For the various compounding conventions, they are defined as follows:

(a) **Yearly**   For yearly compounding,

$$d_k = \frac{1}{(1 + s_k)^k} .$$

(b) m **periods per year**   For compounding m periods per year,

$$d_k = \frac{1}{(1 + s_k/m)^{mk}} .$$

(c) **Continuous**   For continuous compounding,

$$d_t = e^{-s_t t} .$$

The discount factors transform future cash flows directly into an equivalent present value. Hence given any cash flow stream $(x_0, x_1, x_2, \ldots, x_n)$, the present value, relative to the prevailing spot rates, is

$$\text{PV} = x_0 + d_1 x_1 + d_2 x_2 + \cdots + d_n x_n .$$

The discount factor d_k acts like a *price* for cash received at time k. We determine the value of a stream by adding up "price times quantity" for all the cash components of the stream.

TABLE 4.1
Bond Evaluation

Year	1	2	3	4	5	6	7	8	9	10	Total PV
Discount	.947	.889	.827	.764	.701	.641	.583	.528	.477	.431	
Cash flow	8	8	8	8	8	8	8	8	8	108	
PV	7.58	7.11	6.61	6.11	5.61	5.12	4.66	57.05	3.82	46.50	97.34

Each cash flow is discounted by the discount factor for its time.

Example 4.1 (Price of a 10-year bond)   Using the spot rate curve of Figure 4.2, let us find the value of an 8% bond maturing in 10 years.

Normally, for bonds we would use the rates and formulas for 6-month compounding; but for this example let us assume that coupons are paid only at the end of each year, starting a year from now, and that 1-year compounding is consistent with our general evaluation method. We write the cash flows together with the discount factors, take their products, and then sum, as shown in Table 4.1. The value of the bond is found to be 97.34.

Example 4.2 (Simplico gold mine)   Consider the lease of the Simplico gold mine discussed in Chapter 2, Example 2.6, but now let us assume that interest rates follow the term structure pattern of Figure 4.2. We shall find the present value of the lease.

The cash flow stream is identical to that of the earlier example; namely, $2M each year for 10 years. The present value is therefore just the sum of the first 10 discount figures multiplied by $2M, for a total of $13.58M.

Determining the Spot Rate

The obvious way to determine a spot rate curve is to find the prices of a series of zero-coupon bonds with various maturity dates. Unfortunately the set of available zero-coupon bonds is typically rather sparse, and, indeed, until recently there were essentially no "zeros" available with long maturities. Thus it is not always practical to determine a complete set of spot rates this way. However, the existence of zero-coupon bonds is not necessary for the concept of spot rates to be useful, nor are they needed as data to determine the spot rate value.

The spot rate curve can be determined from the prices of coupon-bearing bonds by beginning with short maturities and working forward toward longer maturities. We illustrate the process for the 1-year compounding convention (and assuming coupons are paid only once a year). First determine s_1 by direct observation of the 1-year interest rate—as determined, for example, by the 1-year Treasury bill rate. Next consider a 2-year bond. Suppose that bond has price P, makes coupon payments of amount C at the end of both years, and has a face value F. The price should equal the discounted value of the cash flow stream, so we can write

$$P = \frac{C}{1 + s_1} + \frac{C + F}{(1 + s_2)^2}.$$

Since s_1 is already known, we can solve this equation for s_2. Working forward this way, by next considering 3-year bonds, then 4-year bonds, and so forth, we can determine $s_3, s_4, \ldots$, step by step.

Spot rates can also be determined by a subtraction process. Two bonds of different coupon rates but identical maturity dates can be used to construct the equivalent of a zero-coupon bond. The following example illustrates the method.

Example 4.3 (Construction of a zero)   Bond A is a 10-year bond with a 10% coupon. Its price is $P_A = 98.72$. Bond B is a 10-year bond with an 8% coupon. Its price is $P_B = 85.89$. Both bonds have the same face value, normalized to 100.

Consider a portfolio with $-.8$ unit of bond A and 1 unit of bond B. This portfolio will have a face value of 20 and a price of $P = P_B - .8P_A = 6.914$. The coupon payments cancel, so this is a zero-coupon portfolio. The 10-year spot rate s_{10} must satisfy $(1 + s_{10})^{10} P = 20$. Thus $s_{10} = 11.2\%$.

In practice, since spot rates are an idealization, and the spot rates implied by different bonds may differ slightly from one another, it is advisable to modify these procedures to incorporate an averaging method when estimating the spot rates. (See Exercise 4.)

4.3 FORWARD RATES

An elegant and useful concept emerges directly from the definition of spot rates; namely, the concept of forward rates. **Forward rates** are interest rates for money to be borrowed between two dates in the future, *but under terms agreed upon today.*

It is easiest to explain the concept for a 2-year situation. Suppose that s_1 and s_2 are known. If we leave \$1 in a 2-year account it will, by definition, grow to $\$(1 + s_2)^2$ at the end of the 2 years. Alternatively, we might place the \$1 in a 1-year account and simultaneously make arrangements that the proceeds, which will be $\$(1 + s_1)$, will be lent for 1 year starting a year from now. That loan will accrue interest at a prearranged rate (agreed upon now) of say f. The rate f is the forward rate for money to be lent in this way. The final amount of money we receive at the end of 2 years under this compound plan is $\$(1 + s_1)(1 + f)$.

We now invoke the comparison principle. We have two alternative methods for investing \$1 for 2 years. The first returns $(1 + s_2)^2$ and the second returns $(1 + s_1)(1 + f)$.

These two should be equal, since both are available.[1] Thus we have

$$(1 + s_2)^2 = (1 + s_1)(1 + f)$$

or

$$f = \frac{(1 + s_2)^2}{1 + s_1} - 1.$$

Hence the forward rate is determined by the two spot rates.

We can justify the use of the comparison principle here through an **arbitrage argument.** If these two methods of investing money did not return the same amount, then there would be an opportunity to make arbitrage profits—defined to be either instantaneous profit or sure future profit with zero net investment. In the preceding example, if $(1 + s_1)(1 + f) > (1 + s_2)^2$, meaning that the second method of investment returned more than the first, then an arbitrageur could reverse the first plan (by *borrowing* for 2 years) and then carry out the second plan by investing the money that was borrowed. This arbitrageur would have zero net investment because he or she used only borrowed capital, but after repaying the loan the arbitrageur would have a profit factor of $(1 + s_1)(1 + f) - (1 + s_2)^2 > 0$. This arbitrage scheme could be carried out at any magnitude, and hence, in theory, the arbitrageur could make very large sums of money from no initial capital. We assume that it is not possible to implement this scheme in the market because potential arbitrageurs are always on the lookout for such discrepancies. If a slight discrepancy does arise, they take advantage of it, and this action tends to close the gap in rates. If the inequality were in the other direction, the arbitageur could just reverse the procedure. Thus equality must hold.

The arbitrage argument assumes that there are no transaction costs—either real costs such as brokerage fees or opportunity costs related to the time and effort of finding the discrepancy and arranging for the trades. The argument also assumes that the borrowing and lending rates are identical. If there were transaction costs or unequal rates, there could be a slight "wedge" between the 2-year rates associated with the two alternative strategies. However, in practice the transaction cost associated with a highly liquid security such as a U.S. Treasury is a very small fraction of the security's total cost, especially if large amounts are involved; and borrowing and lending rates are quite close, again if large amounts of capital are involved. So although the arbitrage argument represents an idealization, it is in practice a reasonable approximation.

The comparison principle can be used to argue that the two overall rates must be equal even in the absence of arbitrageurs. If there were a difference in rates, then investors seeking to loan money for 2 years would choose the best alternative—and so would borrowers. Market forces would tend to equalize the rates.

Example 4.4   Suppose that the spot rates for 1 and 2 years are, respectively, $s_1 = 7\%$ and $s_2 = 8\%$. We then find that the forward rate is $f = (1.08)^2/1.07 - 1 = .0901 = 9.01\%$. Hence the 2-year 8% rate can be obtained either as a direct 2-year investment, or by investing for 1 year at 7% followed by a second year at 9.01%.

---

[1] Forward contracts of this type are actually implemented by the use of futures contracts on Treasury securities, as explained in Chapter 10. They are highly liquid, so forwards of this type are obtained easily.

This discussion can be generalized to define other forward rates between different time periods. The rate f used earlier is more completely labeled as $f_{1,2}$ because it is the forward rate between years 1 and 2. In general we use the following:

Forward rate definition   *The forward rate between times t_1 and t_2 with $t_1 < t_2$ is denoted by f_{t_1,t_2}. It is the rate of interest charged for borrowing money at time t_1 which is to be repaid (with interest) at time t_2.*

In general, forward rates are expressed on an annualized basis, like other interest rates, unless another basis is explicitly specified.

In the market there could be more than one rate for any particular forward period. For example, the forward rate for borrowing may differ from that for lending. Thus when discussing market rates one must be specific. However, in theoretical discussions the definition of forward rates is based on an underlying set of spot rates (which themselves generally represent idealizations or averages of market conditions). These calculated forward rates are often termed **implied forward rates** to distinguish them from **market forward rates.**

The implied forward rates are found by extending the logic given earlier for assigning the value $f_{1,2}$. If we use 1-year compounding, the basic forward rates are defined between various yearly periods. They are defined to satisfy the following equation (for $i < j$):

$$(1 + s_j)^j = (1 + s_i)^i (1 + f_{i,j})^{j-i} .$$

The left side of this equation is the factor by which money grows if it is directly invested for j years. This amount is determined by the spot rate s_j. The right side of the equation is the factor by which money grows if it is invested first for i years and then in a forward contract (arranged now) between years i and j. The term $(1 + f_{i,j})$ is raised to the $(j - i)$th power because the forward rate is expressed in yearly terms.

The extension to other compounding conventions is straightforward. For completeness, the formulas for forward rates (expressed as yearly rates) under various compounding conventions are listed here:

Forward rate formulas   *The implied forward rate between times t_1 and $t_2 > t_1$ is the rate of interest between those times that is consistent with a given spot rate curve. Under various compounding conventions the forward rates are specified as follows:*

(a) **Yearly**   *For yearly compounding, the forward rates satisfy, for $j > i$,*

$$(1 + s_j)^j = (1 + s_i)^i (1 + f_{i,j})^{j-i} .$$

Hence,

$$f_{i,j} = \left[\frac{(1 + s_j)^j}{(1 + s_i)^i} \right]^{1/(j-i)} - 1 .$$

(b) *m* **periods per year**   *For m period-per-year compounding, the forward rates satisfy, for j > i, expressed in periods,*

$$(1 + s_j/m)^j = (1 + s_i/m)^i (1 + f_{i,j}/m)^{(j-i)}.$$

Hence,

$$f_{i,j} = m \left[\frac{(1 + s_j/m)^j}{(1 + s_i/m)^i} \right]^{1/(j-i)} - m.$$

(c) **Continuous**   *For continuous compounding, the forward rates f_{t_1,t_2} are defined for all t_1 and t_2, with $t_2 > t_1$, and satisfy*

$$e^{s_{t_2} t_2} = e^{s_{t_1} t_1} e^{f_{t_1,t_2}(t_2 - t_1)}.$$

Hence,

$$f_{t_1,t_2} = \frac{s_{t_2} t_2 - s_{t_1} t_1}{t_2 - t_1}.$$

Note again that continuous compounding produces the simplest formula. As a further convention, it is useful to define spot rates, discount factors, and forward rates when one of the time points is zero, representing current time. Hence we define $s_{t_0} = 0$ and correspondingly $d_{t_0} = 1$, where t_0 is the current time. (Alternatively we write $s_0 = 0$ and $d_0 = 1$ when denoting time by period integers.) For forward rates, we write similarly $f_{t_0,t_1} = s_{t_1}$. The forward rates from time zero are the corresponding spot rates.

There are a large number of forward rates associated with a spot rate curve. In fact, if there are n periods, there are n spot rates (excluding s_0); and there are $n(n + 1)/2$ forward rates (including the basic spot rates.) However, all these forward rates are derived from the n underlying spot rates.

The forward rates are introduced partly because they represent rates of actual transactions. Forward contracts do in fact serve a very important hedging role, and their use in this manner is discussed further in Chapter 10. They are introduced here, however, mainly because they are important for the full development of the term structure theory. They are used briefly in the next section and then extensively in the section following that.

4.4 TERM STRUCTURE EXPLANATIONS

The yield curve can be observed, at least roughly, by looking at a series of bond quotes in the financial press. The curve is almost never *flat* but, rather, it usually slopes gradually upward as maturity increases. The spot rate curve has similar characteristics. Typically it, too, slopes rapidly upward at short maturities and continues to slope upward, but more gradually as maturities lengthen. It is natural to ask if there is a simple explanation for this typical shape. Why is the curve not just flat at a common interest rate?

There are three standard explanations (or "theories") for the term structure, each of which provides some important insight. We outline them briefly in this section.

Expectations Theory

The first explanation is that spot rates are determined by expectations of what rates will be in the future. To visualize this process, suppose that, as is usually the case, the spot rate curve slopes upward, with rates increasing for longer maturities. The 2-year rate is greater than the 1-year rate. It is argued that this is so because the market (that is, the collective of all people who trade in the interest rate market) believes that the 1-year rate will most likely go up next year. (This belief may, for example, be because most people believe inflation will rise, and thus to maintain the same real rate of interest, the nominal rate must increase.) This majority belief that the interest rate will rise translates into a market *expectation*. An expectation is only an average guess; it is not definite information—for no one knows for sure what will happen next year—but people on average assume, according to this explanation, that the rate will increase.

This argument is made more concrete by expressing the expectations in terms of forward rates. This more precise formulation is the **expectations hypothesis.** To outline this hypothesis, consider the forward rate $f_{1,2}$, which is the implied rate for money loaned for 1 year, a year from now. According to the expectations hypothesis, this forward rate is *exactly* equal to the market expectation of what the 1-year spot rate will be next year. Thus the expectation can be inferred from existing rates.

Earlier we considered a situation where $s_1 = 7\%$ and $s_2 = 8\%$. We found that the implied forward rate was $f_{1,2} = 9.01\%$. According to the unbiased expectations hypothesis, this value of 9.01% is the market's expected value of next year's 1-year spot rate s_1'.

The same argument applies to the other rates as well. As additional spot rates are considered, they define corresponding forward rates for next year. Specifically, s_1, s_2, and s_3 together determine the forward rates $f_{1,2}$ and $f_{1,3}$. The second of these is the forward rate for borrowing money for 2 years, starting next year. This rate is assumed to be equal to the current expectation of what the 2-year spot rate s_2' will be next year. In general, then, the current spot rate curve leads to a set of forward rates $f_{1,2}, f_{1,3}, \ldots, f_{1,n}$, which define the expected spot rate curve $s_1', s_2', \ldots, s_{n-1}'$ for next year. The expectations are inherent in the current spot rate structure.

There are two ways of looking at this construction. One way is that the current spot rate curve implies an expectation about what the spot rate curve will be next year. The other way is to turn this first view around and say that the expectation of next year's curve determines what the current spot rate curve must be. Both views are intertwined; expectations about future rates are part of today's market and influence today's rates.

This theory or hypothesis is a nice explanation of the spot rate curve, even though it has some important weaknesses. The primary weakness is that, according to this explanation, the market expects rates to increase whenever the spot rate curve slopes upward; and this is practically all the time. Thus the expectations cannot be right even on average, since rates do not go up as often as expectations would imply. Nevertheless, the expectations explanation is plausible, although the expectations may themselves be skewed.

The expectations explanation of the term structure can be regarded as being (loosely) based on the comparison principle. To see this, consider again the 2-year situation. An investor can invest either in a 2-year instrument or in a 1-year instrument followed by another 1-year investment. The follow-on investment can also be carried out two ways. It can be arranged currently through a forward contract at rate $f_{1,2}$, or it can simply be "rolled over" by reinvesting the following year at the then prevailing 1-year rate. A wise investor would compare the two alternatives. If the investor expects that next year's 1-year rate will equal the current value of $f_{1,2}$, then he or she will be indifferent between these two alternatives. Indeed, the fact that both are viable implies that they must seem (approximately) equal.

Liquidity Preference

The liquidity preference explanation asserts that investors usually prefer short-term fixed income securities over long-term securities. The simplest justification for this assertion is that investors do not like to tie up capital in long-term securities, since those funds may be needed before the maturity date. Investors prefer their funds to be **liquid** rather than tied up. However, the term *liquidity* is used in a slightly nonstandard way in this argument. There are large active markets for bonds of major corporations and of the Treasury, so it is easy to sell any such bonds one might hold. Short-term and long-term bonds of this type are equally liquid.

Liquidity is used in this explanation of the term structure shape instead to express the fact that most investors prefer short-term bonds to long-term bonds. The reason for this preference is that investors anticipate that they may need to sell their bonds soon, and they recognize that long-term bonds are more sensitive to interest rate changes than are short-term bonds. Hence an investor who may need funds in a year or so will be be reluctant to place these funds in long-term bonds because of the relatively high near-term risk associated with such bonds. To lessen risk, such an investor prefers short-term investments. Hence to induce investors into long-term instruments, better rates must be offered for long bonds. For this reason, according to the theory, the spot rate curve rises.

Market Segmentation

The market segmentation explanation of the term structure argues that the market for fixed-income securities is segmented by maturity dates. This argument assumes that investors have a good idea of the maturity date that they desire, based on their projected need for future funds or their risk preference. The argument concludes that the group of investors competing for long-term bonds is different from the group competing for short-term bonds. Hence there need be no relation between the prices (defined by interest rates) of these two types of instruments; short and long rates can move around rather independently. Taken to an extreme, this viewpoint suggests that all points on the spot rate curve are mutually independent. Each is determined by the forces of supply and demand in its own market.

A moderated version of this explanation is that, although the market is basically segmented, individual investors are willing to shift segments if the rates in an adjacent segment are substantially more attractive than those of the main target segment. Adjacent rates cannot become grossly out of line with each other. Hence the spot rate curve must indeed be a curve rather than a jumble of disjointed numbers, but this curve can bend in various ways, depending on market forces.

Discussion

Certainly each of the foregoing explanations embodies an element of truth. The whole truth is probably some combination of them all.

The expectations theory is the most analytical of the three, in the sense that it offers concrete numerical values for expectations, and hence it can be tested. These tests show that it works reasonably well with a deviation that seems to be explained by liquidity preference. Hence expectations tempered by the risk considerations of liquidity preference seem to offer a good straightforward explanation.

4.5 EXPECTATIONS DYNAMICS

The concept of market expectations introduced in the previous section as an explanation for the shape of the spot rate curve can be developed into a useful tool in its own right. This tool can be used to form a plausible **forecast** of future interest rates.

Spot Rate Forecasts

The basis of this method is to assume that the expectations implied by the current spot rate curve will actually be fulfilled. Under this assumption we can then predict next year's spot rate curve from the current one. This new curve implies yet another set of expectations for the following year. If we assume that these, too, are fulfilled, we can predict ahead once again. Going forward in this way, an entire future of spot rate curves can be predicted. Of course, it is understood that these predicted spot rate curves are based on the assumption that expectations will be fulfilled (and we recognize that this may not happen), but once made, the assumption does provides a logical forecast.

Let us work out some of the details. We begin with the current spot rate curve $s_1, s_2, \ldots, s_n$, and we wish to estimate next year's spot rate curve $s'_1, s'_2, \ldots, s'_{n-1}$. The current forward rate $f_{1,j}$ can be regarded as the expectation of what the interest rate will be next year—measured from next year's current time to a time $j - 1$ years ahead—in other words, $f_{1,j}$ is next year's spot rate s'_{j-1}. Explicitly,[2]

$$s'_{j-1} = f_{1,j} = \left[\frac{(1 + s_j)^j}{1 + s_1} \right]^{1/(j-1)} - 1 \tag{4.1}$$

---

[2]Recall that this formula for $f_{i,j}$ was given in Section 4.3. It is derived from the relation $(1 + s_j)^j = (1 + f_{1,j})^{j-1}(1 + s_1)$.

for $1 < j \leq n$. This is the basic formula for updating a spot rate curve under the assumption that expectations are fulfilled. Starting with the current curve, we obtain an estimate of next year's curve.

We term this transformation **expectations dynamics,** since it gives an explicit characterization of the dynamics of the spot rate curve based on the expectations assumption. Other assumptions are certainly possible. For instance, we could assume that the spot rate curve will remain unchanged, or that it will shift upward by a fixed amount, and so forth; however, expectations dynamics has a nice logical appeal.

The expectations process can be carried out for another step to obtain the spot rate curve for the third year, and so forth. Note, however, that if the original curve has finite length, each succeeding curve is shorter by one term—and hence the curves eventually become quite short. This problem can be rectified by initially assuming a very long (or infinite) spot rate curve, or by adding a new s_n term each year. This latter approach would require an additional hypothesis.

Example 4.5 (A simple forecast)   Let us take as given the spot rate curve shown in the first row of the table. The second row is then the forecast of next year's spot rate curve under expectations dynamics. This row is found using (4.1).

	s_1	s_2	s_3	s_4	s_5	s_6	s_7
Current	6.00	6.45	6.80	7.10	7.36	7.56	7.77
Forecast	6.90	7.20	7.47	7.70	7.88	8.06	

The first two entries in the second row were computed as follows:

$$f_{1,2} = \frac{(1.0645)^2}{1.06} - 1 = .069$$

$$f_{1,3} = \left[\frac{(1.068)^3}{1.06} \right]^{1/2} - 1 = .072 \,.$$

All future spot rate curves implied by an initial spot rate curve can be displayed by listing all of the forward rates associated with the initial spot rate curve. Such a list is shown in a triangular array:

$$
\begin{array}{llllll}
f_{0,1} & f_{0,2} & f_{0,3} & \cdots & f_{0,n-2} & f_{0,n-1} & f_{0,n} \\
f_{1,2} & f_{1,3} & f_{1,4} & \cdots & f_{1,n-1} & f_{1,n} \\
f_{2,3} & f_{2,4} & f_{2,5} & \cdots & f_{2,n} \\
\vdots & \vdots \\
f_{n-2,n-1} & f_{n-2,n} \\
f_{n-1,n}.
\end{array}
$$

The first row of the array lists the forward rates from the initial time. These are identical to the spot rates themselves; that is, $s_j = f_{0,j}$ for all j with $0 < j \leq n$.

The next row lists the forward rates from time 1. These will be next year's spot rates according to expectations dynamics. The third row will be the spot rates for the third year, and so forth.

Discount Factors

Another important concept is that of a **discount factor** between two times. The discount factors are, of course, fundamental quantities used in present value calculations.

It is useful to apply a double indexing system to the discount factors paralleling the system used for forward rates. Accordingly, the symbol $d_{j,k}$ denotes the discount factor used to discount cash received at time k back to an equivalent amount of cash at time j. The normal, time zero, discount factors are $d_1 = d_{0,1}, d_2 = d_{0,2}, \ldots, d_n = d_{0,n}$. The discount factors can be expressed in terms of the forward rates as

$$d_{j,k} = \left[\frac{1}{1 + f_{j,k}}\right]^{k-j}.$$

The discount factors are related by a compounding rule: to discount from time k back to time i, one can first discount from time k back to an intermediate time j and then discount from j back to i. In other words, $d_{i,k} = d_{i,j}d_{j,k}$ for $i < j < k$.

 Discount factor relation *The discount factor between periods i and j is defined as*

$$d_{i,j} = \left[\frac{1}{1 + f_{i,j}}\right]^{j-i}.$$

These factors satisfy the compounding rule

$$d_{i,k} = d_{i,j}d_{j,k}$$

for $i < j < k$.

Short Rates

Short rates are the forward rates spanning a single time period. The short rate at time k is accordingly $r_k = f_{k,k+1}$; that is, it is the forward rate from k to $k + 1$. The short rates can be considered fundamental just as spot rates, for a complete set of short rates fully specifies a term structure.

The spot rate s_k is found from the short rates from the fact that interest earned from time zero to time k is identical to the interest that would be earned by rolling over an investment each year. Specifically,

$$(1 + s_k)^k = (1 + r_0)(1 + r_1) \cdots (1 + r_{k-1}).$$

The relation generalizes because all forward rates can be found from the short rates in a similar way. Specifically,

$$(1 + f_{i,j})^{j-i} = (1 + r_i)(1 + r_{i+1}) \cdots (1 + r_{j-1}).$$

Hence the short rates form a convenient basis for generating all other rates.

The short rates are especially appealing in the context of expectations dynamics, because they do not change from year to year, whereas spot rates do. Given the initial short rates $r_0, r_1, r_2, \ldots, r_{n-1}$, next year (under expectations dynamics) the short rates will be $r_1, r_2, \ldots, r_{n-1}$. The short rate for a specific year does not change; however, that year is 1 year closer to the sliding current time. For example, if we are at the beginning of year 2020, the short rate r_4 is the rate for the year beginning January 2024. A year later, in 2021, the new r_3 will be the rate for the year 2024 and this short rate will be identical (under expectations dynamics) to the previous r_4.

An example of a complete set of forward rates, discount factors, and short rates is shown in Table 4.2. Here the rows represent the rates or factors for a given year: the top row of each array contains the initial rates or factors for 7 years forward. The forward rate array is, as discussed, identical to the spot rate array. Hence the basic spot rate curve is defined by the top line of the forward rate array. Everything else is derived from that single row. The discount factors for the current time are those listed in the top row of the discount factor array. These are the values used to find the present values of future cash flows. Note that successive rows of the short rate table are just shifted versions of the rows above. Short rates remain fixed in absolute time.

TABLE 4.2
Forward Rates, Discount Factors, and Short Rates

Forward rates							Short rates						
6.00	6.45	6.80	7.10	7.36	7.56	7.77	6.00	6.90	7.50	8.00	8.40	8.60	9.00
6.90	7.20	7.47	7.70	7.88	8.06		6.90	7.50	8.00	8.40	8.60	9.00	
7.50	7.75	7.97	8.12	8.30			7.50	8.00	8.40	8.60	9.00		
8.00	8.20	8.33	8.50				8.00	8.40	8.60	9.00			
8.40	8.50	8.67					8.40	8.60	9.00				
8.60	8.80						8.60	9.00					
9.00							9.00						

Discount factors						
.943	.883	.821	.760	.701	.646	.592
.935	.870	.806	.743	.684	.628	
.930	.861	.795	.732	.671		
.926	.854	.787	.722			
.923	.849	.779				
.921	.845					
.917						

The original spot rate curve is defined by the top row of the forward rate array. All other terms are derived from this row.

Invariance Theorem

Suppose that you have a sum of money to invest in fixed-income securities, and you will not draw from these funds for n periods (say, n years). You will invest only in Treasury instruments, and there is a current known spot rate curve for these securities. You have a multitude of choices for structuring a portfolio using your available money. You may select some bonds with long maturities, some zero-coupon bonds, and some bonds with short maturities. If you select a mix of these securities, then, as time passes, you will obtain income from coupons and from the redemption of the short maturity bonds. You may also elect to sell some bonds early, before maturity. As income is generated in these ways, you will reinvest this income in other bonds; again you have a multitude of choices. Finally you will cash out everything at time period n. How should you invest in order to obtain the maximum amount of money at the terminal time?

To address this question, you must have a model of how interest rates will change in the intervening years, since future rates will determine the prices for bonds that you sell early and those that you buy when reinvesting income. There are a variety of models you could select (some of which might involve randomness, as discussed in Chapter 14), but a straightforward choice is to assume expectations dynamics—so let us make that assumption. Let us assume that the initial spot rate curve is transformed, after 1 year, to a new curve in accordance with the updating formula presented earlier. This updating is repeated each year. Now, how should you invest?

The answer is revealed by the title of this subsection. It makes absolutely *no* difference how you invest (as long as you remain fully invested). All choices will produce exactly the same result. In particular, investing in a single zero-coupon bond will produce this invariant amount, which is, accordingly, $(1+s_n)^n$ times your original sum of money. This result is spelled out in the following theorem:

Invariance theorem   *Suppose that interest rates evolve according to expectations dynamics. Then (assuming a yearly compounding convention) a sum of money invested in the interest rate market for n years will grow by a factor of $(1 + s_n)^n$ independent of the investment and reinvestment strategy (so long as all funds are fully invested).*

> ***Proof:***   The conclusion is easiest to see from the example used earlier. Suppose that $n = 2$. You have two basic choices for investment. You can invest in a 2-year zero-coupon bond, or you can invest in a 1-year bond and then reinvest the proceeds at the end of the year. Under expectations dynamics, the reinvestment rate after 1 year will be equal to the current forward rate $f_{1,2}$. Both of these choices lead to a growth of $(1 + s_2)^2$. Any other investment, such as a 2-year bond that makes a coupon payment after 1 year that must be reinvested, will be a combination of these two basic strategies. It should be clear that a similar argument applies for any n. ∎

The simplest way to internalize this result is to think in terms of the short rates. Every investment earns the relevant short rates over its duration. A 10-year zero-coupon bond earns the 10 short rates that are defined initially. An investment rolled over year by year for 10 years earns the 10 short rates that happen to occur. Under expectations dynamics, the short rates do not change; that is, the rate initially implied for a specified period in the future will be realized when that period arrives. Hence no matter how an initial sum is invested, it will progress step by step through each of the short rates.

This theorem is very helpful in discussing how to structure an actual portfolio. It shows that the motivation for selecting a mixture of bonds must be due to anticipated deviations from expectations dynamics—deviations of the realized short rates from their originally implied values. Expectations dynamics is, therefore, in a sense the *simplest* assumption about the future because it implies invariance of portfolio growth with respect to strategy.

4.6 RUNNING PRESENT VALUE

The present value of a cash flow stream is easily calculated in the term structure framework. One simply multiplies each cash flow by the discount factor associated with the period of the flow and then sums these discounted values; that is, present value is obtained by appropriately discounting all future cash flows.

There is a special, alternative way to arrange the calculations of present value, which is sometimes quite convenient and which has a useful interpretation. This different way is termed **running present value.** It calculates present value in a recursive manner starting with the final cash flow and working backward to the present. This method uses the concepts of expectations dynamics from the previous section, although it is not necessary to assume that interest rates actually follow the expectations dynamics pattern to use the method. Although this method is presented, at this point, as just an alternative to the standard method of calculation, it will be the preferred—indeed standard—method of calculation in later chapters.

To work out the process, suppose $(x_0, x_1, x_2, \ldots, x_n)$ is a cash flow stream. We denote the present value of this stream PV(0), meaning the present value at time zero. Now imagine that k time periods have passed and we are anticipating the remainder of the cash flow stream, which is $(x_k, x_{k+1}, \ldots, x_n)$. We could calculate the present value (as viewed at time k) using the discount factors that would be applicable then. We denote this present value by PV(k). In general, then, we can imagine the present value running along in time—each period's value being the present value of the remaining stream, but calculated using that period's discount factors. These running values are related to each other in a simple way, which is the basis for the method we describe.

The original present value can be expressed explicitly as

$$PV(0) = x_0 + d_1 x_1 + d_2 x_2 + \cdots + d_n x_n$$

where the d_k's are the discount factors at time zero. This formula can be written in the alternative form

$$PV(0) = x_0 + d_1 [x_1 + (d_2/d_1)x_2 + \cdots + (d_n/d_1)x_n]. \tag{4.2}$$

The values d_k/d_1, $k = 2, 3, \ldots, n$, are the discount factors *1 year from now* under an assumption of expectations dynamics (as shown later). Hence,

$$PV(0) = x_0 + d_1 PV(1).$$

To show how this works in general, for arbitrary time points, we employ the double-indexing system for discount factors introduced in the previous section. The present values at time k is

$$PV(k) = x_k + d_{k,k+1}x_{k+1} + d_{k,k+2}x_{k+2} + \cdots + d_{k,n}x_n.$$

Using the discount compounding formula, it follows that $d_{k,k+j} = d_{k,k+1}d_{k+1,k+j}$. Hence we may write this equation as

$$PV(k) = x_k + d_{k,k+1}(x_{k+1} + d_{k+1,k+2}x_{k+2} + \cdots + d_{k+1,n}x_n).$$

We can therefore write

$$PV(k) = x_k + d_{k,k+1}PV(k + 1).$$

This equation states that the present value at time k is the sum of the current cash flow and a one-period discount of the next present value. Note that $d_{k,k+1} = 1/(1 + f_{k,k+1})$, where $f_{k,k+1}$ is the short rate at time k. Hence in this method discounting always uses short rates to determine the discount factors.

 Present value updating   *The running present values satisfy the recursion*

$$PV(k) = x_k + d_{k,k+1}PV(k + 1)$$

where $d_{k,k+1} = 1/(1 + f_{k,k+1})$ is the discount factor for the short rate at k.

To carry out the computation in a recursive manner, the process is initiated by starting at the *final* time. One first calculates $PV(n)$ as $PV(n) = x_n$ and then $PV(n - 1) = x_{n-1} + d_{n-1,n}PV(n)$, and so forth until $PV(0)$ is found.

You can visualize the process in terms of n people standing strung out, on a time line. You are at the head of the line, at time zero. Each person can observe only the cash flow that occurs at that person's time point. Hence you can observe only the current, time zero, cash flow. How can you compute the present value? Use the running method.

The last person, person n, computes the present value seen then and passes that value to the first person behind. That person, using the short rate at that time, discounts the value announced by person n, then adds the observed cash flow at $n - 1$ and passes this new present value back to person $n - 2$. This process continues, each person discounting according to their short rate, until the running present value is passed to you. Once you hear what the person in front of you announces, you discount it using the initial short rate and add the current cash flow. That is the overall present value.

The running present value $PV(k)$ is, of course, somewhat of a fiction. It will be the actual present value of the remaining stream at time k only if interest rates follow expectations dynamics. Otherwise, entirely different discount rates will apply at that

TABLE 4.3
Example of Running Present Value

				Year k				
	0	**1**	**2**	**3**	**4**	**5**	**6**	**7**
Cash flow	20	25	30	35	40	30	20	10
Discount	.943	.935	.93	.926	.923	.921	.917	
PV(k)	168.95	157.96	142.20	120.64	92.49	56.87	29.17	10.00

The present value is found by starting at the final time and working backward, discounting one period at a time.

time. However, when computing a present value at time zero, that is, when computing PV(0), the running present value method can be used since it is a mathematical identity.

Example 4.6 (Constant running rate)   Suppose that the spot rate curve is flat, with $s_k = r$ for all $k = 1, 2, \ldots, n$. Let $(x_0, x_1, x_2, \ldots, x_n)$ be a cash flow stream. In the flat case, all forward rates are also equal to r. (See Exercise 9.) Hence the present value can be calculated as

$$PV(n) = x_n$$

$$PV(k) = x_k + \frac{1}{1+r}PV(k+1).$$

This recursion is run from the terminal time backward to $k = 0$.

Example 4.7 (General running)   A sample present value calculation is shown in Table 4.3. The basic cash flow stream is the first row of the table. We assume that the current term structure is that of Table 4.2, and the appropriate one-period discount rates (found in the first column of the discount factor table in Table 4.2) are listed in the second row of Table 4.3.

The present value at any year k is computed by multiplying the discount factor listed under that year times the present value of the next year, and then adding the cash flow for year k. This is done by beginning with the final year and working backward to time zero. Thus we first find PV(0) = 10.00. Then PV(9) = 20+.917×10.00 = 29.17, PV(8) = 30 + .921 × 29.17 = 56.87, and so forth. The present value of the entire stream is PV(0) = 168.95.

4.7 FLOATING RATE BONDS

A floating rate note or bond has a fixed face value and fixed maturity, but its coupon payments are tied to current (short) rates of interest. Consider, for example, a floating rate bond that makes coupon payments every 6 months. When the bond is issued, the coupon rate for the first 6 months is set equal to the current 6-month interest rate. At the end of 6 months a coupon payment at that rate is paid; specifically, the coupon is the rate times the face value divided by 2 (because of the 6-month schedule). Then, after that payment, the rate is **reset**: the rate for the next 6 months is set equal to the then current 6-month (short) rate. The process continues until maturity.

Clearly, the exact values of future coupon payments are uncertain until 6 months before they are due. It seems, therefore, that it may be difficult to assess the value of such a bond. In fact at the reset times, the value is easy to deduce—it is equal to par. We highlight this important result.

Theorem 4.1 (Floating rate value)   *The value of a floating rate bond is equal to par at any reset point.*

Proof: It is simplest to prove this by working backward using a running present value argument. Look first at the last reset point, 6 months before maturity. We know that the final payment, in 6 months, will be the face value plus the 6-month rate of interest on this amount. The present value at the last reset point is obtained by discounting the total final payment at the 6-month rate—leading to the face value—so the present value is par at that point. Now move back another 6 months to the previous reset point. The present value there is found by discounting the sum of the next present value and the next coupon payment, again leading to a value of par. We can continue this argument back to time zero. ∎

4.8 DURATION

The concept of duration presented in Chapter 3, Section 3.5, can be extended to a term structure framework. We recall that duration is a measure of interest rate sensitivity, which in the earlier development was expressed as sensitivity with respect to yield. In the term structure framework, yield is not a fundamental quantity, but a different, yet similar, measure of risk can be constructed.

The alternative is to consider parallel shifts in the spot rate curve. Specifically, given the spot rates $s_1, s_2, \ldots, s_n$ we imagine that these rates all change together by an additive amount λ. Hence the new spot rates are $s_1 + \lambda, s_2 + \lambda, \ldots, s_n + \lambda$. This is a hypothetical *instantaneous* change, for the new spot rates are for the same periods as before. This parallel shift of the spot rate curve generalizes a change in the yield because if the spot rate curve were flat, all spot rates would be equal to the common value of yield. Figure 4.3 shows the shifted spot rate curve in the case of a continuous spot rate curve.

Given this notion of a potential change in spot rates, we then can measure the sensitivity of price with respect to the change.

Fisher–Weil Duration

The details work out most nicely for the case of continuous compounding, and we shall present that case first. Given a cash flow sequence $(x_{t_0}, x_{t_1}, x_{t_2}, \ldots, x_{t_n})$ and the

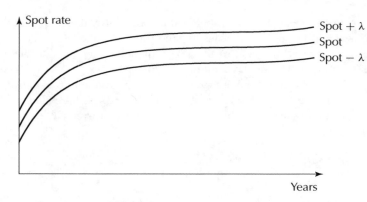

FIGURE 4.3 **Shifted spot rate curves.** The original spot rate curve is the middle curve. This curve is shifted upward and downward by an amount λ to obtain the other curves. It is possible to immunize a portfolio against such shifts for small values of λ.

spot rate curve s_t, $t_0 \leq t \leq t_n$, the present value is

$$\text{PV} = \sum_{i=0}^{n} x_{t_i} e^{-s_{t_i} t_i} .$$

The **Fisher–Weil duration** is then defined as

$$D_{\text{FW}} = \frac{1}{\text{PV}} \sum_{i=0}^{n} t_i x_{t_i} e^{-s_{t_i} t_i} .$$

Note that this corresponds exactly to the general definition of duration as a present-value-weighted average of the cash flow times. Clearly D_{FW} has the units of time and satisfies $t_0 \leq D \leq t_n$ when all $x_{t_i} \geq 0$.

    We now consider the sensitivity of price (present value) to a parallel shift of the yield curve and show that it is determined by the Fisher–Weil duration. For arbitrary λ the price is

$$P(\lambda) = \sum_{i=0}^{n} x_{t_i} e^{-(s_{t_i} + \lambda) t_i} .$$

We then differentiate to find

$$\left. \frac{dP(\lambda)}{d\lambda} \right|_{\lambda=0} = - \sum_{i=0}^{n} t_i x_{t_i} e^{-s_{t_i} t_i}$$

so immediately we find that the **relative price sensitivity** is

$$\frac{1}{P(0)} \frac{dP(0)}{d\lambda} = -D_{\text{FW}} .$$

This essentially duplicates the formula that holds for yield sensitivity presented in Chapter 3.

Fisher–Weil formulas   *Under continuous compounding, the Fisher–Weil duration of a cash flow stream* $(x_{t_0}, x_{t_1}, \ldots, x_{t_n})$ *is*

$$D_{\text{FW}} = \frac{1}{\text{PV}} \sum_{i=0}^{n} t_i x_{t_i} e^{-s_{t_i} t_i}$$

where PV *denotes the present value of the stream. If all spot rates change to* $s_{t_i} + \lambda$, $i = 0, 1, 2, \ldots, n$, *the corresponding present value function* $P(\lambda)$ *satisfies*

$$\frac{1}{P(0)} \frac{dP(0)}{d\lambda} = -D_{\text{FW}} .$$

Discrete-Time Compounding*

Now we work out the details under the convention of compounding m times per year. The spot rate in period k is s_k (expressed as a yearly rate). Again, we have a cash flow stream $(x_0, x_1, x_2, \ldots, x_n)$ (where the indexing is by period). The price is

$$P(\lambda) = \sum_{k=0}^{n} x_k \left(1 + \frac{s_k + \lambda}{m} \right)^{-k} .$$

We then find that

$$\frac{dP(0)}{d\lambda} \equiv \frac{dP(\lambda)}{d\lambda} \bigg|_0 = \sum_{k=1}^{n} -\left(\frac{k}{m} \right) x_k \left(1 + \frac{s_k}{m} \right)^{-(k+1)} .$$

We can relate this to a duration measure by dividing by $-P(0)$. Thus we define

$$D_Q \equiv -\frac{1}{P(0)} \frac{dP(0)}{d\lambda} = \frac{\sum_{k=1}^{n} (k/m) x_k (1 + s_k/m)^{-(k+1)}}{\sum_{i=0}^{n} x_k (1 + s_k/m)^{-k}} . \qquad (4.3)$$

We term the quantity D_Q the **quasi-modified duration.** It does have the units of time; however, it is not exactly an average of the cash flow times because $(1 + s_k/m)^{-(k+1)}$ appears in the numerator instead of $(1 + s_k/m)^{-k}$, which is the discount factor. There is an extra factor of $(1 + s_k/m)^{-1}$ in each numerator term. In the earlier case, where s_k was constant for all k, it was possible to pull this extra term outside the summation sign. That led to modified duration. Here such a step is not possible, since the extra factor depends on k, so we call this rather cumbersome expression by an equally cumbersome name—the quasi-modified duration. It does give the relative price sensitivity to a parallel shift in the spot rate curve. An example is given in the next section.

Quasi-modified duration   *Under compounding m times per year, the quasi-modified duration of a cash flow stream* $(x_0, x_1, \ldots, x_n)$ *is*

$$D_Q = \frac{1}{\text{PV}} \sum_{k=1}^{n} \left(\frac{k}{m} \right) x_k \left(1 + \frac{s_k}{m} \right)^{-(k+1)}$$

where PV *denotes the present value of the stream. If all spot rates change to* $s_k + \lambda$, $k = 1, 2, \ldots, n$, *the corresponding present value function* $P(\lambda)$ *satisfies*

$$\frac{1}{P(0)} \frac{dP(0)}{d\lambda} = -D_Q .$$

Duration is used extensively by investors and professional bond portfolio managers. It serves as a convenient and accurate proxy for interest rate risk. Frequently an institution specifies a guideline that duration should not exceed a certain level, or sometimes a target duration figure is prescribed.

4.9 IMMUNIZATION

The term structure of interest rates leads directly to a new, more robust method for portfolio immunization. This new method does not depend on selecting bonds with a common yield, as in Chapter 3; indeed, yield does not even enter the calculations. The process is best explained through an example.

Example 4.8 (A million dollar obligation) Suppose that we have a $1 million obligation payable at the end of 5 years, and we wish to invest enough money today to meet this future obligation. We wish to do this in a way that provides a measure of protection against interest rate risk. To solve this problem, we first determine the current spot rate curve. A hypothetical spot rate curve s_k is shown as the column labeled **spot** in Table 4.4.

We use a yearly compounding convention in this example in order to save space in the table. We decide to invest in two bonds described as follows: B_1 is a 12-year 6% bond with price 65.95 (in decimal form), and B_2 is a 5-year 10% bond with price 101.66. The prices of these bonds are consistent with the spot rates; and the details of the price calculation are given in Table 4.4. The cash flows are multiplied by the discount factors (column d), and the results are listed and summed in columns headed PV_1 and PV_2 for the two bonds.

TABLE 4.4
Worksheet for Immunization Problem

Year	Spot	d	B_1	PV_1	$-PV_1'$	B_2	PV_2	$-PV_2'$
1	7.67	.929	6	5.57	5.18	10	9.29	8.63
2	8.27	.853	6	5.12	9.45	10	8.53	15.76
3	8.81	.776	6	4.66	12.84	10	7.76	21.40
4	9.31	.700	6	4.20	15.38	10	7.00	25.63
5	9.75	.628	6	3.77	17.17	110	69.08	314.73
6	10.16	.560	6	3.36	18.29			
7	10.52	.496	6	2.98	18.87			
8	10.85	.439	6	2.63	18.99			
9	11.15	.386	6	2.32	18.76			
10	11.42	.339	6	2.03	18.26			
11	11.67	.297	6	1.78	17.55			
12	11.89	.260	106	27.53	295.26			
Total				65.95	466.00		101.66	386.15
Duration					7.07			3.80

The present values and durations of two bonds are found as transformations of cash flows.

We decide to immunize against a parallel shift in the spot rate curve. We calculate $dP/d\lambda$, denoted by $-PV'$ in Table 4.4, by multiplying each cash flow by t and by $(1+s_t)^{-(t+1)}$ and then summing these. The quasi-modified duration is then the quotient of these two numbers; that is, it equals $-(1/P)\ dP/d\lambda$. The quasi-modified duration of bond 1 is, accordingly, $466/65.95 = 7.07$.

We also find the present value of the obligation to be $627,903.01 and the corresponding quasi-modified duration is $5/(1 + s_5) = 4.56$.

To determine the appropriate portfolio we let x_1 and x_2 denote the number of units of bonds 1 and 2, respectively, in the portfolio (assuming, for simplicity, face values of $100). We then solve the two equations[3]

$$P_1x_1 + P_2x_2 = PV$$

$$P_1D_1x_1 + P_2D_2x_2 = PV \times D$$

where the D's are the quasi-modified durations. This leads to $x_1 = 2,208.17$ and $x_2 = 4,744.03$. We round the solutions to determine the portfolio. The results are shown in the first column of Table 4.5, where it is clear that, to within rounding error, the present value condition is met.

To check the immunization properties of this portfolio we change the spot rate curve by adding 1% to each of the spot rate numbers in the first column of Table 4.4. Using these new spot rates, we can again calculate all present values. Likewise, we subtract 1% from the spot rates and calculate present values. The results are shown in the final two columns of Table 4.5. These results show that the immunization property does hold: the change in net present value is only a second-order effect.

TABLE 4.5
Immunization Results

	Lambda		
	0	**1%**	**−1%**
Bond 1			
Shares	2,208.00	2,208.00	2,208.00
Price	65.94	51.00	70.84
Value	145,602.14	135,805.94	156,420.00
Bond 2			
Shares	4,744.00	4,744.00	4,744.00
Price	101.65	97.89	105.62
Value	482,248.51	464,392.47	501,042.18
Obligation value	627,903.01	600,063.63	657,306.77
Bonds minus obligation	−$52.37	$134.78	$155.40

The overall portfolio of bonds and obligations is immunized against parallel shifts in the spot rate curve.

---

[3] Alternatively, but equivalently, one could solve the equations $V_1 + V_2 = PV$ and $D_1V_1 + D_2V_2 = PV \times D$. Then let $x_1 = V_1/P_1$ and $x_2 = V_2/P_2$.

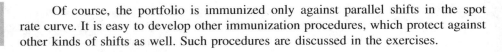

Of course, the portfolio is immunized only against parallel shifts in the spot rate curve. It is easy to develop other immunization procedures, which protect against other kinds of shifts as well. Such procedures are discussed in the exercises.

4.10 SUMMARY

If observed yield is plotted as a function of time to maturity for a variety of bonds within a fixed risk class, the result is a scatter of points that can be approximated by a curve—the yield curve. This curve typically rises gradually with increasing maturity, reflecting the fact that long maturity bonds typically offer higher yields than short maturity bonds. The shape of the yield curve varies continually, and occasionally it may take on an inverted shaped, where yields decrease as the time to maturity increases.

Fixed-income securities are best understood through the concept of the term structure of interest rates. In this structure there is, at any time, a specified interest rate for every maturity date. This is the rate, expressed on an annual basis, that would apply to a zero-coupon bond of the specified maturity. These underlying interest rates are termed spot rates, and if they are plotted as a function of time to maturity, they determine a spot rate curve, similar in character to the yield curve. However, spot rates are fundamental to the whole interest rate market—unlike yields, which depend on the payout pattern of the particular bonds used to calculate them. Once spot rates are determined, it is straightforward to define discount factors for every time, and the present value of a future cash flow is found by discounting that cash flow by the appropriate discount factor. Likewise, the present value of a cash flow stream is found by summing the present values of the individual flow elements.

A series of forward rates can be inferred from a spot rate curve. The forward rate between future times t_1 and t_2 is the interest rate that would be charged for borrowing money at time t_1 and repaying it at time t_2, but at terms arranged today. These forward rates are important components of term structure theory.

There are three main explanations of the characteristic upward sloping spot rate curve. The first is expectations theory. It asserts that the current implied forward rates for 1 year ahead—that is, the forward rates from year 1 to future dates—are good estimates of next year's spot rates. If these estimates are higher than today's values, the current spot rate curve must slope upward. The second explanation is liquidity preference theory. It asserts that people prefer short-term maturities to long-term maturities because the interest rate risk is lower with short-term maturities. This preference drives up the prices of short-term maturities. The third explanation is the market segmentation theory. According to this theory, there are separate supply and demand forces in every range of maturities, and prices are determined in each range by these forces. Hence the interest rate within any maturity range is more or less independent of that in other ranges. Overall it is believed that the factors in all three of these explanations play a role in the determination of the observed spot rate curve.

Expectations theory forms the basis of the concept of expectations dynamics, which is a particular model of how spot rates might change with time. According to expectations dynamics, next year's spot rates will be equal to the current implied forward rates for 1 year ahead—the rates between year 1 and future years. In other words, the forward rates for 1 year ahead actually will be realized in 1 year. This prediction can be repeated for the next year, and so on. This means that all future spot rates are determined by the set of current forward rates. Expectations dynamics is only a model, and future rates will most likely deviate from the values it delivers; but it provides a logical simple prediction of future rates. As a special case, if the current spot rate curve is flat—say, at 12%—then according to expectations dynamics, the spot rate curve next year will also be flat at 12%. The invariance theorem states that if spot rates evolve according to expectations dynamics, the interest earned on funds committed to the interest rate market for several years is independent of how those funds are invested.

Present value can be calculated by the running method, which starts from the final cash flow and works backward toward the first cash flow. At any stage k of the process, the present value is calculated by discounting the next period's present value using the short rate at time k that is implied by the term structure. This backward moving method of evaluation is fundamental to advanced methods of calculation in various areas of investment science.

Duration can be extended to the term structure framework. The key idea is to consider parallel shifts of the spot rate curve, shifts defined by adding a constant λ to every spot rate. Duration is then defined as $(-1/P)\,dP/d\lambda$ evaluated at $\lambda = 0$. Fisher–Weil duration is based on continuous-time compounding, which leads to a simple formula. In discrete time, the appropriate, somewhat complicated formula is termed quasi-modified duration.

Once duration is defined, it is possible to extend the process of immunization to the term structure framework. A portfolio of assets designed to fund a stream of obligations can be immunized against a parallel shift in the spot rate curve by matching both the present values and the durations of the assets and the obligations.

EXERCISES

1. (One forward rate)   If the spot rates for 1 and 2 years are $s_1 = 6.3\%$ and $s_2 = 6.9\%$, what is the forward rate $f_{1,2}$?

2. (Spot update)   Given the (yearly) spot rate curve $\mathbf{s} = (5.0, 5.3, 5.6, 5.8, 6.0, 6.1)$, find the spot rate curve for next year.

3. (Construction of a zero)   Consider two 5-year bonds: one has a 9% coupon and sells for 101.00; the other has a 7% coupon and sells for 93.20. Find the price of a 5-year zero-coupon bond.

4. (Spot rate project ⊕)   It is November 5 in the year 2011. The bond quotations of Table 4.6 are available. Assume that all bonds make semiannual coupon payments on the 15th of the month. The fractional part of a bond's price is quoted in 1/32nd's. Estimate the (continuous-time) term structure in the form of a 4th-order polynomial,

$$r(t) = a_0 + a_1 t + a_2 t^2 + a_3 t^3 + a_4 t^4$$

TABLE 4.6
Bond Quotes

Coupon	Maturity	Ask price
$6\frac{5}{8}$	Feb-2012	100:0
$9\frac{1}{8}$	Feb-2012	100:22
$7\frac{7}{8}$	Aug-2012	100:24
$8\frac{1}{4}$	Aug-2012	101:1
$8\frac{1}{4}$	Feb-2013	101:7
$8\frac{3}{8}$	Feb-2013	101:12
8	Aug-2013	100:26
$8\frac{3}{4}$	Aug-2013	102:1
$6\frac{7}{8}$	Feb-2014	98:5
$8\frac{7}{8}$	Feb-2014	102:9
$6\frac{7}{8}$	Aug-2014	97:13
$8\frac{5}{8}$	Aug-2014	101:23
$7\frac{3}{4}$	Feb-2015	99:5
$11\frac{1}{4}$	Feb-2015	109:4
$8\frac{1}{2}$	Aug-2015	101:13
$10\frac{1}{2}$	Aug-2015	107:27
$7\frac{7}{8}$	Feb-2016	99:13
$8\frac{7}{8}$	Feb-2016	103:0

where t is time in units of years from today. The discount rate for cash flows at time t is accordingly $d(t) = e^{-r(t)t}$. Recall that accrued interest must be added to the price quoted to get the total price. Estimate the coefficients of the polynomial by minimizing the sum of squared errors between the total price and the price predicted by the estimated term structure curve. Plot the curve and give the five polynomial coefficients.

5. (Instantaneous rates ◇)   Let $s(t)$, $0 \le t \le \infty$, denote a spot rate curve; that is, the present value of a dollar to be received at time t is $e^{-s(t)t}$. For $t_1 < t_2$, let $f(t_1, t_2)$ be the forward rate between t_1 and t_2 implied by the given spot rate curve.

(a) Find an expression for $f(t_1, t_2)$.

(b) Let $r(t) = \lim_{t_2 \to t} f(t, t_2)$. We can call $r(t)$ the instantaneous interest rate at time t. Show that $r(t) = s(t) + s'(t)t$.

(c) Suppose an amount x_0 is invested in a bank account at $t = 0$ which pays the instantaneous rate of interest $r(t)$ at all t (compounded). Then the bank balance $x(t)$ will satisfy $\mathrm{d}x(t)/\mathrm{d}t = r(t)x(t)$. Find an expression for $x(t)$. [*Hint:* Recall in general that $y\mathrm{d}z + z\mathrm{d}y = \mathrm{d}(yz)$.]

6. (Discount conversion)   At time zero the one-period discount rates $d_{0,1}, d_{1,2}, d_{2,3}, \ldots, d_{5,6}$ are known to be 0.950, 0.940, 0.932, 0.925, 0.919, 0.913. Find the time zero discount factors $d_{0,1}, d_{0,2}, \ldots, d_{0,6}$.

7. **(Bond taxes)**   An investor is considering the purchase of 10-year U.S. Treasury bonds and plans to hold them to maturity. Federal taxes on coupons must be paid during the year they are received, and tax must also be paid on the capital gain realized at maturity (defined as the difference between face value and original price). Federal bonds are exempt from state taxes. This investor's federal tax bracket rate is $t = 30\%$, as it is for most individuals. There are two bonds that meet the investor's requirements. Bond 1 is a 10-year, 10% bond with a price (in decimal form) of $P_1 = 92.21$. Bond 2 is a 10-year, 7% bond with a price of $P_2 = 75.84$. Based on the price information contained in those two bonds, the investor would like to compute the theoretical price of a hypothetical 10-year zero-coupon bond that had no coupon payments and required tax payment only at maturity equal in amount to 30% of the realized capital gain (the face value minus the original price). This theoretical price should be such that the price of this bond and those of bonds 1 and 2 are mutually consistent on an after-tax basis. Find this theoretical price, and show that it does not depend on the tax rate t. (Assume all cash flows occur at the end of each year.)

8. **(Real zeros)**   Actual zero-coupon bonds are taxed as if implied coupon payments were made each year (or really every 6 months), so tax payments are made each year, even though no coupon payments are received. The implied coupon rate for a bond with n years to maturity is $(100 - P_0)/n$, where P_0 is the purchase price. If the bond is held to maturity, there is no realized capital gain, since all gains are accounted for in the implied coupon payments. Compute the theoretical price of a real 10-year zero-coupon bond. This price is to be consistent on an after-tax basis with the prices of bonds 1 and 2 of Exercise 7.

9. **(Flat forwards)**   Show explicitly that if the spot rate curve is flat [with $s(k) = r$ for all k], then all forward rates also equal r.

10. **(Orange County blues)**   Orange County managed an investment pool into which several municipalities made short-term investments. A total of $7.5 billion was invested in this pool, and this money was used to purchase securities. Using these securities as collateral, the pool borrowed $12.5 billion from Wall Street brokerages, and these funds were used to purchase additional securities. The $20 billion total was invested primarily in long-term fixed-income securities to obtain a higher yield than the short-term alternatives. Furthermore, as interest rates slowly declined, as they did in 1992–1994, an even greater return was obtained. Things fell apart in 1994, when interest rates rose sharply.

    Hypothetically, assume that initially the duration of the invested portfolio was 10 years, the short-term rate was 6%, the average coupon interest on the portfolio was 8.5% of face value, the cost of Wall Street money was 7%, and short-term interest rates were falling at $\frac{1}{2}\%$ per year.

    (a) What was the rate of return that pool investors obtained during this early period? Does it compare favorably with the 6% that these investors would have obtained by investing normally in short-term securities?

    (b) When interest rates had fallen two percentage points and began increasing at 2% per year, what rate of return was obtained by the pool?

11. **(Running PV example)**   A (yearly) cash flow stream is $\mathbf{x} = (-40, 10, 10, 10, 10, 10, 10)$. The spot rates are those of Exercise 2.

    (a) Find the current discount factors $d_{0,k}$ and use them to determine the (net) present value of the stream.

(*b*) Find the series of expectations dynamics short-rate discount factors and use the running present value method to evaluate the stream.

12. (Pure duration ⋄)   It is sometimes useful to introduce variations of the spot rates that are different from an additive variation. Let $\mathbf{s}^0 = (s_1^0, s_2^0, s_3^0, \ldots, s_n^0)$ be an initial spot rate sequence (based on m periods per year). Let $\mathbf{s}(\lambda) = (s_1, s_2, \ldots, s_n)$ be spot rates parameterized by λ, where

$$1 + s_k/m = e^{\lambda/m}(1 + s_k^0/m)$$

for $k = 1, 2, \ldots, n$. Suppose a bond price $P(\lambda)$, is determined by these spot rates. Show that

$$-\frac{1}{P}\frac{dP}{d\lambda} = D$$

is a pure duration; that is, find D and describe it in words.

13. (Stream immunization ⊕)   A company faces a stream of obligations over the next 8 years as shown: where the numbers denote thousands of dollars. The spot rate curve is that of

Year	1	2	3	4	5	6	7	8
	500	900	600	500	100	100	100	50

Example 4.8. Find a portfolio, consisting of the two bonds described in that example, that has the same present value as the obligation stream and is immunized against an additive shift in the spot rate curve.

14. (Mortgage division)   Often a mortgage payment stream is divided into a principal payment stream and an interest payment stream, and the two streams are sold separately. We shall examine the component values. Consider a standard mortgage of initial value $M = M(0)$ with equal periodic payments of amount B. If the interest rate used is r per period, then the mortgage principal after the kth payment satisfies

$$M(k) = (1+r)M(k-1) - B$$

for $k = 0, 1, \ldots$. This equation has the solution

$$M(k) = (1+r)^k M - \left[\frac{(1+r)^k - 1}{r}\right]B.$$

Let us suppose that the mortgage has n periods and B is chosen so that $M(n) = 0$; namely,

$$B = \frac{r(1+r)^n M}{(1+r)^n - 1}.$$

The kth payment has an interest component of

$$I(k) = rM(k-1)$$

and a principal component of

$$P(k) = B - rM(k-1).$$

(*a*) Find the present value V (at rate r) of the principal payment stream in terms of B, r, n, M.

(*b*) Find V in terms of r, n, M only.

(*c*) What is the present value W of the interest payment stream?

(*d*) What is the value of V as $n \to \infty$?

(*e*) Which stream do you think has the larger duration—principal or interest?

15. (Short rate sensitivity)   Gavin Jones sometimes has flashes of brilliance. He asked his instructor if duration would measure the sensitivity of price to a parallel shift in the short rate curve. (That is, $r_k \to r_k + \lambda$.) His instructor smiled and told him to work it out. He was unsuccessful at first because his formulas became very complicated. Finally he discovered a simple solution based on the running present value method. Specifically, letting P_k be the present value as seen at time k and $S_k = dP_k/d\lambda|_{\lambda=0}$, the S_k's can be found recursively by an equation of the form $S_{k-1} = -a_k P_k + b_k S_k$, while the P_k's are found by the running method. Find a_k and b_k.

REFERENCES

For general discussions of term structure theory, see [1–3]. Critical analyses of the expectations explanation are contained in [4] and [5]. The liquidity preference explanation is explored in [6]. Immunization in a term structure environment was originated in [7].

1. Fabozzi, F. J., and F. Modigliani (1992), *Capital Markets: Institutions and Instruments*, Prentice Hall, Englewood Cliffs, NJ.
2. Homer, S., and M. Liebowitz (1972), *Inside the Yield Book: New Tools for Bond Market Strategy*, Prentice Hall, Englewood Cliffs, NJ.
3. Van Horne, J. C. (1990), *Financial Market Rates & Flows*, Prentice Hall, Englewood Cliffs, NJ.
4. Russell, S. (July/August 1992), "Understanding the Term Structure of Interest Rates: The Expectations Theory," *Federal Reserve Bank of St. Louis Review*, 36–51.
5. Cox, J., J. Ingersoll, and S. Ross (September 1981), "A Reexamination of Traditional Hypotheses about the Term Structure of Interest Rates," *Journal of Finance*, **36**, 769–99.
6. Fama, E. (1984), "The Information in the Term Structure," *Journal of Financial Economics*, **13**, 509–28.
7. Fisher, L., and R. L. Weil (October 1977), "Coping with the Risk of Market-Rate Fluctuations: Returns to Bondholders from Naive and Optimal Strategies," *Journal of Business*, **44**, 408–431.

5 APPLIED INTEREST RATE ANALYSIS

Ultimately, the practical purpose of investment science is to improve the investment process. This process includes identification, selection, combination, and ongoing management. In the ideal case, these process components are integrated and handled as a craft—a craft rooted in scientific principles and meaningful experience, and executed through a combination of intuition and formal problem-solving procedures. This chapter highlights the formal procedures for structuring investments.

The previous chapters provide the groundwork for the analysis of a surprisingly broad set of investment problems. Indeed, interest rate theory alone provides the basis of the vast majority of actual investment studies. Therefore mastery of the previous chapters is adequate preparation to address a wide assortment of investment situations—and appropriate analyses can be conducted with simple practical tools, such as spreadsheet programs, or more complex tools, such as parallel processor computers. To illustrate the range of problems that can be meaningfully treated by the theory developed in earlier chapters, this chapter considers a few typical problem areas. Our treatment of these subjects is only introductory, for indeed there are textbooks devoted to each of these topics. Nevertheless, the solid grounding of the previous chapters allows us to enter these problems at a relatively high level, and to convey quickly the essence of the subject. We consider capital budgeting, bond portfolio construction, management of dynamic investments, and valuation of firms from accounting data. These subjects all represent important investment issues.

To resolve an investment issue with quantitative methods, the issue must first be formulated as a specific problem. There are usually a number of ways to do this, but frequently the best formulation is a version of **optimization.** It is entirely consistent with general investment objectives to try to devise the "ideal" portfolio, to select the "best" combination of projects, to manage an investment to attain the "most favorable" outcome, or to hedge assets to attain the "least" exposure to risk. All of these are, at least loosely, statements of optimization. Indeed, optimization and investment seem like perfect partners. We begin to explore the possibilities of this happy relationship in this chapter.

5.1 CAPITAL BUDGETING

The capital allocation problem consists of allocating a (usually fixed) budget among a number of investments or projects. We distinguish between **capital budgeting** treated here and **portfolio problems** treated in the next section, although the two are related. Capital budgeting typically refers to allocation among projects or investments for which there are not well-established markets and where the projects are *lumpy* in that they each require discrete lumps of cash (as opposed to securities, where virtually any number of shares can be purchased).

Capital budgeting problems often arise in a firm where several proposed projects compete for funding. The projects may differ considerably in their scale, their cash requirements, and their benefits. The critical point, however, is that even if all proposed projects offer attractive benefits, they cannot all be funded because of a budget limitation. Our earlier study of investment choice, in Chapter 2, focused on situations where the budget was not fixed, and the choice options were mutually exclusive, such as the choice between a red and a green car. In capital budgeting the alternatives may or may not be mutually exclusive, and budget is a definite limitation.

Independent Projects

The simplest, and classic, type of a capital budgeting problem is that of selecting from a list of independent projects. The projects are independent in the sense that it is reasonable to select any combination from the list. It is not a question of selecting between a red and a green car; we can choose both if we have the required budget. Likewise, the value of one project does not depend on another project also being funded. This standard capital budgeting problem is quite easy to formulate.

Suppose that there are m potential projects. Let b_i be the total benefit (usually the net present value) of the ith project, and let c_i denote its initial cost. Finally, let C be the total capital available—the budget. For each $i = 1, 2, \ldots, m$ we introduce the **zero–one variable** x_i, which is zero if the project is rejected and one if it is accepted. The problem is then that of solving

$$\text{maximize} \sum_{i=1}^{m} b_i x_i$$

$$\text{subject to} \sum_{i=1}^{m} c_i x_i \leq C$$

$$x_i = 0 \text{ or } 1 \quad \text{for } i = 1, 2, \ldots, m.$$

This is termed a **zero–one programming problem,** since the variables are zero–one variables. It is a formal representation of the fact that projects can either be selected or not, but for those that are selected, both the benefits and the costs are directly additive.

There is an easy way to obtain an approximate solution to this problem, which is quite accurate in many cases. We shall describe this method under the assumption (which can be weakened) that each project requires an initial outlay of funds (a negative cash flow) that is followed by a stream of benefits (a stream of positive cash flows). We define the **benefit–cost ratio** as the ratio of the present worth of the benefits to the magnitude of the initial cost. We then rank projects in terms of this benefit–cost ratio. Projects with the highest ratios offer the best return per dollar invested—the biggest "bang for the buck"—and hence are excellent candidates for inclusion in the final list of selected projects. Once the projects are ranked this way, they are selected one at a time, by order of the ranking, until no additional project can be included without violating the given budget. This method will produce the best value for the amount spent. However, despite this property, the solution found by this approximate method is not always optimal since it may not use the entire available budget. Better solutions may be found by skipping over some high-cost projects so that other projects, with almost as high a benefit–cost ratio, can be included. To obtain true optimality, the zero–one optimization problem can be solved exactly by readily available software programs. However, the simpler method based on the benefit–cost ratio is helpful in a preliminary study. (Some spreadsheet packages have integer programming routines suitable for modest-sized problems.)

Example 5.1 (A selection problem)   During its annual budget planning meeting, a small computer company has identified several proposals for independent projects that could be initiated in the forthcoming year. These projects include the purchase of equipment, the design of new products, the lease of new facilities, and so forth. The projects all require an initial capital outlay in the coming year. The company management believes that it can make available up to $500,000 for these projects. The financial aspects of the projects are shown in Table 5.1.

For each project the required initial outlay, the present worth of the benefits (the present value of the remainder of the stream after the initial outlay), and the ratio of these two are shown. The projects are already listed in order of decreasing benefit–cost ratio. According to the approximate method the company would select projects 1, 2, 3, 4, and 5 for a total expenditure of $370,000 and a total net

TABLE 5.1
Project Choices

Project	Outlay ($1,000)	Present worth ($1,000)	Benefit–cost ratio
1	100	300	3.00
2	20	50	2.50
3	150	350	2.33
4	50	110	2.20
5	50	100	2.00
6	150	250	1.67
7	150	200	1.33

The outlays are made immediately, and the present worth is the present value of the future benefits. Projects with a high benefit–cost ratio are desirable.

Project	Outlay	Present worth	Net PV	Optimal x-value	Cost	Optimal PV
1	100	300	200	1	100	200
2	20	50	30	0	0	0
3	150	350	200	1	150	200
4	50	110	60	1	50	60
5	50	100	50	1	50	50
6	150	250	100	1	150	100
7	150	200	50	0	0	0
Totals					500	610

FIGURE 5.1 Spreadsheet for project choices. The x-values are listed in one column. These values are multiplied by the corresponding elements of outlay and net present value to obtain the components of cost and optimal present value in the total package of projects. A zero–one program (within the spreadsheet) adjusts these x-values to find the optimal set.

present value of $\$910,000 - \$370,000 = \$540,000$. However, this solution is not optimal.

The proper method of solution is to formulate the problem as a zero–one optimization problem. Accordingly, we define the variables x_i, $i = 1, 2, \ldots, 7$, with x_i equal to 1 if it is to be selected and 0 if not. The problem is then

$$\text{maximize } 200x_1 + 30x_2 + 200x_3 + 60x_4 + 50x_5 + 100x_6 + 50x_7$$

$$\text{subject to } 100x_1 + 20x_2 + 150x_3 + 50x_4 + 50x_5 + 150x_6 + 150x_7 \leq 500$$

$$x_i = 0 \text{ or } 1 \quad \text{for each } i.$$

Note that the terms of the objective for maximization are present worth minus outlay—present value.

The problem and its solution are displayed in spreadsheet form in Figure 5.1. It is seen that the solution is to select projects 1, 3, 4, 5, and 6 for a total expenditure of $500,000 and a total net present value of $610,000. The approximate method does not account for the fact that using project 2 precludes the use of the more costly, but more beneficial, project 6. Specifically, by replacing 2 by 6 the full budget can be used and, hence, a greater total benefit achieved.

Interdependent Projects*

Sometimes various projects are interdependent, the feasibility of one being dependent on whether others are undertaken. We formulate a problem of this type by assuming that there are several independent goals, but each goal has more than one possible method of implementation. It is these implementation alternatives that define the projects. This formulation generalizes the problems studied in Chapter 2, where there was only one goal (such as buying a new car) but several ways to achieve that goal. The more general problem can be treated as a zero–one programming problem.

As an example of the formulation using goals and projects, suppose a transportation authority wishes to construct a road between two cities. Corresponding projects might detail whether the road were concrete or asphalt, two lanes or four, and so forth. Another, independent, goal might be the improvement of a bridge.

In general, assume that there are m goals and that associated with the ith goal there are n_i possible projects. Only one project can be selected for any goal. As before, there is a fixed available budget.

We formulate this problem by introducing the zero–one variables x_{ij} for $i = 1, 2, \ldots, m$ and $j = 1, 2, \ldots, n_i$. The variable x_{ij} equals 1 if goal i is chosen and implemented by project j; otherwise it is 0. The problem is then

$$\text{maximize} \quad \sum_{i=1}^{m} \sum_{j=1}^{n_i} b_{ij} x_{ij}$$

$$\text{subject to} \quad \sum_{i=1}^{m} \sum_{j=1}^{n_i} c_{ij} x_{ij} \leq C$$

$$\sum_{j=1}^{n_i} x_{ij} \leq 1, \quad \text{for } i = 1, 2, \ldots, m$$

$$x_{ij} = 0 \text{ or } 1 \quad \text{for all } i \text{ and } j.$$

The exclusivity of the individual projects is captured by the second set of constraints— one constraint for each objective. This constraint states that the sum of the x_{ij} variables over j (the sum of the variables corresponding to projects associated with objective i) must not exceed 1. Since the variables are all either 0 or 1, this means that at most one x_{ij} variable can be 1 for any i. In other words, at most one project associated with goal i can be chosen.

In general this is a more difficult zero–one programming problem than that for independent projects. This new problem has more constraints, hence it is not easy to obtain a solution by inspection. In particular, the approximate solution based on benefit–cost ratios is not applicable. However, even large-scale problems of this type can be readily solved with modern computers.

Example 5.2 (County transportation choices)   Suppose that the goals and specific projects shown in Table 5.2 are being considered by the County Transportation Authority.

There are three independent goals and a total of 10 projects. Table 5.2 shows the cost and the net present value (after the cost has been deducted) for each of the projects. The total available budget is $5 million. To formulate this problem we introduce a zero–one variable for each project. (However, for simplicity we index these variables consecutively from 1 through 10, rather than using the double indexing procedure of the general formulation presented earlier.) The problem formulation can be expressed as

$$\text{maximize} \quad 4x_1 + 5x_2 + 3x_3 + 4.3x_4 + x_5 + 1.5x_6 + 2.5x_7 + .3x_8 + x_9 + 2x_{10}$$

$$\text{subject to} \quad 2x_1 + 3x_2 + 1.5x_3 + 2.2x_4 + .5x_5 + 1.5x_6 + 2.5x_7 + .1x_8 + .6x_9 + x_{10} \leq 5$$

$$x_1 + x_2 + x_3 + x_4 \leq 1$$

$$x_5 + x_6 + x_7 \leq 1$$

$$x_8 + x_9 + x_{10} \leq 1$$

$$x_1, x_2, x_3, x_4, x_5, x_6, x_7, x_8, x_9, x_{10} = 0 \text{ or } 1.$$

TABLE 5.2
Transportation Alternatives

	Cost ($1,000)	NPV ($1,000)
Road between Augen and Burger		
1 Concrete, 2 lanes	2,000	4,000
2 Concrete, 4 lanes	3,000	5,000
3 Asphalt, 2 lanes	1,500	3,000
4 Asphalt, 4 lanes	2,200	4,300
Bridge at Cay Road		
5 Repair existing	500	1,000
6 Add lane	1,500	1,500
7 New structure	2,500	2,500
Traffic Control in Downsberg		
8 Traffic lights	100	300
9 Turn lanes	600	1,000
10 Underpass	1,000	2,000

At most one project can be selected for each major objective.

This problem and its solution are clearly displayed by a spreadsheet, as illustrated in Figure 5.2. The solution is that projects 2, 5, and 10 should be selected, for a cost of $4,500,000 and a total present value of $8,000,000.

This method for treating dependencies among projects can be extended to situations where precedence relations apply (that is, where one project cannot be chosen unless another is also chosen) and to capital budgeting problems with additional

	Project	Cost ($1,000)	NPV ($1,000)	Optimal x-values	Cost	NPV	Goals
1	Concrete, 2 lanes	2,000	4,000	0	0	0	
2	Concrete, 4 lanes	3,000	5,000	1	3,000	5,000	
3	Asphalt, 2 lanes	1,500	3,000	0	0	0	
4	Asphalt, 4 lanes	2,200	4,300	0	0		1
5	Repair existing	500	1,000	1	500	1,000	
6	Add lane	1,500	1,500	0	0	0	
7	New structure	2,500	2,000	0	0	0	1
8	Traffic lights	100	300	0	0	0	
9	Turn lanes	600	1,000	0	0	0	
10	Underpass	1,000	2,000	1	1,000	2,000	1
Totals					4,500	8,000	

FIGURE 5.2   Transportation spreadsheet. The x-values are shown in one column; the corresponding elements of cost and net present value in the next columns. Also, the number of projects included for each goal are shown in the final column. These numbers are constrained to be less than or equal to 1. The optimal x-values are found by a zero–one programming package.

financial constraints. Typically these more general problems merely impose additional constraints among the variables.

Although capital budgeting is a useful concept, its basic formulation is somewhat flawed. The *hard* budget constraint is inconsistent with the underlying assumption that it is possible for the investor (or organization) to borrow unlimited funds at a given interest rate. Indeed, in theory one should carry out *all* projects that have positive net present value. In practice, however, the assumption that an unlimited supply of capital is available at a fixed interest rate does not hold. A bank may impose a limited credit line, or in a large organization investment decisions may be decentralized by passing down budgets to individual organizational units. It is therefore often useful to in fact solve the capital budgeting problem. However, it is usually worth solving the problem for various values of the budget to measure the sensitivity of the benefit to the budget level.

5.2 OPTIMAL PORTFOLIOS

Portfolio optimization is another capital allocation problem, similar to capital budgeting. The term **optimal portfolio** usually refers to the construction of a portfolio of financial securities. However, the term is also used more generally to refer to the construction of any portfolio of financial assets, including a "portfolio" of projects. When the assets are freely traded in a market, certain pricing relations apply that may not apply to more general, nontraded assets. This feature is an important distinction that is highlighted by using the term **portfolio optimization** for problems involving securities.

This section considers only portfolios of fixed-income instruments. As we know, a fixed-income instrument that returns cash at known points in time can be described by listing the stream of promised cash payments (and future cash outflows, if any). Such an instrument can be thought of as corresponding to a list or a vector, with the payments as components, defining an associated cash flow stream. A portfolio is just a combination of such streams, and can be represented as a combination of the individual lists or vectors representing the securities. Spreadsheets offer one convenient way to handle such combinations.

The Cash Matching Problem

A simple optimal portfolio problem is the **cash matching problem.** To describe this problem, suppose that we face a known sequence of future monetary obligations. (If we manage a pension fund, these obligations might represent required annuity payments.) We wish to invest now so that these obligations can be met as they occur; and accordingly, we plan to purchase bonds of various maturities and use the coupon payments and redemption values to meet the obligations. The simplest approach is to design a portfolio that will, without future alteration, provide the necessary cash as required.

To formulate this problem mathematically, we first establish a basic time period length, with cash flows occurring at the end of these periods. For example, we might use 6-month periods. Our obligation is then a stream $\mathbf{y} = (y_1, y_2, \ldots, y_n)$, starting one period from now. (We use boldface letters to denote an entire stream.) Likewise each bond has an associated cash flow stream of receipts, starting one period from now. If there are m bonds, we denote the stream associated with one unit of bond j by $\mathbf{c}_j = (c_{1j}, c_{2j}, \ldots, c_{nj})$. The price of bond j is denoted by p_j. We denote by x_j the amount of bond j to be held in the portfolio. The cash matching problem is to find the x_j's of minimum total cost that guarantee that the obligations can be met. Specifically,

$$\text{minimize} \sum_{j=1}^{m} p_j x_j$$

$$\text{subject to} \sum_{j=1}^{m} c_{ij} x_j \geq y_i \quad \text{for } i = 1, 2, \ldots, n$$

$$x_j \geq 0 \quad \text{for } j = 1, 2, \ldots, m.$$

The objective function to be minimized is the total cost of the portfolio, which is equal to the sum of the prices of the bonds times the amounts purchased. The main set of constraints are the cash matching constraints. For a given i the corresponding constraint states that the total amount of cash generated in period i from all m bonds must be at least equal to the obligation in period i. The final constraint rules out the possibility of selling bonds short.

This problem can be clearly visualized in terms of an array of numbers in a spreadsheet, as in the following example.

Example 5.3 (A 6-year match) We wish to match cash obligations over a 6-year period. We select 10 bonds for this purpose (and for simplicity all accounting is done on a yearly basis). The cash flow structure of each bond is shown in the corresponding column in Table 5.3. Below this column is the bond's current price. For example, the first column represents a 10% bond that matures in 6 years. This bond is selling at 109. The second to last column shows the yearly cash requirements (or obligations) for cash to be generated by the portfolio. We formulate the standard cash matching problem as a linear programming problem and solve for the optimal portfolio. (The solution can be found easily by use of a standard linear programming package such as those available on some spreadsheet programs.) The solution is given in the bottom row of Table 5.3. The actual cash generated by the portfolio is shown in the right-hand column. This column is computed by multiplying each bond column j by its solution value x_j and then summing these results. The minimum total cost of the portfolio is also indicated in the table.

Note that in two of the years extra cash, beyond what is required, is generated. This is because there are high requirements in some years, and so a large number of bonds must be purchased that mature at those dates. However, these bonds generate coupon payments in earlier years and only a portion of these payments is needed to

TABLE 5.3
Cash Matching Example

Yr	Bonds										Req'd	Actual
	1	2	3	4	5	6	7	8	9	10		
1	10	7	8	6	7	5	10	8	7	100	100	171.74
2	10	7	8	6	7	5	10	8	107		200	200.00
3	10	7	8	6	7	5	110	108			800	800.00
4	10	7	8	6	7	105					100	119.34
5	10	7	8	106	107						800	800.00
6	110	107	108								1,200	1,200.00
p	109	94.8	99.5	93.1	97.2	92.9	110	104	102	95.2	2,381.14	
x	0	11.2	0	6.81	0	0	0	6.3	0.28	0	Cost	

A spreadsheet layout clearly shows the problem and its solution. In this example, the cash flow streams of 10 different bonds are shown, year by year, as 10 columns in the array. The current price of each bond is listed below the stream, and the amount to be included in a portfolio is listed below the price. Cash flows required to be generated by the portfolio are shown in the penultimate column, and those actually generated are show in the last column.

meet obligations in those early years. A smoother set of cash requirements would not lead to such surpluses.

There is a fundamental flaw in the cash matching problem as formulated here, as evidenced by the surpluses generated in our example. The surpluses amount to extra cash, which is essentially thrown away since it is not used to meet obligations and is not reinvested. In reality, such surpluses would be immediately reinvested in instruments that were available at that time. Such reinvestment can be accommodated by a slight modification of the problem formulation, but some assumptions about the nature of future investment opportunities must be introduced. The simplest is to assume that extra cash can be carried forward at zero interest; that it can, so to speak, be put under the mattress to be recovered when needed. This flexibility is introduced by adjoining artificial "bonds" having cash flow streams of the form $(0, \ldots, 0, -1, 1, 0, \ldots, 0)$. Such a bond is "purchased" in the year with the -1 (since it absorbs cash) and is "redeemed" the next year. An even better formulation would allow surplus cash to be invested in actual bonds, but to incorporate this feature an assumption about future interest rates (or, equivalently, about future bond prices) must be made. One logical approach is to assume that prices follow expectations dynamics based on the current spot rate curve. Then if r' is the estimate of what the 1-year interest rate will be a year from now, which under expectations dynamics is the current forward rate $f_{1,2}$, a bond of the form $(0, -1, 1 + r', 0, \ldots, 0)$ would be introduced. The addition of such future bonds allows surpluses to be reinvested, and this addition will lead to a different solution than the simple cash matching solution given earlier.

Other modifications to the basic cash matching problem are possible. For example, if the sums involved are not large, then account might be made of the integer nature of the required solution; that is, the x_i variables might be restricted to be integers. Other modifications combine immunization with cash matching.

5.3 DYNAMIC CASH FLOW PROCESSES

To produce excellent results, many investments require deliberate ongoing management. For example, the course of a project within a firm might be guided by a series of operational decisions. Likewise, a portfolio of financial instruments might (and should be) modified systematically over time. The selection of an appropriate sequence of actions that affect an investment's cash flow stream is the problem of dynamic management.

Imagine, for example, that you have purchased an oil well. This is an investment project, and to obtain good results from it, it must be carefully managed. In this case you must decide, each month, whether to pump oil from your well or not. If you do pump oil, you will incur operational costs and receive revenue from the sale of oil, leading to a profit; but you will also reduce the oil reserves. Your current pumping decision clearly influences the future possibilities of production. If you believe that current oil prices are low, you may wisely choose not to pump now, but rather to save the oil for a time of higher prices.

Discussion of this type of problem within the context of deterministic cash flow streams is especially useful—both because it is an important class of problems, and because the method used to solve these problems, **dynamic programming,** is used also in Part 3 of the book. This simpler setting provides a good foundation for that later work.

Representation of Dynamic Choice

A deterministic investment is defined by its cash flow stream, say, $\mathbf{x} = (x_0, x_1, x_2, \ldots, x_n)$, but the magnitudes of the cash flows in this stream often depend on management choices in a complex fashion. In order to solve dynamic management problems, we need a way to represent the possible choices at each period, and the effect that those choices have on future cash flows. In short, we need a **dynamic model.** There are several mathematical structures that can be used to construct such a model, but the simplest is a **graph.** In this structure, the time points at which cash flows occur are represented by points along the horizontal direction, as usual. In the vertical direction above each such time point is laid out a set of **nodes,** which represent the different possible **states** or conditions of the process at that time. Nodes from one time to the next are connected by **branches** or **arcs.** A branch represents a possible path from a node at one time to another node at the next time. Different branches correspond to different management actions, which guide the course of the process. Simple examples of such graphs are that of a **binomial tree** and a **binomial lattice,** illustrated in Figure 5.3(*a*) and (*b*). In such a tree there are exactly two branches leaving each node. The leftmost node corresponds to the situation at the initial time, the next vertical pair of nodes represent the two possibilities at time 1, and so forth. (In the figure only four time points are shown.)

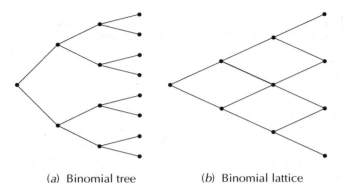

FIGURE 5.3 Graph representations. A tree is a general way to represent dynamic choice.

(*a*) Binomial tree   (*b*) Binomial lattice

The best way to describe the meaning of the tree is to walk through an example. Let us again consider the management of the oil well you recently purchased. At any time you can either pump oil or not. A node in the tree represents the condition of the well, defined by the size of its reserves, the state of repair, and so forth. To model your choices as a tree, you should start at the leftmost node of the tree, which represents the initial condition of the well. You have only two choices at that time: pump or don't pump. Assign one of these choices to an upward movement and the other to a downward movement; suppose that pumping corresponds to moving upward and nonpumping corresponds to moving downward. At the next time point your well is at one of the two nodes for that time. Again you make a choice and move either up or down. As you make your decisions, you move through the tree, from left to right, from node to node, along a particular path of branches. The path is uniquely determined by your choices; that is, the condition of the well through time and the magnitude of your overall profit are determined by your choices and represented by this unique path through the tree.

Suppose, specifically, that the well has initial reserves of 10 million barrels of oil. Each year it is possible to pump out 10% of the current reserves, but to do so a crew must be hired and paid. However, if a crew is already on hand, because it was used in the previous year, the hiring expenses are avoided. Therefore, to calculate the profit that can be obtained in any year, it is necessary to know the level of oil reserves and whether a crew is already on hand. Hence we label each node of the tree showing the reserve level and the status of a crew. For example, the label (9, YES) means that the reserves are 9,000,000 barrels and there is a crew on hand. A complete tree for the two periods is shown in Figure 5.3(*a*).

If crews can be assembled with no hiring cost, it is not necessary to keep track of the crew status. We can therefore drop one component from the node labels and keep only the reserve level. If we do that, some nodes that had distinct labels in the original tree will now have identical labels. In the example illustrated in Figure 5.4, two of the nodes at the final time both have a reserve level of 9 (meaning 9 million barrels). Since the labels are identical, we can combine these nodes into a single node, as shown in Figure 5.4(*b*). If the tree were extended for additional time periods, this combining effect would happen frequently, and as a

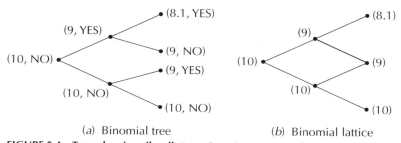

(a) Binomial tree   (b) Binomial lattice

FIGURE 5.4   Trees showing oil well states. Pumping corresponds to an upward movement; no pumping corresponds to a downward movement. The tree in (a) accounts for both the level of reserves and the status of a crew. If only the reserve levels affect the profit, some nodes combine, forming a binomial lattice, as shown in (b).

result the tree could be collapsed to a binomial lattice. A typical binomial lattice is shown in Figure 5.3(b). In such a graph, moving up and then down leads to the same node as moving down and then up. There are fewer nodes in a binomial lattice than in a binomial tree.

In terms of the oil well, if the only relevant factor for determining profit is the reserve level, it is clear that starting at any node, an upward movement in the tree (corresponding to pumping) followed by a downward movement (corresponding to not pumping) is identical in its influence on reserves to a downward movement followed by an upward movement. Both combinations deplete the reserves by the same amount. Hence a binomial lattice can be used to represent the management choices, as in Figure 5.4(b).

We used a binomial tree or a binomial lattice for the oil well example, which is appropriate when there are only two possible choices at each time. If there were three choices, we could form a **trinomial tree** or a **trinomial lattice,** having three branches emanating from each node. Clearly, any finite number of choices can be accommodated. (It is only reasonable to draw small trees on paper, but a computer can handle larger trees quite effectively, up to a point.)

Cash Flows in Graphs

The description of the nodes of a graph as states of a process is only an intermediate step in the representation of a dynamic investment situation. The essential part of the final representation is an assignment of cash flows to the various branches of the graph. These cash flows are used to evaluate management alternatives.

In the first oil well example, where crew hiring costs are not zero, suppose that the cost of hiring a crew is $100,000. (This represents just the initial hiring cost, not the wages paid.) Suppose the profit from oil production is $5.00 per barrel. Finally, suppose that at the beginning of a year the level of reserves in the well is x. Then the net profit for a year of production is $5 \times .10 \times x - 100,000$ if a crew must be hired, and $5 \times .10 \times x$ if a crew is already on hand. We can enter these values on the branches of the tree, indicating that much profit is attained if that branch is selected. These values are shown in Figure 5.5 in units of millions of dollars.

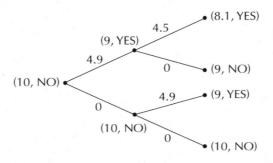

FIGURE 5.5 Oil well cash flow tree. The cash flow corresponding to a decision is listed on the branch corresponding to that decision. These cash flow values are determined by the node state and the decision.

Since only the cash flow values on the branches are important for analysis, it would be possible (conceptually) to bypass the step of describing the nodes as states of the process. However, in practice the node description is important because the cash flow values are determined from these descriptions by an accounting formula. If someone gave us the tree with cash flow values specified on all branches, that would be sufficient; we would not need the node descriptions. In practice, someone must first characterize the nodes, as we did earlier, so that the cash flows can be determined.

In representations of this kind it must also be stated whether the cash flow of a branch occurs at the beginning or at the end of the corresponding time period. In reality, a branch cash flow is often spread out over the entire period, but the model assigns a lump value at one end or the other (or sometimes a part at the beginning and another part at the end). The choice may vary with the situation being represented.

In some cases there is cash flow associated with the termination of the process, whose value varies with the final node achieved. This is a **final reward** or **salvage value.** These values are placed on the graph at the corresponding final nodes. In the oil well example, the final value might be the value for which the well could be sold.

5.4 OPTIMAL MANAGEMENT

Once we have a graph representation of the cash flow process associated with an investment, we can apply the principles of earlier chapters to determine the optimal management plan. Each path through the tree determines a specific cash flow stream; hence it is only necessary to select the path that is best. Usually this is the path that has the largest present value. So one way to solve the problem is to list all the possible streams, corresponding to all the possible paths, compute their respective present values, and select the largest one. We then manage the investment by following the path that corresponds to that maximal present value.

Although this method will work well for small problems, it is plagued by the **curse of dimensionality** for large problems. The number of possible paths in a tree grows exponentially with the number of periods. For example, in an n-period binomial tree the number of nodes is $2^{n+1} - 1$. So if $n = 12$ (say, 1 year of monthly decisions), there are 8,191 possible paths. And if there were 10 possible choices each month, this figure would rise to $10^{13} - 1$, which is beyond the capability of straightforward computation. We can use the computational procedure of **dynamic programming** to search much more efficiently.

Running Dynamic Programming

Dynamic programming solves a problem step by step, starting at the termination time and working back to the beginning. For this reason, dynamic programming is sometimes characterized by the phrase, "it solves the problem backward."

A special version of dynamic programming, based on the running present value method of Section 4.6, is especially convenient for investment problems. We call this method **running dynamic programming.** It is the method that we develop here and that is used throughout the text.

Suppose an investment with a dynamic cash flow is represented by a graph as described earlier. For simplicity, we assume periods are 1 year in length, and we use yearly compounding. A path through the graph generates a cash flow stream $c_0, c_1, \ldots, c_{n-1}$ (with each flow occurring at the beginning of the period), corresponding to the arcs that it passes along, and the path also determines a termination flow V_n at the final node. The present value of this complete stream is

$$\text{PV} = c_0 + \frac{c_1}{1 + s_1} + \frac{c_2}{(1 + s_2)^2} + \cdots + \frac{c_{n-1}}{(1 + s_{n-1})^{n-1}} + \frac{V_n}{(1 + s_n)^n}$$

where the s_k's are the spot rates. A path is defined by a particular series of decisions—one choice at each node. We wish to determine those choices that maximize the resulting present value.

In the running method, we use the one-period discount factors $d_k = 1/(1 + r_k)$, where r_k is the short rate $r_k = f_{k,k+1}$, and we evaluate the present value step by step. In particular, in running dynamic programming we assign to each node a value equal to the best running present value that can be obtained from that node, neglecting all previous cash flows. For the ith node at time k, denoted by (k, i), the best running value is called V_{ki}. We refer to these values as V-values.

The V-values at the final nodes are just the terminal values of the investment process. These values are clearly the present values—as seen at time n—that can be attained neglecting the past. Hence the V-values at the final nodes are already given as part of the problem description.

The dynamic programming procedure next addresses the nodes at time $n - 1$. For any node i at time $n - 1$, we pretend that the underlying investment process has taken us to that node. The decisions for previous nodes have already been made, and the corresponding previous cash flows $c_0, c_1, \ldots, c_{n-2}$ have already occurred. Only one decision remains: we must determine which arc to follow from node $(n - 1, i)$ to some final node at time n. Since we can do nothing about past decisions (in this pretending viewpoint), it is clear that we should select the arc that maximizes the present value as seen at time $n - 1$ (the running present value). Specifically, if we index the arcs by the node number a they reach at time n, we should look at the values $c_{n-1}^a + d_n V_{n,a}$. (Here c_{n-1}^a is the cash flow associated with arc a and $V_{n,a}$ is the V-value at the node

$$V_{n-1,1} = \max_{a=1,2} \left(c_{n-1}^a + d_{n-1} V_{n,a} \right)$$

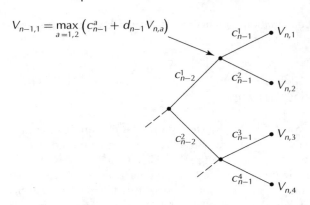

FIGURE 5.6   First recursive step of dynamic programming. Assuming that the first $n-1$ steps of the process have been completed, we evaluate the best that can be done for the last step. For any node at time $n-1$ we find the maximum running present value from that node.

to which arc a leads.) After calculating these sums for every arc a emanating from node $(n-1, i)$, we select the largest of these values and denote that value by $V_{n-1,i}$. This is the best running present value that can be attained from node $(n-1, i)$; and hence it is the correct V-value. This procedure, illustrated in Figure 5.6, is repeated for each of the nodes at time $n-1$.

Next the same procedure is carried out at time $n-2$. We assume that the investment process is at a particular node $(n-2, i)$. Each branch a emanating from that node produces a cash flow and takes the process to a corresponding node a at time $n-1$. If c_{n-2}^a is the cash flow associated with this choice, the total contribution to (running) present value, accounting for the future as well, is $c_{n-2}^a + d_{n-2} V_{n-1,a}$ because the running present value is equal to the current cash flow plus a discounted version of the running present value of the next period. We compute these new values for all possible arcs and select the largest. This maximal value is defined to be $V_{n-2,i}$. This procedure, illustrated in Figure 5.7, is carried out for every node at time $n-2$.

This procedure is continued, working backward until time zero is reached, where there is only one node. The V-value determined there is the optimal present value as seen at time zero, and hence it is the overall best value. The optimal decisions and cash flows can easily be determined as a by-product of the dynamic programming

$$V_{n-2,1} = \max_{a=1,2} \left(c_{n-2}^a + d_{n-2} V_{n-1,a} \right)$$

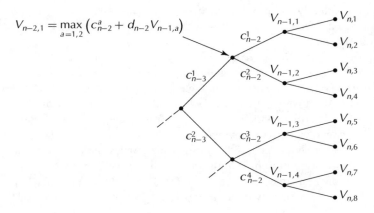

FIGURE 5.7   Second stage of dynamic programming. Assuming that the first $n-2$ stages of the process have been completed, we evaluate the best running present value for the remaining two stages.

procedure, either by recording them at the nodes as the V-values are computed, or by working forward, using the known future V-values.

The running dynamic programming method can be written very succinctly by a recurrence relation. Define c_{ki}^a to be the cash flow generated by moving from node (k, i) to node $(k + 1, a)$. The recursion procedure is

$$V_{ki} = \underset{a}{\text{maximize}} \left(c_{ki}^a + d_k V_{k+1,a} \right).$$

An example will make all of this clear.

Examples

Example 5.4 (Fishing problem) Suppose that you own both a lake and a fishing boat as an investment package. You plan to profit by taking fish from the lake. Each season you decide either to fish or not to fish. If you do not fish, the fish population in the lake will flourish, and in fact it will double by the start of the next season. If you do fish, you will extract 70% of the fish that were in the lake at the beginning of the season. The fish that were not caught (and some before they are caught) will reproduce, and the fish population at the beginning of the next season will be the same as at the beginning of the current season. So corresponding to whether you abstain or fish, the fish population will either double or remain the same, and you get either nothing or 70% of the beginning-season fish population. The initial fish population is 10 tons. Your profit is $1 per ton. The interest rate is constant at 25%, which means that the discount factor is .8 each year. Unfortunately you have only three seasons to fish. The management problem is that of determining in which of those seasons you should fish.

The situation can be described by the binomial lattice shown in Figure 5.8. The nodes are marked with the fish population. A lattice, rather than a tree, is appropriate because only the fish population in the lake is relevant at any time. The manner by which that population was achieved has no effect on future cash flows. The value on

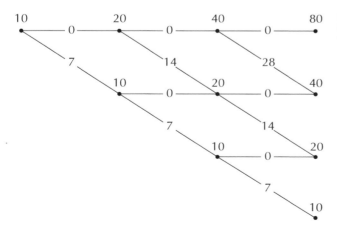

FIGURE 5.8 Fishing problem. The node values are the tonnage of fish in the lake; the branch values are cash flows.

a branch indicates the catch (and hence the cash flow) associated with that branch. Horizontal branches correspond to no fishing and no catch, whereas downward directed branches correspond to fishing.

The problem is solved by working backward. We assign the value of 0 to each of the final nodes, since once we are there we can no longer fish. Then at each of the nodes one step from the end we determine the maximum possible cash flow. (Clearly, we fish in every case.) This determines the cash flow received that season, and we assume that we obtain that cash at the beginning of the season. Hence we do *not* discount the profit. The value obtained is the (running) present value, as viewed from that time. These values are indicated on a copy of the lattice in Figure 5.9.

Next we back up one time period and calculate the maximum present values at that time. For example, for the node just to the right of the initial node, we have

$$V = \max(.8 \times 28, \quad 14 + .8 \times 14).$$

The maximum is attained by the second choice, corresponding to the downward branch, and hence $V = 14 + .8 \times 14 = 25.2$. The discount rate of $1/1.25 = .8$ is applicable at every stage since the spot rate curve is flat. (See Section 4.6.) Finally, a similar calculation is carried out for the initial node. The value there gives the maximum present value. The optimal path is the path determined by the optimal choices we discovered in the procedure. The optimal path for this example is indicated in Figure 5.9 by the heavy line. In words, the solution is not to fish the first season (to let the fish population increase) and then fish the next two seasons (to harvest the population).

The lattice structure can accommodate any finite number of branches emanating from a node. The limit of this kind of construction is a continuous lattice, having a continuum of nodes at any stage and a continuum of possible decisions at any node. For example, in the case of the oil well discussed in the previous section, from a total reserve R you might pump any amount z between, say, 0 and M, leading to a new reserve of

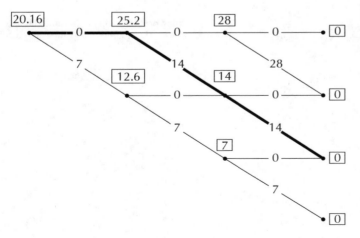

FIGURE 5.9   Calculations for fish problem. The node values are now the optimal running present values, found by working backward from the terminal nodes. The branch values are cash flows.

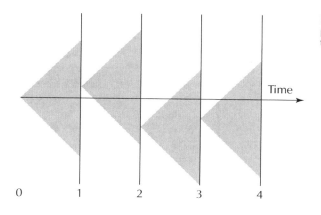

FIGURE 5.10 Continuous lattice. A continuous lattice is a powerful way to represent situations where there is a continuum of possible choices every period.

Time

0 1 2 3 4

$R - z$. Your choice z is continuous, and so is the level of reserves. This type of lattice is illustrated schematically in Figure 5.10. Here each vertical line represents the continuum of nodes possible at a particular time. (At the initial time there is only one node.) The fan emanating from a node represents the fan of possibilities for traveling to a subsequent node. Only one fan is indicated for each time, whereas actually there is such a fan emanating from every point on the vertical line. This dynamic structure works very much like the finite-node case: The process starts at the initial node, and one of the possible choices is selected. This leads to a specific node point on the line for the next time, and the process continues. Optimizing such a process by dynamic programming works in the reverse direction, just like in the finite case, but is made more difficult by the fact that a V-value must be assigned to every point on each node line. Hence V is a function defined on the line. In some cases this function has a simple analytic form, and then the dynamic programming procedure can be carried out explicitly. An illustration of this kind is shown in the next example, which, by the way, is the next in our continuing sequence of gold mine examples.

Example 5.5 (Complexico mine) The Complexico mine is for lease. This mine has been worked heavily and is approaching depletion. It is becoming increasingly difficult to extract rich ore. In fact, if x is the amount of gold remaining in the mine at the beginning of a year, the cost to extract $z < x$ ounces of gold in that year is $\$500z^2/x$. (Note that as x decreases, it becomes more difficult to obtain gold.) It is estimated that the current amount of gold remaining in the mine is $x_0 = 50,000$ ounces. The price of gold is \$400/oz. We are contemplating the purchase of a 10-year lease of the Complexico mine. The interest rate is 10%. How much is this lease worth?

To solve this problem we must know how to operate the mine optimally over the 10-year period. In particular, we must determine how much gold to mine each year in order to obtain the maximum present value. To find this optimal operating plan, we represent the mine by a continuous lattice, with the nodes at any time representing the amount of gold remaining in the mine at the beginning of that year. We denote this amount by x. This amount determines the optimal value of the remaining lease from that point on.

We index the time points by the number of years since the beginning of the lease. The initial time is 0, the end of the first year is 1, and so forth. The end of the lease is time 10. We also assume, for simplicity, that the cash flow from mining operations is obtained at the *beginning* of the year.

We begin by determining the value of a lease on the mine at time 9, when the remaining deposit is x_9. Only 1 year remains on the lease, so the value is obtained by maximizing the profit for that year. If we extract z_9 ounces, the revenue from the sale of the gold will be gz_9, where g is the price of gold, and the cost of mining will be $500z_9^2/x_9$. Hence the optimal value of the mine at time 9 if x_9 is the remaining deposit level is

$$V_9(x_9) = \max_{z_9} \, (gz_9 - 500z_9^2/x_9).$$

We find the maximum by setting the derivative with respect to z_9 equal to zero. This yields[1]

$$z_9 = gx_9/1{,}000.$$

We substitute this value in the formula for profit to find

$$V_9(x_9) = \frac{g^2 x_9}{1{,}000} - \frac{500g^2 x_9}{1{,}000 \times 1{,}000} = \frac{g^2 x_9}{2{,}000}.$$

We write this as $V_9(x_9) = K_9 x_9$, where $K_9 = g^2/2{,}000$ is a constant. Hence the value of the lease is directly proportional to how much gold remains in the mine; the proportionality factor is K_9.

Next we back up and solve for $V_8(x_8)$. In this case we account for the profit generated during the ninth year and also for the value that the lease will have at the end of that year—a value that depends on how much gold we leave in the mine. Hence,

$$V_8(x_8) = \max_{z_8} \left[gz_8 - 500z_8^2/x_8 + d \cdot V_9(x_8 - z_8) \right].$$

Note that we have discounted the value associated with the mine at the next year by a factor d. As in the previous example, the discount rate is constant because the spot rate curve is flat. In this case $d = 1/1.1$.

Using the explicit form for the function V_9, we may write

$$V_8(x_8) = \max_{z_8} \left[gz_8 - 500z_8^2/x_8 + dK_9(x_8 - z_8) \right].$$

We again set the derivative with respect to z_8 equal to zero and obtain

$$z_8 = \frac{(g - dK_9)x_8}{1{,}000}.$$

This value can be substituted into the expression for V_8 to obtain

$$V_8(x_8) = \left[\frac{(g - dK_9)^2}{2{,}000} + dK_9 \right] x_8.$$

This is proportional to x_8, and we may write it as $V_8(x_8) = K_8 x_8$.

---

[1] We should check that $z_9 \le x_9$, which does hold with the values we use.

TABLE 5.4
K-Values for
Complexico Mine

Years	K-values
0	213.81
1	211.45
2	208.17
3	203.58
4	197.13
5	187.96
6	174.79
7	155.47
8	126.28
9	80.00

We can continue backward in this way, determining the functions $V_7, V_6, \ldots, V_0$. Each of these functions will be of the form $V_j(x_j) = K_j x_j$. It should be clear that the same algebra applies at each step, and hence we have the recursive formula

$$K_j = \frac{(g - d K_{j+1})^2}{2,000} + d K_{j+1}.$$

If we use the specific values $g = 400$ and $d = 1/1.1$, we begin the recursion with $K_9 = g^2/2,000 = 80$. We can then easily solve for all the other values, as shown in Table 5.4, working from the bottom to the top.

It is the last value calculated (that is, K_0) that determines the value of the original lease. That value is determined by finding the value of the lease when there is 50,000 ounces of gold remaining. Hence $V_0(50,000) = 213.82 \times 50,000 = \$10,691,000$.

The optimal plan is determined as a by-product of the dynamic programming procedure. At any time j, the amount of gold to extract is the value z_j found in the optimization problem. Hence $z_9 = g x_9/1,000$ and $z_8 = (g - d K_9) x_9/1,000$. In general, $z_j = (g - d K_{j+1}) x_{j+1}/1,000$.

Dynamic programming problems using a continuous lattice do not always work out as well as in the preceding example, because it is not always possible to find a simple expression for the V functions. (The specific functional form for the cost in the gold mine example led to the linear form for the V functions.) But dynamic programming is a general problem-solving technique that has many variations and many applications. The general idea is used repeatedly in Parts 3 and 4 of this book.

5.5 THE HARMONY THEOREM*

We know that there is a difference between the present value criterion for selecting investment opportunities and the internal rate of return criterion, and that it is strongly believed by theorists that the present value criterion is the better of the two, provided that account is made for the entire cash flow stream of the investment over all its periods. But if you are asked to consider an investment of a fixed amount of dollars (say, in your friend's new venture), you probably would not evaluate this proposition in terms of present value; you would more likely focus on potential return. In fact, if you do make the investment, you are likely to encourage your friend to maximize the return on your investment, not the present value of the firm. Your friend might insist on maximizing present value. Is there a conflict here?

We will try to shed some light on this important issue by working through a hypothetical situation. Suppose your friend has invented a new gismo for which he holds the patent rights. To profit from this invention, he must raise capital and carry out certain operations. The cost for the operations occurs immediately; the reward occurs at the end of a year. In other words, the cash flow stream has just two elements: a negative amount now and a positive amount at the end of a year.

Your friend recognizes that there are many different ways that he can operate his venture, and these entail different costs and different rewards. Hence there are many possible cash flow streams corresponding to different operating plans. He must select one. The possibilities can be described by points on a graph showing the reward (at the end of a year) versus the current cost of operations, as in Figure 5.11(a). Your friend can select any one of the points.

Suppose also that the 1-year interest rate is $r = 10\%$. The possibility of depositing money in the bank can be represented on the graph as a straight line with slope 1.10: the current deposit is a cost, and the reward is 1.10 times that amount. This slope will be used to evaluate the present value of a cash flow stream.

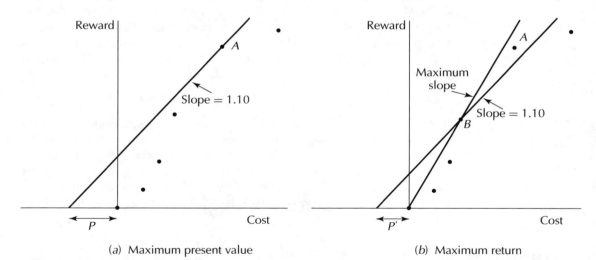

(a) Maximum present value   (b) Maximum return

FIGURE 5.11 Comparison of criteria. (a) Plan A is selected because it has the greatest present value. It is the point corresponding to the highest line of slope, equal to 1.10. (b) Plan B is selected because it is the point on the line from the origin of greatest slope. As the text demonstrates, the analysis in (b) is faulty, and when corrected, the maximum return criterion will correspond to the present value criterion.

If your friend decides to maximize the present value of his venture, he will draw lines with slopes $1 + r = 1.10$ and find the highest one that goes through a possible operating plan. The plan that lies on that line is the optimal one. This optimal line and plan are shown in Figure 5.11(a); point A is the optimal plan. Using a bank, it is possible to move along the line through A. In particular, it is possible to move all the way down to the horizontal axis. At this point, no money will be received next year, but an amount P of net profit is obtained now.

Suppose your friend asks you to invest in his venture, supplying a portion of the operating cost and getting that portion of the reward. You would measure the return on your investment. The operating point that achieves the maximum return is found by swinging a line upward, pivoting around the origin, reaching an operating point of greatest possible slope. The result of this process is shown in Figure 5.11(b). The optimal point according to this criterion is the point B in the figure. The maximum return is the slope of this maximum-slope line. Note that this slope is greater than 110%. So point B achieves a higher rate of return than point A. Its present value, however, is just P', which is less than P. There seems to be a conflict.

Here is how the conflict is resolved. Your friend currently owns the rights to his gismo. He has not yet committed any money for operations; but his present value analysis shows that he could go to the bank, take out a loan sufficient to cover the expenses for plan A, and then, at the end of the year, he could pay back the loan and pocket the profit of $1.10P$ (which is worth P now). He doesn't care about the rate of return, since he is not investing any money; he is just taking out a loan. Alternatively, he could borrow the money from you, but he would not pay you any more than the current interest rate.

But you are not being asked to make a loan; you are being asked to invest in the venture—to have ownership in it. As an extreme case, suppose your friend asks you to buy the whole venture. You will then have the rights to the gismo. He is willing to stay on and operate the venture (if you provide the necessary operating costs), but you will have the power to decide what operating plan to use.

If your friend sells you the venture, he will charge you an amount P because that is what it would be worth to him if he kept ownership. So if you decide to buy the venture, the total expense of an operating plan is now P plus the actual operating cost. If you want to maximize your return, you will maximize reward/(cost + P). You can find this new best operating plan by swinging a line upward, pivoting around the point $-P$, reaching the operating point with the greatest possible slope. That point will be point A, the point that maximized the present value. [Look again at Figure 5.11(a).] Alternatively, once you are the owner, you might consider maximizing the present value. That will lead to point A as well. Therefore if you decide to buy the venture, and you pay the full value P, you will maximize the return on your investment by operating under plan A; and your return will be 110%. (It does not matter if you decide to borrow some of the operating costs instead of funding them yourself; still you will want to operate at A, and your return will still be 110%.)

We summarize the preceding discussion by a general result that we term the *harmony theorem*. It states that there is harmony between the present value criterion and the rate of return criterion when account is made for ownership.

Harmony theorem *Current owners of a venture should want to operate the venture to maximize the present value of its cash flow stream. Potential new owners, who must pay the full value of their prospective share of the venture, will want the company to operate in the same way, in order to maximize the return on their investment.*

The harmony theorem is justification for operating a venture (such as a company) in the way that maximizes the present value of the cash flow stream it generates. Both current owners and potential investors will agree on this policy.

The presentation in this section considered only deterministic cash flow streams with two flows. The harmony theorem generalizes to multiple periods and to random streams as well—under certain conditions. A multiperiod generalization is discussed in Exercise 10.

5.6 VALUATION OF A FIRM*

The principles of cash flow analysis can be used to evaluate the worth of publicly traded corporations; indeed almost all analytic valuation methods do use some form of cash flow analysis. However, as straightforward as that may sound, the general idea is subject to a variety of interpretations, each leading to a different result. These differences spring from the question of just which cash flows should form the basis of analysis: should they be the dividends that flow to a stockholder, the net earnings to the company, or the flow that could be captured by a single individual or group who owned the company and was free to extract the cash according to the group's own policy? If these various quantities are defined by standard accounting practice, they can lead to significantly different inferred firm values.

Another weakness of this kind of analysis is that it is based on an assumption that future cash flows are known deterministically, which, of course, is usually not the case. Often uncertainty is recognized in an analysis, but treated in a simplistic way (for instance, by increasing the interest rate used for discounting above the risk-free rate). We discuss other, more solidly based approaches to evaluation under uncertainty in later chapters. This section assumes that the cash flows are deterministic.

Dividend Discount Models

The owner of a share of stock in a company can expect to receive periodic dividends. Suppose that it is known that in year k, $k = 1, 2, \ldots,$ a dividend of D_k will be received. If the interest rate (or the discount rate) is fixed at r, it is reasonable to assign a value of the firm to the stock holders as the present value of this dividend stream; namely,

$$V_0 = \frac{D_1}{1 + r} + \frac{D_2}{(1 + r)^2} + \frac{D_3}{(1 + r)^3} + \cdots .$$

This formula is straightforward, but it requires that the future dividends be known.

A popular way to specify dividends is to use the **constant-growth dividend model,** where dividends grow at a constant rate g. In particular, given D_1 and the relation $D_{k+1} = (1 + g)D_k$, the present value of the stream is

$$V_0 = \frac{D_1}{1 + r} + \frac{D_1(1 + g)}{(1 + r)^2} + \frac{D_1(1 + g)^2}{(1 + r)^3} + \cdots = D_1 \sum_{k=1}^{\infty} \frac{(1 + g)^{k-1}}{(1 + r)^k}.$$

This summation is similar to that of an annuity, except that there is the extra growth term in the numerator. The summation will have finite value only if the dividend growth rate is less than the rate used for discounting; that is, if $g < r$. In that case we have the explicit **Gordon formula** (see Exercise 11) for the summation

$$V_0 = \frac{D_1}{r - g}. \tag{5.1}$$

Note that, according to this formula, the value of a firm's stock increases if g increases, if the current dividend D_1 increases, or if the discount rate r decreases. All of these properties are intuitively clear.

If we project D_1 from a current dividend (already paid) of D_0, we can rewrite (5.1) by including the first-year's growth. We highlight this as follows:

Discounted growth formula   *Consider a dividend stream that grows at a rate of g per period. Assign $r > g$ as the discount rate per period. Then the present value of the stream, starting one period from the present, with the dividend D_1, is*

$$V_0 = \frac{(1 + g)D_0}{r - g} \tag{5.2}$$

where D_0 is the current dividend.

To use the constant-growth dividend model one must estimate the growth rate g and assign an appropriate value to the discount rate r. Estimation of g can be based on the history of the firm's dividends and on future prospects. Frequently a value is assigned to r that is larger than the actual risk-free interest rate to reflect the idea that uncertain cash flows should be discounted more heavily than certain cash flows. (In Chapters 15 and 16, we study better ways to account for uncertainty.)

Example 5.6 (The XX Corporation)   The XX Corporation has just paid a dividend of \$1.37M. The company is expected to grow at 10% for the foreseeable future, and hence most analysts project a similar growth in dividends. The discount rate used for this type of company is 15%. What is the value of a share of stock in the XX Corporation?

The total value of all shares is given by (5.2). Hence this value is

$$V_0 = \frac{1.37\text{M} \times 1.10}{.15 - .10} = \$30,140,000.$$

Assume that there are 1 million shares outstanding. Each share is worth \$30.14 according to this analysis.

Free Cash Flow*

A conceptual difficulty with the dividend discount method is that the dividend rate is set by the board of directors of the firm, and this rate may not be representative of the firm's financial status. A different perspective to valuation is obtained by imagining that you were the sole owner and could take out cash as it is earned. From this perspective the value of the firm might be the discounted value of the net earnings stream.

The net earnings of a firm is defined by accounting practice. In the simplest case it is just revenue minus cost, and then minus taxes; but things are rarely this simple. Account must be made for depreciation of plant and equipment, payment of interest on debt, taxes, and other factors. The final net earnings figure may have little relation to the cash flow that can be extracted from the firm.

Within the limitations of a deterministic approach, the best way to value a firm is to determine the cash flow stream of maximum present value that can be taken out of the company and distributed to the owners. The corresponding cash flow in any year is termed that year's **free cash flow** (FCF). Roughly, free cash flow is the cash generated through operations minus the investments necessary to sustain those operations and their anticipated growth.

It is difficult to obtain an accurate measure of the free cash flow. First, it is necessary to assess the firm's potential for generating cash under various policies. Second, it is necessary to determine the optimal rate of investment—the rate that will generate the cash flow stream of maximum present value. Usually this optimal rate is merely estimated; but since the relation between growth rate and present value is complex, the estimated rate may be far from the true optimum. We shall illustrate the ideal process with a highly idealized example.

Suppose that a company has gross earnings of Y_n in year n and decides to invest a portion u of this amount each year in order to attain earnings growth. The growth rate is determined by the function $g(u)$, which is a property of the firm's characteristics. On a (simplified) accounting basis, depreciation is a fraction α of the current capital account ($\alpha \approx .10$, for example). In this case the capital C_n follows the formula $C_{n+1} = (1 - \alpha)C_n + uY_n$. With these ideas we can set up a general income statement for a firm, as shown in Table 5.5.

Example 5.7 (Optimal growth) We can go further with the foregoing analysis and calculate Y_n and C_n in explicit form. Since $Y_{n+1} = [1 + g(u)]Y_n$, it is easy to see that $Y_n = [1 + g(u)]^n Y_0$. Likewise, it can be shown that

$$C_n = (1 - \alpha)^n C_0 + uY_0 \left\{ \frac{-(1 - \alpha)^n + [1 + g(u)]^n}{g(u) + \alpha} \right\}.$$

If we ignore the two terms having $(1 - \alpha)^n$ (since they will nearly cancel) we have

$$C_n = \frac{uY_0[1 + g(u)]^n}{g(u) + \alpha}. \tag{5.3}$$

TABLE 5.5
Free Cash Flow

Income statement	
Before-tax cash flow from operations	Y_n
Depreciation	αC_n
Taxable income	$Y_n - \alpha C_n$
Taxes (34%)	$.34(Y_n - \alpha C_n)$
After-tax income	$.66(Y_n - \alpha C_n)$
After-tax cash flow (after-tax income plus depreciation)	$.66(Y_n - \alpha C_n) + \alpha C_n$
Sustaining investment	$u Y_n$
Free cash flow	$.66(Y_n - \alpha C_n) + \alpha C_n - u Y_n$

Depreciation is assumed to be α times the amount in the capital account.

Putting the expressions for Y_n and C_n in the bottom line of Table 5.5, we find the free cash flow at time n to be

$$\text{FCF} = \left[.66 + .34\frac{\alpha u}{g(u) + \alpha} - u\right][1 + g(u)]^n Y_0. \tag{5.4}$$

This is a growing geometric series. We can use the Gordon formula to calculate its present value at interest rate r. This gives

$$\text{PV} = \left[.66 + .34\frac{\alpha u}{g(u) + \alpha} - u\right]\frac{1}{r - g(u)}Y_0. \tag{5.5}$$

It is not easy to see by inspection what value of u would be best. Let us consider another example.

Example 5.8 (XX Corporation)   Assume that the XX Corporation has current earnings of $Y_0 = \$10$ million, and the initial capital[2] is $C_0 = \$19.8$ million. The interest rate is $r = 15\%$, the depreciation factor is $\alpha = .10$, and the relation between investment rate and growth rate is $g(u) = .12[1 - e^{5(\alpha - u)}]$. Notice that $g(\alpha) = 0$, reflecting the fact that an investment rate of α times earnings just keeps up with the depreciation of capital.

Using (5.5) we can find the value of the company for various choices of the investment rate u. For example, for $u = 0$, no investment, the company will slowly shrink, and the present value under that policy will be $29 million. If $u = .10$, the company will just maintain its current level, and the present value under that plan will be $39.6 million. Or if $u = .5$, the present value will be $52 million.

It is possible to maximize (5.5) (by trial and error or by a simple optimization routine as is available in some spreadsheet packages). The result is $u = 37.7\%$ and $g(u) = 9.0\%$. The corresponding present value is $58.3 million. This is the company value.

---

[2]This value of C_0 will make the terms that were canceled in deriving (5.3) cancel exactly.

Here is a question to consider carefully. Suppose that during the first year, the firm operates according to this plan, investing 37.7% of its gross earnings in new capital. Suppose also, for simplicity, that no dividends are paid that year. What will be the value of the company after 1 year? Recall that during this year, capital and earnings expand by 9%. Would you guess that the company value will increase by 9% as well? Remember the harmony theorem. Actually, the value will increase by the rate of interest, which is 15%. Investors must receive this rate, and they do. The reason this may seem strange is that we assumed that no dividends were paid. The free cash flow that was generated, but not taken out of the company, is held for the year (itself earning 15%), and this must be added to the present value calculation of future cash flows. If the free cash flow generated in the first year were distributed as dividends, the company value would increase by 9%, but the total return to investors, including the dividend and the value increase, again would be 15%.

Although this example is highly idealized, it indicates the character of a full valuation procedure (under an assumption of certainty). The free cash flow stream must be projected, accounting for future opportunities. Furthermore, this cash flow stream must be optimized by proper selection of a capital investment policy. Because the impact of current investment on future free cash flow is complex, effective optimization requires the use of formal models and formal optimization techniques.

5.7 SUMMARY

Interest rate theory is probably the most widely used financial tool. It is used to determine the value of projects, to allocate money among alternatives, to design complex bond portfolios, to determine how to manage investments effectively, and even to determine the value of a firm.

Interest rate theory is most powerful when it is combined with general problem-solving methods, particularly methods of optimization. With the aid of such methods, interest rate theory provides more than just a static measure of value; it guides us to find the decision or structure with the highest value.

One class of problems that can be approached with this combination is capital budgeting problems. In the classic problem of this class, a fixed budget is to be allocated among a set of independent projects in order to maximize net present value. This problem can be solved approximately by selecting projects with the highest benefit–cost ratio. The problem can be solved exactly by formulating it as a zero–one optimization problem and using an integer programming package. More complex capital budgeting problems having dependencies among projects can be also be solved by the zero–one programming method.

The selection of a bond portfolio to meet certain requirements can be conveniently formulated as an optimization problem—but there are several possible formulations. A particularly simple problem within this class is the cash-matching problem, where a portfolio is constructed to generate a required cash flow in each period. This formulation has the weakness that in some periods extra cash may be generated, beyond that required, and this extra cash is essentially wasted. More complex formulations do not have this weakness.

To produce excellent results, many investments require deliberate ongoing management. The relation between a series of management decisions and the resulting cash flow stream frequently can be modeled as a graph. (Especially useful types of graphs are trees and lattices.) In such a graph the nodes correspond to states of the process, and a branch leading from a node corresponds to a particular choice made from that node. Associated with each branch is a cash flow value.

Optimal dynamic management consists of following the special path of arcs through the graph that produces the greatest present value. This optimal path can be found efficiently by the method of dynamic programming. A particularly useful version of dynamic programming for investment problems uses the running method for evaluation of present value.

Dynamic programming works backward in time. For a problem with n time periods, the running version of the procedure starts by finding the best decision at each of the nodes i at time $n - 1$ and assigns a V-value, denoted by $V_{n-1,i}$, to each such node. This V-value is the optimal present value that could be obtained if the investment process were initiated at that node. To find that value, each possible arc emanating from node i is examined. The sum of the cash flow of the arc and the one-period discounted V-value at the node reached by the arc is evaluated. The V-value of the originating node i is the maximum of those sums. After completing this procedure for all the nodes at $n - 1$, the procedure then steps back to the nodes at time $n - 2$. Optimal V-values are found for each of those nodes by a procedure that exactly parallels that for the nodes at $n - 1$. The procedure continues by working backward through all time periods, and it ends when an optimal V-value is assigned to the initial node at time zero.

When operating a venture it is appropriate to maximize the present value. On the other hand, investors may be most interested in the rate of return. These criteria might seem to be in conflict, but the harmony theorem states that the criteria are equivalent under the assumption that investors pay the full value for their ownership of the venture.

Present value analysis is commonly used to estimate the value of a firm. One such procedure is the dividend discount method, where the value to a stockholder is assumed to be equal to the present value of the stream of future dividend payments. If dividends are assumed to grow at a rate g per year, a simple formula gives the present value of the resulting stream.

The better method of firm evaluation bases the evaluation on free cash flow, which is the amount of cash that can be taken out of the firm while maintaining optimal operations and investment strategies. In idealized form, this method requires that the present value of free cash flow be maximized with respect to all possible management decisions, especially those related to investment that produces earnings growth.

Valuation methods based on present value suffer the defect that future cash flows are treated as if they were known with certainty, when in fact they are usually uncertain. The deterministic theory is therefore not adequate. This defect is widely recognized; and to compensate for it, it is common practice to discount predicted, but uncertain, cash flows at higher interest rates than the risk-free rate. There is some theoretical justification for this, but a completely consistent approach to uncertainty is more subtle. The exciting story of uncertainty in investment begins with the next chapter and continues throughout the remainder of the text.

EXERCISES

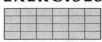

1. (Capital budgeting)   A firm is considering funding several proposed projects that have the financial properties shown in Table 5.6. The available budget is $600,000. What set of projects would be recommended by the approximate method based on benefit–cost ratios? What is the optimal set of projects?

TABLE 5.6
Financial Properties of Proposed Projects

Project	Outlay ($1,000)	Present worth ($1,000)
1	100	200
2	300	500
3	200	300
4	150	200
5	150	250

2. (The road ⊕)   Refer to the transportation alternatives problem of Example 5.2. The bridge at Cay Road is actually part of the road between Augen and Burger. Therefore it is not reasonable for the bridge to have fewer lanes than the road itself. This means that if projects 2 or 4 are carried out, either projects 6 or 7 must also be carried out. Formulate a zero–one programming problem that includes this additional requirement. Solve the problem.

3. (Two-period budget ⊕)   A company has identified a number of promising projects, as indicated in Table 5.7. The cash flows for the first 2 years are shown (they are all negative).

TABLE 5.7
A List of Projects

Project	Cash flow 1	2	NPV
1	−90	−58	150
2	−80	−80	200
3	−50	−100	100
4	−20	−64	100
5	−40	−50	120
6	−80	−20	150
7	−80	−100	240

The cash flows in later years are positive, and the net present value of each project is shown. The company managers have decided that they can allocate up to $250,000 in each of the first 2 years to fund these projects. If less than $250,000 is used the first year, the balance can be invested at 10% and used to augment the next year's budget. Which projects should be funded?

4. (Bond matrix ◇)   The cash matching and other problems can be conveniently represented in matrix form. Suppose there are m bonds. We define for each bond j its associated yearly cash flow stream (column) vector $\mathbf{c}_j$, which is n-dimensional. The yearly obligations are likewise represented by the n-dimensional vector $\mathbf{y}$. We can stack the $\mathbf{c}_j$ vectors side by side to form the columns of a bond matrix $\mathbf{C}$. Finally we let $\mathbf{p}$ and $\mathbf{x}$ be m-dimensional column vectors. The cash matching problem can be expressed as

$$\text{maximize} \quad \mathbf{p}^T\mathbf{x}$$

$$\text{subject to} \quad \mathbf{Cx} \geq \mathbf{y}$$

$$\mathbf{x} \geq \mathbf{0}.$$

(a) Identify $\mathbf{C}$, $\mathbf{y}$, $\mathbf{p}$, and $\mathbf{x}$ in Table 5.3.
(b) Show that if all bonds are priced according to a common term structure of interest rates, there is a vector $\mathbf{v}$ satisfying

$$\mathbf{C}^T\mathbf{v} = \mathbf{p}.$$

What are the components of $\mathbf{v}$?
(c) Suppose $\mathbf{b}$ is a vector whose components represent obligations in each period. Show that a portfolio $\mathbf{x}$ meeting these obligations exactly satisfies

$$\mathbf{Cx} = \mathbf{b}.$$

(d) With $\mathbf{x}$ and $\mathbf{v}$ defined as before, show that the price of the portfolio $\mathbf{x}$ is $\mathbf{v}^T\mathbf{b}$. Interpret this result.

5. (Trinomial lattice)   A trinomial lattice is a special case of a trinomial tree. From each node three moves are possible: up, middle, and down. The special feature of the lattice is that certain pairs of moves lead to identical nodes two periods in the future. We can express these equivalences as

$$\begin{aligned} \text{up–down} \;&=\; \text{down–up} \;=\; \text{middle–middle} \\ \text{middle–down} \;&=\; \text{down–middle} \\ \text{middle–up} \;&=\; \text{up–middle.} \end{aligned}$$

Draw a trinomial lattice spanning three periods. How many nodes does it contain? How many nodes are contained in a full trinomial tree of the same number of periods?

6. (A bond project ⊕)   You are the manager of XYZ Pension Fund. On November 5, 2011, XYZ must purchase a portfolio of U.S. Treasury bonds to meet the fund's projected liabilities in the future. The bonds available at that time are those of Exercise 4 in Chapter 4. Short selling is not allowed. Following the procedure of the earlier exercise, a 4th-order polynomial estimate of the term structure is constructed as $r(t) = \alpha_0 + \alpha_1 t + \alpha_2 t^2 + \alpha_3 t^3 + \alpha_4 t^4$. The liabilities of XYZ are as listed in Table 5.8.

TABLE 5.8
Liabilities of XYC Pension Fund

Liabilities	Occur on 15th
Feb 2012	$2,000
Aug 2012	$20,000
Feb 2013	$0
Aug 2013	$25,000
Feb 2014	$1,000
Aug 2014	$0
Feb 2015	$20,000
Aug 2015	$1,000
Feb 2016	$15,000

(a) (Simple cash matching)   Construct a minimum-cost liability-matching portfolio by buying Treasury bonds assuming that excess periodic cash flows may be held only at *zero* interest to meet future liabilities.

(b) (Complex cash matching)   Construct a minimum-cost liability-matching portfolio by buying Treasury bonds assuming that all excess periodic cash flows may be reinvested at the expected interest rates (implied by the current term structure) to meet future liabilities. No borrowing is allowed.

(c) (Duration matching)   Construct a minimum-cost portfolio with present value equal to that of the liability stream. Immunize against a change in the term structure parameters. Do this for five cases. Case 1 is to guard against a change in α_1, case 2 to guard against changes in α_1 and α_2, and so on.

7. (The fishing problem)   Find the solution to the fishing problem of Example 5.4 when the interest rate is 33%. Are the decisions different than when the interest rate is 25%? At what critical value of the discount factor does the solution change?

8. (Complexico mine ⊕)   Consider the Complexico mine and assume a 10% constant interest rate; also assume the price of gold is constant at $400/oz.

(a) Find the value of the mine (not a 10-year lease) if the current deposit is x_0. In particular, how much is the mine worth initially when $x_0 = 50,000$ ounces? [*Hint:* Consider the recursive equation for K_k as $k \to \infty$.]

(b) For the 10-year lease considered in the text, how much gold remains in the mine at the end of the lease; and how much is the mine worth at that time?

(c) If the mine were not leased, but instead operated optimally by an owner, what would the mine be worth after 10 years?

9. (Little Bear Oil)   You have purchased a lease for the Little Bear Oil well. This well has initial reserves of 100 thousand barrels of oil. In any year you have three choices of how to operate the well: (a) you can *not* pump, in which case there is no operating cost and no change in oil reserves; (b) you can pump normally, in which case the operating cost is $50 thousand and you will pump out 20% of what the reserves were at

the beginning of the year; or (c) you can use enhanced pumping using water pressure, in which case the operating cost is $120 thousand and you will pump out 36% of what the reserves were at the beginning of the year. The price of oil is $10 per barrel and the interest rate is 10%. Assume that both your operating costs and the oil revenues come at the beginning of the year (through advance sales). Your lease is for a period of 3 years.

(a) Show how to set up a trinomial lattice to represent the possible states of the oil reserves.

(b) What is the maximum present value of your profits, and what is the corresponding optimal pumping strategy?

10. (Multiperiod harmony theorem ◇)   The value of a firm is the maximum present value of its possible cash flow streams. This can be expressed as

$$V_0 = \max\left[x_0 + \frac{x_1}{1+s_1} + \frac{x_2}{(1+s_2)^2} + \cdots + \frac{x_n}{(1+s_n)^n} \right]$$

where the maximization is with respect to all possible streams $x_0, x_1, \ldots, x_n$, and the s_i's are the spot rates. Let x_0^* be the first cash flow in the optimal plan. If the firm chooses an arbitrary plan that results in an initial cash flow of x_0 (distributed to the owners), the value of the firm after 1 year is

$$V_1(x_0) = \max\left\{ x_1 + \frac{x_2}{1+s_1'} + \frac{x_3}{(1+s_2')^2} + \cdots + \frac{x_n}{(1+s_n')^{n-1}} \right\}$$

where now that maximum is with respect to all feasible cash flows that start with x_0 and the s_i''s are the spot rates after 1 year. An investor purchasing the firm at its full fair price has initial cash flow $x_0 - V_0$ and achieves a value of $V_1(x_0)$ after 1 year. Hence the 1-year total return to the investor is

$$R = \frac{V_1(x_0)}{V_0 - x_0}.$$

The investor would urge that x_0 be chosen to maximize R. Call this value $\overline{x}_0$. Assuming that interest rates follow expectation dynamics and that $V_1(\overline{x}_0) > 0$, show that the maximum R is $1 + s_1$ and that this return is achieved by the same x_0^* that determines V_0.

11. (Growing annuity)   Show that for $g < r$,

$$\sum_{k=1}^{\infty} \frac{(1+g)^{k-1}}{(1+r)^k} = \frac{1}{r-g}.$$

$$\left[\text{Hint: Let } S \text{ be the value of the sum. Note that } S = 1/(1+r) + S(1+g)/(1+r).\right]$$

12. (Two-stage growth)   It is common practice in security analysis to modify the basic dividend growth model by allowing more than one stage of growth, with the growth factors being different in the different stages. As an example consider company Z, which currently distributes dividends of $10M annually. The dividends are expected to grow at the rate of 10% for the next 5 years and at a rate of 5% thereafter.

(a) Using a dividend discount approach with an interest rate of 15%, what is the value of the company?

(b) Find a general formula for the value of a company satisfying a two-stage growth model. Assume a growth rate of G for k years, followed by a growth rate of g thereafter, and an initial dividend of D_1.

REFERENCES

Capital budgeting is a classic topic in financial planning. Some good texts are [1–4]; good surveys are [5], [6]. Bond portfolio construction is considered in [6–8] and in other references given for Chapters 3 and 4. Dynamic programming was developed by Bellman (see [9, 10]). The classic reference on stock valuation is [11]. See [12–16] for other presentations. A vivid discussion of how improper analysis techniques led to disastrous overvaluation in the 1980s is in [17].

1. Dean, J. (1951), *Capital Budgeting,* Columbia University Press, New York.
2. Brealey, R., and S. Myers (1984), *Principles of Corporate Finance,* McGraw-Hill, New York.
3. Bierman, H., Jr., and S. Smidt (1984), *The Capital Budgeting Decision*, 6th ed., Macmillan, New York.
4. Martin, J. D., S. H. Cox, Jr., and R. D. MacMinn (1988), *The Theory of Finance, Evidence and Applications*, Dryden Press, Chicago, IL.
5. Schall, L. D., G. L. Sundem, and W. R. Geijsbeek (1978), "Survey and Analysis of Capital Budgeting Methods," *Journal of Finance*, **33**, 281–287.
6. Weingartner, H. M. (1966), "Capital Budgeting of Interrelated Projects: Survey and Synthesis," *Management Science*, **12**, 485–516.
7. Bierwag, G. O., G. G. Kaufman, R. Schweitzer, and A. Toevs (1981), "The Art of Risk Management in Bond Portfolios," *Journal of Portfolio Management*, **7**, 27–36.
8. Fabozzi, F. J., and T. D. Fabozzi (1989), *Bond Markets, Analysis and Strategies,* Prentice Hall, Englewood Cliffs, NJ.
9. Bellman, R. (1957), *Dynamic Programming,* Princeton University Press, Princeton, NJ.
10. Bellman R., and S. Dreyfus (1962), *Applied Dynamic Programming*, Princeton University Press, Princeton, NJ.
11. Graham, B., D. L. Dodd, and S. Cottle (1962), *Security Analysis*, McGraw-Hill, New York.
12. Williams, J. B. (1938), *The Theory of Investment Value,* North-Holland, Amsterdam, The Netherlands.
13. Gordon, M. J. (1959), "Dividends, Earnings, and Stock Prices," *Review of Economics and Statistics*, **41**, 99–195.
14. Molodovsky, N., C. May, and S. Chottiner (1965), "Common Stock Valuation: Principles, Tables and Application," *Financial Analysts Journal*, **21**, 104–123.
15. Foster, G. (1986), *Financial Statement Analysis,* Prentice Hall, Englewood Cliffs, NJ.
16. Black, F. (1980), "The Magic in Earnings: Economic Earnings versus Accounting Earnings," *Financial Analysts Journal*, **36**, 19–24.
17. Klarman, S. A. (1991), *Margin of Safety: Risk-Averse Value Investing Strategies for the Thoughtful Investor,* Harper Business.

PART II

SINGLE-PERIOD RANDOM CASH FLOWS

6 MEAN–VARIANCE PORTFOLIO THEORY

Typically, when making an investment, the initial outlay of capital is known, but the amount to be returned is uncertain. Such situations are studied in this part of the text. In this part, however, we restrict attention to the case of a single investment period: money is invested at the initial time, and payoff is attained at the end of the period.

The assumption that an investment situation comprises a single period is sometimes a good approximation. An investment in a zero-coupon bond that will be held to maturity is an example. Another is an investment in a physical project that will not provide payment until it is completed. However, many common investments, such as publicly traded stocks, are not tied to a single period, since they can be liquidated at will and may return dividends periodically. Nevertheless, such investments are often analyzed on a single period basis as a simplification; but this type of analysis should be regarded only as a prelude to Parts 3 and 4 of the text, which are more comprehensive.

This part of the text treats uncertainty with three different mathematical methods: (1) mean–variance analysis, (2) utility function analysis, and (3) arbitrage (or comparison) analysis. Each of these methods is an important component of investment science.

This first chapter of the second part of the text treats uncertainty by **mean–variance** analysis. This method uses probability theory only slightly, and leads to convenient mathematical expressions and procedures. Mean–variance analysis forms the basis for the important *capital asset pricing model* discussed in Chapter 7.

6.1 ASSET RETURN

An investment instrument that can be bought and sold is frequently called an **asset.** We introduce a fundamental concept concerning such assets.

Suppose that you purchase an asset at time zero, and 1 year later you sell the asset. The **total return** on your investment is defined to be

$$\text{total return} = \frac{\text{amount received}}{\text{amount invested}}.$$

Or if X_0 and X_1 are, respectively, the amounts of money invested and received and R is the total return, then

$$R = \frac{X_1}{X_0}.$$

Often, for simplicity, the term *return* is used for total return.

The **rate of return** is

$$\text{rate of return} = \frac{\text{amount received} - \text{amount invested}}{\text{amount invested}}.$$

Or, again, if X_0 and X_1 are, respectively, the amounts of money invested and received and r is the rate of return, then

$$r = \frac{X_1 - X_0}{X_0}. \tag{6.1}$$

The shorter expression *return* is also frequently used for the rate of return.

We distinguish the two definitions by using upper- or lowercase letters, such as R and r, respectively, for total return and rate of return; and usually the context makes things clear if we use the shorthand phrase *return*.

It is clear that the two notions are related by

$$R = 1 + r$$

and that (6.1) can be rewritten as

$$X_1 = (1 + r)X_0.$$

This shows that a rate of return acts much like an interest rate.

Short Sales

Sometimes it is possible to sell an asset that you do not own through the process of **short selling,** or **shorting,** the asset. To do this, you borrow the asset from someone who owns it (such as a brokerage firm). You then sell the borrowed asset to someone else, receiving an amount X_0. At a later date, you repay your loan by purchasing the asset for, say, X_1 and return the asset to your lender. If the later amount X_1 is lower than the original amount X_0, you will have made a profit of $X_0 - X_1$. Hence short selling is profitable if the asset price declines.

Short selling is considered quite risky—even dangerous—by many investors. The reason is that the potential for loss is unlimited. If the asset value increases, the loss is $X_1 - X_0$; since X_1 can increase arbitrarily, so can the loss. For this reason (and others) short selling is prohibited within certain financial institutions, and it is purposely avoided as a policy by many individuals and institutions. However, it is not universally forbidden, and there is, in fact, a considerable level of short selling of stock market securities.

When short selling a stock, you are essentially duplicating the role of the issuing corporation. You sell the stock to raise immediate capital. If the stock pays dividends during the period that you have borrowed it, you too must pay that same dividend to the person from whom you borrowed the stock.

In practice, the pure process of short selling is supplemented by certain restrictions and safeguards. (For example, you must post a security deposit with the broker from whom you borrowed the asset.) But for theoretical work, we typically assume that the pure shorting of an asset is allowed.

Let us determine the return associated with short selling. We *receive* X_0 initially and *pay* X_1 later, so the outlay is $-X_0$ and the final receipt is $-X_1$, and hence the total return is

$$R = \frac{-X_1}{-X_0} = \frac{X_1}{X_0}.$$

The minus signs cancel out, so we obtain the same expression as that for purchasing the asset. Hence the return value R applies algebraically to both purchases and short sales. We can write this as

$$-X_1 = -X_0 R = -X_0(1 + r)$$

to show that final receipt is related to initial outlay.

Example 6.1 (A short sale)   Suppose I decide to short 100 shares of stock in company CBA. This stock is currently selling for $10 per share. I borrow 100 shares from my broker and sell these in the stock market, receiving $1,000. At the end of 1 year the price of CBA has dropped to $9 per share. I buy back 100 shares for $900 and give these shares to my broker to repay the original loan. Because the stock price fell, this has been a favorable transaction for me. I made a profit of $100.

Someone who purchased the stock at the beginning of the year and sold it at the end would have lost $100. That person would easily compute

$$R = \frac{900}{1,000} = .90$$

or

$$r = \frac{900 - 1,000}{1,000} = -.10.$$

The rate of return is clearly negative as $r = -10\%$. Shorting converts a negative rate of return into a profit because the original investment is also negative. For my shorting activity on CBA my original outlay was $-\$1,000$; hence my profit is $-\$1,000 \times r = \$100$.

It is a bit strange to refer to a rate of return associated with the idealized shorting procedure, since there is no initial commitment of resources. Nevertheless, it is the proper notion. In practice, shorting does require an initial commitment of margin, and the proceeds from the initial sale are held until the short is cleared. This modified procedure will have a different rate of return. (See Exercise 1.) For basic theoretical work, however, we shall often assume that the idealized procedure is available.

Portfolio Return

Suppose now that n different assets are available. We can form a **master asset,** or **portfolio,** of these n assets. Suppose that this is done by apportioning an amount X_0 among the n assets. We then select amounts X_{0i}, $i = 1, 2, \ldots, n$, such that $\sum_{i=1}^{n} X_{0i} = X_0$, where X_{0i} represents the amount invested in the ith asset. If we are allowed to sell an asset short, then some of the X_{0i}'s can be negative; otherwise we restrict the X_{0i}'s to be nonnegative.

The amounts invested can be expressed as fractions of the total investment. Thus we write

$$X_{0i} = w_i X_0, \qquad i = 1, 2, \ldots, n$$

where w_i is the **weight** or fraction of asset i in the portfolio. Clearly,

$$\sum_{i=1}^{n} w_i = 1$$

and some w_i's may be negative if short selling is allowed.

Let R_i denote the total return of asset i. Then the amount of money generated at the end of the period by the ith asset is $R_i X_{0i} = R_i w_i X_0$. The total amount received by this portfolio at the end of the period is therefore $\sum_{i=1}^{n} R_i w_i X_0$. Hence we find that the overall total return of the portfolio is

$$R = \frac{\sum_{i=1}^{n} R_i w_i X_0}{X_0} = \sum_{i=1}^{n} w_i R_i \;.$$

Equivalently, since $\sum_{i=1}^{n} w_i = 1$, we have

$$r = \sum_{i=1}^{n} w_i r_i \;.$$

This is a basic result concerning returns, and so we highlight it here:

Portfolio return   *Both the total return and the rate of return of a portfolio of assets are equal to the weighted sum of the corresponding individual asset returns, with the weight of an asset being its relative weight (in purchase cost) in the portfolio; that is,*

$$R = \sum_{i=1}^{n} w_i R_i \;, \qquad r = \sum_{i=1}^{n} w_i r_i \;.$$

An example calculation of portfolio weights and the associated expected rate of return of the portfolio are shown in Table 6.1.

TABLE 6.1
Calculation of Portfolio Return

Security	Number of shares	Price	Total cost	Weight in portfolio
Jazz, Inc.	100	$40	$4,000	0.25
Classical, Inc.	400	$20	$8,000	0.50
Rock, Inc.	200	$20	$4,000	0.25
Portfolio total values			$16,000	1.00

Security	Weight in portfolio	Rate of return	Weighted rate
Jazz, Inc.	.25	17%	4.25%
Classical, Inc.	.50	13%	6.50%
Rock, Inc.	.25	23%	5.75%
Portfolio rate of return			16.50%

The weight of a security in a portfolio is its proportion of total cost, as shown in the upper table. These weights then determine the rate of return of the portfolio, as shown in the lower table.

6.2 RANDOM VARIABLES

Frequently the amount of money to be obtained when selling an asset is uncertain at the time of purchase. In that case the return is random and can be described in probabilistic terms. In preparation for the study of random returns, we briefly introduce some concepts of probability. (For more detail on basic probability theory, see Appendix A.)

Suppose x is a random quantity that can take on any one of a finite number of specific values, say, $x_1, x_2, \ldots, x_m$. Assume further that associated with each possible x_i, there is a probability p_i that represents the relative chance of an occurrence of x_i. The p_i's satisfy $\sum_{i=1}^{m} p_i = 1$ and $p_i \geq 0$ for each i. Each p_i can be thought of as the relative frequency with which x_i would occur if an experiment of observing x were repeated infinitely often. The quantity x, characterized in this way before its value is known, is called a **random variable.**

A simple example is that of rolling an ordinary six-sided die, with the number of spots obtained being x. The six possibilities are 1, 2, 3, 4, 5, 6, and each has probability $1/6$.

It is common to display the probabilities associated with a random variable graphically as a density. The possible values of x are indicated on the horizontal axis, and the height of the line at a point represents the probability of that point. Some examples are shown in Figure 6.1. Figure 6.1(a) shows the density corresponding to the outcome of a roll of a die, where the six possibilities each have a probability of $1/6$. Figure 6.1(b) shows a more general case with several possible outcomes of various probabilities.

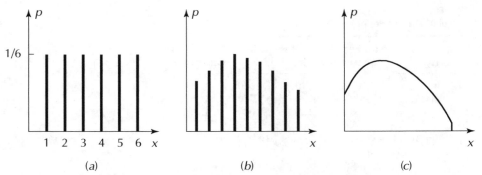

FIGURE 6.1 Probability distributions. Probability distributions are shown for (*a*) the outcome of a roll of a die, (*b*) another random variable with a finite number of possible outcomes, and (*c*) a continuous random variable.

If the outcome variable can take any real value in an interval as, for example, the temperature of a room, a **probability density function** $p(x)$ describes the probability. The probability that the variable's value will lie in any segment of the line is equal to the area of the vertical region bounded by this segment and the density function. An example is shown in Figure 6.1(*c*).

Expected Value

The **expected value** of a random variable x is just the average value obtained by regarding the probabilities as frequencies. For the case of a finite number of possibilities, it is defined as

$$\mathrm{E}(x) = \sum_{i=1}^{m} x_i \, p_i \, .$$

For convenience $\mathrm{E}(x)$ is often denoted by $\bar{x}$. Also the terms **mean** or **mean value** are often used for the expected value. So we say x has mean $\bar{x}$.

Example 6.2 (A roll of the die) The expected value of the number of spots on a roll of a die is

$$\tfrac{1}{6}(1 + 2 + 3 + 4 + 5 + 6) = 3.5 \, .$$

Note that the expected value is not necessarily a possible outcome of a roll.

The expected value operation is the main operation used in probability calculations, so it is useful to note its basic properties:

1. Certain value If y is a known value (not random), then $\mathrm{E}(y) = y$.
   This states that the expected value of a nonrandom quantity is equal to the quantity itself.

2. **Linearity**   If y and z are random, then $E(\alpha y + \beta z) = \alpha E(y) + \beta E(z)$ for any real values of α and β.

   This states that the expected (or mean) value of the sum of two random variables is the sum of their corresponding means; and the mean value of the multiple of a random variable is the same multiple of the original mean. For example, the expected value for the total number of spots on two dice is $3.5 + 3.5 = 7$.

3. **Nonnegativity**   If x is random but never less than zero, then $E(x) \geq 0$.

   This is a sign-preserving property.

Variance

The expected value of a random variable provides a useful summary of the probabilistic nature of the variable. However, typically one wants, in addition, to have a measure of the degree of possible deviation from the mean. One such measure is the **variance.**

   Given a random variable y with expected value $\overline{y}$, the quantity $y - \overline{y}$ is itself random, but has an expected value of zero. [This is because $E(y - \overline{y}) = E(y) - E(\overline{y}) = \overline{y} - \overline{y} = 0$.] The quantity $(y - \overline{y})^2$ is always nonnegative and is large when y deviates greatly from $\overline{y}$ and small when it is near $\overline{y}$. The expected value of this squared variable $(y - \overline{y})^2$ is a useful measure of how much y tends to vary from its expected value.

   In general, for any random variable y the variance of y is defined as

$$\mathrm{var}(y) = E\left[(y - \overline{y})^2\right].$$

In mathematical expressions, variance is represented by the symbol σ^2. Thus we write $\sigma_y^2 = \mathrm{var}(y)$, or if y is understood, we simply write $\sigma^2 = \mathrm{var}(y)$.

   We frequently use the square root of the variance, denoted by σ and called the **standard deviation.** It has the same units as the quantity y and is another measure of how much the variable is likely to deviate from its expected value. Thus, formally,

$$\sigma_y = \sqrt{E\left[(y - \overline{y})^2\right]}.$$

   There is a simple formula for variance that is useful in computations. We note that

$$\begin{aligned}
\mathrm{var}(x) &= E\left[(x - \overline{x})^2\right] \\
&= E(x^2) - 2E(x)\overline{x} + \overline{x}^2 \\
&= E(x^2) - \overline{x}^2.
\end{aligned} \tag{6.2}$$

This result is used in the following example.

Example 6.3 (A roll of the die)   Let us compute the variance of the random variable y defined as the number of spots obtained by a roll of a die. Recalling that $\overline{y} = 3.5$

we find

$$\sigma^2 = E(y^2) - \overline{y}^2$$
$$= \tfrac{1}{6}[1 + 4 + 9 + 16 + 25 + 36] - (3.5)^2 = 2.92.$$

Hence $\sigma = \sqrt{2.92} = 1.71$.

Several Random Variables

Suppose we are interested in two random variables, such as the outside temperature and the barometric pressure. To describe these random variables we must have probabilities for all possible combinations of the two values. If we denote the variables by x and y, we must consider the possible pairs (x, y). Suppose x can take on the possible values $x_1, x_2, \ldots, x_n$ and y can take on the values $y_1, y_2, \ldots, y_m$. (By assuming limited measurement precision, temperature and pressure can easily be assumed to take on only a finite number of values.) Then we must specify the probabilities p_{ij} for combinations (x_i, y_j) for $i = 1, 2, \ldots, n$ and $j = 1, 2, \ldots, m$. Hence for temperature and barometric pressure we need the probabilities of all possible combinations.

If we are interested in three random variables, such as outside temperature, barometric pressure, and humidity, we would need probabilities over all possible combinations of the three variables. For more variables, things get progressively more complicated.

There is an important special case where the probability description of several variables simplifies. Two random variables x and y are said to be **independent random variables** if the outcome probabilities for one variable do not depend on the outcome of the other. For example, consider the roll of two dice. The probability of an outcome of, say, 4 on the second die is 1/6, no matter what the outcome of the first die. Hence the two random variables corresponding to the spots on the two dice are independent. On the other hand, outside temperature and barometric pressure are not independent, since if pressure is high, temperature is more likely to be high as well.

Covariance

When considering two or more random variables, their mutual dependence can be summarized conveniently by their **covariance.**

Let x_1 and x_2 be two random variables with expected values $\overline{x}_1$ and $\overline{x}_2$. The covariance of these variables is defined to be

$$\mathrm{cov}(x_1, x_2) = E\big[(x_1 - \overline{x}_1)(x_2 - \overline{x}_2)\big].$$

The covariance of two random variables x and y is frequently denoted by σ_{xy}. Hence for random variables x_1 and x_2 we write $\mathrm{cov}(x_1, x_2) = \sigma_{x_1, x_2}$ or, alternatively, $\mathrm{cov}(x_1, x_2) = \sigma_{12}$. Note that, by symmetry, $\sigma_{12} = \sigma_{21}$.

Analogous to (6.2), there is an alternative shorter formula for covariance that is easily derived; namely,

$$\text{cov}(x_1, x_2) = \text{E}(x_1 x_2) - \overline{x}_1 \overline{x}_2. \tag{6.3}$$

This is useful in computations.

If two random variables x_1 and x_2 have the property that $\sigma_{12} = 0$, then they are said to be **uncorrelated.** This is the situation (roughly) where knowledge of the value of one variable gives no information about the other. If two random variables are independent, then they are uncorrelated. If $\sigma_{12} > 0$, the two variables are said to be **positively correlated.** In this case, if one variable is above its mean, the other is likely to be above its mean as well. On the other hand, if $\sigma_{12} < 0$, the two variables are said to be **negatively correlated.**

Figure 6.2 illustrates the concept of correlation by showing collections of random samples of two variables x and y under the conditions (*a*) positive correlation, (*b*) negative correlation, and (*c*) no correlation.

The following result gives an important bound on the covariance.

Covariance bound   *The covariance of two random variables satisfies*

$$|\sigma_{12}| \leq \sigma_1 \sigma_2 .$$

In the preceding inequality, if $\sigma_{12} = \sigma_1 \sigma_2$, the variables are **perfectly correlated.** In this situation, the covariance is as large as possible for the given variances. If one variable were a fixed positive multiple of the other, the two would be perfectly correlated. Conversely, if $\sigma_{12} = -\sigma_1 \sigma_2$, the two variables exhibit **perfect negative correlation.**

Another useful construct is the **correlation coefficient** of two variables, defined as

$$\rho_{12} = \frac{\sigma_{12}}{\sigma_1 \sigma_2} .$$

From the covariance bound above, we see that $|\rho_{12}| \leq 1$.

Note that the variance of a random variable x is the covariance of that variable with itself. Hence we write $\sigma_x^2 = \sigma_{xx}$.

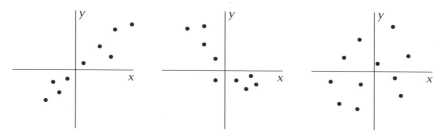

(*a*) Positively correlated   (*b*) Negatively correlated   (*c*) Uncorrelated

FIGURE 6.2   Correlations of data. Samples are drawn of the pair of random variables x and y, and these pairs are plotted on an x–y diagram. A typical pattern of points obtained is shown in the three cases: (*a*) positive correlation, (*b*) negative correlation, and (*c*) no correlation.

Variance of a Sum

When we know the covariance between two random variables, it is possible to compute the variance of the sum of the variables. This is a computation that is used frequently in what follows.

Suppose that x and y are random variables. We have, by linearity, that $E(x+y) = \overline{x} + \overline{y}$. Also by definition,

$$
\begin{aligned}
\text{var}\,(x+y) &= E[(x - \overline{x} + y - \overline{y})^2] \\
&= E[(x - \overline{x})^2] + 2E[(x - \overline{x})(y - \overline{y})] + E[(y - \overline{y})^2] \\
&= \sigma_x^2 + 2\sigma_{xy} + \sigma_y^2.
\end{aligned} \tag{6.4}
$$

This formula is easy to remember because it looks similar to the standard expression for the square of the sum of two algebraic quantities. We just substitute variance for the square and the covariance for the product.

An important special case is where the two variables are uncorrelated. In that case $\sigma^2 = \sigma_x^2 + \sigma_y^2$.

Example 6.4 (Two rolls of the die)   Suppose that a die is rolled twice and the average of the two numbers of spots is recorded as a quantity z. What are the mean value and the variance of z? We let x and y denote the values obtained on the first and second rolls, respectively. Then $z = \frac{1}{2}(x + y)$. Also x and y are uncorrelated, since the rolls of the die are independent. Therefore $\overline{z} = \frac{1}{2}(\overline{x} + \overline{y}) = 3.5$, and var$(z) = \frac{1}{4}(\sigma_x^2 + \sigma_y^2) = 2.92/2 = 1.46$. Hence $\sigma_z = 1.208$, which is somewhat smaller than the corresponding 1.71 value for a single roll.

6.3 RANDOM RETURNS

When an asset is originally acquired, its rate of return is usually uncertain. Accordingly, we consider the rate of return r to be a random variable. For analytical purposes we shall, in this chapter, summarize the uncertainty of the rate of return by its expected value (or mean) $E(r) \equiv \overline{r}$, by its variance $E[(r - \overline{r}^2)] \equiv \sigma^2$, and by its covariance with other assets of interest. We can best illustrate how rates of return are represented by considering a few examples.

Example 6.5 (Wheel of fortune)   Consider the wheel of fortune shown in Figure 6.3. It is unlike any wheel you are likely to find in an amusement park since its payoffs are quite favorable. If you bet \$1 on the wheel, the payoff you receive is that shown in the segment corresponding to the landing spot. The chance of landing on a given segment is proportional to the area of the segment. For this wheel the probability of each segment is $1/6$.

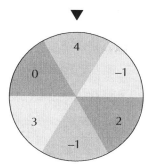

FIGURE 6.3 Wheel of fortune. If you bet $1 on the wheel, you will receive the amount equal to the value shown in the segment under the marker after the wheel is spun.

Let us first compute the mean and the variance of the payoff of the wheel. We denote the payoff of segment i by Q_i. Therefore the expected payoff is

$$\overline{Q} = \sum_i p_i Q_i = \tfrac{1}{6}(4 - 1 + 2 - 1 + 3) = 7/6.$$

The variance can be found from the short formula (6.2) to be

$$\sigma_Q^2 = \mathrm{E}(Q^2) - \overline{Q}^2 = \tfrac{1}{6}(16 + 1 + 4 + 1 + 9) - (7/6)^2 = 3.81.$$

The payoff of the wheel is the same as the total return under the assumption of a $1 bet. Therefore $Q = R$ and the rate of return is $r = Q - 1$. From this we find

$$\overline{r} = \mathrm{E}(r) = \overline{Q} - 1 = 1/6$$
$$\sigma_r^2 = \mathrm{E}\left[(r - \overline{r})^2\right] = \mathrm{E}\left\{[Q - 1 - (\overline{Q} - 1)]^2\right\} = \sigma_Q^2 = 3.81.$$

Example 6.6 (Rate of return on a stock)   Let us consider a share of stock in a major corporation (such as General Motors, AT&T, or IBM) as an asset. Imagine that we are attempting to describe the rate of return that applies if we were to buy it now and sell it at the end of one year. We ignore transactions costs. As an estimate, we might take $\mathrm{E}(r) = .12$; that is, we estimate that the expected rate of return is 12%. This is a reasonable value for the stock of a major corporation, based on the past performance of stocks in the overall market. Now what about the standard deviation? We recognize that the 12% figure is not likely to be hit exactly, and that there can be significant deviations. In fact it is quite possible that the 1-year rate of return could be -5% in one year and $+25\%$ in the next. A reasonable estimate for the standard deviation is about .15, or 15%. Hence, loosely, we might say that the rate of return is likely to be 12% plus or minus 15%. We discuss the process of estimating expected values and standard deviations for stocks in Chapter 8, but this example gives a rough idea of typical magnitudes.

The probability density for the rate of return of this typical stock is shown in Figure 6.4. It has a mean value of .12, but the return can become arbitrarily large. However, the rate of return can never be less than -1, since that represents complete loss of the original investment.

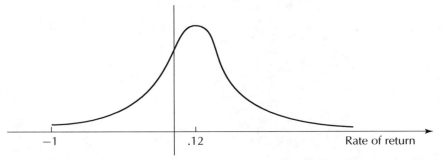

FIGURE 6.4   Probability density of the rate of return of a stock. The mean rate of return may be about 12% and the standard deviation about 15%. The rate of return cannot be less than −1.

Example 6.7 (Betting wheel)   Two kinds of wheels are useful for the study of investment problems. The wheel of fortune of Example 6.5 is one form of wheel. For that type, one bets on (invests in) the wheel as a whole, and the payoff is determined by the landing segment.

The other kind of wheel is a **betting wheel,** an example of which is shown in Figure 6.5. For this kind of wheel one bets on (invests in) the individual segments of the wheel. For example, for the wheel shown, if one invests $1 in the white segment, then $3 will be the payoff if white is the landing segment; otherwise the payoff is zero and the original $1 is lost. One is allowed to bet different amounts on different segments. A roulette wheel is a betting wheel. From a theoretical viewpoint, a betting wheel is interesting because the returns from different segments are correlated.

For the wheel shown, we may bet on: (1) white, (2) black, or (3) gray, with payoffs 3, 2, or 6, respectively. Note that the bet on white has quite favorable odds.

We can work out the expected rates of return for the three possible bets. It is much easier here to work first with total returns and then subtract 1. For example, for white the return is $3 with probability $\frac{1}{2}$ and 0 with probability $\frac{1}{2}$.

The three expected values are:

$$\overline{R}_1 = \tfrac{1}{2}(3) + \tfrac{1}{2}(0) = \tfrac{3}{2}$$

$$\overline{R}_2 = \tfrac{1}{3}(2) + \tfrac{2}{3}(0) = \tfrac{2}{3}$$

$$\overline{R}_3 = \tfrac{1}{6}(6) + \tfrac{5}{6}(0) = 1 \,.$$

Likewise, the three variances are, from (6.2),

$$\sigma_1^2 = \tfrac{1}{2}(3^2) - (\tfrac{3}{2})^2 = 2.25$$

$$\sigma_2^2 = \tfrac{1}{3}(2)^2 - (\tfrac{2}{3})^2 = .889$$

$$\sigma_3^2 = \tfrac{1}{6}6^2 - 1 = 5 \,.$$

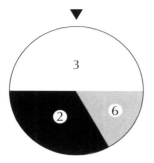

FIGURE 6.5 Betting wheel. It is possible to bet on any segment of the wheel. If that segment is chosen by the spin, the better receives the amount indicated times the bet.

Finally, we can calculate the covariances using (6.3). The expected value of products such as $E(R_1 R_2)$ are all zero, so we easily find

$$\sigma_{12} = -\tfrac{3}{2}(\tfrac{2}{3}) = -1.0$$

$$\sigma_{13} = -\tfrac{3}{2}(1) = -1.5$$

$$\sigma_{23} = -\tfrac{2}{3}(1) = -.67.$$

Mean–Standard Deviation Diagram

The random rates of return of assets can be represented on a two-dimensional diagram, as shown in Figure 6.6. An asset with mean rate of return $\bar{r}$ [or m or $E(r)$] and standard deviation σ is represented as a point in this diagram. The horizontal axis is used for the standard deviation, and the vertical axis is used for the mean. This diagram is called a mean–standard deviation diagram, or simply $\bar{r}$–σ diagram.

In such a diagram the standard deviation, rather than the variance, is used as the horizontal axis. This gives both axes comparable units (such as percent per year). Such diagrams are used frequently in mean–variance investment analysis.

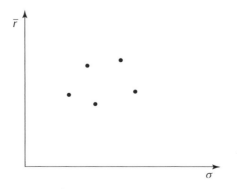

FIGURE 6.6 Mean–standard deviation diagram. Assets are described as points on the diagram.

6.4 PORTFOLIO MEAN AND VARIANCE

Now that we have the concepts of expected value (or mean) and variance for returns of individual assets and covariances between pairs of assets, we show how these can be used to determine the corresponding mean and variance of the return of a portfolio.

Mean Return of a Portfolio

Suppose that there are n assets with (random) rates of return $r_1, r_2, \ldots, r_n$. These have expected values $E(r_1) = \bar{r}_1, E(r_2) = \bar{r}_2, \ldots, E(r_n) = \bar{r}_n$.

Suppose that, as in Section 6.1, we form a portfolio of these n assets using the weights w_i, $i = 1, 2, \ldots, n$. The rate of return of the portfolio in terms of the return of the individual returns is

$$r = w_1 r_1 + w_2 r_2 + \cdots + w_n r_n.$$

We may take the expected values of both sides, and using linearity (property 2 of the expected value in Section 6.2), we obtain

$$E(r) = w_1 E(r_1) + w_2 E(r_2) + \cdots + w_n E(r_n).$$

In other words, the expected rate of return of the portfolio is found by taking the weighted sum of the individual expected rates of return. So, finding the expected return of a portfolio is easy once we have the expected rates of return of the individual assets from which the portfolio is composed.

Variance of Portfolio Return

Now let us determine the variance of the rate of return of the portfolio.

We denote the variance of the return of asset i by σ_i^2, the variance of the return of the portfolio by σ^2, and the covariance of the return of asset i with asset j by σ_{ij}. We perform a straightforward calculation:

$$\sigma^2 = E[(r - \bar{r})^2]$$

$$= E\left[\left(\sum_{i=1}^{n} w_i r_i - \sum_{i=1}^{n} w_i \bar{r}_i\right)^2\right]$$

$$= E\left[\left(\sum_{i=1}^{n} w_i (r_i - \bar{r}_i)\right)\left(\sum_{j=1}^{n} w_j (r_j - \bar{r}_j)\right)\right]$$

$$= E\left[\sum_{i,j=1}^{n} w_i w_j (r_i - \bar{r}_i)(r_j - \bar{r}_j)\right]$$

$$= \sum_{i,j=1}^{n} w_i w_j \sigma_{ij}.$$

This important result shows how the variance of a portfolio's return can be calculated easily from the covariances of the pairs of asset returns and the asset weights used in the portfolio. (Recall, $\sigma_{ii} = \sigma_i^2$.)

Example 6.8 (Two-asset portfolio)   Suppose that there are two assets with $\bar{r}_1 = .12$, $\bar{r}_2 = .15$, $\sigma_1 = .20$, $\sigma_2 = .18$, and $\sigma_{12} = .01$ (values typical for two stocks). A portfolio is formed with weights $w_1 = .25$ and $w_2 = .75$. We can calculate the mean and the variance of the portfolio. First we have the mean,

$$\bar{r} = .25(.12) + .75(.15) = .1425 .$$

Second we calculate the variance,

$$\sigma^2 = (.25)^2(.20)^2 + .25(.75)(.01) + .75(.25)(.01) + (.75)^2(.18)^2 = .024475 .$$

Note that the two cross terms are equal (since $w_i w_j = w_j w_i$). Hence,

$$\sigma = .1564 .$$

Diversification*

Portfolios with only a few assets may be subject to a high degree of risk, represented by a relatively large variance. As a general rule, the variance of the return of a portfolio can be reduced by including additional assets in the portfolio, a process referred to as **diversification.** This process reflects the maxim, "Don't put all your eggs in one basket."

   The effects of diversification can be quantified by using the formulas for combining variances. Suppose as an example that there are many assets, all of which are mutually uncorrelated. That is, the return of each asset is uncorrelated with that of any other asset in the group. Suppose also that the rate of return of each of these assets has mean m and variance σ^2. Now suppose that a portfolio is constructed by taking equal portions of n of these assets; that is, $w_i = 1/n$ for each i. The overall rate of return of this portfolio is

$$r = \frac{1}{n} \sum_{i=1}^{n} r_i .$$

The mean value of this is $\bar{r} = m$, which is independent of n. The corresponding variance is

$$\text{var}(r) = \frac{1}{n^2} \sum_{i=1}^{n} \sigma^2 = \frac{\sigma^2}{n}$$

where we have used the fact that the individual returns are uncorrelated. The variance decreases rapidly as n increases, as shown in Figure 6.7(a). This chart shows the variance as a function of n, the number of assets (when $\sigma^2 = 1$). Note that considerable improvement is obtained by including about six uncorrelated assets.

   The situation is somewhat different if the returns of the available assets are correlated. As a simple example suppose again that each asset has a rate of return with mean

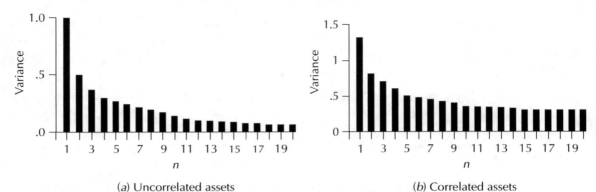

FIGURE 6.7   Effects of diversification. If assets are uncorrelated, the variance of a portfolio can be made very small. If assets are positively correlated, there is likely to be a lower limit to the variance that can be achieved.

m and variance σ^2, but now each return pair has a covariance of $\text{cov}(r_i, r_j) = .3\sigma^2$ for $i \neq j$. Again we form a portfolio by taking equal portions of n of these assets. In this case,

$$\text{var}(r) = \text{E}\left[\sum_{i=1}^{n}\frac{1}{n}(r_i - \overline{r})\right]^2$$

$$= \frac{1}{n^2}\text{E}\left\{\left[\sum_{i=1}^{n}(r_i - \overline{r})\right]\left[\sum_{j=i}^{n}(r_j - \overline{r})\right]\right\}$$

$$= \frac{1}{n^2}\sum_{i,j}\sigma_{ij} = \frac{1}{n^2}\left\{\sum_{i=j}\sigma_{ij} + \sum_{i \neq j}\sigma_{ij}\right\}$$

$$= \frac{1}{n^2}\left\{n\sigma^2 + .3(n^2 - n)\sigma^2\right\}$$

$$= \frac{\sigma^2}{n} + .3\sigma^2\left(1 - \frac{1}{n}\right)$$

$$= \frac{.7\sigma^2}{n} + .3\sigma^2$$

This result is shown in Figure 6.7(b) (where again $\sigma^2 = 1$). In this case it is impossible to reduce the variance below $.3\sigma^2$, no matter how large n is made.

This analysis of diversification is somewhat crude, for we have assumed that all expected rates of return are equal. In general, diversification may reduce the overall expected return while reducing the variance. Most people do not want to sacrifice much expected return for a small decrease in variance, so blind diversification, without an understanding of its influence on both the mean and the variance of return, is not necessarily desirable. This is the motivation behind the general mean–variance approach developed by Markowitz. It makes the trade-offs between mean and variance explicit.

Nevertheless, there is an important lesson to be learned from this simple analysis. Namely, if returns are uncorrelated, it is possible through diversification to reduce portfolio variance essentially to zero by taking n large. Conversely, if returns are positively correlated, it is more difficult to reduce variance, and there may be a lower limit to what can be achieved.

Diagram of a Portfolio

Suppose that two assets are represented on a mean–standard deviation diagram. These two assets can be combined, according to some weights, to form a portfolio—a new asset. The mean value and the standard deviation of the rate of return of this new asset can be calculated from the mean, variances, and covariances of the returns of the original assets. However, since covariances are not shown on the diagram, the exact location of the point representing the new asset cannot be determined from the location on the diagram of the original two assets. There are many possibilities, depending on the covariance of these asset returns.

We analyze the possibilities as follows. We begin with two assets as indicated in Figure 6.8. We then define a whole family of portfolios by introducing the variable α, which defines weights as $w_1 = 1 - \alpha$ and $w_2 = \alpha$. Thus as α varies from 0 to 1, the portfolio goes from one that contains only asset 1 to one that contains a mixture of assets 1 and 2, and then to one that contains only asset 2. Values of α outside the range $0 \leq \alpha \leq 1$ make one or the other of the weights negative, corresponding to short selling.

As α varies, the new portfolios trace out a curve that includes assets 1 and 2. This curve will look something like the curved shape shown in Figure 6.8, but its exact shape depends on σ_{12}. The solid portion of the curve corresponds to positive combinations of the two assets; the dashed portion corresponds to the shorting of one of them (the one at the opposite end of the solid curve). It can be shown in fact that the solid portion of the curve must lie within the shaded region shown in the figure; that is, it must lie within a triangular region defined by the vertices 1, 2, and a point A on the

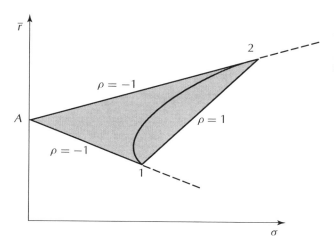

FIGURE 6.8 Combinations of two assets. When two assets are combined in various combinations, the resulting portfolios sweep out a curve between the points representing the original assets. This curve must lie in the shaded triangular region shown.

vertical axis. We state this property formally, but it is not essential that you absorb the details at first reading. It is only necessary to understand the general shape of the curve.

Portfolio diagram lemma   *The curve in an $\bar{r}$–σ diagram defined by nonnegative mixtures of two assets 1 and 2 lies within the triangular region defined by the two original assets and the point on the vertical axis of height $A = (\bar{r}_1\sigma_2 + \bar{r}_2\sigma_1)/(\sigma_1 + \sigma_2)$.*

Proof: The rate of return of the portfolio defined by α is $r(\alpha) = (1-\alpha)r_1 + \alpha r_2$. The mean value of this return is

$$\bar{r}(\alpha) = (1-\alpha)\bar{r}_1 + \alpha\bar{r}_2 \, .$$

This says that the mean value is between the original means, in direct proportion to the proportions of the assets. In a 50–50 mix, for example, the new mean will be midway between the original means.

Let us compute the standard deviation of the portfolio. We have, from the general formula of the previous section,

$$\sigma(\alpha) = \sqrt{(1-\alpha)^2\sigma_1^2 + 2\alpha(1-\alpha)\sigma_{12} + \alpha^2\sigma_2^2} \, .$$

Using the definition of the correlation coefficient $\rho = \sigma_{12}/(\sigma_1\sigma_2)$, this equation can be written

$$\sigma(\alpha) = \sqrt{(1-\alpha)^2\sigma_1^2 + 2\rho\alpha(1-\alpha)\sigma_1\sigma_2 + \alpha^2\sigma_2^2} \, .$$

This is quite a messy expression. However, we can determine its bounds. We know that ρ can range over $-1 \le \rho \le 1$. Using $\rho = 1$ we find the upper bound

$$\sigma(\alpha)^* = \sqrt{(1-\alpha)^2\sigma_1^2 + 2\alpha(1-\alpha)\sigma_1\sigma_2 + \alpha^2\sigma_2^2}$$

$$= \sqrt{[(1-\alpha)\sigma_1 + \alpha\sigma_2]^2}$$

$$= (1-\alpha)\sigma_1 + \alpha\sigma_2 \, .$$

Using $\rho = -1$ we likewise obtain the lower bound

$$\sigma(\alpha)_* = \sqrt{(1-\alpha)^2\sigma_1^2 - 2\alpha(1-\alpha)\sigma_1\sigma_2 + \alpha^2\sigma_2^2}$$

$$= \sqrt{}$$

is positive, so we can replace that term by $(1 - \alpha)\sigma_1 - \alpha\sigma_2$. This remains positive until $\alpha = \sigma_1/(\sigma_1 + \sigma_2)$. After that it reverses sign, and so the absolute value becomes $\alpha\sigma_2 - (1 - \alpha)\sigma_1$. The reversal occurs at the point A given by the expression in the proposition statement. The two linear expressions, together with the linear expression for the mean, imply that the lower bound traces out the kinked line shown in Figure 6.8. We conclude that the curve traced out by the portfolio points must lie within the shaded region; and for an intermediate value of ρ, it looks like the curve shown. ∎

6.5 THE FEASIBLE SET

Suppose now that there are n basic assets. We can plot them as points on the mean–standard deviation diagram. Next imagine forming portfolios from these n assets, using every possible weighting scheme. Hence there are portfolios consisting of each of the n assets alone, combinations of two assets, combinations of three, and so forth, all the way to arbitrary combinations of all n. These portfolios are made by letting the weighting coefficients w_i range over all possible combinations such that $\sum_{i=1}^{n} w_i = 1$.

The set of points that correspond to portfolios is called the **feasible set** or **feasible region.** The feasible set satisfies two important properties.

1. If there are at least three assets (not perfectly correlated and with different means), the feasible set will be a solid two-dimensional region.

Figure 6.9 shows why the region will be solid. There are three basic assets: 1, 2, and 3. We know that any two assets define a (curved) line between them as combination portfolios are formed. The three lines between the possible three pairs are shown in Figure 6.9. Now if a combination of, say, assets 2 and 3 is formed to produce asset 4, this can be combined with 1 to form a line connecting 1 and 4. As 4 is moved between 2 and 3, the line between 1 and 4 traces out a solid region.

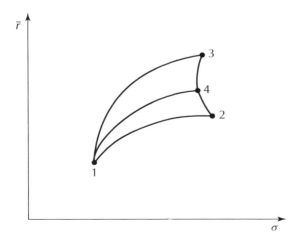

FIGURE 6.9 Three points form a region. Combinations of assets 2 and 3 sweep out a curve between them. Combination of one of these assets, such as 4, together with asset 1 sweeps out another curve. The family of all these curves forms a solid region.

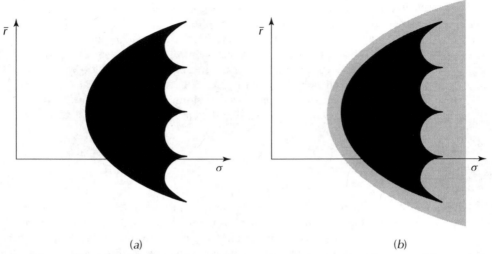

(a)   (b)

FIGURE 6.10   Feasible region. The feasible region is the set of all points representing portfolios made from n original assets. Two such regions can be defined: (a) no shorting and (b) shorting allowed.

2. The feasible region is convex to the left.

  This means that given any two points in the region, the straight line connecting them does not cross the left boundary of the feasible set. This follows from the fact that all portfolios (with positive weights) made from two assets lie on or to the left of the line connecting them. A typical feasible region is shown in Figure 6.10(a).

  There are two natural, but alternative, definitions of the feasible region, corresponding to whether short selling of assets is allowed or not allowed. The two general conclusions about the shape of the region hold in either case. However, in general the feasible region defined with short selling allowed will contain the region defined without short selling, as shown in Figure 6.10(b). (In general, the leftmost edges of these two regions may partially coincide—unlike the case shown in Figure 6.10.)

The Minimum-Variance Set and the Efficient Frontier

The left boundary of a feasible set is called the **minimum-variance set,** since for any value of the mean rate of return, the feasible point with the smallest variance (or standard deviation) is the corresponding left boundary point. The minimum-variance set has a characteristic **bullet** shape, as shown in Figure 6.11(a). There is a special point on this set having minimum variance. It is termed the **minimum-variance point** (MVP).

  Suppose that an investor's choice of portfolio is restricted to the feasible points on a given horizontal line in the $\bar{r}$–σ plane. All portfolios on this line have the same mean rate of return, but different standard deviations (or variances). Most investors will prefer the portfolio corresponding to the leftmost point on the line; that is, the point with the smallest standard deviation for the given mean. An investor who agrees

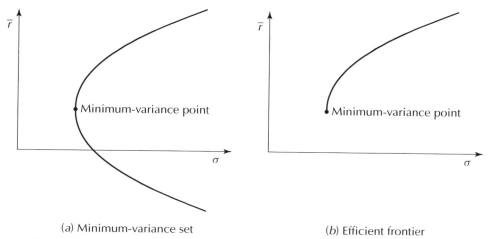

(a) Minimum-variance set   (b) Efficient frontier

FIGURE 6.11   Special sets. The minimum-variance set has a characteristic bullet shape. The minimum-variance point is the point with lowest possible variance. The efficient frontier is the upper portion of the minimum-variance set.

with this viewpoint is said to be **risk averse,** since he or she seeks to minimize risk (as measured by standard deviation). An investor who would select a point other than the one of minimum standard deviation is said to be **risk preferring.** We direct our analysis to risk-averse investors who, accordingly, prefer to minimize the standard deviation. Such investors are interested in points on the minimum-variance set.

We can turn the argument around 90 degrees and consider portfolios corresponding to the various points on a vertical line; that is, the portfolios with a fixed standard deviation and various mean values. Most investors will prefer the highest point on such a line. In other words, they would select the portfolio of the largest mean for a given level of standard deviation. This property of investors is termed **nonsatiation,** which reflects the idea that, everything else being equal, investors always want more money; hence they want the highest possible expected return for a given standard deviation.

These arguments imply that only the upper part of the minimum-variance set will be of interest to investors who are risk averse and satisfy nonsatiation. This upper portion of the minimum-variance set is termed the **efficient frontier** of the feasible region. It is illustrated in Figure 6.11(b). These are the efficient portfolios, in the sense that they provide the best mean–variance combinations for most investors. We can therefore limit our investigation to this frontier. The next section explains how to calculate points on this frontier.

6.6 THE MARKOWITZ MODEL

We are now in a position to formulate a mathematical problem that leads to minimum-variance portfolios. Again assume that there are n assets. The mean (or expected) rates of return are $\bar{r}_1, \bar{r}_2, \ldots, \bar{r}_n$ and the covariances are σ_{ij}, for $i, j = 1, 2, \ldots, n$. A portfolio is defined by a set of n weights w_i, $i = 1, 2, \ldots, n$, that sum to 1. (We allow negative weights, corresponding to short selling.) To find a minimum-variance portfolio, we fix the mean value at some arbitrary value $\bar{r}$. Then we find the feasible portfolio of minimum variance that has this mean. Hence we formulate the problem

$$\text{minimize} \quad \tfrac{1}{2} \sum_{i,j=1}^{n} w_i w_j \sigma_{ij}$$

$$\text{subject to} \quad \sum_{i=1}^{n} w_i \bar{r}_i = \bar{r}$$

$$\sum_{i=1}^{n} w_i = 1 \, .$$

The factor of $\tfrac{1}{2}$ in front of the variance is for convenience only. It makes the final form of the equations neater.

The Markowitz problem provides the foundation for single-period investment theory. The problem explicitly addresses the trade-off between expected rate of return and variance of the rate of return in a portfolio. Once the Markowitz problem is formulated, it can be solved numerically to obtain a specific numerical solution. It is also useful to solve the problem analytically because some strong additional conclusions are obtained from the analytic solution. However, as we move to the next chapter, the Markowitz problem is used mainly when a risk-free asset as well as risky assets are available. The existence of a risk-free asset greatly simplifies the nature of the feasible set and also simplifies the analytic solution.

Solution of the Markowitz Problem*

We can find the conditions for a solution to this problem using **Lagrange multipliers** λ and μ. We form[1] the **Lagrangian**

$$L = \tfrac{1}{2} \sum_{i,j=1}^{n} w_i w_j \sigma_{ij} - \lambda \left(\sum_{i=1}^{n} w_i \bar{r}_i - \bar{r} \right) - \mu \left(\sum_{i=1}^{n} w_i - 1 \right).$$

We then differentiate the Lagrangian with respect to each variable w_i and set this derivative to zero.

The differentiation may be a bit difficult if this type of structure is unfamiliar to you. Therefore we shall do it for the two-variable case, after which it will be easy to generalize to n variables. For two variables,

$$L = \tfrac{1}{2} \left(w_1^2 \sigma_1^2 + w_1 w_2 \sigma_{12} + w_2 w_1 \sigma_{21} + w_2^2 \sigma_2^2 \right)$$
$$- \lambda (\bar{r}_1 w_1 + \bar{r}_2 w_2 - \bar{r}) - \mu (w_1 + w_2 - 1) \, .$$

---

[1] In general, the Lagrangian is formed by first converting each constraint to one with a zero right-hand side. Then each left-hand side is multiplied by its Lagrange multiplier and subtracted from the objective function. In our problem, λ and μ are the multipliers for the first and second constraints, respectively. (See Appendix B.)

Hence,

$$\frac{\partial L}{\partial w_1} = \frac{1}{2}\left(2\sigma_1^2 w_1 + \sigma_{12}w_2 + \sigma_{21}w_2\right) - \lambda \overline{r}_1 - \mu$$

$$\frac{\partial L}{\partial w_2} = \frac{1}{2}\left(\sigma_{12}w_1 + \sigma_{21}w_1 + 2\sigma_2^2 w_2\right) - \lambda \overline{r}_2 - \mu.$$

Using the fact that $\sigma_{12} = \sigma_{21}$ and setting these derivatives to zero, we obtain

$$\sigma_1^2 w_1 + \sigma_{12}w_2 - \lambda \overline{r}_1 - \mu = 0$$

$$\sigma_{21}w_1 + \sigma_2^2 w_2 - \lambda \overline{r}_2 - \mu = 0.$$

This gives us two equations. In addition, there are the two equations of the constraints, so we have a total of four equations. These can be solved[2] for the four unknowns w_1, w_2, λ, and μ.

The general form for n variables now can be written by obvious generalization. We state the conditions here:

Equations for efficient set *The n portfolio weights w_i for $i = 1, 2, \ldots, n$ and the two Lagrange multipliers λ and μ for an efficient portfolio (with short selling allowed) having mean rate of return $\overline{r}$ satisfy*

$$\sum_{j=1}^{n} \sigma_{ij}w_j - \lambda \overline{r}_i - \mu = 0 \quad \text{for } i = 1, 2, \ldots, n \tag{6.5a}$$

$$\sum_{i=1}^{n} w_i \overline{r}_i = \overline{r} \tag{6.5b}$$

$$\sum_{i=1}^{n} w_i = 1. \tag{6.5c}$$

We have n equations in (6.5a), plus the two equations of the constraints (6.5b) and (6.5c), for a total of $n + 2$ equations. Correspondingly, there are $n + 2$ unknowns: the w_i's, λ, and μ. The solution to these equations will produce the weights for an efficient portfolio with mean $\overline{r}$. Notice that all $n + 2$ equations are linear, so they can be solved with linear algebra methods.

Example 6.9 (Three uncorrelated assets)   Suppose there are three uncorrelated assets. Each has variance 1, and the mean values are 1, 2, and 3, respectively. There is

---

[2]The case of two assets is actually degenerate because the two unknowns w_1 and w_2 are uniquely determined by the two constraints. The degeneracy (usually) disappears when there are three or more assets. Nevertheless, the equations obtained for the two-asset case foreshadow the pattern of the corresponding equations for n assets.

a bit of simplicity and symmetry in this situation, which makes it relatively easy to find an explicit solution.

We have $\sigma_1^2 = \sigma_2^2 = \sigma_3^2 = 1$ and $\sigma_{12} = \sigma_{23} = \sigma_{13} = 0$. Thus (6.5a–c) become

$$w_1 - \lambda - \mu = 0$$
$$w_2 - 2\lambda - \mu = 0$$
$$w_3 - 3\lambda - \mu = 0$$
$$w_1 + 2w_2 + 3w_3 = \bar{r}$$
$$w_1 + w_2 + w_3 = 1.$$

The top three equations can be solved for w_1, w_2, and w_3 and substituted into the bottom two equations. This leads to

$$14\lambda + 6\mu = \bar{r}$$
$$6\lambda + 3\mu = 1.$$

These two equations can be solved to yield $\lambda = (\bar{r}/2) - 1$ and $\mu = 2\frac{1}{3} - \bar{r}$. Then

$$w_1 = \tfrac{4}{3} - (\bar{r}/2)$$
$$w_2 = \tfrac{1}{3}$$
$$w_3 = (\bar{r}/2) - \tfrac{2}{3}.$$

The standard deviation at the solution is $\sqrt{w_1^2 + w_2^2 + w_3^2}$, which by direct substitution gives

$$\sigma = \sqrt{\frac{7}{3} - 2\bar{r} + \frac{\bar{r}^2}{2}}. \tag{6.6}$$

The minimum-variance point is, by symmetry, at $\bar{r} = 2$, with $\sigma = \sqrt{3}/3 = .58$. The feasible region is the region bounded by the bullet-shaped curve shown in Figure 6.12.

The foregoing analysis assumes that shorting of assets is allowed. If shorting is not allowed, the feasible set will be smaller, as discussed in the next subsection.

Nonnegativity Constraints*

In the preceding derivation, the signs of the w_i variables were not restricted, which meant that short selling was allowed. We can prohibit short selling by restricting

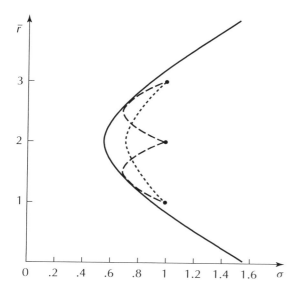

FIGURE 6.12 Three-asset example. The feasible region with shorting contains the feasible region without shorting. The outside curve is the minimum-variance set with shorting allowed. The short curved lines are portfolios made up of two of the assets at a time.

each w_i to be nonnegative. This leads to the following alternative statement of the Markowitz problem:

$$\text{minimize} \quad \tfrac{1}{2} \sum_{i,j=1}^{n} \sigma_{ij} w_i w_j \tag{6.7a}$$

$$\text{subject to} \quad \sum_{i=1}^{n} \overline{r}_i w_i = \overline{r} \tag{6.7b}$$

$$\sum_{i=1}^{n} w_i = 1 \tag{6.7c}$$

$$w_i \geq 0 \quad \text{for } i = 1, 2, \dots, n. \tag{6.7d}$$

This problem cannot be reduced to the solution of a set of linear equations. It is termed a **quadratic program,** since the objective is quadratic and the constraints are linear equalities and inequalities. Special computer programs are available for solving such problems, but small to moderate-sized problems of this type can be solved readily with spreadsheet programs. In the financial industry there are a multitude of special-purpose programs designed to solve this problem for hundreds or even thousands of assets.

A significant difference between the two formulations is that when short selling is allowed, most, if not all, of the optimal w_i's have nonzero values (either positive or negative), so essentially all assets are used. By contrast, when short selling is not allowed, typically many weights are equal to zero.

Example 6.10 (The three uncorrelated assets) Consider again the assets of Example 6.9, but with shorting not allowed. Efficient points must solve problem (6.7a) with the parameters of the earlier example. In this case the problem cannot be reduced to a system of equations, but by considering combinations of pairs of assets, the efficient frontier can be found. The general solution is as follows:

$1 \le \bar{r} \le \frac{4}{3}$	$\frac{4}{3} \le \bar{r} \le \frac{8}{3}$	$\frac{8}{3} \le \bar{r} \le 3$
$w_1 = 2 - \bar{r}$	$\frac{4}{3} - \dfrac{\bar{r}}{2}$	0
$w_2 = \bar{r} - 1$	$\frac{1}{3}$	$3 - \bar{r}$
$w_3 = 0$	$\dfrac{\bar{r}}{2} - \dfrac{2}{3}$	$\bar{r} - 2$
$\sigma = \sqrt{2\bar{r}^2 - 6\bar{r} + 5}$	$\sqrt{\dfrac{2}{3} - 2\bar{r}_1 + \dfrac{\bar{r}^2}{2}}$	$\sqrt{2\bar{r}^2 - 10\bar{r} + 13}$.

6.7 THE TWO-FUND THEOREM*

The minimum-variance set has an important property that greatly simplifies its computation. Recall that points in this set satisfy the system of $n + 2$ linear equations [Eqs. (6.5a–c)], which is repeated here:

$$\sum_{j=1}^{n} \sigma_{ij} w_j - \lambda \bar{r}_i - \mu = 0 \quad \text{for } i = 1, 2, \ldots, n \tag{6.8a}$$

$$\sum_{i=1}^{n} w_i \bar{r}_i = \bar{r} \tag{6.8b}$$

$$\sum_{i=1}^{n} w_i = 1. \tag{6.8c}$$

Suppose that there are two known solutions, $\mathbf{w}^1 = (w_1^1, w_2^1, \ldots, w_n^1)$, λ^1, μ^1 and $\mathbf{w}^2 = (w_1^2, w_2^2, \ldots, w_n^2)$, λ^2, μ^2, with expected rates of return $\bar{r}^1$ and $\bar{r}^2$, respectively. Let us form a combination by multiplying the first by α and the second by $(1 - \alpha)$. By direct substitution, we see that the result is also a solution to the $n + 2$ equations, corresponding to the expected value $\alpha \bar{r}^1 + (1 - \alpha)\bar{r}^2$. To check this in detail, notice that $\alpha \mathbf{w}^1 + (1 - \alpha)\mathbf{w}^2$ is a legitimate portfolio with weights that sum to 1; hence (6.8c) is satisfied. Next notice that the expected return is in fact $\alpha \bar{r}_1 + (1 - \alpha)\bar{r}_2$; hence (6.8$b$) is satisfied for that value. Finally, notice that since both solutions make the left side of (6.8a) equal to zero, their combination does also; hence (6.8a) is satisfied. This implies that the combination portfolio $\alpha \mathbf{w}^1 + (1 - \alpha)\mathbf{w}^2$ is also a solution; that is, it also represents a point in the minimum-variance set. This simple result is usually quite surprising to most people on their first exposure to the subject, but it highlights an important property of the minimum-variance set.

To use this result, suppose $\mathbf{w}^1$ and $\mathbf{w}^2$ are two different portfolios in the minimum-variance set. Then as α varies over $-\infty < \alpha < \infty$, the portfolios defined by $\alpha\mathbf{w}^1 + (1 - \alpha)\mathbf{w}^2$ sweep out the entire minimum-variance set. We can, of course, select the two original solutions to be efficient (that is, on the upper portion of the minimum-variance set), and these will generate all other efficient points (as well as all other points in the minimum-variance set). This result is often stated in a form that has operational significance for investors:

The two-fund theorem   *Two efficient funds (portfolios) can be established so that any efficient portfolio can be duplicated, in terms of mean and variance, as a combination of these two. In other words, all investors seeking efficient portfolios need only invest in combinations of these two funds.*

This result has dramatic implications. According to the two-fund theorem, two **mutual funds**[3] could provide a complete investment service for everyone. There would be no need for anyone to purchase individual stocks separately; they could just purchase shares in the mutual funds. This conclusion, however, is based on the assumption that everyone cares only about mean and variance; that everyone has the same assessment of the means, variances, and covariances; and that a single-period framework is appropriate. All of these assumptions are quite tenuous. Nevertheless, if you are an investor without the time or inclination to make careful assessments, you might choose to find two funds managed by people whose assessments you trust, and invest in those two funds.

The two-fund theorem also has implications for computation. In order to solve (6.5a–c) for all values of $\bar{r}$ it is only necessary to find two solutions and then form combinations of those two. A particularly simple way to specify two solutions is to specify values of λ and μ. Convenient choices are (*a*) $\lambda = 0$, $\mu = 1$ and (*b*) $\lambda = 1$, $\mu = 0$. In either of these solutions the constraint $\sum_{i=1}^{n} w_i = 1$ may be violated, but this can be remedied later by normalizing all w_i's by a common scale factor. The solution obtained by choice (*a*) ignores the constraint on the expected mean rate of return; hence this is the minimum-variance point. The overall procedure is illustrated in the following example.

Example 6.11 (A securities portfolio)   The information concerning the 1-year co-variances and mean values of the rates of return on five securities is shown in the top part of Table 6.2. The mean values are expressed on a percentage basis, whereas the covariances are expressed in units of (percent)^2/100. For example, the first security has an expected rate of return of $15.1\% = .151$ and a variance of return of .023, which translates into a standard deviation of $\sqrt{.023} = .152 = 15.2\%$ per year.

---

[3] A mutual fund is an investment company that accepts investment capital from individuals and reinvests that capital in a diversity of individual stocks. Each individual is entitled to his or her proportionate share of the fund's portfolio value, less certain operating fees and commissions.

TABLE 6.2
A Securities Portfolio

Security	Covariance V					$\bar{r}$
1	2.30	.93	.62	.74	−.23	15.1
2	.93	1.40	.22	.56	.26	12.5
3	.62	.22	1.80	.78	.27	14.7
4	.74	.56	.78	3.40	−.56	9.02
5	−.23	.26	−.27	−.56	2.60	17.68

	$\mathbf{v}^1$	$\mathbf{v}^2$	$\mathbf{w}^1$	$\mathbf{w}^2$
	.141	3.652	.088	.158
	.401	3.583	.251	.155
	.452	7.248	.282	.314
	.166	.874	.104	.038
	.440	7.706	.275	.334
Mean			14.413	15.202
Variance			.625	.659
Std. dev.			.791	.812

The covariances and mean rates of return are shown for five securities. The portfolio $\mathbf{w}^1$ is the minimum-variance point, and $\mathbf{w}^2$ is another efficient portfolio made from these five securities.

We shall find two funds in the minimum-variance set. First we set $\lambda = 0$ and $\mu = 1$ in (6.5). We thus solve the system of equations

$$\sum_{j=1}^{5} \sigma_{ij} v_j^1 = 1$$

for the vector $\mathbf{v}^1 = (v_1^1, v_2^1, \ldots, v_5^1)$. This solution can be found using a spreadsheet package that solves linear equations. The coefficients of the equation are those of the covariance matrix, and the right-hand sides are all 1's. The resulting v_j^2's are listed in the first column of the bottom part of Table 6.2 as components of the vector $\mathbf{v}^1$.

Next we normalize the v_i^1's so that they sum to 1, obtaining w_i^1's as

$$w_i^1 = \frac{v_i^1}{\sum_{j=1}^{n} v_j^1}.$$

The vector $\mathbf{w}^1 = (w_1^1, w_2^1, \ldots, w_5^1)$ defines the minimum-variance point.

Second we set $\mu = 0$ and $\lambda = 1$. We thus solve the system of equations

$$\sum_{j=1}^{5} \sigma_{ij} v_j^2 = \bar{r}_i, \qquad i = 1, 2, \ldots, 5$$

for a solution $\mathbf{v}^2 = (v_1^2, v_2^2, \ldots, v_5^2)$. Again we normalize the resulting vector $\mathbf{v}^2$ so its components sum to 1, to obtain $\mathbf{w}^2$. The vectors $\mathbf{v}^1$, $\mathbf{v}^2$, $\mathbf{w}^1$, $\mathbf{w}^2$ are shown in the bottom part of Table 6.2. Also shown are the means, variances, and standard deviations corresponding to the portfolios defined by $\mathbf{w}^1$ and $\mathbf{w}^2$. All efficient portfolios are combinations of these two.

6.8 INCLUSION OF A RISK-FREE ASSET

In the previous few sections we have implicitly assumed that the n assets available are all risky; that is, they each have $\sigma > 0$. A **risk-free asset** has a return that is deterministic (that is, known with certainty) and therefore has $\sigma = 0$. In other words, a risk-free asset is a pure interest-bearing instrument; its inclusion in a portfolio corresponds to lending or borrowing cash at the risk-free rate. Lending (such as the purchase of a bond) corresponds to the risk-free asset having a positive weight, whereas borrowing corresponds to its having a negative weight.

The inclusion of a risk-free asset in the list of possible assets is necessary to obtain realism. Investors invariably have the opportunity to borrow or lend. Fortunately, as we shall see shortly, inclusion of a risk-free asset introduces a mathematical degeneracy that greatly simplifies the shape of the efficient frontier.

To explain the degeneracy condition, suppose that there is a risk-free asset with a (deterministic) rate of return r_f. Consider any other risky asset with rate of return r, having mean $\bar{r}$ and variance σ^2. Note that the covariance of these two returns must be zero. This is because the covariance is defined to be $\mathrm{E}\big[(r - \bar{r})(r_f - r_f)\big] = 0$.

Now suppose that these two assets are combined to form a portfolio using a weight of α for the risk-free asset and $1 - \alpha$ for the risky asset, with $\alpha \leq 1$. The mean rate of return of this portfolio will be $\alpha r_f + (1 - \alpha)\bar{r}$. The standard deviation of the return will be $\sqrt{(1 - \alpha)^2 \sigma^2} = (1 - \alpha)\sigma$. This is because the risk-free asset has no variance and no covariance with the risky asset. The only term left in the formula is that due to the risky asset.

If we define, just for the moment, $\sigma_f = 0$, we see that the portfolio rate of return has

$$\text{mean} = \alpha r_f + (1 - \alpha)\bar{r}$$

$$\text{standard deviation} = \alpha \sigma_f + (1 - \alpha)\sigma .$$

These equations show that both the mean and the standard deviation of the portfolio vary linearly with α. This means that as α varies, the point representing the portfolio traces out a straight line in the $\bar{r}$–σ plane.

Suppose now that there are n risky assets with known mean rates of return $\bar{r}_i$ and known covariances σ_{ij}. In addition, there is a risk-free asset with rate of return r_f. The inclusion of the risk-free asset in the list of available assets has a profound effect on the shape of the feasible region. The reason for this is shown in Figure 6.13(a). First we construct the ordinary feasible region, defined by the n risky assets. (This region may be either the one constructed with shorting allowed or the one constructed without shorting.) This region is shown as the darkly shaded region in the figure. Next,

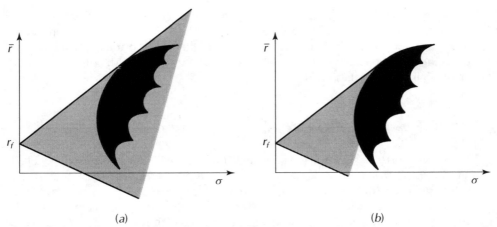

(a) (b)

FIGURE 6.13   Effect of a risk-free asset. Inclusion of a risk-free asset adds lines to the feasible region. (a) If both borrowing and lending are allowed, a complete infinite triangular region is obtained. (b) If only lending is allowed, the region will have a triangular front end, but will curve for larger σ.

for each asset (or portfolio) in this region we form combinations with the risk-free asset. In forming these combinations we allow borrowing or lending of the risk-free asset, but only purchase of the risky asset. These new combinations trace out the infinite straight line originating at the risk-free point, passing through the risky asset, and continuing indefinitely. There is a line of this type for every asset in the original feasible set. The totality of these lines forms a triangularly shaped feasible region, indicated by the light shading in the figure.

This is a beautiful result. The feasible region is an infinite triangle whenever a risk-free asset is included in the universe of available assets.

If borrowing of the risk-free asset is not allowed (no shorting of this asset), we can adjoin only the finite line segments between the risk-free asset and points in the original feasible region. We cannot extend these lines further, since this would entail borrowing of the risk-free asset. The inclusion of these finite line segments leads to a new feasible region with a straight-line front edge but a rounded top, as shown in Figure 6.13(b).

6.9 THE ONE-FUND THEOREM

When risk-free borrowing and lending are available, the efficient set consists of a single straight line, which is the top of the triangular feasible region. This line is tangent to the original feasible set of risky assets. (See Figure 6.14.) There will be a point F in the original feasible set that is on the line segment defining the overall efficient set. It is clear that *any* efficient point (any point on the line) can be expressed as a combination of this asset and the risk-free asset. We obtain different efficient points by changing the weighting between these two (including negative weights of the risk-free asset to borrow money in order to leverage the buying of the risky asset). The portfolio

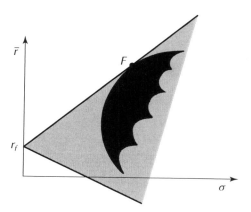

FIGURE 6.14 One-fund theorem. When both borrowing and lending at the risk-free rate are allowed, there is a unique fund F of risky assets that is efficient. All points on the efficient frontier are combinations of F and the risk-free asset.

represented by the tangent point can be thought of as a fund made up of assets and sold as a unit. The role of this fund is summarized by the following statement:

The one-fund theorem *There is a single fund F of risky assets such that any efficient portfolio can be constructed as a combination of the fund F and the risk-free asset.*

This is a final conclusion of mean–variance portfolio theory, and this conclusion is the launch point for the next chapter. It is fine to stop reading here, and (after doing some exercises) to go on to the next chapter. But if you want to see how to calculate the special efficient point F, read the specialized subsection that follows.

Solution Method*

How can we find the tangent point that represents the efficient fund? We just characterize that point in terms of an optimization problem. Given a point in the feasible region, we draw a line between the risk-free asset and that point. We denote the angle between that line and the horizontal axis by θ. For any feasible (risky) portfolio p, we have

$$\tan \theta = \frac{\bar{r}_p - r_f}{\sigma_p}.$$

The tangent portfolio is the feasible point that maximizes θ or, equivalently, maximizes $\tan \theta$. It turns out that this problem can be reduced to the solution of a system of linear equations.

To develop the solution, suppose, as usual, that there are n risky assets. We assign weights $w_1, w_2, \ldots, w_n$ to the risky assets such that $\sum_{i=1}^n w_i = 1$. There is zero weight on the risk-free asset in the tangent fund. (Note that we are allowing short selling among the risky assets.) For $r_p = \sum_{i=1}^n w_i r_i$, we have $\bar{r}_p = \sum_{i=1}^n w_i \bar{r}_i$ and $r_f = \sum_{i=1}^n w_i r_f$. Thus,

$$\tan \theta = \frac{\sum_{i=1}^n w_i (\bar{r}_i - r_f)}{\left(\sum_{i,j=1}^n \sigma_{ij} w_i w_j \right)^{1/2}}.$$

It should be clear that multiplication of all w_i's by a constant will not change the expression, since the constant will cancel. Hence it is not necessary to impose the constraint $\sum_{i=1}^{n} w_i = 1$ here.

We then set the derivative of $\tan \theta$ with respect to each w_k equal to zero. This leads (see Exercise 10) to the following equations:

$$\sum_{i=1}^{n} \sigma_{ki} \lambda w_i = \bar{r}_k - r_f, \qquad k = 1, 2, \ldots, n \qquad (6.9)$$

where λ is an (unknown) constant. Making the substitution $v_i = \lambda w_i$ for each i, (6.9) becomes

$$\sum_{i=1}^{n} \sigma_{ki} v_i = \bar{r}_k - r_f, \qquad k = 1, 2, \ldots, n. \qquad (6.10)$$

We solve these linear equations for the v_i's and then normalize to determine the w_i's; that is,

$$w_i = \frac{v_i}{\sum_{k=1}^{n} v_k}.$$

Example 6.12 (Three uncorrelated assets)   We consider again Example 6.9, where the three risky assets were uncorrelated and each had variance equal to 1. The three mean rates of return were $\bar{r}_1 = 1$, $\bar{r}_2 = 2$, and $\bar{r}_3 = 3$. We assume in addition that there is a risk-free asset with rate $r_f = .5$.

We apply (6.9), which is very simple in this case because the covariances are all zero, to find

$$v_1 = 1 - .5 = .5$$
$$v_2 = 2 - .5 = 1.5$$
$$v_3 = 3 - .5 = 2.5.$$

We then normalize these values by dividing by their sum, 4.5, and find

$$w_1 = \tfrac{1}{9}, \qquad w_2 = \tfrac{1}{3}, \qquad w_3 = \tfrac{5}{9}.$$

Example 6.13 (A larger portfolio)   Consider the five risky assets of Example 6.11. Assume also that there is a risk-free asset with $r_f = 10\%$. We can easily find the special fund F.

We note that the system of equations (6.10) is identical to those used to find $\mathbf{v}^1$ and $\mathbf{v}^2$ in Example 6.11, but with a different right-hand side. Actually the right-hand side is a linear combination of those used for $\mathbf{v}^1$ and $\mathbf{v}^2$; namely, $\bar{r}_k - r_f = 1 \times \bar{r}_k - r_f \times 1$. Therefore the solution to (6.10) is $\mathbf{v} = \mathbf{v}^2 - r_f \mathbf{v}^1$. Thus (using $r_f = 10$ to be consistent with the units used in the earlier example), $\mathbf{v} = (2.242, -.427, 2.728, -.786, 3.306)$. We normalize this to obtain the final result $\mathbf{w} = (.317, -.060, .386, -.111, .468)$.

Basically, we have used the fact that portfolio F is a combination of two known efficient points.

6.10 SUMMARY

The study of one-period investment situations is based on asset and portfolio returns. Both total returns and rates of return are used. The return of an asset may be uncertain, in which case it is useful to consider it formally as a random variable. The probabilistic properties of such random returns can be summarized by their expected values, their variances, and their covariances with each other.

A portfolio is defined by allocating fractions of initial wealth to individual assets. The fractions (or weights) must sum to 1; but some of these weights may be negative if short selling is allowed. The return of a portfolio is the weighted sum of the returns of its individual assets, with the weights being those that define the portfolio. The expected return of the portfolio is, likewise, equal to the weighted average of the expected returns of the individual assets. The variance of the portfolio is determined by a more complicated formula: $\sigma^2 = \sum_{i,j=1}^{n} w_i w_j \sigma_{ij}$, where the w_i's are the weights and the σ_{ij}'s are the covariances.

From a given collection of n risky assets, there results a set of possible portfolios made from all possible weights of the n individual assets. If the mean and the standard deviation of these portfolios are plotted on a diagram with vertical axis $\bar{r}$ (the mean) and horizontal axis σ (the standard deviation), the region so obtained is called the feasible region. Two alternative feasible regions are defined: one allowing shorting of assets and one not allowing shorting.

It can be argued that investors who measure the value of a portfolio in terms of its mean and its standard deviation, who are risk averse, and who have the nonsatiation property will select portfolios on the upper left-hand portion of the feasible region—the efficient frontier.

Points on the efficient frontier can be characterized by an optimization problem originally formulated by Markowitz. This problem seeks the portfolio weights that minimize variance for a given value of mean return. Mathematically, this is a problem with a quadratic objective and two linear constraints. If shorting is allowed (so that the weights may be negative as well as positive), the optimal weights can be found by solving a system of $n+2$ linear equations and $n+2$ unknowns. Otherwise if shorting is not allowed, the Markowitz problem can be solved by special quadratic programming packages.

An important property of the Markowitz problem, when shorting is allowed, is that if two solutions are known, then any weighted combination of these two solutions is also a solution. This leads to the fundamental two-fund theorem: investors seeking efficient portfolios need only invest in two master efficient funds.

Usually it is appropriate to assume that, in addition to n risky assets, there is available a risk-free asset with fixed rate of return r_f. The inclusion of such an asset greatly simplifies the shape of the feasible region, transforming the upper boundary into a straight line. This line is the efficient frontier. The straight-line frontier touches the original feasible region (the region defined by the risky assets only) at a single point F. This leads to the important one-fund theorem: investors seeking efficient portfolios need only invest in one master fund of risky assets and in the risk-free asset. Different investors may prefer different combinations of these two.

The single efficient fund of risky assets F can be found by solving a system of n linear equations and n unknowns. When the solution to this system is normalized so that its components sum to 1, the resulting components are the weights of the risky assets in the master fund.

EXERCISES

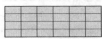

1. (Shorting with margin) Suppose that to short a stock you are required to deposit an amount equal to the initial price X_0 of the stock. At the end of 1 year the stock price is X_1 and you liquidate your position. You receive your profit from shorting equal to $X_0 - X_1$ and you recover your original deposit. If R is the total return of the stock, what is the total return on your short?

2. (Dice product) Two dice are rolled and the two resulting values are multiplied together to form the quantity z. What are the expected value and the variance of the random variable z? [*Hint:* Use the independence of the two separate dice.]

3. (Two correlated assets) The correlation ρ between assets A and B is .1, and other data are given in Table 6.3. [*Note:* $\rho = \sigma_{AB}/(\sigma_A\sigma_B)$.]

TABLE 6.3
Two Correlated Cases

Asset	$\bar{r}$	σ
A	10.0%	15%
B	18.0%	30%

(*a*) Find the proportions α of A and $(1-\alpha)$ of B that define a portfolio of A and B having minimum standard deviation.
(*b*) What is the value of this minimum standard deviation?
(*c*) What is the expected return of this portfolio?

4. (Two stocks) Two stocks are available. The corresponding expected rates of return are $\bar{r}_1$ and $\bar{r}_2$; the corresponding variances and covariances are σ_1^2, σ_2^2, and σ_{12}. What percentages of total investment should be invested in each of the two stocks to minimize the total variance of the rate of return of the resulting portfolio? What is the mean rate of return of this portfolio?

5. (Rain insurance) Gavin Jones's friend is planning to invest $1 million in a rock concert to be held 1 year from now. The friend figures that he will obtain $3 million revenue from his $1 million investment—unless, my goodness, it rains. If it rains, he will lose his entire investment. There is a 50% chance that it will rain the day of the concert. Gavin suggests that he buy rain insurance. He can buy one unit of insurance for $.50, and this unit pays $1 if it rains and nothing if it does not. He may purchase as many units as he wishes, up to $3 million.

(a) What is the expected rate of return on his investment if he buys u units of insurance? (The cost of insurance is in addition to his $1 million investment.)

(b) What number of units will minimize the variance of his return? What is this minimum value? And what is the corresponding expected rate of return? [*Hint:* Before calculating a general expression for variance, think about a simple answer.]

6. (**Wild cats**)   Suppose there are n assets which are uncorrelated. (They might be n different "wild cat" oil well prospects.) You may invest in any one, or in any combination of them. The mean rate of return $\bar{r}$ is the same for each asset, but the variances are different. The return on asset i has a variance of σ_i^2 for $i = 1, 2, \ldots, n$.

(a) Show the situation on an $\bar{r}$–σ diagram. Describe the efficient set.

(b) Find the minimum-variance point. Express your result in terms of

$$\bar{\sigma}^2 = \left(\sum_{i=1}^{n} \frac{1}{\sigma_i^2} \right)^{-1}.$$

7. (**Markowitz fun**)   There are just three assets with rates of return r_1, r_2, and r_3, respectively. The covariance matrix and the expected rates of return are

$$\mathbf{V} = \begin{bmatrix} 2 & 1 & 0 \\ 1 & 2 & 1 \\ 0 & 1 & 2 \end{bmatrix}, \qquad \bar{\mathbf{r}} = \begin{bmatrix} .4 \\ .8 \\ .8 \end{bmatrix}.$$

(a) Find the minimum-variance portfolio. [*Hint:* By symmetry $w_1 = w_3$.]

(b) Find another efficient portfolio by setting $\lambda = 1$, $\mu = 0$.

(c) If the risk-free rate is $r_f = .2$, find the efficient portfolio of risky assets.

8. (**Tracking**)   Suppose that it is impractical to use all the assets that are incorporated into a specified portfolio (such as a given efficient portfolio). One alternative is to find the portfolio, made up of a given set of n stocks, that tracks the specified portfolio most closely—in the sense of minimizing the variance of the difference in returns.

Specifically, suppose that the target portfolio has (random) rate of return r_M. Suppose that there are n assets with (random) rates of return $r_1, r_2, \ldots, r_n$. We wish to find the portfolio rate of return

$$r = \alpha_1 r_1 + \alpha_2 r_2 + \cdots + \alpha_n r_n$$

(with $\sum_{i=1}^{n} \alpha_i = 1$) minimizing $\mathrm{var}(r - r_M)$.

(a) Find a set of equations for the α_i's.

(b) Although this portfolio tracks the desired portfolio most closely in terms of variance, it may sacrifice the mean. Hence a logical approach is to minimize the variance of the tracking error subject to achieving a given mean return. As the mean is varied, this results in a family of portfolios that are efficient in a new sense—say, tracking efficient. Find the equation for the α_i's that are tracking efficient.

9. (**Betting wheel**)   Consider a general betting wheel with n segments. The payoff for a $1 bet on a segment i is A_i. Suppose you bet an amount $B_i = 1/A_i$ on segment i for each i. Show that the amount you win is independent of the outcome of the wheel. What is the risk-free rate of return for the wheel? Apply this to the wheel in Example 6.7.

10. (Efficient portfolio ◇) Derive (6.9). [*Hint:* Note that

$$\frac{\partial}{\partial w_i} \left(\sum_{ij}^{n} \sigma_{ij} w_i w_j \right)^{1/2} = \left(\sum_{ij}^{n} \sigma_{ij} w_i w_j \right)^{-1/2} \sum_{j=1}^{n} \sigma_{ij} w_j. \Bigg]$$

REFERENCES

Mean–variance portfolio theory was initially devised by Markowitz [1–4]. Other important developments were presented in [5–8]. The one-fund argument is due to Tobin [9]. For comprehensive textbook presentations, see [10–11] and the other general investment textbooks listed as references for Chapter 2.

1. Markowitz, H. M. (1952), "Portfolio Selection," *Journal of Finance*, **7,** no. 1, 77–91.
2. Markowitz, H. M. (1956), "The Optimization of a Quadratic Function Subject to Linear Constraints," *Naval Research Logistics Quarterly*, **3,** nos. 1–2, 111–133.
3. Markowitz, H. M. (1987), *Portfolio Selection*, Wiley, New York.
4. Markowitz, H. M. (1987), *Mean-Variance Analysis in Portfolio Choice and Capital Markets*, Basil Blackwell, New York.
5. Hester, D. D., and J. Tobin (1967), *Risk Aversion and Portfolio Choice*, Wiley, New York.
6. Fama, E. F. (1976), *Foundations of Finance*, Basic Books, New York.
7. Sharpe, W. F. (1967), "Portfolio Analysis," *Journal of Financial and Quantitative Analysis*, **2,** 76–84.
8. Levy, H. (1979), "Does Diversification Always Pay?" *TIMS Studies in Management Science*.
9. Tobin, J. (1958), "Liquidity Preference as Behavior Toward Risk," *Review of Economic Studies*, **26,** February, 65–86.
10. Francis, J. C., and G. Alexander (1986), *Portfolio Analysis*, 3rd ed., Prentice Hall, Englewood Cliffs, NJ.
11. Elton, E. J., and M. J. Gruber (1991), *Portfolio Theory and Investment Analysis*, 4th ed., Wiley, New York.

7 THE CAPITAL ASSET PRICING MODEL

Two main problem types dominate the discipline of investment science. The first is to determine the best course of action in an investment situation. Problems of this type include how to devise the best portfolio, how to devise the optimal strategy for managing an investment, how to select from a group of potential investment projects, and so forth. Several examples of such problems were treated in Part 1 of this book. The second type of problem is to determine the correct, arbitrage-free, fair, or equilibrium price of an asset. We saw examples of this in Part 1 as well, such as the formula for the correct price of a bond in terms of the term structure of interest rates, and the formula for the appropriate value of a firm.

This chapter concentrates mainly on the pricing issue. It deduces the correct price of a risky asset within the framework of the mean–variance setting. The result is the **capital asset pricing model** (CAPM) developed primarily by Sharpe, Lintner, and Mossin, which follows logically from the Markowitz mean–variance portfolio theory described in the previous chapter. Later in this chapter we discuss how this result can be applied to investment decision problems.

7.1 MARKET EQUILIBRIUM

Suppose that everyone is a mean–variance optimizer as described in the previous chapter. Suppose further that everyone agrees on the probabilistic structure of assets; that is, everyone assigns to the returns of assets the same mean values, the same variances, and the same covariances. Furthermore, assume that there is a unique risk-free rate of borrowing and lending that is available to all, and that there are no transactions costs. With these assumptions what will happen?

From the one-fund theorem we know that everyone will purchase a single fund of risky assets, and they may, in addition, borrow or lend at the risk-free rate. Furthermore, since everyone uses the same means, variances, and covariances, everyone will use the same risky fund. The mix of these two assets, the risky fund and the risk-free asset, will likely vary across individuals according to their individual tastes for risk. Some will seek to avoid risk and will, accordingly, have a high percentage of the risk-free asset in their portfolios; others, who are more aggressive, will have a high percentage of the risky fund. However, every individual will form a portfolio that is a mix of the risk-free asset and the single, risky *one fund*. Hence the *one fund* in the theorem is really the *only fund* that is used.

If everyone purchases the same fund of risky assets, what must that fund be? The answer to this question is the key insight underlying the CAPM. A bit of reflection reveals that the answer is that this fund must equal the **market portfolio.** The market portfolio is the summation of all assets. In the world of equity securities, it is the totality of shares of IBM, GM, DIS, and so forth. If everyone buys just one fund, and their purchases add up to the market, then that one fund must be the market as well; that is, it must contain shares of every stock in proportion to that stock's representation in the entire market.

An asset's weight in a portfolio is defined as the proportion of portfolio capital that is allocated to that asset. Hence the weight of an asset in the market portfolio is equal to the proportion of that asset's total capital value to the total market capital value. These weights are termed **capitalization weights.** It is these weights that we usually denote by w_i. In other words, the w_i's of the market portfolio are the capitalization weights of the assets.

The exact definition of the market portfolio is illustrated as follows. Suppose there are only three stocks in the market: Jazz, Inc., Classical, Inc., and Rock, Inc. Their outstanding shares and prices are shown in Table 7.1. The market weights are proportional to the total market capitalization, not to the number of shares.

In the situation where everyone follows the mean–variance methodology with the same estimates of parameters, we know that the efficient fund of risky assets will be the market portfolio. Hence under these assumptions there is no need for us to formulate the mean–variance problem, to estimate the underlying parameters, or to solve the system of equations that define the optimal portfolio. We know that the optimal portfolio will turn out to be the market portfolio.

TABLE 7.1
Market Capitalization Weights

Security	Shares outstanding	Relative shares in market	Price	Capitalization	Weight in market
Jazz, Inc.	10,000	1/8	$6.00	$60,000	3/20
Classical, Inc.	30,000	3/8	$4.00	$120,000	3/10
Rock, Inc.	40,000	1/2	$5.50	$220,000	11/20
Total	80,000	1		$400,000	1

The percentage of shares of a stock in the market portfolio is a share-weighted proportion of total shares. These percentages are not *the market portfolio weights. The market portfolio weight of a stock is proportional to capitalization. If the price of an asset changes, the share proportions do not change, but the capitalization weights do change.*

How does this happen? How can it be that we solve the problem even without knowing the required data? The answer is based on an **equilibrium** argument. If everyone else (or at least a large number of people) solves the problem, we do not need to. It works like this: The return on an asset depends on both its initial price and its final price. The other investors solve the mean–variance portfolio problem using their common estimates, and they place orders in the market to acquire their portfolios. If the orders placed do not match what is available, the prices must change. The prices of assets under heavy demand will increase; the prices of assets under light demand will decrease. These price changes affect the estimates of asset returns directly, and hence investors will recalculate their optimal portfolios. This process continues until demand exactly matches supply; that is, it continues until there is equilibrium.

In the idealized world, where every investor is a mean–variance investor and all have the same estimates, everyone buys the same portfolio, and that must be equal to the market portfolio. In other words, prices adjust to drive the market to efficiency. Then after other people have made the adjustments, we can be sure that the efficient portfolio is the market portfolio, so we need not make any calculations.

This theory of equilibrium is usually applied to assets that are traded repeatedly over time, such as the stock market. In this case it is argued that individuals adjust their return estimates slowly, and only make a series of minor adjustments to their calculations rather than solving the entire portfolio optimization problem at one time.

Finally, in such equilibrium models it is argued that the appropriate equilibrium need be calculated by only a few devoted (and energetic) individuals. They move prices around to the proper value, and other investors follow their lead by purchasing the market portfolio.

These arguments about the equilibrium process all have a degree of plausibility, and all have weaknesses. Deeper analysis can be carried out, but for our purposes we will merely consider that equilibrium occurs. Hence the ultimate conclusion of the mean–variance approach is that the *one fund* must be the market portfolio.

7.2 THE CAPITAL MARKET LINE

Given the preceding conclusion that the single efficient fund of risky assets is the market portfolio, we can label this fund on the $\bar{r}$–σ diagram with an M for *market*. The efficient set therefore consists of a single straight line, emanating from the risk-free point and passing through the market portfolio. This line, shown in Figure 7.1, is called the **capital market line.**

This line shows the relation between the expected rate of return and the risk of return (as measured by the standard deviation) for efficient assets or portfolios of assets. It is also referred to as a pricing line, since prices should adjust so that efficient assets fall on this line.

The line has great intuitive appeal. It states that as risk increases, the corresponding expected rate of return must also increase. Furthermore, this relationship can be

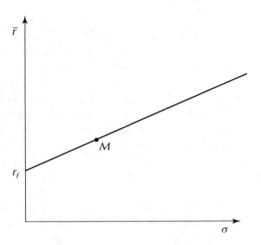

FIGURE 7.1   Capital market line. Efficient assets must all lie on the line determined by the risk-free rate and the market portfolio.

described by a straight line if risk is measured by standard deviation. In mathematical terms the capital market line states that

$$\bar{r} = r_f + \frac{\bar{r}_M - r_f}{\sigma_M}\sigma \tag{7.1}$$

where $\bar{r}_M$ and σ_M are the expected value and the standard deviation of the market rate of return and $\bar{r}$ and σ are the expected value and the standard deviation of the rate of return of an arbitrary efficient asset.

The slope of the capital market line is $K = (\bar{r}_M - r_f)/\sigma_M$, and this value is frequently called the **price of risk.** It tells by how much the expected rate of return of a portfolio must increase if the standard deviation of that rate increases by one unit.

Example 7.1 (The impatient investor)   Mr. Smith is young and impatient. He notes that the risk-free rate is only 6% and the market portfolio of risky assets has an expected return of 12% and a standard deviation of 15%. He figures that it would take about 60 years for his $1,000.00 nest egg to increase to $1 million if it earned the market rate of return. He can't wait that long. He wants that $1 million in 10 years.

Mr. Smith easily determines that he must attain an average rate of return of about 100% per year to achieve his goal (since $1,000 \times 2^{10} = \$1,048,000$). Correspondingly, his yearly standard deviation according to the capital market line would be the value of σ satisfying

$$1.0 = .06 + \frac{.12 - .06}{.15}\sigma$$

or $\sigma = 10$. This corresponds to $\sigma = 1,000\%$. So this young man is certainly not guaranteed success (even if he could borrow the amount required to move far beyond the market on the capital market line).

Example 7.2 (An oil venture)   Consider an oil drilling venture. The price of a share of this venture is $875. It is expected to yield the equivalent of $1,000 after 1 year, but due to high uncertainty about how much oil is at the drilling site, the standard deviation of the return is $\sigma = 40\%$. Currently the risk-free rate is 10%. The expected rate of return on the market portfolio is 17%, and the standard deviation of this rate is 12%.

Let us see how this venture compares with assets on the capital market line. Given the level of σ, the expected rate of return predicted by the capital market line is

$$\bar{r} = .10 + \frac{.17 - .10}{.12} .40 = 33\%.$$

However, the actual expected rate of return is only $\bar{r} = 1,000/875 - 1 = 14\%$. Therefore the point representing the oil venture lies well below the capital market line. (This does *not* mean that the venture is necessarily a poor one, as we shall see later, but it certainly does not, by itself, constitute an efficient portfolio.)

7.3 THE PRICING MODEL

The capital market line relates the expected rate of return of an efficient portfolio to its standard deviation, but it does not show how the expected rate of return of an individual asset relates to its individual risk. This relation is expressed by the capital asset pricing model.

We state this major result as a theorem. The reader may wish merely to glance over the proof at first reading since it is a bit involved. We shall discuss the implications of the result following the proof.

The capital asset pricing model (CAPM)   *If the market portfolio M is efficient, the expected return $\bar{r}_i$ of any asset i satisfies*

$$\bar{r}_i - r_f = \beta_i(\bar{r}_M - r_f) \tag{7.2}$$

where

$$\beta_i = \frac{\sigma_{iM}}{\sigma_M^2}. \tag{7.3}$$

Proof: For any α consider the portfolio consisting of a portion α invested in asset i and a portion $1 - \alpha$ invested in the market portfolio M. (We allow $\alpha < 0$, which corresponds to borrowing at the risk-free rate.) The expected rate of return of this portfolio is

$$\bar{r}_\alpha = \alpha \bar{r}_i + (1 - \alpha)\bar{r}_M$$

and the standard deviation of the rate of return is

$$\sigma_\alpha = [\alpha^2 \sigma_i^2 + 2\alpha(1 - \alpha)\sigma_{iM} + (1 - \alpha)^2 \sigma_M^2]^{1/2}.$$

As α varies, these values trace out a curve in the $\bar{r}$–σ diagram, as shown in Figure 7.2. In particular, $\alpha = 0$ corresponds to the market portfolio M. This

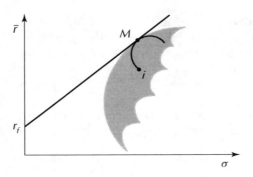

FIGURE 7.2 Portfolio curve. The family of portfolios traces out a curve on the diagram. This curve cannot cross the capital market line, and hence must be tangent to that line.

curve cannot cross the capital market line. If it did, the portfolio corresponding to a point above the capital market line would violate the very definition of the capital market line as being the efficient boundary of the feasible set. Hence as α passes through zero, the curve must be tangent to the capital market line at M. This tangency is the condition that we exploit to derive the formula.

The tangency condition can be translated into the condition that the slope of the curve is equal to the slope of the capital market line at the point M. To set up this condition we need to calculate a few derivatives.

First we have

$$\frac{d\bar{r}_\alpha}{d\alpha} = \bar{r}_i - \bar{r}_M$$

$$\frac{d\sigma_\alpha}{d\alpha} = \frac{\alpha\sigma_i^2 + (1 - 2\alpha)\sigma_{iM} + (\alpha - 1)\sigma_M^2}{\sigma_\alpha}.$$

Thus,

$$\left.\frac{d\sigma_\alpha}{d\alpha}\right|_{\alpha=0} = \frac{\sigma_{iM} - \sigma_M^2}{\sigma_M}.$$

We then use the relation

$$\frac{d\bar{r}_\alpha}{d\sigma_\alpha} = \frac{d\bar{r}_\alpha/d\alpha}{d\sigma_\alpha/d\alpha}$$

to obtain

$$\left.\frac{d\bar{r}_\alpha}{d\sigma_\alpha}\right|_{\alpha=0} = \frac{(\bar{r}_i - \bar{r}_M)\sigma_M}{\sigma_{iM} - \sigma_M^2}.$$

This slope must equal the slope of the capital market line. Hence,

$$\frac{(\bar{r}_i - \bar{r}_M)\sigma_M}{\sigma_{iM} - \sigma_M^2} = \frac{\bar{r}_M - r_f}{\sigma_M}.$$

We now just solve for $\bar{r}_i$, obtaining the final result

$$\bar{r}_i = r_f + \left(\frac{\bar{r}_M - r_f}{\sigma_M^2}\right)\sigma_{iM} = r_f + \beta_i(\bar{r}_M - r_f).$$

This is clearly equivalent to the stated formula.   ∎

The value β_i is referred to as the **beta** of an asset. When the asset is fixed in a discussion, we often just write beta without a subscript—β. An asset's beta is all that need be known about the asset's risk characteristics to use the CAPM formula.

The value $\bar{r}_i - r_f$ is termed the **expected excess rate of return** of asset i; it is the amount by which the rate of return is expected to exceed the risk-free rate. Likewise, $\bar{r}_M - r_f$ is the expected excess rate of return of the market portfolio. In terms of these expected excess rates of return, the CAPM says that the expected excess rate of return of an asset is proportional to the expected excess rate of return of the market portfolio, and the proportionality factor is β. So with r_f taken as a base point, the expected returns of a particular asset and of the market above that base are proportional.

An alternative interpretation of the CAPM formula is based on the fact that β is a normalized version of the covariance of the asset with the market portfolio. Hence the CAPM formula states that the expected excess rate of return of an asset is directly proportional to its covariance with the market. It is this covariance that determines the expected excess rate of return.

To gain insight into this result, let us consider some extreme cases. Suppose, first, that the asset is completely *uncorrelated* with the market; that is, $\beta = 0$. Then, according to the CAPM, we have $\bar{r} = r_f$. This is perhaps at first sight a surprising result. It states that even if the asset is very risky (with large σ), the expected rate of return will be that of the risk-free asset—there is no premium for risk. The reason for this is that the risk associated with an asset that is uncorrelated with the market can be diversified away. If we had many such assets, each uncorrelated with the others and with the market, we could purchase small amounts of each of them, and the resulting total variance would be small. Since the final composite return would have small variance, the corresponding expected rate of return should be close to r_f.

Even more extreme is an asset with a negative value of β. In that case $\bar{r} < r_f$; that is, even though the asset may have very high risk (as measured by its σ), its expected rate of return should be even less than the risk-free rate. The reason is that such an asset reduces the overall portfolio risk when it is combined with the market. Investors are therefore willing to accept the lower expected value for this risk-reducing potential. Such assets provide a form of insurance. They do well when everything else does poorly.

The CAPM changes our concept of the risk of an asset from that of σ to that of β. It is still true that, overall, we measure the risk of a portfolio in terms of σ, but this does not translate into a concern for the σ's of individual assets. For those, the proper measure is their β's.

Example 7.3 (A simple calculation)   We illustrate how simple it is to use the CAPM formula to calculate an expected rate of return. Let the risk-free rate be $r_f = 8\%$. Suppose the rate of return of the market has an expected value of 12% and a standard deviation of 15%.

Now consider an asset that has covariance of .045 with the market. Then we find $\beta = .045/(.15)^2 = 2.0$. The expected return of the asset is $\bar{r} = .08 + 2 \times (.12 - .08) = .16 = 16\%$.

Betas of Common Stocks

The concept of beta is well established in the financial community, and it is referred to frequently in technical discussions about particular stocks. Beta values are estimated by various financial service organizations. Typically, these estimates are formed by using a record of past stock values (usually about 6 or 18 months of weekly values) and computing, from the data, average values of returns, products of returns, and squares of returns in order to approximate expected returns, covariances, and variances. The beta values so obtained drift around somewhat over time, but unless there are drastic changes in a company's situation, its beta tends to be relatively stable.

Table 7.2 lists some well-known U.S. companies and their corresponding beta (β) and volatility (σ) values as estimated at a particular date. Try scanning the list and see if the values given support your intuitive impression of the company's market

TABLE 7.2
Some U.S. Companies: Their Betas and Sigmas

Ticker sym	Company name	Beta	Volatility
KO	Coca-Cola Co	1.19	18%
DIS	Disney Productions	2.23	22%
EK	Eastman Kodak	1.43	34%
XON	Exxon Corp	.67	18%
GE	General Electric CO	1.26	15%
GM	General Motors Corp	.81	19%
GS	Gillette Co	1.09	21%
HWP	Hewlett-Packard Co	1.65	21%
HIA	Holiday Inns Inc	2.56	39%
KM	K-Mart Corp	.82	20%
LK	Lockheed Corp	3.02	43%
MCD	McDonalds Corp	1.56	21%
MRK	Merck & Co	.94	20%
MMM	Minnesota Mining & Mfg	1.00	17%
JCP	Penny J C Inc	1.22	20%
MO	Phillip Morris Inc.	.87	21%
PG	Procter & Gamble	.70	14%
SA	Safeway Stores Inc	.72	14%
S	Sears Roebuck & Co	1.04	19%
SD	Standard Oil of Calif	.85	24%
SYN	Syntex Corp	1.18	31%
TXN	Texas Instruments	1.46	23%
X	US Steel Corp	1.03	26%
UNP	Union Pacific Corp	.65	18%
ZE	Zenith Radio Corp	2.01	32%

Source: *Dailygraph Stock Option Guide,* William O'Neil & Co, Inc., Los Angeles, December 7, 1979. Reprinted with permission of Daily Graphs, P.O. Box 66919, Los Angeles, CA 90066.

properties. Generally speaking, we expect aggressive companies or highly leveraged companies to have high betas, whereas conservative companies whose performance is unrelated to the general market behavior are expected to have low betas. Also, we expect that companies in the same business will have similar, but not identical, beta values. Compare, for instance, JC Penny with Sears Roebuck, or Exxon with Standard Oil of California.

Beta of a Portfolio

It is easy to calculate the overall beta of a portfolio in terms of the betas of the individual assets in the portfolio. Suppose, for example, that a portfolio contains n assets with the weights $w_1, w_2, \ldots, w_n$. The rate of return of the portfolio is $r = \sum_{i=1}^{n} w_i r_i$. Hence $\operatorname{cov}(r, r_M) = \sum_{i=1}^{n} w_i \operatorname{cov}(r_i, r_M)$. It follows immediately that

$$\beta_p = \sum_{i=1}^{n} w_i \beta_i . \tag{7.4}$$

In other words, the portfolio beta is just the weighted average of the betas of the individual assets in the portfolio, with the weights being identical to those that define the portfolio.

7.4 THE SECURITY MARKET LINE

The CAPM formula can be expressed in graphical form by regarding the formula as a linear relationship. This relationship is termed the **security market line.** Two versions are shown in Figure 7.3.

Both graphs show the linear variation of $\bar{r}$. The first expresses it in covariance form, with $\operatorname{cov}(r, r_M)$ being the horizontal axis. The market portfolio corresponds to the point σ_M^2 on this axis. The second graph shows the relation in beta form, with beta being the horizontal axis. In this case the market corresponds to the point $\beta = 1$.

Both of these lines highlight the essence of the CAPM formula. Under the equilibrium conditions assumed by the CAPM, any asset should fall on the security market line.

The security market line expresses the risk–reward structure of assets according to the CAPM, and emphasizes that the risk of an asset is a function of its covariance with the market or, equivalently, a function of its beta.

Systematic Risk

The CAPM implies a special structural property for the return of an asset, and this property provides further insight as to why beta is the most important measure of risk. To develop this result we write the (random) rate of return of asset i as

$$r_i = r_f + \beta_i (r_M - r_f) + \varepsilon_i . \tag{7.5}$$

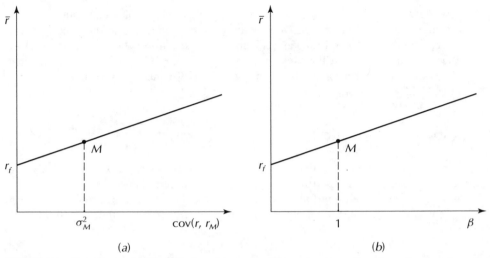

FIGURE 7.3　Security market line. The expected rate of return increases linearly as the covariance with the market increases or, equivalently, as β increases.

This is just an arbitrary equation at this point. The random variable ε_i is chosen to make it true. However, the CAPM formula tells us several things about ε_i.

First, taking the expected value of (7.5), the CAPM says that $\mathrm{E}(\varepsilon_i) = 0$. Second, taking the correlation of (7.5) with r_M (and using the definition of β_i), we find $\mathrm{cov}(\varepsilon_i, \sigma_M) = 0$. We can therefore write

$$\sigma_i^2 = \beta_i^2 \sigma_M^2 + \mathrm{var}(\varepsilon_i)$$

and we see that σ_i^2 is the sum of two parts. The first part, $\beta_i^2 \sigma_M^2$, is termed the **systematic risk.** This is the risk associated with the market as a whole. This risk cannot be reduced by diversification because every asset with nonzero beta contains this risk. The second part, $\mathrm{var}(\varepsilon_i)$, is termed the **nonsystematic, idiosyncratic,** or **specific risk.** This risk is uncorrelated with the market and can be reduced by diversification. It is the systematic (or nondiversifiable) risk, measured by beta, that is most important, since it directly combines with the systematic risk of other assets.

Consider an asset on the capital market line[1] with a value of β. The standard deviation of this asset is $\beta\sigma_M$. It has only systematic risk; there is no nonsystematic risk. This asset has an expected rate of return equal to $\bar{r} = r_f + \beta(\bar{r}_M - r_f)$. Now consider a whole group of other assets, all with the same value of β. According to CAPM, these all have the same expected rate of return, equal to $\bar{r}$. However, if these assets carry nonsystematic risk, they will not fall on the capital market line. Indeed, as the nonsystematic risk increases, the points on the $\bar{r}$–σ plane representing these assets drift to the right, as shown in Figure 7.4. The horizontal distance of a point from the capital market line is therefore a measure of the nonsystematic risk.

---

[1] Of course, to be exactly on the line, the asset must be equivalent to a combination of the market portfolio and the risk-free asset.

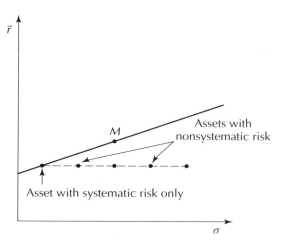

FIGURE 7.4 Systematic and nonsystematic risk. An asset on the capital market line has only systematic risk. Assets with nonsystematic risk fall to the right of the capital market line.

7.5 INVESTMENT IMPLICATIONS

The question of interest for the investor is: Can the CAPM help with investment decisions? There is not a simple answer to this question.

The CAPM states (or assumes), based on an equilibrium argument, that the solution to the Markowitz problem is that the market portfolio is the *one fund* (and *only fund*) of risky assets that anyone need hold. This fund is supplemented only by the risk-free asset. The investment recommendation that follows this argument is that an investor should simply purchase the market portfolio. That is, ideally, an investor should purchase a little bit of every asset that is available, with the proportions determined by the relative amounts that are issued in the market as a whole. If the world of equity securities is taken as the set of available assets, then each person should purchase some shares in every available stock, in proportion to the stocks' monetary share of the total of all stocks outstanding. It is not necessary to go to the trouble of analyzing individual issues and computing a Markowitz solution. Just buy the market portfolio.

Since it would be rather cumbersome for an individual to assemble the market portfolio, mutual funds have been designed to match the market portfolio closely. These funds are termed **index funds,** since they usually attempt to duplicate the portfolio of a major stock market index, such as the *Standard & Poor's 500* (S&P 500), an average of 500 stocks that as a group is thought to be representative of the market as a whole. Other indices use even larger numbers of stocks. A CAPM purist (that is, one who fully accepts the CAPM theory as applied to publicly traded securities) could just purchase one of these index funds (to serve as the *one fund*) as well as some risk-free securities such as U.S. Treasury bills.

Some people believe that they can do better than blindly purchasing the market portfolio. The CAPM, after all, assumes that everyone has identical information about the (uncertain) returns of all assets. Clearly, this is not the case. If someone believes that he or she possesses superior information, then presumably that person could form a portfolio that would outperform the market. We return to this issue in the next chapter, where questions concerning data and information are explicitly addressed. It is shown there that it is not at all easy to obtain accurate data for use in a Markowitz model, and hence the solution computed from such a model is likely to be somewhat nonsensical. For now we just state that the best designs seem to be those formulated as deviations or extensions of the basic CAPM idea, rather than as bold new beginnings. In other words, in constructing a portfolio, one probably should begin with the market portfolio and alter it systematically, rather than attempting to solve the full Markowitz problem from scratch.

One area where the CAPM approach has direct application is in the analysis of assets that do not have well-established market prices. In this case the CAPM can be used to find a *reasonable* price. An important class of problems of this type are the project evaluation problems (variations of capital budgeting problems) that arise in firms. This application is considered explicitly in Section 7.8.

7.6 PERFORMANCE EVALUATION

The CAPM theory can be used to evaluate the performance of an investment portfolio, and indeed it is now common practice to evaluate many institutional portfolios (such as pension funds and mutual funds) using the CAPM framework. We shall present the main ideas by going through a simple hypothetical example. The primary purpose of this section, however, is to use these performance measure ideas to illustrate the CAPM.

Example 7.4 (ABC fund analysis)   The ABC mutual fund has the 10-year record of rates of return shown in the column labeled ABC in Table 7.3. We would like to evaluate this fund's performance in terms of mean–variance portfolio theory and the CAPM. Is it a good fund that we could recommend? Can it serve as the *one fund* for a prudent mean–variance investor?

Step 1. We begin our analysis by computing the three quantities shown in Table 7.3 below the given return data: the average rate of return, the standard deviation of the rate as implied by the 10 samples, and the geometric mean rate of return. These quantities are estimates based on the available data.

In general, given $r_i, i = 1, 2, \ldots, n$, the average rate of return is

$$\hat{\bar{r}} = \frac{1}{n} \sum_{i=1}^{n} r_i$$

and this serves as an estimate of the true expected return $\bar{r}$. The average variance is[2]

$$s^2 = \frac{1}{n-1} \sum_{i=1}^{n} (r_i - \hat{\bar{r}})^2$$

---

[2]The reason that $n - 1$ is used in the denominator instead of n is discussed in the next chapter.

TABLE 7.3
ABC Fund Performance

| Year | Rate of return percentages | | |
	ABC	S&P	T-bills
1	14	12	7
2	10	7	7.5
3	19	20	7.7
4	−8	−2	7.5
5	23	12	8.5
6	28	23	8
7	20	17	7.3
8	14	20	7
9	−9	−5	7.5
10	19	16	8
Average	13	12	7.6
Standard deviation	12.4	9.4	.5
Geometric mean	12.3	11.6	7.6
Cov(ABC, S&P)	.0107		
Beta	1.20375	1	
Jensen	0.00104	0.00000	
Sharpe	0.43577	0.46669	

The top part of the table shows the rate of return achieved by ABC, S&P 500, and T-bills over a 10-year period. The lower portion shows the Jensen and Sharpe indices.

and the estimate s of the standard deviation is the square root of that. It is also useful to calculate the geometric mean rate of return, which is

$$\mu = \left[(1 + r_1)(1 + r_2) \cdots (1 + r_n)\right]^{1/n} - 1.$$

This measures the actual rate of return over the n years, accounting for compounding. This value will generally be somewhat lower than the average rate of return.

Step 2. Next we obtain data on both the market portfolio and the risk-free rate of return over the 10-year period. We use the *Standard & Poor's 500* stock average and the 1-year Treasury bill rate, respectively. These are shown in Table 7.3. We calculate average rates of return and standard deviations of these by the same method as for ABC. We also calculate an estimate of the covariance of the ABC fund with the S&P 500 by using the estimate

$$\text{cov}(r, r_M) = \frac{1}{n-1} \sum_{i=1}^{n} (r_i - \hat{\bar{r}})(r_{Mi} - \hat{\bar{r}}_M).$$

We then calculate beta from the standard formula,

$$\beta = \frac{\text{cov}(r, r_M)}{\text{var}(r_M)}.$$

This gives us enough information to carry out an interesting analysis.

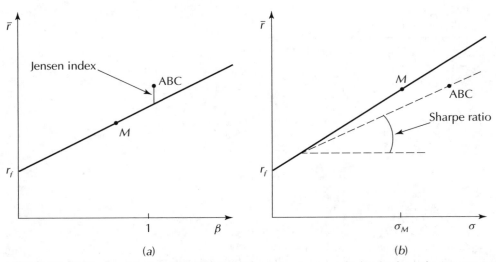

(a)   (b)

FIGURE 7.5   Performance indices for ABC. The Jensen index measures the height above the security market line; the Sharpe ratio measures the angle in the $\bar{r}$–σ plane.

Step 3. (The Jensen index)   We write the formula

$$\hat{\bar{r}} - r_f = J + \beta(\hat{\bar{r}}_M - r_f).$$

This looks like the CAPM pricing formula (7.2), except that we have replaced expected rates of return by measured average returns (for that is the best that can be done in this situation), and we have added an error term J. The J here stands for **Jensen's index.**

According to the CAPM, the value of J should be zero when true expected returns are used. Hence J measures, approximately, how much the performance of ABC has deviated from the theoretical value of zero. A positive value of J presumably implies that the fund did better than the CAPM prediction (but of course we recognize that approximations are introduced by the use of a finite amount of data to estimate the important quantities).

The Jensen index can be indicated on the security market line, as shown in Figure 7.5(a). For ABC, we find that indeed $J > 0$, and hence we might conclude that ABC is an excellent fund. But is this really a correct inference?

Aside from the difficulties inherent in using short histories of data this way, the inference that ABC is a good mutual fund is not entirely warranted. It is *not* clear that it can serve as the one fund of risky assets in an efficient portfolio. The fact that $J > 0$ is nice, and may tell us that ABC is a good *asset,* but it does not say that the ABC fund is, by itself, efficient.[3]

---

[3] It can be argued that the Jensen index tells us nothing about the fund, but instead is a measure of the validity of the CAPM. If the CAPM is valid, then every security (or fund) must satisfy the CAPM formula exactly, since the formula is an identity if the market portfolio is efficient. If we find a security with a nonzero Jensen index, then that is a sign that the market is not efficient. The CAPM formula is often applied to (new) financial instruments or projects that are not traded and hence not part of the market portfolio. In this case, the Jensen index can be a useful measure.

Step 4. (The Sharpe index)   In order to measure the efficiency of ABC we must see where it falls relative to the capital market line. Only portfolios on that line are efficient. We do this by writing the formula

$$\hat{r} - r_f = S\sigma.$$

The value of S is the slope of the line drawn between the risk-free point and the ABC point on the $\bar{r}$–σ diagram. The S stands for **Sharpe index.** For ABC we find $S = .43577$. This must be compared with the corresponding value for the market—represented by the S&P 500. We find the value for the S&P 500 is $S = .46669$. The situation is shown in Figure 7.5(*b*). Clearly ABC is not efficient, at least as revealed by the available data.

We conclude that ABC may be worth holding in a portfolio. By itself it is not quite efficient, so it would be necessary to supplement this fund with other assets or funds to achieve efficiency. Or, to attain efficiency, an investor could simply invest in a broad-based fund instead of the ABC fund.

7.7 CAPM AS A PRICING FORMULA

The CAPM is a **pricing model.** However, the standard CAPM formula does not contain prices explicitly—only expected rates of return. To see why the CAPM is called a pricing model we must go back to the definition of return.

Suppose that an asset is purchased at price P and later sold at price Q. The rate of return is then $r = (Q - P)/P$. Here P is known and Q is random. Putting this in the CAPM formula, we have

$$\frac{\overline{Q} - P}{P} = r_f + \beta(\bar{r}_M - r_f).$$

Solving for P we obtain

$$P = \frac{\overline{Q}}{1 + r_f + \beta(\bar{r}_M - r_f)}.$$

This gives the price of the asset according to the CAPM. We highlight this important result:

Pricing form of the CAPM   *The price P of an asset with payoff Q is*

$$P = \frac{\overline{Q}}{1 + r_f + \beta(\bar{r}_M - r_f)} \tag{7.6}$$

where β is the beta of the asset.

This pricing formula has a form that very nicely generalizes the familiar discounting formula for deterministic situations. In the deterministic case, it is appropriate to discount the future payment at the interest rate r_f, using a factor of $1/(1 + r_f)$. In the random case the appropriate interest rate is $r_f + \beta(\bar{r}_M - r_f)$, which can be regarded as a risk-adjusted interest rate.

Example 7.5 (The price is right)   Gavin Jones is good at math, but his friends tell him that he doesn't always see the *big picture*. Right now, Gavin is thinking about investing in a mutual fund. This fund invests 10% of its funds at the risk-free rate of 7% and the remaining 90% in a widely diversified portfolio that closely approximates the market portfolio, which has an expected rate of return equal to 15%. One share of the mutual fund represents $100 of assets in the fund. Having just studied the CAPM, Gavin wants to know how much such a share should cost.

Gavin figures out that the beta of the fund must be .90. The value of a share after 1 year is expected to be $10 \times 1.07 + 90 \times 1.15 = 114.20$. Hence, according to (7.6),

$$P = \frac{114.20}{1.07 + .90 \times .08} = \$100.$$

Yes, the price of a share will be equal to the value of the funds it represents. Gavin is reassured (but suspects he could have figured that out more simply).

Example 7.6 (The oil venture)   Consider again, as in Example 7.2, the possibility of investing in a share of a certain oil well that will produce a payoff that is random because of the uncertainty associated with whether or not there is oil at that site and because of the uncertainty in future oil prices. The expected payoff is $1,000 and the standard deviation of return is a relatively high 40%. The beta of the asset is $\beta = .6$, which is relatively low because, although the uncertainty in return due to oil prices is correlated with the market portfolio, the uncertainty associated with exploration is not. The risk-free rate is $r_f = 10\%$, and the expected return on the market portfolio is .17. What is the value of this share of the oil venture, based on CAPM? (Recall that earlier it was stated that the offered price was $875.) We have immediately

$$P = \frac{\$1,000}{1.10 + .6(.17 - .10)} = \$876$$

and σ does not enter the calculation.

The venture may be quite risky in the traditional sense of having a high standard deviation associated with its return. But, nevertheless, it is fairly priced because of the relatively low beta.

Linearity of Pricing and the Certainty Equivalent Form

We now discuss a very important property of the pricing formula—namely, that it is **linear.** This means that the price of the sum of two assets is the sum of their prices, and the price of a multiple of an asset is the same multiple of the price. This is really quite startling because the formula does not *look* linear at all (at least for sums). For example, if

$$P_1 = \frac{\overline{Q}_1}{1 + r_f + \beta_1(\overline{r}_M - r_f)}, \qquad P_2 = \frac{\overline{Q}_2}{1 + r_f + \beta_2(\overline{r}_M - r_f)}$$

it does not seem obvious that

$$P_1 + P_2 = \frac{\overline{Q}_1 + \overline{Q}_2}{1 + r_f + \beta_{1+2}(\overline{r}_M - r_f)}$$

where β_{1+2} is the beta of a new asset, which is the sum of assets 1 and 2. Furthermore, based on our recognition that the covariance between assets is important in assessing how to use them in a portfolio, it may seem *unreasonable* that the pricing formula should be linear. We can easily take care of the first doubt by converting the formula into another form, which appears linear; then we will discuss the intuition behind the result.

The form of the CAPM pricing formula that clearly displays linearity is called the **certainty equivalent form.** Suppose that we have an asset with price P and final value Q. Here again P is known and Q is uncertain. Using the fact that $r = Q/P - 1$, the value of beta is

$$\beta = \frac{\text{cov}[(Q/P - 1), r_M]}{\sigma_M^2}.$$

This becomes

$$\beta = \frac{\text{cov}(Q, r_M)}{P\sigma_M^2}.$$

Substituting this into the pricing formula (7.6) and dividing by P yields

$$1 = \frac{\overline{Q}}{P(1 + r_f) + \text{cov}(Q, r_M)(\overline{r}_M - r_f)/\sigma_M^2}.$$

Finally, solving for P we obtain the following formula:

Certainty equivalent pricing formula   *The price P of an asset with payoff Q is*

$$P = \frac{1}{1 + r_f}\left[\overline{Q} - \frac{\text{cov}(Q, r_M)(\overline{r}_M - r_f)}{\sigma_M^2}\right]. \tag{7.7}$$

The term in brackets is called the **certainty equivalent** of Q. This value is treated as a certain amount, and then the normal discount factor $1/(1 + r_f)$ is applied to obtain P. The certainty equivalent form shows clearly that the pricing formula is linear because both terms in the brackets depend linearly on Q.

The reason for linearity can be traced back to the principle of no arbitrage: if the price of the sum of two assets were not equal to the sum of the individual prices, it would be possible to make arbitrage profits. For example, if the combination asset were priced lower than the sum of the individual prices, we could buy the combination (at the low price) and sell the individual pieces (at the higher price), thereby making a profit. By doing this in large quantities, we could make arbitrarily large profits. If the reverse situation held—if the combination asset were priced higher than the sum of the two assets—we would buy the assets individually and sell the combination, again making arbitrage profits. Such arbitrage opportunities are ruled out if and only if the pricing of assets is linear. This linearity of pricing is therefore a fundamental tenet of financial theory (in the context of perfect markets), and we shall return to it frequently throughout the text.

Example 7.7 (Gavin tries again)   Gavin Jones decides to use the certainty equivalent form of the pricing equation to calculate the share price of the mutual fund considered in Example 7.5. In this case he notes that $\text{cov}(Q, r_M) = 90\sigma_M^2$, where Q is the value of the fund after 1 year. Hence,

$$P = \frac{114.20 - 90 \times .08}{1.07} = \$100.$$

All is well again, according to his math.

7.8 PROJECT CHOICE*

A firm can use the CAPM as a basis for deciding which projects it should carry out. Suppose, for example, that a potential project requires an initial outlay of P and will generate a net amount Q after 1 year. As usual, P is known and Q is random, with expected value $\overline{Q}$. It is natural to define the net present value (NPV) of this project by the formula

$$\text{NPV} = -P + \frac{1}{1 + r_f}\left[\overline{Q} - \frac{\text{cov}(Q, r_M)(\overline{r}_M - r_f)}{\sigma_M^2}\right]. \tag{7.8}$$

This formula is based on the certainty equivalent form of the CAPM: the first (negative) term is the initial outlay and the second term is the certainty equivalent of the final payoff.

The firm may have many different projects from which it will select a few. What criterion should the firm employ in making its selection? Extending our knowledge of the deterministic case, it seems appropriate for the firm to select the group of projects that maximize NPV. Indeed this is the advice that is normally given to firms.

How would potential investors view the situation? For them a particular firm is only one of a whole group of firms in which they may choose to invest. Investors are concerned with the overall performance of their portfolios, and only incidentally with the internal decisions of a particular firm. If investors base their investment decisions on a mean–variance criterion, they want an individual firm to operate so as to push the efficient frontier, of the entire universe of assets, as far upward and leftward as possible. This would improve the efficient frontier and hence the performance of a mean–variance efficient portfolio. Therefore potential investors will urge the management teams of firms to select projects that will shift the efficient frontier outward as far as possible, then they will invest in the efficient portfolio. For firms to do this, they must account for the selections made by all other firms, for it is the combined effect, accounting for interactions, that determines the efficient frontier.

The two criteria—net present value and maximum expansion of the efficient frontier—may, it seems, be in conflict. The NPV criterion focuses on the firm itself; the efficient frontier criterion focuses on the joint effect of all firms. But really, there is no conflict. The two criteria are essentially equivalent, as stated by the following version of the harmony theorem:

Harmony theorem *If a firm does not maximize* NPV, *then the efficient frontier can be expanded.*

Proof: Suppose firm i is planning to operate in a manner that leads to a net present value of Δ which does not maximize the net present value available. The initial cost of the project is P_i^0. Investors pay $P_i = P_i^0 + \Delta$ and plan to receive the reward Q_i, obtaining a rate of return $r_i = (Q_i - P_i)/P_i$. We assume that firm i has a very small weight in the market portfolio of risky assets and that projects have positive initial cost.

The current rate of return r_i satisfies the CAPM relation

$$\overline{r}_i - r_f = \beta_i(\overline{r}_M - r_f)$$

which as shown earlier is equivalent to

$$0 = -P_i + \frac{\overline{Q} - \mathrm{cov}(Q, r_M)(\overline{r}_M - r_f)/\sigma_M^2}{1 + r_f}.$$

Hence from the viewpoint of investors, the current net present value is zero.

Suppose now that the firm could operate to increase the present value by using a project with cost $P_i^{0'}$ and reward Q_i'. Investors pay Δ to buy the company and pay the operating cost $P_i^{0'}$. The total $P_i' = P_i^{0'} + \Delta$ satisfies

$$-P_i' + \frac{\overline{Q}_i' - \mathrm{cov}(Q_i', r_M)(\overline{r}_M - r_f)/\sigma_M^2}{1 + r_f} > 0$$

which, since $P_i' > 0$, implies that

$$r_i' - r_f - \mathrm{cov}(r_i', r_M)(\overline{r}_M - r_f)/\sigma_M^2 > 0.$$

Now consider the portfolio with return $r_\alpha = r_M + \alpha r_i' - \alpha r_i$ where α is the original weight of the firm i in the market portfolio. This portfolio corresponds to dropping the old firm project and replacing it by the same weight of the new.

We want to show that this portfolio lies above the old efficient frontier. To show this we evaluate

$$\tan \theta_\alpha = \frac{\overline{r}_\alpha - r_f}{\sigma_\alpha}$$

for small $\alpha > 0$. Differentiation gives

$$\frac{d \tan \theta_\alpha}{d\alpha} = \frac{1}{\sigma_\alpha}\frac{d\overline{r}_\alpha}{d\alpha} - \frac{\overline{r}_\alpha - r_f}{\sigma_\alpha^2}\frac{d\sigma_\alpha}{d\alpha}.$$

Using

$$\left.\frac{d\bar{r}_\alpha}{d\alpha}\right|_{\alpha=0} = \bar{r}_i' - \bar{r}_i$$

$$\left.\frac{d\sigma_\alpha}{d\alpha}\right|_{\alpha=0} = \frac{\sigma_{Mi'} - \sigma_{Mi}}{\sigma_M}$$

we find

$$\left.\frac{d\tan\theta_\alpha}{d\alpha}\right|_{\alpha=0} = \frac{\bar{r}_i' - \bar{r}_i}{\sigma_M} - \frac{\bar{r}_M - r_f}{\sigma_M^2}\frac{\sigma_{Mi'} - \sigma_{Mi}}{\sigma_M}$$

$$= \frac{1}{\sigma_M}[\bar{r}_i' - \beta_i'(\bar{r}_M - r_f)] - \frac{1}{\sigma_M}[\bar{r}_i - \beta_i(\bar{r}_M - r_f)] > 0.$$

The final inequality follows because the first bracketed term is positive and the second is zero. Since α is small this means that $\tan\theta_\alpha > \tan\theta_0$. Hence the efficient frontier is larger than it was originally. ∎

7.9 SUMMARY

If everybody uses the mean–variance approach to investing, and if everybody has the same estimates of the asset's expected returns, variances, and covariances, then everybody must invest in the same fund F of risky assets and in the risk-free asset. Because F is the same for everybody, it follows that, in equilibrium, F must correspond to the market portfolio M—the portfolio in which each asset is weighted by its proportion of total market capitalization. This observation is the basis for the capital asset pricing model (CAPM).

If the market portfolio M is the efficient portfolio of risky assets, it follows that the efficient frontier in the $\bar{r}$–σ diagram is a straight line that emanates from the risk-free point and passes through the point representing M. This line is the capital market line. Its slope is called the market price of risk. Any efficient portfolio must lie on this line.

The CAPM is derived directly from the condition that the market portfolio is a point on the edge of the feasible region that is tangent to the capital market line; in other words, the CAPM expresses the tangency conditions in mathematical form. The CAPM result states that the expected rate of return of any asset i satisfies

$$\bar{r}_i - r_f = \beta_i(\bar{r}_M - r_f)$$

where $\beta_i = \text{cov}(r_i, r_M)/\sigma_M^2$ is the beta of the asset.

The CAPM can be represented graphically as a security market line: the expected rate of return of an asset is a straight-line function of its beta (or, alternatively, of its covariance with the market); greater beta implies greater expected return. Indeed, from the CAPM view it follows that the risk of an asset is fully characterized by its beta. It follows, for example, that an asset that is uncorrelated with the market ($\beta = 0$) will have an expected rate of return equal to the risk-free rate.

The beta of the market portfolio is by definition equal to 1. The betas of other stocks take other values, but the betas of most U.S. stocks range between .5 and 2.5.

The beta of a portfolio of stocks is equal to the weighted average of the betas of the individual assets that make up the portfolio.

One application of CAPM is to the evaluation of mutual fund performance. The Jensen index measures the historical deviation of a fund from the security market line. (This measure has dubious value for funds of publicly traded stocks, however.) The Sharpe index measures the slope of the line joining the fund and the risk-free asset on the $\bar{r}$–σ diagram, so that this slope can be compared with the market price of risk.

The CAPM can be converted to an explicit formula for the price of an asset. In the simplest version, this formula states that price is obtained by discounting the expected payoff, but the interest rate used for discounting must be $r_f + \beta(\bar{r}_M - r_f)$, where β is the beta of the asset. An alternative form expresses the price as a discounting of the certainty equivalent of the payoff, and in this formula the discounting is based on the risk-free rate r_f.

It is important to recognize that the pricing formula of CAPM is linear, meaning that the price of a sum of assets is the sum of their prices, and the price of a multiple of an asset is that same multiple of the basic price. The certainty equivalent formulation of the CAPM clearly exhibits this linear property.

The CAPM can be used to evaluate single-period projects within firms. Managers of firms should maximize the net present value of the firm, as calculated using the pricing form of the CAPM formula. This policy will generate the greatest wealth for existing owners and provide the maximum expansion of the efficient frontier for all mean–variance investors.

EXERCISES

1. (Capital market line)   Assume that the expected rate of return on the market portfolio is 23% and the rate of return on T-bills (the risk-free rate) is 7%. The standard deviation of the market is 32%. Assume that the market portfolio is efficient.

   (a) What is the equation of the capital market line?
   (b) (i) If an expected return of 39% is desired, what is the standard deviation of this position? (ii) If you have $1,000 to invest, how should you allocate it to achieve the above position?
   (c) If you invest $300 in the risk-free asset and $700 in the market portfolio, how much money should you expect to have at the end of the year?

2. (A small world)   Consider a world in which there are only two risky assets, A and B, and a risk-free asset F. The two risky assets are in equal supply in the market; that is, $M = \frac{1}{2}(A + B)$. The following information is known: $r_F = .10$, $\sigma_A^2 = .04$, $\sigma_{AB} = .01$, $\sigma_B^2 = .02$, and $\bar{r}_M = .18$.

   (a) Find a general expression (without substituting values) for σ_M^2, β_A, and β_B.
   (b) According to the CAPM, what are the numerical values of $\bar{r}_A$ and $\bar{r}_B$?

3. (Bounds on returns)   Consider a universe of just three securities. They have expected rates of return of 10%, 20%, and 10%, respectively. Two portfolios are known to lie on

the minimum-variance set. They are defined by the portfolio weights

$$\mathbf{w} = \begin{bmatrix} .60 \\ .20 \\ .20 \end{bmatrix}, \qquad \mathbf{v} = \begin{bmatrix} .80 \\ -.20 \\ .40 \end{bmatrix}.$$

It is also known that the market portfolio is efficient.

(a) Given this information, what are the minimum and maximum possible values for the expected rate of return on the market portfolio?

(b) Now suppose you are told that $\mathbf{w}$ represents the minimum-variance portfolio. Does this change your answers to part (a)?

4. (Quick CAPM derivation)   Derive the CAPM formula for $\bar{r}_k - r_f$ by using Equation (6.9) in Chapter 6. [*Hint:* Note that

$$\sum_{i=1}^{n} \sigma_{ik} w_i = \text{cov}(r_k, r_M).$$

Apply (6.9) both to asset k and to the market itself.

5. (Uncorrelated assets)   Suppose there are n mutually uncorrelated assets. The return on asset i has variance σ_i^2. The expected rates of return are unspecified at this point. The total amount of asset i in the market is X_i. We let $T = \sum_{i=1}^{n} X_i$ and then set $x_i = X_i/T$, for $i = 1, 2, \ldots, n$. Hence the market portfolio in normalized form is $\mathbf{x} = (x_1, x_2, \ldots, x_n)$. Assume there is a risk-free asset with rate of return r_f. Find an expression for β_j in terms of the x_i's and σ_i's.

6. (Simpleland)   In Simpleland there are only two risky stocks, A and B, whose details are listed in Table 7.4.

TABLE 7.4
Details of Stocks A and B

	Number of shares outstanding	Price per share	Expected rate of return	Standard deviation of return
Stock A	100	$1.50	15%	15%
Stock B	150	$2.00	12%	9%

Furthermore, the correlation coefficient between the returns of stocks A and B is $\rho_{AB} = \frac{1}{3}$. There is also a risk-free asset, and Simpleland satisfies the CAPM exactly.

(a) What is the expected rate of return of the market portfolio?

(b) What is the standard deviation of the market portfolio?

(c) What is the beta of stock A?

(d) What is the risk-free rate in Simpleland?

7. (Zero-beta assets)   Let $\mathbf{w}_0$ be the portfolio (weights) of risky assets corresponding the minimum-variance point in the feasible region. Let $\mathbf{w}_1$ be any other portfolio on the efficient frontier. Define r_0 and r_1 to be the corresponding returns.

(a) There is a formula of the form $\sigma_{01} = A\sigma_0^2$. Find A. [*Hint:* Consider the portfolios $(1 - \alpha)\mathbf{w}_0 + \alpha\mathbf{w}_1$, and consider small variations of the variance of such portfolios near $\alpha = 0$.]

(b) Corresponding to the portfolio $\mathbf{w}_1$ there is a portfolio $\mathbf{w}_z$ on the minimum-variance set that has zero beta with respect to $\mathbf{w}_1$; that is, $\sigma_{1,z} = 0$. This portfolio can be expressed as $\mathbf{w}_z = (1 - \alpha)\mathbf{w}_0 + \alpha\mathbf{w}_1$. Find the proper value of α.

(c) Show the relation of the three portfolios on a diagram that includes the feasible region.

(d) If there is no risk-free asset, it can be shown that other assets can be priced according to the formula

$$\bar{r}_i - \bar{r}_z = \beta_{iM}\left(\bar{r}_M - \bar{r}_z\right)$$

where the subscript M denotes the market portfolio and $\bar{r}_z$ is the expected rate of return on the portfolio that has zero beta with the market portfolio. Suppose that the expected returns on the market and the zero-beta portfolio are 15% and 9%, respectively. Suppose that a stock i has a correlation coefficient with the market of .5. Assume also that the standard deviation of the returns of the market and stock i are 15% and 5%, respectively. Find the expected return of stock i.

8. (Wizards ◇) Electron Wizards, Inc. (EWI) has a new idea for producing TV sets, and it is planning to enter the development stage. Once the product is developed (which will be at the end of 1 year), the company expects to sell its new process for a price p, with expected value $\bar{p} = \$24M$. However, this sale price will depend on the market for TV sets at the time. By examining the stock histories of various TV companies, it is determined that the final sales price p is correlated with the market return as $E[(p - \bar{p})(r_M - \bar{r}_M)] = \$20M\sigma_M^2$.

To develop the process, EWI must invest in a research and development project. The cost c of this project will be known shortly after the project is begun (when a technical uncertainty will be resolved). The current estimate is that the cost will be either $c = \$20M$ or $c = \$16M$, and each of these is equally likely. (This uncertainty is uncorrelated with the final price and is also uncorrelated with the market.) Assume that the risk-free rate is $r_f = 9\%$ and the expected return on the market is $\bar{r}_M = 33\%$.

(a) What is the expected rate of return of this project?

(b) What is the beta of this project? [*Hint:* In this case, note that

$$E\left[\left(\frac{p - \bar{p}}{c}\right)(r_M - \bar{r}_M)\right] = E\left(\frac{1}{c}\right)E[(p - \bar{p})(r_M - \bar{r}_M)].\right]$$

(c) Is this an acceptable project based on a CAPM criterion? In particular, what is the excess rate of return (+ or −) above the return predicted by the CAPM?

9. (Gavin's problem)   Prove to Gavin Jones that the results he obtained in Examples 7.5 and 7.7 were not accidents. Specifically, for a fund with return $\alpha r_f + (1 - \alpha)r_M$, show that both CAPM pricing formulas give the price of $100 worth of fund assets as $100.

REFERENCES

The CAPM theory was developed independently in references [1–4]. There are now numerous extensions and textbook accounts of that theory. Consult any of the basic finance textbooks listed as references for Chapter 2. The application of this theory to mutual fund performance evaluation was presented in [5, 6]. An alternative measure, not discussed in this chapter, is due to Treynor [7]. For summaries of the application of CAPM to corporate analysis, see [8, 9]. The idea of using a zero-beta asset, as in Exercise 7, is due to Black [10].

1. Sharpe, W. F. (1964), "Capital Asset Prices: A Theory of Market Equilibrium under Conditions of Risk," *Journal of Finance*, **19,** 425–442.
2. Lintner, J. (1965), "The Valuation of Risk Assets and the Selection of Risky Investment in Stock Portfolios and Capital Budgets," *Review of Economics and Statistics*, **47,** 13–37.
3. Mossin, J. (1966), "Equilibrium in a Capital Asset Market," *Econometrica*, **34,** no. 4, 768–783.
4. Treynor, J. L. (1961), "Towards a Theory of Market Value of Risky Assets," unpublished manuscript.
5. Sharpe, W. F. (1966), "Mutual Fund Performance." *Journal of Business*, **39,** January, 119–138.
6. Jensen, M. C. (1969), "Risk, the Pricing of Capital Assets, and the Evaluation of Investment Portfolios," *Journal of Business*, **42,** April, 167–247.
7. Treynor, J. L. (1965), "How to Rate Management Investment Funds," *Harvard Business Review*, **43,** January–February, 63–75.
8. Rubinstein, M. E. (1973), "A Mean–Variance Synthesis of Corporate Financial Theory," *Journal of Finance*, **28,** 167–182.
9. Fama, E. F. (1977), "Risk-Adjusted Discount Rates and Capital Budgeting under Uncertainty," *Journal of Financial Economics*, **5,** 3–24.
10. Black, F. (1972), "Capital Market Equilibrium with Restricted Borrowing," *Journal of Business,* **45,** 445–454.

11 MODELS OF ASSET DYNAMICS

True multiperiod investments fluctuate in value, distribute random dividends, exist in an environment of variable interest rates, and are subject to a continuing variety of other uncertainties. This chapter initiates the study of such investments by showing how to model asset price fluctuations conveniently and realistically. This chapter therefore contains no investment principles as such. Rather it introduces the mathematical models that form the foundation for the analyses developed in later chapters.

Two primary model types are used to represent asset dynamics: binomial lattices and Ito processes. Binomial lattices are analytically simpler than Ito processes, and they provide an excellent basis for computational work associated with investment problems. For these reasons it is best to study binomial lattice models first. The important investment concepts can all be expressed in terms of these models, and many real investment problems can be formulated and solved using the binomial lattice framework. Indeed, roughly 80% of the material in later chapters is presented in terms of binomial lattice models.

Ito processes are more realistic than binomial lattice models in the sense that they have a continuum of possible stock prices at each period, not just two. Ito process models also allow some problems to be solved analytically, as well as computationally. They also provide the foundation for constructing binomial lattice models in a clear and consistent manner. For these reasons Ito process models are fundamental to dynamic problems. For a complete understanding of investment principles, it is important to understand these models.

The organization of this chapter is based on the preceding viewpoint concerning the roles of different models. The first section presents the binomial lattice model directly. With this background most of the material in later chapters can be studied. Therefore you may wish to read only this first section and then skip to the next chapter.

The remaining sections consider models that have a continuum of price values. These models are developed progressively from discrete-time models to continuous-time models based on Ito processes.

11.1 BINOMIAL LATTICE MODEL

To define a binomial lattice model, a basic period length is established (such as 1 week). According to the model, if the price is known at the beginning of a period, the price at the beginning of the next period is one of only two possible values. Usually these two possibilities are defined to be multiples of the price at the previous period—a multiple u (for up) and a multiple d (for down). Both u and d are positive, with $u > 1$ and (usually) $d < 1$. Hence if the price at the beginning of a period is S, it will be either uS or dS at the next period. The probabilities of these possibilities are p and $1 - p$, respectively, for some given probability p, $0 < p < 1$. That is, if the current price is S, there is a probability p that the new price will be uS and a probability $1 - p$ that it will be dS. This model continues on for several periods.

The general form of such a lattice is shown in Figure 11.1. The stock price can be visualized as moving from node to node in a rightward direction. The probability of an upward movement from any node is p and the probability of a downward movement is $1 - p$. A lattice is the appropriate structure in this case, rather than a tree, because an up movement followed by a down is identical to a down followed by an up. Both produce ud times the price.

The model may at first seem too simple because it permits only two possible values at the next period. But if the period length is small, many values are possible after several short steps.

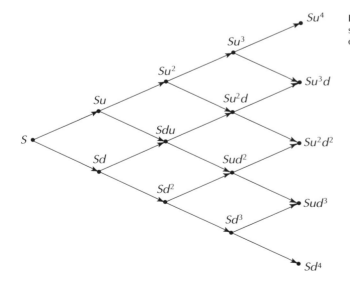

FIGURE 11.1 Binomial lattice stock model. At each step the stock price S either increases to uS or decreases to dS.

To specify the model completely, we must select values for u and d and the probability p. These should be chosen in such a way that the true stochastic nature of the stock is captured as faithfully as possible, as will be discussed.

Because the model is multiplicative in nature (the new value being uS or dS, with $u > 0$, $d > 0$), the price will never become negative. It is therefore possible to consider the logarithm of price as a fundamental variable. For reasons discussed in later sections, use of the logarithm is in fact very helpful and leads to simple formulas for selecting the parameters.

Accordingly, we define ν as the expected yearly growth rate.[1] Specifically,

$$\nu = E\big[\ln(S_T/S_0)\big]$$

where S_0 is the initial stock price and S_T is the price at the end of 1 year.

Likewise, we define σ as the yearly standard deviation. Specifically,

$$\sigma^2 = \text{var}\big[\ln(S_T/S_0)\big].$$

If a period length of Δt is chosen, which is small compared to 1, the parameters of the binomial lattice can be selected as

$$p = \frac{1}{2} + \frac{1}{2}\left(\frac{\nu}{\sigma}\right)\sqrt{\Delta t}$$

$$u = e^{\sigma\sqrt{\Delta t}} \tag{11.1}$$

$$d = e^{-\sigma\sqrt{\Delta t}}.$$

With this choice, the binomial model will closely match the values of ν and σ (as shown later); that is, the expected growth rate of $\ln S$ in the binomial model will be nearly ν, and the variance of that rate will be nearly σ^2. The closeness of the match improves if Δt is made smaller, becoming exact as Δt goes to zero.

Example 11.1 (A volatile stock)   Consider a stock with the parameters $\nu = 15\%$ and $\sigma = 30\%$. We wish to make a binomial model based on weekly periods. According to (11.1), we set

$$u = e^{.30/\sqrt{52}} = 1.04248, \qquad d = 1/u = .95925$$

and

$$p = \frac{1}{2}\left(1 + \frac{.15}{.30}\sqrt{\frac{1}{52}}\right) = .534669.$$

The lattice for this example is shown in Figure 11.2, assuming $S(0) = 100$.

We shall return to the binomial lattice later in this chapter after studying models that allow a continuum of prices. The binomial model will be found to be a natural approximation to these models.

---

[1] If the process were deterministic, then $\nu = \ln(S_T/S_0)$ implies $S_T = S_0 e^{\nu T}$, which shows that ν is the exponential growth rate.

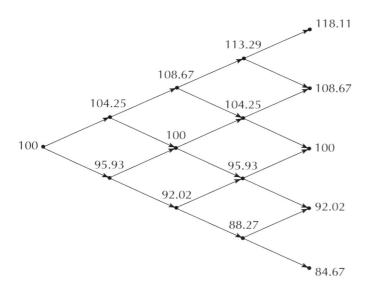

FIGURE 11.2 Lattice for Example 11.1. The parameters are chosen so that the expected growth rate of the logarithm of price and the variance of that growth rate match the known corresponding values for the asset.

11.2 THE ADDITIVE MODEL

We now study models with the property that price can range over a continuum. First we shall consider discrete-time models, beginning with the additive model of this section, and then later we shall consider continuous-time models defined by Ito processes.

Let us focus on $N + 1$ time points, indexed by k, $k = 0, 1, 2, \ldots, N$. We also focus on a particular asset that is characterized by a price at each time. The price at time k is denoted by $S(k)$. Our model will recognize that the price in any one time is dependent to some extent on previous prices.

The simplest model is the **additive model,**

$$S(k + 1) = aS(k) + u(k) \tag{11.2}$$

for $k = 0, 1, 2, \ldots, N$. In this equation a is a constant (usually $a > 1$) and the quantities $u(k)$, $k = 0, 1, \ldots, N - 1$, are random variables. The $u(k)$'s can be thought of as "shocks" or "disturbances" that cause the price to fluctuate. To operate or run this model, an initial price $S(0)$ is specified; then once the random variable $u(0)$ is given, $S(1)$ can be determined. The process then repeats progressively in a stepwise fashion, determining $S(2), S(3), \ldots, S(N)$.

The key ingredient of this model is the sequence of random variables $u(k)$, $k = 1, 2, \ldots, N$. We assume that these are mutually statistically independent.

Note that the price at any time depends only on the price at the most recent previous time and the random disturbance. It does not explicitly depend on other previous prices.

Normal Price Distribution

It is instructive to solve explicitly for a few of the prices from (11.2). By direct substitution we have

$$S(1) = aS(0) + u(0)$$

$$S(2) = aS(1) + u(1)$$

$$= a^2 S(0) + au(0) + u(1).$$

By simple induction it can be seen that for general k,

$$S(k) = a^k S(0) + a^{k-1}u(0) + a^{k-2}u(1) + \cdots + u(k-1). \tag{11.3}$$

Hence $S(k)$ is $a^k S(0)$ plus the sum of k random variables.

Frequently we assume that the random variables $u(k)$, $k = 0, 1, 2, \ldots, N - 1$, are independent normal random variables with a common variance σ^2. Then, since a linear combination of normal random variables is also normal (see Appendix A), it follows from (11.3) that $S(k)$ is itself a normal random variable.

If the expected values of all the $u(k)$'s are zero, then the expected value of $S(k)$ is

$$E[S(k)] = a^k S(0).$$

When $a > 1$, this model has the property that the expected value of the price increases geometrically (that is, according to a^k). Indeed, the constant a is the growth rate factor of the model.

The additive model is structurally simple and easy to work with. The expected value of price grows geometrically, and all prices are normal random variables. However, the model is seriously flawed because it lacks realism. Normal random variables can take on negative values, which means that the prices in this model might be negative as well; but real stock prices are never negative. Furthermore, if a stock were to begin at a price of, say, $1 with a σ of, say, $.50 and then drift upward to a price of $100, it seems very unlikely that the σ would remain at $.50. It is more likely that the standard deviation would be proportional to the price. For these reasons the additive model is not a good general model of asset dynamics. The model is useful for localized analyses, over short periods of time (perhaps up to a few months for common stocks), and it is a useful building block for other models, but it cannot be used alone as an ongoing model representing long- or intermediate-term fluctuations. For this reason we must consider a better alternative, which is the multiplicative model. (However, our understanding of the additive model will be important for that more advanced model.)

11.3 THE MULTIPLICATIVE MODEL

The **multiplicative model** has the form

$$S(k + 1) = u(k)S(k) \tag{11.4}$$

for $k = 0, 1, \ldots, N - 1$. Here again the quantities $u(k)$, $k = 0, 1, 2, \ldots, N - 1$, are mutually independent random variables. The variable $u(k)$ defines the *relative* change in price between times k and $k + 1$. This relative change is $S(k + 1)/S(k)$, which is independent of the overall magnitude of $S(k)$. It is also independent of the units of price. For example, if we change units from U.S. dollars to German marks, the relative price change is still $u(k)$.

The multiplicative model takes a familiar form if we take the natural logarithm of both sides of the equation. This yields

$$\ln S(k + 1) = \ln S(k) + \ln u(k) \tag{11.5}$$

for $k = 0, 1, 2, \ldots, N - 1$. Hence in this form the model is of the additive type with respect to the logarithm of the price, rather than the price itself. Therefore we can use our knowledge of the additive model to analyze the multiplicative model.

It is now natural to specify the random disturbances directly in terms of the $\ln u(k)$'s. In particular we let

$$w(k) = \ln u(k)$$

for $k = 0, 1, 2, \ldots, N - 1$, and we specify that these $w(k)$'s be normal random variables. We assume that they are mutually independent and that each has expected value $\overline{w}(k) = v$ and variance σ^2.

We can express the original multiplicative disturbances as

$$u(k) = e^{w(k)} \tag{11.6}$$

for $k = 0, 1, 2, \ldots, N - 1$. Each of the variables $u(k)$ is said to be a **lognormal** random variable since its logarithm is in fact a normal random variable.

Notice that now there is no problem with negative values. Although the normal variable $w(k)$ may be negative, the corresponding $u(k)$ given by (11.6) is always positive. Since the random factor by which a price is multiplied is $u(k)$, it follows that prices remain positive in this model.

Lognormal Prices

The successive prices of the multiplicative model can be easily found to be

$$S(k) = u(k - 1)u(k - 2) \cdots u(0)S(0).$$

Taking the natural logarithm of this equation we find

$$\ln S(k) = \ln S(0) + \sum_{i=0}^{k-1} \ln u(i) = \ln S(0) + \sum_{i=0}^{k-1} w(i).$$

The term $\ln S(0)$ is a constant, and the $w(i)$'s are each normal random variables. Since the sum of normal random variables is itself a normal random variable (see Appendix A), it follows that $\ln S(k)$ is normal. In other words, all prices are lognormal under the multiplicative model.

If each $w(i)$ has expected value $\overline{w}(i) = \nu$ and variance σ^2, and all are mutually independent, then we find

$$E[\ln S(k)] = \ln S(0) + \nu k \qquad (11.7a)$$

$$\mathrm{var}[\ln S(k)] = k\sigma^2. \qquad (11.7b)$$

Hence both the expected value and the variance increase linearly with k.

Real Stock Distributions

At this point it is natural to ask how well this theoretical model fits actual stock price behavior. Are real stock prices lognormal?

The answer is that, based on an analysis of past stock price records, the price distributions of most stocks are actually quite close to lognormal. To verify this, we select a nominal period length of, say, 1 week and record the differences $\ln S(k+1) - \ln S(k)$ for many values of k; that is, we record the weekly changes in the logarithm of the prices for many weeks. We then construct a histogram of these values and compare it with that of a normal distribution of the same variance. Typically, the measured distribution is quite close to being normal, except that the observed distribution often is slightly smaller near the mean and larger at extremely large values (either positive or negative large values). This slight change in shape is picturesquely termed **fat tails**. (See Figure 11.3.[2]) The observed distribution is larger in the tails than a normal

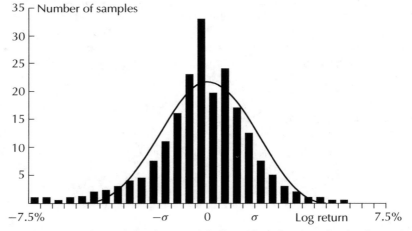

FIGURE 11.3 **Observed distribution of the logarithm of return.** The distribution has "fatter tails" than a normal distribution of the same variance.

---

[2]The figure shows a histogram of American Airlines weekly log stock returns for the 10-year period of 1982–1992. Shown superimposed is the normal distribution with the same (sample) mean and standard deviation. Along with fat tails there is invariably a "skinny middle."

distribution. This implies that large price changes tend to occur somewhat more frequently than would be predicted by a normal distribution of the same variance. For most applications (but not all) this slight discrepancy is not important.

11.4 TYPICAL PARAMETER VALUES*

The return of a stock over the period between k and $k+1$ is $S(k+1)/S(k)$, which under the multiplicative model is equal to $u(k)$. The value of $w(k) = \ln u(k)$ is therefore the logarithm of the return. The mean value of $w(k)$ is denoted by ν and the variance of $w(k)$ by σ^2. Typical values of these parameters for assets such as common stocks can be inferred from our knowledge of corresponding values for returns. Thus for stocks, typical values of $\nu = E[w(k)]$ and $\sigma = \text{stdev}[w(k)]$ might be

$$\nu = 12\%, \qquad \sigma = 15\%$$

when the length of a period is 1 year. If the period length is less than a year, these values scale downward;[3] that is, if the period length is p part of a year, then

$$\nu_p = p\nu, \qquad \sigma_p = \sqrt{p}\sigma.$$

The values can be estimated from historical records in the standard fashion (but with caution as to the validity of these estimates, as raised in Chapter 8). If we have $N + 1$ time points of data, spanning N periods, the estimate of the single-period ν is

$$\hat{\nu} = \frac{1}{N} \sum_{k=0}^{N-1} \ln\left[\frac{S(k+1)}{S(k)}\right] = \frac{1}{N} \sum_{k=0}^{N-1} [\ln S(k+1) - \ln S(k)]$$

$$= \frac{1}{N} \ln\left[\frac{S(N)}{S(0)}\right].$$

Hence all that matters is the ratio of the last to the first price.

The standard estimate of σ^2 is

$$\hat{\sigma}^2 = \frac{1}{N-1} \sum_{k=0}^{N-1} \left\{ \ln\left[\frac{S(k+1)}{S(k)}\right] - \hat{\nu} \right\}^2.$$

As with the estimation of return parameters, the error in these estimates can be characterized by their variances. For ν this variance is

$$\text{var}(\hat{\nu}) = \sigma^2/N$$

and for σ^2 it is [assuming $w(k)$ is normal]

$$\text{var}(\hat{\sigma}^2) = 2\sigma^4/(N-1).$$

---

[3] Using log returns, the scaling is *exactly* proportional. There is no error due to compounding as with returns (without the log). (See Exercise 2.)

Hence for the values assumed earlier, namely, $\nu = .12$ and $\sigma = .15$, we find that 10 years of data is required to reduce the standard deviation of the estimate[4] of ν to .05 (which is still a sizable fraction of the true value). On the other hand, with only 1 year of weekly data we can obtain a fairly good estimate[5] of σ^2.

11.5 LOGNORMAL RANDOM VARIABLES

If u is a lognormal random variable, then the variable $w = \ln u$ is normal. In this case we found that the prices in the multiplicative model are all lognormal random variables. It is therefore useful to study a few important properties of such random variables.

The general shape of the probability distribution of a lognormal random variable is shown in Figure 11.4. Note that the variable is always nonnegative and the distribution is somewhat skewed.

Suppose that w is normal and has expected value $\overline{w}$ and variance σ^2. What is the expected value of $u = e^w$? A quick guess might be $\overline{u} = e^{\overline{w}}$, but this is wrong. Actually $\overline{u}$ is greater than this by the factor $e^{\frac{1}{2}\sigma^2}$; that is,

$$\overline{u} = e^{\overline{w} + \frac{1}{2}\sigma^2} . \tag{11.8}$$

This result can be intuitively understood by noting that as σ is increased, the lognormal distribution will spread out. It cannot spread downward below zero, but it can spread upward unboundedly. Hence the mean value increases as σ increases.

The extra term $\frac{1}{2}\sigma^2$ is actually fairly small for low-volatility stocks. For example, consider a stock with a yearly $\overline{w} = .12$ and a yearly σ of .15. The correction term is

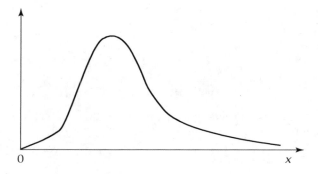

FIGURE 11.4 **Lognormal distribution.** The lognormal distribution is nonzero only for $x > 0$.

---

[4] $\sigma(\hat{\nu}) = \dfrac{\sigma}{\sqrt{N}} = \dfrac{\sigma}{\sqrt{10}} = \dfrac{.15}{3.16} = .05.$

[5] $\mathrm{var}(\hat{\sigma}^2) = (52)^2 \, \mathrm{var}(\hat{\sigma}_w^2) = \dfrac{(52)^2 \times 2\sigma_w^4}{N-1} = \dfrac{(52)^2 \times 2\sigma^4}{(52)^2 \times 51} = \dfrac{2\sigma^4}{51}.$ Hence $\sigma(\hat{\sigma}^2) = \dfrac{\sqrt{2}\sigma^2}{\sqrt{51}} \approx \dfrac{\sigma^2}{5}.$

$\frac{1}{2}\sigma^2 = .0225$, which is small compared to $\overline{w}$. For stocks with high volatility, however, the correction can be significant.

11.6 RANDOM WALKS AND WIENER PROCESSES

In Section 11.7 we will shorten the period length in a multiplicative model and take the limit as this length goes to zero. This will produce a model in continuous time. In preparation for that step, we introduce special random functions of time, called random walks and Wiener processes.

Suppose that we have N periods of length Δt. We define the additive process z by

$$z(t_{k+1}) = z(t_k) + \epsilon(t_k)\sqrt{\Delta t} \tag{11.9}$$

$$t_{k+1} = t_k + \Delta t \tag{11.10}$$

for $k = 0, 1, 2, \ldots, N$. This process is termed a **random walk.** In these equations $\epsilon(t_k)$ is a normal random variable with mean 0 and variance 1—a **standardized normal random variable.** These random variables are mutually uncorrelated; that is, $E[\epsilon(t_j)\epsilon(t_k)] = 0$ for $j \neq k$. The process is started by setting $z(t_0) = 0$. Thereafter a particular realized path wanders around according to the happenstance of the random variables $\epsilon(t_k)$. [The reason for using $\sqrt{\Delta t}$ in (11.9) will become clear shortly.] A particular path of a random walk is shown in Figure 11.5.

Of special interest are the difference random variables $z(t_k) - z(t_j)$ for $j < k$. We can write such a difference as

$$z(t_k) - z(t_j) = \sum_{i=j}^{k-1} \epsilon(t_i)\sqrt{\Delta t} \, .$$

This is a normal random variable because it is the sum of normal random variables. We find immediately that

$$E[z(t_k) - z(t_j)] = 0.$$

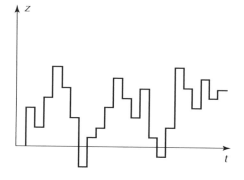

FIGURE 11.5   Possible random walk. The movements are determined by normal random variables.

Also, using the independence of the $\epsilon(t_k)$'s, we find

$$\text{var}[z(t_k) - z(t_j)] = \text{E}\left[\sum_{i=j}^{k-1} \epsilon(t_i)\sqrt{\Delta t}\right]^2$$

$$= \text{E}\left[\sum_{i=j}^{k-1} \epsilon(t_i)^2 \Delta t\right]$$

$$= (k-j)\Delta t = t_k - t_j.$$

Hence the variance of $z(t_k) - z(t_j)$ is exactly equal to the time difference $t_k - t_j$ between the points. This calculation also shows why $\sqrt{\Delta t}$ was used in the definition of the random walk so that Δt would appear in the variance.

It should be clear that the difference variables associated with two different time intervals are uncorrelated if the two intervals are nonoverlapping. That is, if $t_{k_1} < t_{k_2} \leq t_{k_3} < t_{k_4}$, then $z(t_{k_2}) - z(t_{k_1})$ is uncorrelated with $z(t_{k_4}) - z(t_{k_3})$ because each of these differences is made up of different ϵ's, which are themselves uncorrelated.

A Wiener process is obtained by taking the limit of the random walk process (11.9) as $\Delta t \to 0$. In symbolic form we write the equations governing a Wiener process as

$$\text{d}z = \epsilon(t)\sqrt{\text{d}t} \tag{11.11}$$

where each $\epsilon(t)$ is a standardized normal random variable. The random variables $\epsilon(t')$ and $\epsilon(t'')$ are uncorrelated whenever $t' \neq t''$.

This description of a Wiener process is not rigorous because we have no assurance that the limiting operations are defined; but it provides a good intuitive description. An alternative definition of a Wiener process can be made by simply listing the required properties. In this approach we say a process $z(t)$ is a **Wiener process** (or, alternatively, **Brownian motion**) if it satisfies the following:

1. For any $s < t$ the quantity $z(t) - z(s)$ is a normal random variable with mean zero and variance $t - s$.

2. For any $0 \leq t_1 < t_2 \leq t_3 < t_4$, the random variables $z(t_2) - z(t_1)$ and $z(t_4) - z(t_3)$ are uncorrelated.

3. $z(t_0) = 0$ with probability 1.

These properties parallel the properties of the random walk process given earlier.

It is fun to try to visualize the outcome of a Wiener process. A sketch of a possible path is shown in Figure 11.6. Remember that given $z(t)$ at time t, the value of $z(s)$ at time $s > t$ is, on average, the same as $z(t)$ but will vary from that according to a standard deviation equal to $\sqrt{s - t}$.

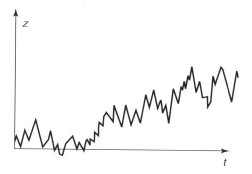

FIGURE 11.6 Path of a Wiener process. A Wiener process moves continuously but is not differentiable.

A Wiener process is not differentiable with respect to time. We can roughly verify this by noting that for $t < s$,

$$E\left[\frac{z(s) - z(t)}{s - t}\right]^2 = \frac{s - t}{(s - t)^2} = \frac{1}{s - t} \to \infty$$

as $s \to t$.

It is, however, useful to have a word for the term dz/dt since this expression appears in many stochastic equations. A common word used, arising from the systems engineering field (the field that motivated Wiener's work), is **white noise.** It is really fun to try to visualize white noise. One depiction is presented in Figure 11.7.

Generalized Wiener Processes and Ito Processes

The Wiener process (or Brownian motion) is the fundamental building block for a whole collection of more general processes. These generalizations are obtained by inserting white noise in an ordinary differential equation.

The simplest extension of this kind is the **generalized Wiener process,** which is of the form

$$dx(t) = a\, dt + b\, dz \tag{11.12}$$

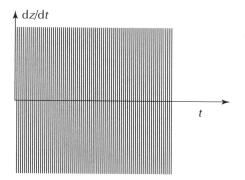

FIGURE 11.7 Fantasizing white noise. White noise is the derivative of a Wiener process, but that derivative does not exist in the normal sense.

where $x(t)$ is a random variable for each t, z is a Wiener process, and a and b are constants.

A generalized Wiener process is especially important because it has an analytic solution (which can be found by integrating both sides). Specifically,

$$x(t) = x(0) + at + bz(t). \tag{11.13}$$

An **Ito process** is somewhat more general still. Such a process is described by an equation of the form

$$dx(t) = a(x, t)\, dt + b(x, t)\, dz. \tag{11.14}$$

As before, z denotes a Wiener process. Now, however, the coefficients $a(x, t)$ and $b(x, t)$ may depend on x and t, and a general solution cannot be written in an analytic form. A special form of Ito process is used frequently to describe the behavior of financial assets, as discussed in the next section.

11.7 A STOCK PRICE PROCESS

We now have the tools necessary to extend the multiplicative model of stock prices to a continuous-time model. Recall that the multiplicative model is

$$\ln S(k + 1) - \ln S(k) = w(k)$$

where the $w(k)$'s are uncorrelated normal random variables. The continuous-time version of this equation is

$$d \ln S(t) = v\, dt + \sigma\, dz \tag{11.15}$$

where v and $\sigma \geq 0$ are constants and z is a standard Wiener process. The whole right-hand side of the equation can be regarded as playing the role of the random variable $w(k)$ in the discrete-time model. This side can be thought of as a constant plus a normal random variable with zero mean, and hence, overall it is a normal random variable. (Although all terms in the equation are differentials or multiples of differentials and thus do not themselves have magnitude in the usual sense, it is helpful to think of dt and dz as being "small" like Δt and Δz.) The term $v\, dt$ is, accordingly, the mean value of the right-hand side. This mean value is proportional to dt, consistent with the fact that in the logarithm version of the multiplicative model the mean value of the change in $\ln S$ is proportional to the length of one period. The standard deviation of the right-hand side is σ times the standard deviation of dz. Hence it is of order of magnitude $\sigma \sqrt{dt}$, which is consistent with the fact that in the logarithm version of the multiplicative model the standard deviation of the change in $\ln S$ is proportional to the square root of the length of one period, as reflected by (11.7a) and (11.7b).

Since equation (11.15) is expressed in terms of $\ln S(t)$, it is actually a generalized Wiener process. Hence we can solve it explicitly using (11.13) as

$$\ln S(t) = \ln S(0) + vt + \sigma z(t). \tag{11.16}$$

This shows that $E[\ln S(t)] = E[\ln S(0)] + vt$, and hence $E[\ln S(t)]$ grows linearly with t. Because the expected logarithm of this process increases linearly with t, just as a continuously compounded bank account, this process is termed **geometric Brownian motion.**

Lognormal Prices

Like the discrete-time multiplicative model, the geometric Brownian motion process described by (11.15) is a lognormal process. This can be seen easily from the solution (11.16). The right-hand side of that equation is a normal random variable with expected value $\ln S(0) + vt$ and standard deviation $\sigma\sqrt{t}$.

We conclude that the price $S(t)$ itself has a lognormal distribution. We can express this formally by $\ln S(t) \sim N(\ln S(0) + vt, \sigma^2 t)$, where $N(m, \sigma^2)$ denotes the normal distribution with mean m and variance σ^2.

Although we can write $S(t) = \exp[\ln S(t)] = S(0)\exp[vt + \sigma z(t)]$, it does *not* follow that the expected value of $S(t)$ is $S(0)e^{vt}$. The mean value must instead be determined by equation (11.8), the general formula that applies to lognormal variables. Hence,

$$\mathrm{E}[S(t)] = S(0)e^{(v + \frac{1}{2}\sigma^2)t}.$$

If we define $\mu = v + \frac{1}{2}\sigma^2$, we have

$$\mathrm{E}[S(t)] = S(0)e^{\mu t}.$$

The standard deviation of $S(t)$ is also given by a general relation for lognormal variables. In the case of the standard deviation, the required calculation is a bit more complex. The formula is (see Exercise 5)

$$\mathrm{stdev}[S(t)] = S(0)e^{vt + \frac{1}{2}\sigma^2 t}\left(e^{\sigma^2 t} - 1\right)^{1/2}.$$

Standard Ito Form

We have defined the random process for $S(t)$ in terms of $\ln S(t)$ rather than directly in terms of $S(t)$. The use of $\ln S(t)$ facilitated the development, and it highlights the fact that the process is a straightforward generalization of the multiplicative model that leads to lognormal distributions. It is, however, useful to express the process in terms of $S(t)$ itself.

In ordinary calculus we know that

$$d\ln[S(t)] = \frac{dS(t)}{S(t)}.$$

Hence we might be tempted to substitute $dS(t)/S(t)$ for $d\ln S(t)$ in the basic equation [Eq. (11.15)], obtaining $dS(t)/S(t) = v\,dt + \sigma\,dz$. This would be almost correct, but there is a correction term that must be applied when changing variables in Ito processes (because Wiener processes are not ordinary functions and do not follow the rules of ordinary calculus). The appropriate Ito process in terms of $S(t)$ is

$$\frac{dS(t)}{S(t)} = \left(v + \frac{1}{2}\sigma^2\right)dt + \sigma\,dz. \tag{11.17}$$

Note that the correction term $\frac{1}{2}\sigma^2$ is exactly the same as needed in the expression for the expected value of a lognormal random variable. Putting $\mu = v + \frac{1}{2}\sigma^2$, we may write the equation in the standard Ito form for price dynamics,

$$\frac{dS(t)}{S(t)} = \mu\, dt + \sigma\, dz. \tag{11.18}$$

The term $dS(t)/S(t)$ can be thought of as the differential return of the stock; hence in this form the differential return has a simple form.

The correction term required when transforming the equation from $\ln S(t)$ to $S(t)$ is a special instance of a general transformation equation defined by **Ito's lemma,** which applies to variables defined by Ito processes. Ito's lemma is discussed in the next section.

Note that if the equation in standard form is written with S in the denominator, as in (11.17), it is an equation for dS/S. This term can be interpreted as the instantaneous rate of return on the stock. Hence the standard form is often referred to as an equation for the instantaneous return.

Example 11.2 (Bond price dynamics)   Let $P(t)$ denote the price of a bond that pays $1 at time $t = T$, with no other payments. Assume that interest rates are constant at r. The price of this bond satisfies

$$\frac{dP(t)}{P(t)} = r\, dt$$

which is a deterministic Ito equation, paralleling the equation for stock prices. The solution to this equation is $P(t) = P(0)e^{rt}$. Using $P(T) = 1$, we find that $P(t) = e^{r(t-T)}$.

We now summarize the relations between $S(t)$ and $\ln S(t)$:

Relations for geometric Brownian motion   *Suppose the geometric Brownian motion process $S(t)$ is governed by*

$$dS(t) = \mu S(t)\, dt + \sigma S(t)\, dz$$

where z is a standard Wiener process. Define $v = \mu - \frac{1}{2}$

$$\bar{t}$$

$$E\{S(t)/S(0)\} = e^{\mu t}$$

$$\text{stdev}\{S(t)/S(0)\} = e^{\mu t}\left(e^{\sigma^2 t} - 1\right)^{1/2}.$$

Simulation

A continuous-time price process can be simulated by taking a series of small time periods and then stepping the process forward period by period. There are two natural ways to do this, and they are *not* exactly equivalent.

First, consider the process in standard form defined by (11.18). We take a basic period length Δt and set $S(t_0) = S_0$, a given initial price at $t = t_0$. The corresponding simulation equation is

$$S(t_{k+1}) - S(t_k) = \mu S(t_k) \Delta t + \sigma S(t_k) \epsilon(t_k) \sqrt{\Delta t}$$

where the $\epsilon(t_k)$'s are uncorrelated normal random variables of mean 0 and standard deviation 1. This leads to

$$S(t_{k+1}) = \left[1 + \mu \Delta t + \sigma \epsilon(t_k) \sqrt{\Delta t} \right] S(t_k) \tag{11.19}$$

which is a multiplicative model, but the random coefficient is normal rather than log-normal, so this simulation method does not produce the lognormal price distributions that are characteristic of the underlying Ito process (in either of its forms).

A second approach is to use the log (or multiplicative) form (11.15). In discrete form this is

$$\ln S(t_{k+1}) - \ln S(t_k) = \nu \Delta t + \sigma \epsilon(t_k) \sqrt{\Delta t}.$$

This leads to

$$S(t_{k+1}) = e^{\nu \Delta t + \sigma \epsilon(t_k) \sqrt{}}$$

$\overline{\Delta t}$ for that week. The second column lists the corresponding multiplicative factors. The value P_1 is the simulated price using the standard method as represented by (11.19). The fourth column shows the appropriate exponential factors for the second method, (11.20). The value P_2 is the simulated price using that method. Note that even at the first step the results are not identical. However, overall the results are fairly close.

TABLE 11.1
Simulation of Price Dynamics

Week	dz	$\mu + \sigma\,dz$	P_1	$\nu + \sigma\,dz$	P_2
0			10.0000		10.0000
1	.06476	.00802	10.0802	.00648	10.0650
2	−.19945	−.00664	10.0132	−.00818	9.9830
3	−.83883	−.04211	9.5916	−.04365	9.5567
4	.49609	.03194	9.8980	.03040	9.8517
5	−.33892	−.01438	9.7557	−.01592	9.6961
6	1.39485	.08180	10.5536	.08026	10.5064
7	.61869	.03874	10.9625	.03720	10.9046
8	.40201	.02672	11.2554	.02518	11.1827
9	−.71118	−.03503	10.8612	−.03656	10.7812
10	.16937	.01382	11.0113	.01228	10.9144
11	1.19678	.07081	11.7910	.06927	11.6973
12	−.14408	−.00357	11.7489	−.00511	11.6377
13	.80590	.04913	12.3261	.04759	12.2049
26	−1.23335	−.06399	13.1428	−.06553	12.9157
39	.68140	.04222	17.6850	.04068	17.3668
52	.69955	.04323	15.1230	.04169	14.7564

The price process is simulated by two methods. Although they differ step by step, the overall results are similar.

11.8 ITO'S LEMMA*

We saw that the two Ito equations—for $S(t)$ and for $\ln S(t)$—are different, and that the difference is not exactly what would be expected from the application of ordinary calculus to the transformation of variables from $S(t)$ to $\ln S(t)$; an additional term $\frac{1}{2}\sigma^2$ is required. This extra term arises because the random variables have order $\sqrt{dt}$, and hence their squares produce first-order, rather than second-order, effects. There is a systematic method for making such transformations in general, and this is encapsulated in Ito's lemma:

Ito's lemma   *Suppose that the random process x is defined by the Ito process*

$$dx(t) = a(x, t)\,dt + b(x, t)\,dz \tag{11.21}$$

where z is a standard Wiener process. Suppose also that the process y(t) is defined by $y(t) = F(x, t)$. Then y(t) satisfies the Ito equation

$$dy(t) = \left(\frac{\partial F}{\partial x}a + \frac{\partial F}{\partial t} + \frac{1}{2}\frac{\partial^2 F}{\partial x^2}b^2\right)dt + \frac{\partial F}{\partial x}b\,dz \tag{11.22}$$

where z is the same Wiener process as in Eq. (11.21).

Proof: Ordinary calculus would give a formula similar to (11.22), but without the term with $\frac{1}{2}$.

We shall sketch a rough proof of the full formula. We expand y with respect to a change Δy. In the expansion we keep terms up to first order in Δt, but since Δx is of order $\sqrt{\Delta t}$, this means that we must expand to second order in Δx. We find

$$y + \Delta y = F(x, t) + \frac{\partial F}{\partial x} \Delta x + \frac{\partial F}{\partial t} \Delta t + \frac{1}{2} \frac{\partial^2 F}{\partial x^2} (\Delta x)^2$$

$$= F(x, t) + \frac{\partial F}{\partial x} (a \, \Delta t + b \, \Delta z) + \frac{\partial F}{\partial t} \Delta t + \frac{1}{2} \frac{\partial^2 F}{\partial x^2} (a \, \Delta t + b \, \Delta z)^2.$$

The quadratic expression in the last term must be treated in a special way. When expanded, it becomes $a^2 (\Delta t)^2 + 2ab \, \Delta t \, \Delta z + b^2 (\Delta z)^2$. The first two terms of this expression are of order higher than 1 in Δt, so they can be dropped. The term $b^2 (\Delta z)^2$ is all that remains. However, Δz has expected value zero and variance Δt, and hence this last term is of order Δt and cannot be dropped. Indeed, it can be shown that, in the limit as Δt goes to zero, the term $(\Delta z)^2$ is nonstochastic and is equal to Δt. Substitution of this into the previous expansion leads to

$$y + \Delta y = F(x, t) + \left(\frac{\partial F}{\partial x} a + \frac{\partial F}{\partial t} + \frac{1}{2} \frac{\partial^2 F}{\partial x^2} b^2 \right) \Delta t + \frac{\partial F}{\partial x} b \, \Delta z.$$

Taking the limit and using $y = F(x, t)$ yields Ito's equation, (11.22). ∎

Example 11.4 (Stock dynamics)   Suppose that $S(t)$ is governed by the geometric Brownian motion

$$dS = \mu S \, dt + \sigma S \, dz.$$

Let us use Ito's lemma to find the equation governing the process $F(S(t)) = \ln S(t)$.
   We have the identifications $a = \mu S$ and $b = \sigma S$. We also have $\partial F / \partial S = 1/S$ and $\partial^2 F / \partial S^2 = -1/S^2$. Therefore according to (11.22),

$$d \ln S = \left(\frac{a}{S} - \frac{1}{2} \frac{b^2}{S^2} \right) dt + \frac{b}{S} dz$$

$$= \left(\mu - \frac{1}{2} \sigma^2 \right) dt + \sigma \, dz$$

which agrees with our earlier result.

11.9 BINOMIAL LATTICE REVISITED

Let us consider again the binomial lattice model shown in Figure 11.8 (which is identical to Figure 11.1). The model is analogous to the multiplicative model discussed earlier in this chapter, since at each step the price is multiplied by a random variable.

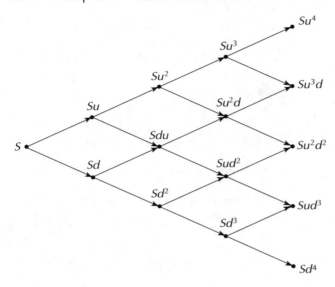

FIGURE 11.8   Binomial lattice stock model. At each step the stock price S either increases to uS or decreases to dS.

In this case, the random variable takes only the two possible values u and d. We can find suitable values for u, d, and p by matching the multiplicative model as closely as possible. This is done by matching both the expected value of the logarithm of a price change and the variance of the logarithm of the price change.[6]

To carry out the matching, it is only necessary to ensure that the random variable S_1, which is the price after the first step, has the correct properties since the process is identical thereafter. Taking $S(0) = 1$, we find by direct calculation that

$$E(\ln S_1) = p \ln u + (1 - p) \ln d$$

$$\mathrm{var}\,(\ln S_1) = p(\ln u)^2 + (1 - p)(\ln d)^2 - [p \ln u + (1 - p) \ln d]^2$$

$$= p(1 - p)(\ln u - \ln d)^2 .$$

Therefore the appropriate parameter matching equations are

$$pU + (1 - p)D = v\,\Delta t \tag{11.23}$$

$$p(1 - p)(U - D)^2 = \sigma^2 \Delta t \tag{11.24}$$

where $U = \ln u$ and $D = \ln d$.

Notice that three parameters are to be chosen: U, D, and p; but there are only two requirements. Therefore there is one degree of freedom. One way to use this freedom is to set $D = -U$ (which is equivalent to setting $d = 1/u$). In this case the

---

[6]For the lattice, the probability of attaining the various end nodes of the lattice is given by the binomial distribution. Specifically, the probability of reaching the value $Su^k d^{n-k}$ is $\binom{n}{k} p^k (1 - p)^{n-k}$, where $\binom{n}{k} = \dfrac{n!}{(n - k)!k!}$ is the binomial coefficient. This distribution approaches (in a certain sense) a normal distribution for large n. The logarithm of the final prices is of the form $k \ln u + (n - k) \ln d$, which is linear in k. Hence the distribution of the end point prices can be considered to be nearly lognormal.

equations (11.23) and (11.24) reduce to

$$(2p - 1)U = v \, \Delta t$$

$$4p(1 - p)U^2 = \sigma^2 \Delta t \, .$$

If we square the first equation and add it to the second, we obtain

$$U^2 = \sigma^2 \, \Delta t + (v \, \Delta t)^2 \, .$$

Substituting this in the first equation, we may solve for p directly, and then $U = \ln u$ can be determined. The resulting solutions to the parameter matching equations are

$$p = \frac{1}{2} + \frac{\frac{1}{2}}{\sqrt{\sigma^2/(v^2 \Delta t) + 1}}$$

$$\ln u = \sqrt{\sigma^2 \Delta t + (v \, \Delta t)^2} \qquad (11.25)$$

$$\ln d = -\sqrt{\sigma^2 \Delta t + (v \, \Delta t)^2} \, .$$

For small Δt (11.25) can be approximated as

$$p = \tfrac{1}{2} + \tfrac{1}{2} \left(\frac{v}{\sigma}\right) \sqrt{\Delta t}$$

$$u = e^{\sigma \sqrt{\Delta t}} \qquad (11.26)$$

$$d = e^{-\sigma \sqrt{\Delta t}} \, .$$

These are the values presented in Section 11.1.

11.10 SUMMARY

A simple and versatile model of asset dynamics is the binomial lattice. In this model an asset's price is assumed to be multiplied either by the factor u or by the factor d, the choice being made each period according to probabilities p and $1-p$, respectively. This model is used extensively in theoretical developments and as a basis for computing solutions to investment problems.

Another broad class of models are those where the asset price may take on values from a continuum of possibilities. The simplest model of this type is the additive model. If the random inputs of this model are normal random variables, the asset prices are also normal random variables. This model has the disadvantage, however, that prices may be negative.

A better model is the multiplicative model of the form $S(k+1) = u(k)S(k)$. If the multiplicative inputs $u(k)$ are lognormal, then the future prices $S(k)$ are also lognormal. The model can be expressed in the alternative form as $\ln S(k + 1) - \ln S(k) = \ln u(k)$.

By letting the period length tend to zero, the multiplicative model becomes the Ito process $d \ln S(t) = v \, dt + \sigma^2 dz(t)$, where z is a normalized Wiener process. This special form of an Ito process is called geometric Brownian motion. This model can be expressed in the alternative (but equivalent) form $dS(t) = \mu S(t)dt + \sigma^2 S(t)dz(t)$, where $\mu = v + \tfrac{1}{2}\sigma^2$.

Ito processes are useful representations of asset dynamics. An important tool for transforming such processes is Ito's lemma: If $x(t)$ satisfies an Ito process, and $y(t)$ is defined by $y(t) = F(x, t)$, Ito's lemma specifies the process satisfied by $y(t)$.

A binomial lattice model can be considered to be an approximation to an Ito process. The parameters of the lattice can be chosen so that the mean and standard deviation of the logarithm of the return agree in the two models.

EXERCISES

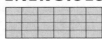

1. (Stock lattice)   A stock with current value $S(0) = 100$ has an expected growth rate of its logarithm of $v = 12\%$ and a volatility of that growth rate of $\sigma = 20\%$. Find suitable parameters of a binomial lattice representing this stock with a basic elementary period of 3 months. Draw the lattice and enter the node values for 1 year. What are the probabilities of attaining the various final nodes?

2. (Time scaling)   A stock price S is governed by the model

$$\ln S(k + 1) = \ln S(k) + w(k)$$

where the period length is 1 month. Let $v = E[w(k)]$ and $\sigma^2 = \mathrm{var}[w(k)]$ for all k. Now suppose the basic period length is changed to 1 year. Then the model is

$$\ln S(K + 1) = \ln S(K) + W(K)$$

where each movement in K corresponds to 1 year. What is the natural definition of $W(K)$? Show that $E[W(K)] = 12v$ and $\mathrm{var}[W(K)] = 12\sigma^2$. Hence parameters scale in proportion to time.

3. (Arithmetic and geometric means)   Suppose that $v_1, v_2, \ldots, v_n$ are positive numbers. The *arithmetic mean* and the *geometric mean* of these numbers are, respectively,

$$v_A = \frac{1}{n} \sum_{i=1}^{n} v_i \quad \text{and} \quad v_G = \left(\prod_{i=1}^{n} v_i \right)^{1/n}.$$

(a) It is always true that $v_A \geq v_G$. Prove this inequality for $n = 2$.

(b) If $r_1, r_2, \ldots, r_n$ are rates of return of a stock in each of n periods, the arithmetic and geometric mean rates of return are likewise

$$r_A = \frac{1}{n} \sum_{i=1}^{n} r_i \quad \text{and} \quad r_G = \left(\prod_{i=1}^{n} (1 + r_i) \right)^{1/n} - 1.$$

Suppose $40 is invested. During the first year it increases to $60 and during the second year it decreases to $48. What are the arithmetic and geometric mean rates of return over the 2 years?

(c) When is it appropriate to use these means to describe investment performance?

4. (Complete the square ◇)   Suppose that $u = e^w$, where w is normal with expected value $\overline{w}$ and variance σ^2. Then

$$\overline{u} = \frac{1}{\sqrt{2\pi\sigma^2}} \int_{-\infty}^{\infty} e^w e^{-(w - \overline{w})^2 / 2\sigma^2} \, dw.$$

Show that

$$w - \frac{(w - \overline{w})^2}{2\sigma^2} = -\frac{1}{2\sigma^2} \left[w - (\overline{w} + \sigma^2) \right]^2 + \overline{w} + \frac{\sigma^2}{2}.$$

Use the fact that

$$\frac{1}{\sqrt{2\pi\sigma^2}} \int_{-\infty}^{\infty} e^{-(x - \bar{x}^2)/2\sigma^2} \, dx = 1$$

to evaluate $\overline{u}$.

5. (Log variance ◊)   Use the method of Exercise 4 to find the variance of a lognormal variable in terms of the parameters of the underlying normal variable.

6. (Expectations)   A stock price is governed by geometric Brownian motion with $\mu = .20$ and $\sigma = .40$. The initial price is $S(0) = 1$. Evaluate the four quantities

$$E[\ln S(1)], \qquad \text{stdev}[\ln S(1)]$$

$$E[S(1)], \qquad \text{stdev}[S(1)].$$

7. (Application of Ito's lemma)   A stock price S is governed by

$$dS = aS\,dt + bS\,dz$$

where z is a standardized Wiener process. Find the process that governs

$$G(t) = S^{1/2}(t).$$

8. (Reverse check)   Gavin Jones was mystified by Ito's lemma when he first studied it, so he tested it. He started with S governed by

$$dS = \mu S\,dt + \sigma S\,dz$$

and found that $Q = \ln S$ satisfies

$$dQ = (\mu - \tfrac{1}{2}\sigma^2)\,dt + \sigma\,dz.$$

He then applied Ito's lemma to this last equation using the change of variable $S = e^Q$. Duplicate his calculations. What did he get?

9. (Two simulations ◊)   A useful expansion is

$$e^x = 1 + x + \tfrac{1}{2}x^2 + \cdots.$$

Use this to express the exponential in equation (11.20) in linear terms of powers of Δt up to first order. Note that this differs from the expression in (11.19), so conclude that the standard form and the multiplicative (or lognormal) form of simulation are different even to first order. Show, however, that the expected values of the two expressions *are* identical to first order, and hence, over the long run the two methods should produce similar results.

10. (A simulation experiment ⊕)   Consider a stock price S governed by the geometric Brownian motion process

$$\frac{dS}{S(t)} = .10\,dt + .30\,dz.$$

(a) Using $\Delta t = 1/12$ and $S(0) = 1$, simulate several (i.e., *many*) years of this process using either method, and evaluate

$$\frac{1}{t} \ln[S(t)]$$

as a function of t. Note that it tends to a limit p. What is the theoretical value of this limit?

(b) About how large must t be to obtain two-place accuracy?

(c) Evaluate

$$\frac{1}{t} \left[\ln S(t) - pt \right]^2$$

as a function of t. Does this tend to a limit? If so, what is its theoretical value?

REFERENCES

For a good overview of stock models similar to this chapter, see [1]. For greater detail on stochastic processes see [2], and for general information of how stock prices actually behave, see [3].

There are numerous textbooks on probability theory that discuss the normal distribution and the lognormal distribution. A classic is [4]. The book by Wiener [5] was responsible for inspiring a great deal of serious theoretical and practical work on issues involving Wiener processes. Ito's lemma was first published in [6] and later in [7].

1. Hull, J. C. (1993), *Options, Futures, and Other Derivative Securities*, 2nd ed., Prentice Hall, Englewood Cliffs, NJ.
2. Malliaris, A. G., and W. A. Brock (1982), *Stochastic methods in Economics and Finance*, North-Holland, Amsterdam, The Netherlands.
3. Cootner, P. H., Ed. (1964), *The Random Character of Stock Market Prices*, M.I.T. Press, Cambridge, MA.
4. Feller, W. (1950), *Probability Theory and Its Applications*, vols 1 and 2, Wiley, New York.
5. Wiener, N. (1950), *Extrapolation, Interpolation, and Smoothing of Stationary Time Series*, Technology Press, M.I.T., Cambridge, MA, and Wiley, New York.
6. Ito, K. (1951), "On a Formula Concerning Stochastic Differentials," *Nagoya Mathematics Journal*, **3**, 55–65.
7. Ito, K. (1961), *Lectures on Stochastic Processes,* Tata Institute of Fundamental Research, India.

12 BASIC OPTIONS THEORY

An **option** is the right, but not the obligation, to buy (or sell) an asset under specified terms. Usually there are a specified price and a specified period of time over which the option is valid. An example is the option to purchase, for a price of $200,000, a certain house, say, the one you are now renting, anytime within the next year. An option that gives the right to purchase something is called a **call** option, whereas an option that gives the right to sell something is called a **put.** Usually an option itself has a price; frequently we refer to this price as the option **premium,** to distinguish it from the purchase or selling price specified in the terms of the option. The premium may be a small fraction of the price of the optioned asset. For example, you might pay $15,000 for the option to purchase the house at $200,000. If the option holder actually does buy or sell the asset according to the terms of the option, the option holder is said to **exercise** the option. The original premium is not recovered in any case.

An option is a derivative security whose underlying asset is the asset that can be bought or sold, such as the house in our example. The ultimate financial value of an option depends on the price of the underlying asset at the time of possible exercise. For example, if the house is worth $300,000 at the end of the year, the $200,000 option is then worth $100,000, because you could buy the house for $200,000 and immediately sell it for $300,000 for a profit of $100,000.

Options have a long history in commerce, since they provide excellent mechanisms for controlling risk, or for locking up resources at a minimal fee. The following story, quoted from Aristotle,[1] is a favorite of professors who write about investments.

> There is an anecdote of Thales the Milesian and his financial device, which involves a principle of universal application, but is attributed to him on account of his reputation for wisdom. He was reproached for his poverty, which was supposed to show that philosophy was of no use. According to the story, he knew by his skill in the stars

---

[1] Aristotle, *Politics*, Book 1, Chapter 11, Jowett translation. Quoted in Gastineau (1975).

while it was yet winter that there would be a great harvest of olives in the coming year; so, having a little money, he gave deposits for the use of all the olive presses in Chios and Miletus, which he hired at a low price because no one bid against him. When the harvest time came, and many wanted them all at once and of a sudden, he let them out at any rate which he pleased, and made a quantity of money. Thus he showed the world that philosophers can easily be rich if they like . . .

Another classic example is associated with the Dutch *tulip mania* in about 1600. Tulips were prized for their beauty, and this led to vigorous speculation and escalation of prices. Put options were used by growers to guarantee a price for their bulbs, and call options were used by dealers to assure future prices. The market was not regulated in any way and finally crashed in 1636, leaving options with a bad reputation.

Options are now available on a wide assortment of financial instruments (such as stocks and bonds) through regulated exchanges. However, options on physical assets are still very important. In addition, there are many implied or hidden options in other financial situations. An example is the option to extract oil from an oil well or leave it in the ground until a better time, or the option to accept a mortgage guarantee or renegotiate. These situations can be fruitfully analyzed using the theory of options explained in this chapter.

12.1 OPTION CONCEPTS

The specifications of an option include, first, a clear description of what can be bought (for a call) or sold (for a put). For options on stock, each option is usually for 100 shares of a specified stock. Thus a call option on IBM is the option to buy 100 shares of IBM. Second, the exercise price, or **strike price,** must be specified. This is the price at which the asset can be purchased upon exercise of the option. For IBM stock the exercise price might be $70, which means that each share can be bought at $70. Third, the period of time for which the option is valid must be specified—defined by the expiration date. Hence an option may be valid for a day, a week, or several months. There are two primary conventions regarding acceptable exercise dates before expiration. An **American option** allows exercise at any time before and including the expiration date. A **European option** allows exercise only on the expiration date. The terms *American* and *European* refer to the different ways most stock options are structured in America and in Europe, but the words have become standard for the two different types of structures, no matter where they are issued. There are some European-style options in America. For example, if the option to buy a house in one year states that the sale must be made in exactly one year and not sooner, the house option can be referred to as a European option.

These four features—the description of the asset, whether a call or a put, the exercise price, and the expiration date (including whether American or European in style)—specify the details of an option. A final, but somewhat separate, feature is the price of the option itself—the premium. If an option is individually tailored, this premium price is established as part of the original negotiation and is part of the contract. If the option is traded on an exchange, the premium is established by the

Option/strike		Exp.	Call		Put	
			Vol.	Last	Vol.	Last
GM	35	Dec	529	$2\frac{7}{8}$	...	...
$37\frac{7}{8}$	35	Jan	93	$3\frac{5}{8}$	90	$\frac{1}{2}$
$37\frac{7}{8}$	35	Mar	36	$4\frac{1}{4}$	49	1
$37\frac{7}{8}$	35	Jun	31	$5\frac{1}{2}$	...	...
$37\frac{7}{8}$	40	Dec	24	$\frac{1}{16}$	549	$2\frac{1}{16}$
$37\frac{7}{8}$	40	Jan	407	$\frac{11}{16}$	284	$2\frac{5}{8}$
$37\frac{7}{8}$	40	Mar	746	$1\frac{5}{8}$	40	3
$37\frac{7}{8}$	40	Jun	91	$2\frac{11}{16}$	135	$3\frac{7}{8}$
$37\frac{7}{8}$	45	Jan	104	$\frac{1}{8}$	49	7
$37\frac{7}{8}$	45	Mar	50	$\frac{1}{2}$	...	...
$37\frac{7}{8}$	45	Jun	110	$1\frac{1}{4}$	15	$7\frac{5}{8}$
$37\frac{7}{8}$	50	Jun	94	$\frac{1}{2}$	...	...

FIGURE 12.1 Options quotations on General Motors stock (December 15, 1995). The first column shows the closing price of the stock. The other columns give information about available options. Source: *The Wall Street Journal,* December 15, 1994.

market through supply and demand, and this premium will vary according to trading activity.

There are two sides to any option: the party that grants the option is said to **write** an option, whereas the party that obtains the option is said to purchase it. The party purchasing an option faces no risk of loss other than the original purchase premium. However, the party that writes the option may face a large loss, since this party must buy or sell this asset at the specified terms if the option is exercised. In the case of an exercised call option, if the writer does not already own the asset, he must purchase it in order to deliver it at the specified strike price, which may be much higher than the current market price. Likewise, in the case of an exercised put option, the writer must accept the asset for the strike price, which could be much lower than the current market price.

Options on many stocks are traded on an exchange. In this case individual option trades are made through a broker who trades on the exchange. The exchange clearing-house guarantees the performance of all parties. Because of the risk associated with options, an option writer is required to post **margin** (a security deposit) guaranteeing performance.[2]

Exchange-traded options are listed in the financial press. A listing of GM (General Motors) options is shown in Figure 12.1. There are several different options available for GM stock. Some are calls and some are puts, and they have a variety of strike prices and expiration dates. In the figure, the first column shows the symbol for the underlying stock and the closing price of the stock itself. The second column shows the exercise (or strike) price of the option. The third column shows the month in

---

[2] The initial margin level is often 50% of the stock value of the option, with a maintenance level of 25%.

which the option expires. The exact expiration date during that month is the Saturday following the third Friday. The fourth and fifth columns give data on a call, showing the volume traded on the day reported and the last reported price for that option. The final two columns give the analogous information for the put. All prices are quoted on a per-share basis, although a single option contract is for 100 shares.

As with futures contracts, options on financial securities are rarely exercised, with the underlying security being bought or sold. Instead, if the price of the security moves in a favorable direction, the option price (the premium) will increase accordingly, and most option holders will elect to sell their options before maturity.

There are many details with regard to options trading, governing special situations such as stock splits, dividends, position limits, and specific margin requirements. These must be checked before engaging in serious trading of options. However, the present overview is sufficient for understanding the basic mechanics of options.

12.2 THE NATURE OF OPTION VALUES

A primary objective of this chapter is to show how to determine the value of an option on a financial security. Such a determination is a fascinating and creative application of the fundamental principles that we have studied so far. Hence options theory is important *partly* because options themselves are important financial instruments, but also partly because options theory shows how the fundamental principles of investment science can be taken to a new level—a level where dynamic structure is fundamental. In this section we examine in a qualitative manner the nature of option prices. This will prepare us for the deeper analysis that follows in subsequent sections.

Suppose that you own a call option on a stock with a strike price of K. Suppose that on the expiration date the price of the underlying stock is S. What is the value of the option at that time? It is easy to see that if $S < K$, then the option value is zero. This is because under the terms of the option, you could exercise the option and purchase the stock for K, but by not exercising the option you could buy the stock on the open market for the lower price of S. Hence you would not exercise the option. The option is worthless. On the other hand, if $S > K$, then the option does have value. By exercising the option you could buy the stock at a price K and then sell that stock on the market for the larger price S. Your profit would be $S - K$, which is therefore the value of the option. We handle both cases together by writing the value of the call at expiration as

$$C = \max(0, \ S - K) \tag{12.1}$$

which means that C is equal to the maximum of the values 0 or $S - K$. We therefore have an explicit formula for the value of a call option at expiration as a function of the price of the underlying security S. This function is shown in Figure 12.2(a). The figure shows that for $S < K$, the value is zero, but for $S > K$, the value of the option increases linearly with the price, on a one–for–one basis.

The result is reversed for a put option. A put option gives one the right, but not the obligation, to sell an asset at a given strike price. Suppose you own a put

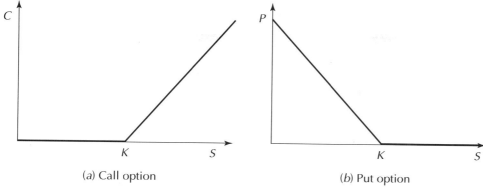

FIGURE 12.2   **Value of option at expiration.** A call has value if $S > K$. A put has value if $S < K$.

option on a stock with a strike price of K. In this case if the price S of the stock at expiration satisfies $S > K$, then this option is worthless. By exercising the option you could sell the stock for a price K, whereas in the open market you could sell the stock for the greater price S. Hence you would not exercise the option. On the other hand, if the price of the stock is less than the strike price, the put option does have value. You could buy the stock on the market for a price S and then exercise the option to sell that same stock for a greater price K. Your profit would be $K - S$, which is therefore the value of the option. The general formula for the value of a put at expiration is

$$P = \max(0, \ K - S).$$ (12.2)

This function is illustrated in Figure 12.2(*b*). Note that the value of a put is bounded, whereas the payoff of a call is unbounded. Conversely, when writing a call, the potential for *loss* is unbounded.

We say that a call option is **in the money, at the money,** or **out of the money,** depending on whether $S > K$, $S = K$, or $S < K$, respectively. The terminology applies at any time; but at expiration the terms describe the nature of the option value. Puts have the reverse terminology, since the payoffs at exercise are positive if $S < K$.

Time Value of Options

The preceding analysis focused on the value of an option at expiration. This value is derived from the basic structure of an option. However, even European options (which cannot be exercised except at expiration) have value at earlier times, since they provide the potential for future exercise. Consider, for example, an option on GM stock with a strike price of $40 and 3 months to expiration. Suppose the current price of GM stock is $37.88. (This situation is approximately that of Figure 12.1 represented by the March 40 call.) It is clear that there is a chance that the price of GM stock might increase to over $40 within 3 months. It would then be possible to exercise the option and obtain a profit. Hence this option has value even though it is currently

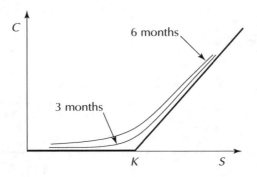

FIGURE 12.3   Option price curve with various times to expiration. At a given stock price S, the value of a call option increases as the time to expiration increases.

out of the money. (In the example represented by the figure, the 40 call is selling for $1.63.)

When there is a positive time to expiration, the value of a call option as a function of the stock price is a smooth curve rather than the decidedly kinked curve that applies at expiration. This smooth curve can be determined by estimation, using data of actual option prices. Such estimation shows that the option price curve for any given expiration period looks something like the curves shown in Figure 12.3. In this figure the heavy kinked line represents the value of a call at expiration. The higher curves correspond to different times to expiration. The first curve is for a call with 3 months to expiration, whereas the next higher one is for 6 months. The curves get higher with increasing length to expiration, since additional time provides a greater chance for the stock to rise in value, increasing the final payoff. However, the effect of additional time is diminished when the stock price is either much smaller or much greater than the strike price K. When the stock price S is much lower than K, there is little chance that S will rise above K, so the option value remains close to zero. When S is much greater than K, there is little advantage in owning the option over owning the stock itself.

A major objective of this chapter is to determine a theory for option prices. This theory will imply a specific set of curves, such as the ones shown in Figure 12.3.

Other Factors Affecting the Value of Options

The volatility of the underlying stock is another factor that influences the value of an option significantly. To see this, imagine that you own similar options on two different stocks. Suppose the prices of the two stocks are both $90, the options have strike prices of $100, and there are 3 months to expiration. Suppose, however, that one of these stocks is very volatile and the other is quite placid. Which option has more value? It is clear that the stock with the high volatility has the greatest chance of rising above $90 in the short period remaining to expiration, and hence its option is the more valuable of the two. We expect therefore that the value of a call option increases with volatility, and we shall verify this in our theoretical development.

What other factors might influence the value of an option? One is the prevailing interest rate (or term structure pattern). Purchasing a call option is in some way a method of purchasing the stock at a reduced price. Hence one saves interest expense. We expect therefore that option prices depend on interest rates.

Another factor that would seem to be important is the growth rate of the stock. It seems plausible that higher values of growth would imply larger values for the option. However, perhaps surprisingly, the growth rate does *not* influence the theoretical value of an option. The reason for this will become clear when the theoretical formula is developed.

12.3 OPTION COMBINATIONS AND PUT–CALL PARITY

It is common to invest in combinations of options in order to implement special hedging or speculative strategies. The payoff curve of such a combination may have any number of connected straight-line segments. This overall payoff curve is formed by combining the payoff functions defined by calls, puts, and the underlying stock itself. The process is best illustrated by an example and a corresponding graph.

Example 12.1 (A butterfly spread)   One of the most interesting combinations of options is the butterfly spread. It is illustrated in Figure 12.4. The spread is constructed by buying two calls, one with strike price K_1 and another with strike price K_3, and by selling two units of a call with strike price K_2, where $K_1 < K_2 < K_3$. Usually K_2 is chosen to be near the current stock price. The figure shows with dashed lines the *profit* (including the payoff and original cost) associated with each of the components. The overall profit function of the combination is the sum of the individual component functions. This particular combination yields a positive profit if the stock price at expiration is close to K_2; otherwise the loss is quite small. The payoff of this spread is obtained by lifting the curve up so that the horizontal portions touch the axis, the displacement distance corresponding to the net cost of the options.

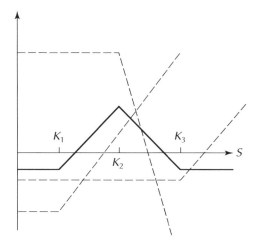

FIGURE 12.4   Profit of butterfly spread. This spread is formed by buying calls with strike prices K_1 and K_3 and writing two units of a call at K_2. This combination is useful if one believes that the underlying stock price will stay in a region near K_2.

The main point here is that by forming combinations of options and stock it is possible to approximate virtually any payoff function by a sequence of straight-line segments. The cost of such a payoff is then just the sum of the costs of the individual components.

Put–Call Parity

For European options there is a simple theoretical relationship between the prices of corresponding puts and calls. The relationship is found by noting that a combination of a put, a call, and a risk-free loan has a payoff identical to that of the underlying stock.

The combination can be easily imagined: buy one call, sell one put, and lend an amount dK. The combination of the first two has a payoff that is a straight line at $45°$, passing through K on the horizontal axis. By lending dK, we obtain an additional payoff of K, which lifts the payoff line up so that it is now a $45°$ line originating at the origin. This final payoff is exactly that of the stock itself, so it must have the value S of the stock. In other words,

$$C - P + dK = S.$$

(See Exercise 3 for more detail.)

Put–call parity   *Let C and P be the prices of a European call and a European put, both with a strike price of K and both defined on the same stock with price S. Put–call parity states that*

$$C - P + dK = S$$

where d is the discount factor to the expiration date.

Example 12.2 (Parity almost)   Consider the GM options of Figure 12.1, and focus on the two 35 March options (with 3 months to expiration). These have $C = 4.25$ and $P = 1.00$, respectively. The interest rate for this period is about 5.5%, so over 3 months we have $d = 1/(1 + .055/4) = .986$. Thus,

$$C - P + dK = 4.25 - 1.0 + .986 \times 35.00 = 37.78.$$

This is a close, but not exact, match with the actual stock price of $37.88. There are several possible explanations for the mismatch. One of the most important is that the stock quotes and option quotes do not come from the same sources. The stock price is the closing price on the stock exchange, whereas the option prices are from the last traded options on the options exchanges; the last trades can occur at different times. Dividends also can influence the parity relation, as discussed in Exercise 2.

12.4 EARLY EXERCISE

An American option offers the possibility of early exercise, that is, exercise before the expiration date of the option. We prove in this section that for call options on a stock that pays no dividends prior to expiration, early exercise is never optimal, provided that prices are such that no arbitrage is possible.

The result can be seen intuitively as follows. Suppose that we are holding a call option at time t and expiration is at time $T > t$. If the current stock price $S(t)$ is less than the strike price K, we would not exercise the option, since we would lose money. If, on the other hand, the stock price is greater than K, we might be tempted to exercise. However, if we do so we will have to pay K now to obtain the stock. If we hold the option a little longer and then exercise, we will still obtain the stock for a price of K, but we will have earned additional interest on the exercise money K—in fact, if the stock declines below K in this waiting period, we will not exercise and be happy that we did not do so earlier.

12.5 SINGLE-PERIOD BINOMIAL OPTIONS THEORY

We now turn to the issue of calculating the theoretical value of an option—an area of work that is called **options pricing theory.** There are several approaches to this problem, based on different assumptions about the market, about the dynamics of stock price behavior, and about individual preferences. The most important theories are based on the no arbitrage principle, which can be applied when the dynamics of the underlying stock take certain forms. The simplest of these theories is based on the binomial model of stock price fluctuations discussed in Chapter 11. This theory is widely used in practice because of its simplicity and ease of calculation. It is a beautiful culmination of the principles discussed in previous chapters.

The basic theory of binomial options pricing has been hinted at in our earlier discussions. We shall develop it here in a self-contained manner, but the reader should notice the connections to earlier sections.

We shall first develop the theory for the single-period case. A single step of a binomial process is all that is used. Accordingly, we suppose that the initial price of a stock is S. At the end of the period the price will either be uS with probability p or dS with probability $1 - p$. We assume $u > d > 0$. Also at every period it is possible to borrow or lend at a common risk-free interest rate r. We let $R = 1 + r$. To avoid arbitrage opportunities, we must have

$$u > R > d.$$

To see this, suppose $R \geq u > d$ and $0 < p < 1$. Then the stock performs worse than the risk-free asset, even in the "up" branch of the lattice. Hence one could short $1.00 of the stock and loan the proceeds, thereby obtaining a profit of either $R - u$ or $R - d$, depending on the outcome state. The initial cost is zero, but in either case the profit is positive, which is not possible if there are no arbitrage opportunities. A similar argument rules out $u > d \geq R$.

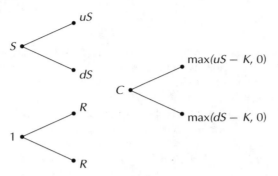

FIGURE 12.5   Three related lattices. The stock price, the value of a risk-free loan, and the value of a call option all move together on a common lattice, represented here as three separate lattices.

Now suppose also that there is a call option on this stock with exercise price K and expiration at the end of the period. To find the value of the call option, we use a no-arbitrage argument by referring to Figure 12.5. This figure shows the binomial lattices for the stock price, the value of a risk-free asset, and the value of the option. All three of these lattices have common arcs, in the sense that all move together along the same arcs. If the stock price moves along the upward arc, then the risk-free asset and the call option both move along their upward arcs as well. The risk-free value is deterministic, but this is treated as if it were a (degenerate) derivative of the stock by just making the value at the end of each arc the same.

Assuming that we know the stock price S, then all values of these one-step lattices are known except the value of the call C. This value will be determined from the other values.

The insight that we use is to note that each of the lattices on the left has only two possible outcomes. By combining various proportions of these two lattices, we can construct any other pattern of outcomes. In particular, we can construct the pattern corresponding to the outcomes of the option.

Let us denote

$$C_u = \max\,(uS - K, 0) \tag{12.3}$$

$$C_d = \max\,(dS - K, 0). \tag{12.4}$$

To duplicate these two outcomes, let us purchase x dollars worth of stock and b dollars worth of the risk-free asset. At the next time period, this portfolio will be worth either $ux + Rb$ or $dx + Rb$, depending on which path is taken. To match the option outcomes we therefore require

$$ux + Rb = C_u \tag{12.5a}$$

$$dx + Rb = C_d. \tag{12.5b}$$

To solve these equations we subtract the second from the first, obtaining

$$x = \frac{C_u - C_d}{u - d}.$$

From this we easily find

$$b = \frac{C_u - ux}{R} = \frac{uC_d - dC_u}{R(u - d)}.$$

Combining these we find that the value of the portfolio is

$$x + b = \frac{C_u - C_d}{u - d} + \frac{uC_d - dC_u}{R(u - d)}$$

$$= \frac{1}{R}\left(\frac{R - d}{u - d}C_u + \frac{u - R}{u - d}C_d\right).$$

We now use the comparison principle (or, equivalently, the no-arbitrage principle) to assert that the value $x + b$ must be the value of the call option C. The reason is that the portfolio we constructed produces exactly the same outcomes as the call option. If the cost of this portfolio were less than the price of the call, we would never purchase the call. Indeed, we could make arbitrage profits by buying this portfolio and selling the call for an immediate gain and no future consequence. If the prices were unequal in the reverse direction, we could just reverse the argument. We conclude therefore that the price of the call is

$$C = \frac{1}{R}\left(\frac{R - d}{u - d}C_u + \frac{u - R}{u - d}C_d\right). \tag{12.6}$$

The portfolio made up of the stock and the risk-free asset that duplicates the outcome of the option is often referred to an a **replicating portfolio.** It replicates the option. This replicating idea can be used to find the value of any security defined on the same lattice; that is, any security that is a derivative of the stock.

There is a simplified way to view equation (12.6). We define the quantity

$$q = \frac{R - d}{u - d}. \tag{12.7}$$

From the relation $u > R > d$ assumed earlier, it follows that $0 < q < 1$. Hence q can be considered to be a probability. Also (12.6) can be written as follows:

Option pricing formula *The value of a one-period call option on a stock governed by a binomial lattice is*

$$C = \frac{1}{R}[qC_u + (1 - q)C_d]. \tag{12.8}$$

Note that (12.8) can be interpreted as stating that C is found by taking the expected value of the option using the probability q, and then discounting this value according to the risk-free rate. The probability q is therefore a **risk-neutral probability.** This procedure of valuation works for all securities. In fact q can be calculated by making sure that the risk-neutral formula holds for the underlying stock itself; that is, we want

$$S = \frac{1}{R}[quS + (1 - q)dS].$$

Solving this equation gives (12.7).

As a suggestive notation, we write (12.8) as

$$C(T - 1) = \frac{1}{R}\hat{E}[C(T)].$$

Here $C(T)$ and $C(T-1)$ are the call values at T and $T-1$, respectively, and $\hat{E}$ denotes expectation with respect to the risk-neutral probabilities q and $1-q$.

An important, and perhaps initially surprising, feature of the pricing formula (12.6) is that it is *independent* of the probability p of an upward move in the lattice. This is because no trade-off among probabilistic events is made. The value is found by perfectly matching the outcomes of the option with a combination of stock and the risk-free asset. Probability never enters this matching calculation.

This derivation of the option pricing formula is really a special case of the risk-neutral pricing concept discussed in Chapter 9. At this point it would be useful for the reader to review that earlier section.

12.6 MULTIPERIOD OPTIONS

We now extend the solution method to multiperiod options by working backward one step at a time.

A two-stage lattice representing a two-period call option is shown in Figure 12.6. It is assumed as before that the initial price of the stock is S, and this price is modified by the up and down factors u and d while moving through the lattice. The values shown in the lattice are those of the corresponding call option with strike price K and expiration time corresponding to the final point in the lattice. The value of the option is known at the final nodes of the lattice. In particular,

$$C_{uu} = \max\left(u^2 S - K, 0\right) \tag{12.9a}$$

$$C_{ud} = \max\left(udS - K, 0\right) \tag{12.9b}$$

$$C_{dd} = \max\left(d^2 S - K, 0\right). \tag{12.9c}$$

We again define the risk-neutral probability as

$$q = \frac{R-d}{u-d}$$

where R is the one-period return on the risk-free asset. Then, assuming that we do not exercise the option early (which we already know is optimal, but will demonstrate

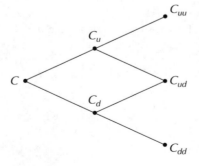

FIGURE 12.6   **Two-period option.** The value is found by working backward a step at a time.

again shortly), we can find the values of C_u and C_d from the single-period calculation given earlier. Specifically,

$$C_u = \frac{1}{R}[qC_{uu} + (1 - q)C_{ud}] \qquad (12.10)$$

$$C_d = \frac{1}{R}[qC_{ud} + (1 - q)C_{dd}] . \qquad (12.11)$$

Then we find C by another application of the same risk-neutral discounting formula. Hence,

$$C = \frac{1}{R}[qC_u + (1 - q)C_d] .$$

For a lattice with more periods, a similar procedure is used. The single-period, risk-free discounting is just repeated at every node of the lattice, starting from the final period and working backward toward the initial time.

Example 12.3 (A 5-month call) Consider a stock with a volatility of its logarithm of $\sigma = .20$. The current price of the stock is \$62. The stock pays no dividends. A certain call option on this stock has an expiration date 5 months from now and a strike price of \$60. The current rate of interest is 10%, compounded monthly. We wish to determine the theoretical price of this call using the binomial option approach.

First we must determine the parameters for the binomial model of the stock price fluctuations. We shall take the period length to be 1 month, which means $\Delta t = 1/12$. The parameters are found from Eqs. (11.1) to be

$$\begin{aligned} u &= e^{\sigma\sqrt{\Delta t}} &= 1.05943 \\ d &= e^{-\sigma\sqrt{\Delta t}} &= .94390 \\ R &= 1 + .1/12 &= 1.00833 . \end{aligned}$$

Then the risk-neutral probability is

$$q = (R - d)/(u - d) = .55770 .$$

We now form the binomial lattice corresponding to the stock price at the beginning of each of six successive months (including the current month). This lattice is shown in Figure 12.7, with the number above a node being the stock price at that node. Note that an up followed by a down always yields a net multiple of 1.

Next we calculate the call option price. We start at the final time and enter the expiration values of the call below the final nodes. This is the maximum of 0 and $S - K$. For example, the entry for the top node is $82.75 - 60 = 22.75$.

The values for the previous time are found by the single-step pricing relation. The value of any node at this time is the discounted expected value of two successive values at the next time. The expected value is calculated using the risk-neutral

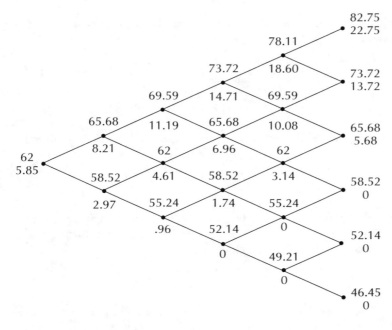

FIGURE 12.7   5-month call using a binomial lattice. The upper numbers are the stock prices, the lower numbers the option values. The option values are found by working backward through the lattice.

probabilities q and $1 - q$. For example, the value at the top node is $[.5577 \times 22.75 + (1 - .5577) \times 13.72]/1.00833 = 18.60$.

We work toward the left, one period at a time, until finally the initial value is reached. In this case we conclude that the price of the option computed this way is $5.85.

Note that the entire process is independent of the expected growth rate of the stock. This value only enters the binomial model of the stock through the probability p; but this probability is not used in the option calculation. Instead it is the risk-neutral probability q that is used. Note, however, that this independence results from using the small Δt approximation for parameter matching. And indeed, in practice this approximation is almost invariably used (even for Δt equal to 1 year). If the more general matching formula were used, the growth rate would (slightly) influence the result.

No Early Exercise*

In the preceding example we assumed (rightly) that the option would never be exercised early. We can prove this directly from the binomial equations. From the basic payoff structure we see that

$$C_{uu} \geq u^2 S - K$$
$$C_{ud} \geq udS - K$$
$$C_{dd} \geq d^2 S - K.$$

Hence,

$$C_u \geq [u^2 q S + ud(1 - q)S - K]/R$$
$$= u[qu + (1 - q)d]S/R - K/R$$
$$> uS - K.$$

Likewise,

$$C_d > dS - K.$$

If the option were exercised at the end of the first period of the two-period lattice shown in Figure 12.6, we would obtain $uS - K$ or $dS - K$, depending on which node was active at the time. These inequalities show that the value of the option at the end of one period is greater than the amount that would be obtained by exercise at that period. Hence we should not exercise the option.

If the lattice had more periods, these inequalities would extend to the next forward period as well. Hence, in general, by an inductive process it can be shown that it is never optimal to exercise the option.

The argument against early exercise does not hold for all options; in some cases an additional operation must be incorporated in the recursive process of value calculation. This is explained in the next section.

12.7 MORE GENERAL BINOMIAL PROBLEMS

The binomial lattice method for calculating the value of an option is extremely simple and highly versatile. For this reason it has become a common tool in the investment and financial community. The method is simplest when applied to a call option on a non-dividend-paying stock, as illustrated in the previous section. This section shows how the basic method can be extended to more complex situations.

Put Options

The method for calculating the values of European put options is analogous to that for call options. The main difference is that the terminal values for the option are different. But once these are specified, the recursive procedure works in a similar way.

For an American put, early exercise may be optimal. This is easily accounted for in the recursive process as follows: At each node, first calculate the value of the put using the discounted risk-neutral formula; then calculate the value that would be obtained by immediate exercise of the put; finally, select the larger of these two values as the value of the put at that node.

Example 12.4 (A 5-month put)   We consider the same stock that was used to evaluate the 5-month call option of Example 12.3, but now we evaluate a 5-month American

62.00	65.68	69.59	73.72	78.11	82.75
	58.52	62.00	65.68	69.59	73.72
		55.24	58.52	62.00	65.68
Stock price			52.14	55.24	58.52
				49.21	52.14
					46.45

1.56	0.61	0.12	0.00	0.00	0.00
	2.79	1.23	0.28	0.00	0.00
		4.80	2.45	0.65	0.00
Put option			**7.86**	**4.76**	**1.48**
				10.79	**7.86**
					13.55

FIGURE 12.8   Calculation of a 5-month put option price. The put values in the lower portion of the figure are found by working backward. Boldface entries indicate points where it is optimal to exercise the option.

put option with a strike price of $K = \$60$. Recall that the critical parameters were $R = 1.008333$, $q = .55770$, $u = 1.05943$, and $d = .94390$. Binomial lattice calculations can be very conveniently carried out with a spreadsheet program. Hence we often show lattices in spreadsheet form rather than as graphical diagrams. This allows us to show larger lattices in a restricted space, and it also indicates more directly how calculations are organized.

The binomial lattice for the stock price is shown in the top portion of Figure 12.8. In this figure an up move is made by moving directly to the right, and a down move is made by moving to the right and down one step.

To calculate the value of the put option, we again work backward, constructing a new lattice below the stock price lattice. The final values (those of the last column) are, in this case, the maximum of 0 and $K - S$. We then work toward the left, one column at a time. To find the value of an element we first calculate the discounted expected value as before, using the risk-neutral probabilities. Now, however, we must also check whether this value would be exceeded by $K - S$, which is what could be obtained by exercising the option at the current point. We assign the larger of the two values to this current node. For example, consider the fourth entry in the second to last column. The discounted expected value there is $[.5577 \times 1.48 + (1 - .5577) \times 7.86]/1.00833 = 4.266$. The exercise value is $60 - 55.24 = 4.76$. The larger of these is 4.76, and that is what is entered in the value lattice. If the larger value is obtained by exercising, we may also wish to indicate this on the lattice, which in our figure is done by using boldface for the entries corresponding to exercise points. (Alternatively, a separate lattice consisting of 0's and 1's can be constructed to indicate the exercise points.) In our example we see that there are several points at which exercise is optimal. The value of the put is the first entry of the lattice, namely, $1.56.

Intuitively, early exercise of a put may be optimal because the upside profit is bounded. Clearly, for example, if the stock price falls to zero, one should exercise there, since no greater profit can be achieved. A continuity argument can be used to infer that it is optimal to exercise if the stock price gets close to zero.

Dividend and Term Structure Problems*

Many other problems can be treated with the binomial lattice model by allowing the parameters of the model to vary from node to node. This does not change the basic structure of the computational method. It merely means that the risk-neutral probabilities and the discount factor may differ from period to period.

One example is the evaluation of a call option on a stock that pays a dividend. If the dividend is proportional to the value of the stock—say, the dividend is δS and is paid at time k—then in the stock price lattice we just change the factors u and d for the period ending at k to $u(1 - \delta)$ and $d(1 - \delta)$. If the dividend is known in advance to be a fixed amount D, then this technique will not work directly, but the lattice approach can still be used. (See Exercise 5.)

The parameters also vary when the interest rate is not constant. In this case the appropriate single-period rate for a given period (the implied short rate) should be used. This will change the value of R and hence also the value of q.

Futures Options*

Are we ready to consider a futures option—that is, an option on a futures contract? This may at first sound complicated; but we shall find that futures options are quite simple to analyze, and study of the analysis should help develop a fuller understanding of the risk-neutral pricing process. The best way to study the analysis is to consider an example.

Example 12.5 (A futures contract) Suppose that a certain commodity (which can be stored without cost and is in ample supply) has a current price of $100, and the price process is described by a monthly binomial lattice with parameters $u = 1.02$, $d = .99$, and $R = 1.01$. The actual probabilities are not important for our analysis. This lattice, for 6 months into the future, is shown in the upper left-hand corner of Figure 12.9. We can immediately calculate the risk-neutral probabilities to be $q = (R - d)/(u - d) = \frac{2}{3}$ and $1 - q = \frac{1}{3}$.

Let us compute the lattice of the corresponding futures prices for a futures contract that expires in the sixth month. This lattice is shown in the lower left-hand side of Figure 12.9. One way to compute this lattice is to use the result of Chapter 10 that the futures price is equal to the current commodity price amplified by interest rate growth over the remaining period of the contract. Hence the futures price at time zero is $100(1.01)^6 = \$106.15$, as shown in the lattice. The futures price for any node in the lattice can be found by the same technique: just multiply the corresponding commodity price by the factor of interest rate growth for the remaining time.

The futures price can also be found recursively by using the risk-neutral probabilities. We know that the final futures price, at month 6, must be identical to the price of the commodity itself at that time, so we can fill in the last column of the array with those values. Let us denote the futures price at the top of the previous column,

0	1	2	3	4	5	6	0	1	2	3	4	5	6
100.00	102.00	104.04	106.12	108.24	110.41	112.62	4.16	5.05	6.04	7.12	8.25	9.42	10.62
	99.00	100.98	103.00	105.06	107.16	109.30		2.50	3.21	4.07	5.07	6.17	7.30
		98.01	99.97	101.97	104.01	106.09			1.14	1.59	2.20	3.02	4.09
Commodity price			97.03	98.97	100.95	102.97	Commodity			0.28	0.42	0.64	0.97
				96.06	97.98	99.94	option				0.00	0.00	0.00
					95.10	97.00						0.00	0.00
						94.15							0.00

0	1	2	3	4	5	6	0	1	2	3	4	5	6
106.15	107.20	108.26	109.34	110.42	111.51	112.62	4.28	5.21	**6.26**	**7.34**	**8.42**	**9.51**	10.62
	104.05	105.08	106.12	107.17	108.23	109.30		2.54	3.27	4.15	**5.17**	**6.23**	7.30
		101.99	103.00	104.02	105.05	106.09			1.15	1.61	2.22	**30.5**	4.09
Futures price			99.97	100.96	101.96	102.97	Futures			0.28	0.42	0.64	0.97
				97.99	98.96	99.94	option				0.00	0.00	0.00
					96.05	97.00						0.00	0.00
						94.15							0.00

FIGURE 12.9   Lattices associated with a commodity. The upper left lattice is the price lattice of a commodity. All other lattices are computed from it by backward risk-neutral evaluation.

at time 5, by F. If one took the long side of a one-period contract with this assigned price, the payoff in the next period would be either $112.62 - F$ or $109.30 - F$, depending on which of the two nodes was attained. These two values should be multiplied by q and $1 - q$, respectively, and the sum discounted one period to find the initial value, at time 5, of such a contract. But since futures contracts are arranged so that the initial value is zero, it follows that $q(112.62 - F) + (1 - q)(109.30 - F) = 0$, which gives $F = q112.62 + (1 - q)109.30$. In other words, F is the weighted average of the next period's prices; the weighting coefficients are the risk-neutral probabilities. We do *not* discount the average.

This process is continued backward a column at a time, computing the weighted average (or expected value) using the risk-neutral probabilities. The final result is again 106.15.

Notice that the original commodity price lattice also can be reconstructed backward by using risk-neutral pricing. Given the final prices, we compute the expected values using the risk-neutral probabilities, but now we *do* discount to find the value at the previous node. Working backward we fill in the entire lattice, duplicating the original figures in the upper left-hand corner.

The backward process for calculating the futures prices and the backward process for computing the commodity prices are identical, except that no discounting is applied in the calculation of futures prices. Hence futures prices will be the same as the commodity prices, but inflated by interest rate growth.

Example 12.6 (Some options)   Now let us consider some options related to the commodity in Example 12.5. First let us consider a call option on the commodity itself, with a strike price of $102 and expiration in month 6. This is now easy for us to calculate using binomial lattice methodology, as shown in the upper right-hand part of Figure 12.9. We just fill in the final column and then work backward with the risk-neutral discounting process. The fair price of the option is $4.16.

Next let us consider a call option on a futures contract with a strike price of $102. If this option is exercised, the call writer must deliver a futures contract with a futures price of $102, but marked to market. Suppose the actual futures price at the time of exercise is $110.42. Then the writer can purchase the futures contract (at zero cost) with the futures price $110.42 and deliver this contract together with the difference of $110.42 − $102.00 = $8.42 to the option holder. This payment compensates for the fact that the writer is delivering a contract at $110.42, instead of at $102.00 as promised. In other words, if the option is exercised, the call holder obtains a current futures contract and cash equal to the difference between the current futures price and the option strike price.

We can compute the value of such a call in the same manner as other calls, as shown in the lattice in the lower right-hand portion of Figure 12.9. At each node we must check whether or not it is desirable to exercise the option. This is done by seeing whether the corresponding futures price minus the strike price is greater than the risk-neutral value that would be obtained by holding the option. If it is optimal to exercise the option, we record the option value in boldface. The option price is found to be $4.28. Notice that even though the final payoff values are identical for the two options. The futures option has a higher value because the higher intermediate futures prices lead to the possibility of early exercise.

12.8 EVALUATING REAL INVESTMENT OPPORTUNITIES

Options theory can be used to evaluate investment opportunities that are not pure financial instruments. We shall illustrate this by again considering our gold mine lease problems. Now, however, the price of gold is assumed to fluctuate randomly, and this fluctuation must be accounted for in our evaluation of the lease prospect.

Example 12.7 (Simplico gold mine)   Recall the Simplico gold mine from Chapter 2. Gold can be extracted from this mine at a rate of up to 10,000 ounces per year at a cost of $200 per ounce. Currently the market price of gold is $400 per ounce, but we recognize that the price of gold fluctuates randomly. The term structure of interest rates is assumed to be flat at 10%. As a convention, we assume that the price obtained for gold mined in a given year is the price that held at the beginning of the year; but all cash flows occur at the end of the year. We wish to determine the value of a 10-year lease of this mine.

We represent future gold prices by a binomial lattice. Each year the price either increases by a factor of 1.2 (with probability .75) or decreases by a factor of .9 (with probability .25). The resulting lattice is shown in Figure 12.10.

How do we solve the problem of finding the lease value by the methods developed for options pricing? The trick is to notice that the gold mine lease can be regarded as a financial instrument. It has a value that fluctuates in time as the price of gold fluctuates. Indeed, the value of the mine lease at any given time can only be

0	1	2	3	4	5	6	7	8	9	10
400.0	480.0	576.0	691.2	829.4	995.3	1194.4	1433.3	1719.9	2063.9	2476.7
	360.0	432.0	518.4	622.1	746.5	895.8	1075.0	1289.9	1547.9	1857.5
		324.0	388.8	466.6	559.9	671.8	806.2	967.5	1161.0	1393.1
			291.6	349.9	419.9	503.9	604.7	725.6	870.7	1044.9
				262.4	314.9	377.9	453.5	544.2	653.0	783.6
Gold price (dollars)					236.2	283.4	340.1	408.1	489.8	587.7
						212.6	255.1	306.1	367.3	440.8
							191.3	229.6	275.5	330.6
								172.2	206.6	247.9
									155.0	186.0
										139.5

FIGURE 12.10 Gold price lattice. Each year the price either increases by a factor of 1.2 or decreases by a factor of .9. The resulting possible values each year are shown in spreadsheet form.

a function of the price of gold and the interest rate (which we assume is fixed). In other words, the lease on the gold mine is a derivative instrument whose underlying security is gold. Therefore the value of the lease can be entered node by node on the gold price lattice.

The lease values on the lattice are determined easily for the final nodes, at the end of the 10 years: the values are zero there because we must return the mine to the owners. At a node representing 1 year to go, the value of the lease is equal to the profit that can be made from the mine that year, discounted back to the beginning of the year. For example, the value at the top node for year 9 is $10,000(2,063.9-200)/1.1 = 16.94$ million. For an earlier node, the value of the lease is the sum of the profit that can be made that year and the risk-neutral expected value of the lease in the next period, both discounted back one period. The risk-neutral probabilities are $q = (1.1-.9)/(1.2-.9) = \frac{2}{3}$, and $1-q = \frac{1}{3}$. The lease values can therefore be calculated by backward recursion using these values. (At nodes where the price of gold is less than $200, we do not mine.) The resulting values are indicated in Figure 12.11. We conclude that the value of the lease is $24,074,548 (showing all the digits).

0	1	2	3	4	5	6	7	8	9	10
24.1	27.8	31.2	34.2	36.5	37.7	37.1	34.1	27.8	16.9	0.0
	17.9	20.7	23.3	25.2	26.4	26.2	24.3	20.0	12.3	0.0
		12.9	15.0	16.7	17.9	18.1	17.0	14.1	8.7	0.0
			8.8	10.4	11.5	12.0	11.5	9.7	6.1	0.0
				5.6	6.7	7.4	7.4	6.4	4.1	0.0
Lease value (millions)					3.2	4.0	4.3	3.9	2.6	0.0
						1.4	2.0	2.1	1.5	0.0
							0.4	0.7	0.7	0.0
								0.0	0.1	0.0
									0.0	0.0
										0.0

FIGURE 12.11 Simplico gold mine. The value of the lease is found by working backward. If the price of gold is greater than $200 per ounce, it is profitable to mine; otherwise no mining is undertaken.

Many readers will be able to see from this example that they have a deeper understanding of investment than they did when they began to study this book. Earlier, in Chapter 2, we discussed the Simplico gold mine under the assumption that the price of gold would remain constant at $400 over the course of the lease. We also assumed a constant 10% interest rate. These assumptions, which are fairly commonly employed in problems of this type, were probably not regarded as being seriously incongruous by most readers. Now, however, we see that they are not just a simplification, but an actual inconsistency. If the price of gold were known to be constant, gold would act as a risk-free asset with zero rate of return. This is incompatible with the assumption that the risk-free rate is 10%. Indeed, in our lattice of gold prices we must select u, d, and R such that $u > R > d$.

Now that we have "mastered" the Simplico gold mine, it is time to move on to even greater challenges. (If you think you have really mastered the Simplico mine, try Exercise 8.)

Example 12.8 (Complexico gold mine$\star$) [3]   The Complexico gold mine was discussed in Chapter 5. In this mine the cost of extraction depends on the amount of gold remaining. Hence if you lease this mine, you must decide how much to mine each period, taking into account that mining in one period affects future mining costs. We also assume now that the price of gold fluctuates according to the binomial lattice of the previous example.

The cost of extraction in any year is $500z^2/x$, where x is the amount of gold remaining at the beginning of the year and z is the amount of gold extracted in ounces. Initially there are $x_0 = 50,000$ ounces of gold in the mine. We again assume that the term structure of interest rates is flat at 10%. Also, the profit from mining is determined on the basis of the price of gold at the beginning of the period, and in this example all cash flows occur at the beginning of the period.

To solve this problem we must do some preliminary analysis. At the final time the value of the lease is clearly zero. If we are at a node representing the end of year 9, we must determine the optimal amount of gold to mine during the tenth year. Accordingly, we must compute the profit

$$V_9(x_9) = \max_{z_9}(gz_9 - 500z_9^2/x_9)$$

where g is the price of gold at that particular node. From the calculations of Example 5.5 we know that the maximization gives

$$V_9(x_9) = \frac{g^2 x_9}{2,000}.$$

This shows that the value of the lease is proportional to x_9, the amount of gold remaining. We therefore write $V_9(x_9) = K_9 x_9$, where

$$K_9 = \frac{g^2}{2,000}.$$

---

[3] This is a more difficult example, which should be studied only after you are fairly comfortable with the material of this chapter.

0	1	2	3	4	5	6	7	8	9	10
324.4	393.8	478.1	580.8	706.6	862.3	1058.7	1313.4	1656.1	2129.9	0.0
	272.5	329.9	398.6	480.7	578.4	694.4	831.7	995.0	1198.0	0.0
		225.8	272.2	327.0	390.7	463.4	542.9	621.9	673.9	0.0
			182.8	218.9	260.0	305.2	351.1	387.3	379.1	0.0
				143.6	169.5	197.0	222.5	237.3	213.2	0.0
K-value					108.1	124.4	138.1	142.8	119.9	0.0
						76.9	84.1	84.6	67.5	0.0
							50.3	49.5	37.9	0.0
								28.7	21.3	0.0
									12.0	0.0
										0.0

FIGURE 12.12   Complexico gold mine solution. The value of the mine is proportional to the amount of gold remaining in the mine. The proportionality factor K is found by backward recursion.

We set up a lattice of K values with nodes corresponding to various gold prices. We put $K_{10} = 0$ for all elements in the last column and put the values of K_9 in the ninth column. In a similar way, following the analysis of the earlier example, we find that for a node at time 8,

$$V_8(x_8) = \max_{z_8}[g z_8 - 500 z_8^2/x_8 + d\hat{K}_9 \times (x_8 - z_8)]$$

where

$$\hat{K}_9 = q K_9 + (1-q) K_9'$$

and where K_9 is the value on the node directly to the right, and K_9' is the value on the node just below that. This leads to

$$z_8 = \frac{(g - d\hat{K}_9)x_8}{1,000}$$

and $V_8(x_8) = K_8 x_8$, where

$$K_8 = \frac{(g - \hat{K}_9/R)^2}{2,000} + \hat{K}_9/R .$$

Again, there will be a different value of K_8 for each node at period 8. We work backward with this same formula to complete the lattice shown in Figure 12.12, obtaining $K_0 = 324.4$. The value of the lease is then found as $V_0 = 50,000 \times K_0 = \$16,220,000$.

Real Options

Sometimes options are associated with investment opportunities that are not financial instruments. For example, when operating a factory, a manager may have the option of hiring additional employees or buying new equipment. As another example, if one acquires a piece of land, one has the option to drill for oil, and then later the option of extracting oil if oil is found. In fact, it is possible to view almost any process that allows control as a process with a series of operational options. These operational options are often termed **real options** to emphasize that they involve *real* activities or *real* commodities, as opposed to purely financial commodities, as in the case, for instance, of stock options. The term *real option* when applied to a general investment problem is also used to imply that options theory can (and should) be used to analyze the problem.

Example 12.9 (A plant manager's problem)   Some manufacturing plants can be described by a **fixed cost** per month (for equipment, management, and rent) and a **variable cost** (for material, labor, and utilities) that is proportional to the level of production. The total cost is therefore $T = F + Vx$, where F is the fixed cost, V is the rate of variable cost, and x is the amount of product produced. The profit of the plant in a month in which it operates at level x is $\pi = px - F - Vx$, where p is the market price of its product. Clearly, if $p > V$, the firm will operate at x equal to the maximum capacity of the plant; if $p < V$, it will not operate. Hence the firm has a continuing option to operate, with a strike price equal to the rate of variable cost. (The Simplico gold mine in Example 12.7 is of this type.)

Real options usually can be analyzed by the same methods used to analyze financial options. Specifically, one sets up an appropriate representation of uncertainty, usually with a binomial lattice, and works backward to find the value. This solution process is really more fundamental than its particular application to options, so it seems unnecessary and sometimes artificial to force all opportunities for control into options—real or otherwise. Instead, the seasoned analyst takes problems as they come and attacks them directly.

The Simplico mine can be used to illustrate a complex real option associated with the timing of an investment.

Example 12.10 (Enhancement of the Simplico mine★)   Recall that the Simplico mine is capable of producing 10,000 ounces of gold per year at a cost of $200 per ounce. This mine already consists of a whole series of real options—namely, the yearly options to carry out mining operations. In fact, the value of the lease can be expressed as a sum of the values of these individual options (although this viewpoint is not particularly helpful). In this example we wish to consider another option, which is truly in the spirit of a real option.

Suppose that there is a possibility of enhancing the production rate of the Simplico mine by purchasing a new mining machine and making some structural changes in the mine. This enhancement would cost $4 million but would raise the mine capability by 25% to 12,500 ounces per year, at a total operating cost of $240 per ounce.

This enhancement alternative is an option, since it need not be carried out. Furthermore, it is an option that is available throughout the term of the lease. The enhancement can be undertaken (that is, exercised) at the beginning of any year, and once in place it applies to all future years. We assume, however, that at the termination of the lease, the enhancement becomes the property of the original mine owner.

Figure 12.13 shows how to calculate the value of the lease when the enhancement option is available. We first calculate the value of the lease assuming that the enhancement is already in place. This calculation is made by constructing the upper lattice of the figure, using exactly the same technique used for the Simplico mine of Example 12.7, but with the new capacity and operating cost figures. The value of the mine under these conditions is $27.0 million. This figure does not include the cost of the enhancement, so if we were to enhance the mine at time zero, the net value of the lease would be $23.0 million, which is somewhat less than the value of $24.1 found earlier without the enhancement. Hence it is not useful to carry out the enhancement immediately.

To find the value of the enhancement option, we construct another lattice, as shown in the lower part of the figure. Here we use the original parameters for production capability and operating cost: 100,000 ounces per year and $200 per ounce. However, at each node, in addition to the usual calculation of value, we see if it would be useful to jump up to the upper lattice by paying $4 million. Specifically, we first calculate the value at a node in the lower lattice in the normal way using risk-neutral probabilities. Then we compare this value with the value at the corresponding node in the upper lattice minus $4 million. We then put the larger of these two values at the node in the lower lattice.

0	1	2	3	4	5	6	7	8	9	10
27.0	31.8	36.4	40.4	43.5	45.2	44.8	41.4	33.9	20.7	0.0
	19.5	23.3	26.6	29.3	31.0	31.2	29.2	24.1	14.9	0.0
		13.5	16.3	18.7	20.4	21.0	20.0	16.8	10.5	0.0
			8.6	10.8	12.5	13.4	13.2	11.3	7.2	0.0
				4.9	6.5	7.7	8.0	7.2	4.7	0.0
Lease value					2.3	3.4	4.1	4.1	2.8	0.0
assuming enhancement						0.8	1.3	1.8	1.4	0.0
in place							0.1	0.2	0.4	0.0
								0.0	0.0	0.0
									0.0	0.0
										0.0
24.6	28.6	32.6	**36.4**	**39.5**	**41.2**	**40.8**	**37.4**	**29.9**	16.9	0
	18.0	20.9	23.5	25.6	**27.0**	**27.2**	**25.2**	**20.1**	12.3	0
		12.9	15.0	16.7	17.9	18.1	17.0	14.1	8.7	0
			8.8	10.4	11.5	12.0	11.5	9.7	6.1	0
				5.6	6.7	7.4	7.4	6.4	4.1	0
Lease with option					3.1	4.0	4.3	3.9	2.6	0
for enhancement						1.3	2.0	2.1	1.5	0
							0.0	0.7	0.7	0
								0.0	0.1	0
									0.0	0
										0

FIGURE 12.13 Option to enhance mine operation. The top array is computed just as for the Simplico mine, but with parameters of enhancement. The lower array refers to the top one to determine when to carry out the enhancement.

The figures in boldface type show nodes where it is advantageous to jump to the upper lattice by carrying out the enhancement. Note that these values are exactly $4 million less than their upper counterparts.

The overall value of the lease with the option is given by the value at the first node, and the $4 million is already taken out. Hence the value of the lease with the enhancement option is $24.6 million—a slight improvement over the original value of $24.1 million.

Linear Pricing

Although we generally use risk-neutral pricing to evaluate derivative securities, it is important to recognize that this evaluation is based on linear pricing; that is, we match a particular derivative to securities we know and then add up the values. The following example highlights the basic simplicity of the method.

Example 12.11 (Gavin explains)   Mr. D. Jones was curious about quantitative work on Wall Street. He brought it up with his son Gavin.

"What are they calculating with all those fancy computers?"

Gavin said that it was all based on linear pricing. "They break a security into its separate pieces, price each piece, and then add them up."

"Are you kidding me? I don't see why you need a supercomputer to do that."

"It gets complicated quickly." Gavin remembered something he had worked out when studying options theory. "I'll show you an example," he said, as he fished in his pocket for a twenty-five cent piece.

Holding the coin up, Gavin began, "Consider this proposition: You pay $1. I flip this coin. If it is heads, you get $3; if it is tails, you get nothing. You can participate at any level you wish, and the payoff scales accordingly."

Mr. Jones nodded. Gavin continued. "The coin flip is like a stock. It has a price, and its outcome is uncertain; but it has a positive expected value—otherwise nobody would invest in it."

"That's simple enough."

"Alternatively, as a second proposition, you can just keep your dollar in your pocket. This is equivalent to paying $1. I flip the coin. If it is heads, you get $1; if it is tails you get $1. Clear?"

"Sure."

"Those are the basic ones. Now here is a new proposition to evaluate: I flip the coin twice. If at least one of the flips is a head, you get $9; otherwise you get nothing. How much is this proposition worth?"

Mr. Jones scratched his head, and after a few seconds said, "I could work out the probabilities."

"It has nothing to do with actual probabilities. This proposition can be expressed as combinations of the other two. We just add up the pieces."

"Okay, show me."

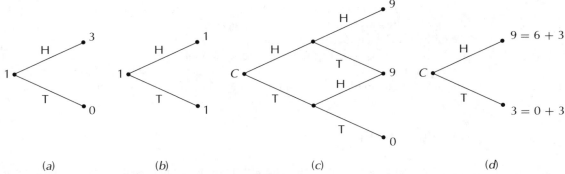

FIGURE 12.14   A proposition and its parts. Tree (a) is a basic risky proposition; tree (b) is a risk-free opportunity; and tree (c) represents a new, more complex proposition. The value C can be found by breaking it into its parts. The final piece is shown in (d).

Gavin drew four trees on the edge of a newspaper, as shown in Figure 12.14. He explained that tree (a) is the original proposition; (b) is keeping money in your pocket, and (c) is the new proposition, with an unknown price C.

If the first flip is heads, the tree from that point has payoff of $9 in each direction, which looks like nine times the payoff of the pocket alternative. It is worth $9 to be there. If the first flip is tails, the tree from that point looks like three times the original proposition, so it is worth $3 to be there. Hence the whole thing is equivalent to tree (d) having payoffs of $9 and $3. "Clear?"

"Very."

Gavin showed that the payoff of 9 and 3 could be broken into 6 and 0 plus 3 and 3. The first of these is twice the original proposition. The second is three times the pocket alternative. Hence $C = 2 + 3 = \$5$. "Okay?"

"Well, I'll be."

Gavin concluded. "That is what those computers are doing. Derivative securities are evaluated by using hundreds of coin flips to represent the daily movements of a stock. The computers work through the big tree just like we did in this example."

[As an exercise, it is useful to determine the risk-neutral probabilities for this example and work through the risk-neutral valuation.]

12.9 GENERAL RISK-NEUTRAL PRICING*

A general principle of risk-neutral pricing can be inferred from the analysis and methods of the previous few sections. This principle provides a compact formula for the price of a derivative security under the binomial lattice formulation.

Suppose that the price S of an asset is described by a binomial lattice, and suppose that f is a security whose cash flow at any time k is a function only of the node at time k. Then the arbitrage-free price of the asset is

$$f_{val} = \hat{E}\left(\sum_{k=0}^{N} d_k f_k\right).$$ (12.12)

In this equation the summation represents the discounted cash flow, with the d_k's being the risk-free discount factors as seen at time 0. The f_k's are the period cash flows, which depend on the particular node at k that occurs. Hence the f_k's are random. The expectation $\hat{E}$ is taken with respect to the risk-neutral probabilities associated with the lattice of the underlying asset.

Consider a European call option with strike price K. The pricing formula, Eq. (12.12), becomes

$$C = \frac{1}{R_T}\hat{E}[\max(S_T - K, 0)]$$ (12.13)

where R_T is the risk-free return for the whole time to expiration. In this case there is only a single cash flow, $\max(S_T - K, 0)$, occurring at the final time. We take the risk-neutral expected value of this and discount it to the present. Note that actual calculation using this formula is best done by working backward from the end. We use the running present value method to back the formula up one stage at a time.

In many situations the cash flow stream can be influenced by our actions as well as by chance. For instance, we may have the opportunity to exercise an option before expiration, decide how much gold to mine, or add enhancements. In such cases the general pricing formula becomes

$$f_{val} = \max\left[\hat{E}\left(\sum_{k=0}^{N} d_k f_k\right)\right]$$

where the maximization is taken with respect to the available actions. We have seen in the examples of this chapter how this maximization can in many cases be carried out as part of the backward recursion process, although the size of the lattice sometimes must be increased. This general formula has great power, for it provides a way to formulate and solve many interesting and important investment problems.

12.10 SUMMARY

An option is the right, but not the obligation, to buy (or sell) an asset under specified terms. Options have had a checkered past, but for the past two decades they have played an important role in finance. Used wisely, they can control risk and enhance the performance of a portfolio. Used carelessly, options can greatly increase risk and lead to substantial losses.

Options terminology includes: call, put, exercise, strike price, expiration, writing a call, premium, in the money, out of the money, American option, and European option.

A major topic of options theory is the determination of the correct price (or premium) of an option. This price depends on the price of the underlying asset, the strike price, the time to expiration, the volatility of the underlying asset, the cash flow generated by the asset (such as dividend payments), and the prevailing interest rate. Although determination of an appropriate option price can be difficult, certain relations can be derived from simple no-arbitrage arguments. For example, for European-style options there is parity between a put and a call with the same strike price. Likewise, the value of a combination of options (such as in a butterfly spread) must be the same combination of the prices of the component options.

One important result is that it is never optimal to exercise, before expiration, an American call option on a stock that does not pay a dividend before expiration.

A general way to find the price of an option is to use the binomial lattice methodology. The random process of the underlying asset is modeled as a binomial lattice. The value of the option at expiration is entered on the final nodes of a corresponding option lattice. The other nodes in the option lattice are computed one at a time by working backward through the periods. For a European-style option (without the possibility of early exercise) the value at any node in the option lattice is found by computing the expected value of the value next period using risk-neutral probabilities. This expected value is then discounted by the effect of one period's interest rate. If the option is an American-style option, the value computed as before must be compared with the value that could be obtained by exercise at that time, and the greater of the two compared values is taken to be the final value for that node.

The risk-neutral probabilities are easy to calculate. The risk-neutral probability for an up move is $q = (R - d)/(u - d)$. The easiest way to derive this formula is to find the q that makes the price of the underlying security equal to the discounted expected value of its next period value.

The binomial lattice methodology can be used to find the value of other investments besides options. Indeed, it can be used to evaluate any project whose cash flow stream is determined by an underlying traded asset. Examples include futures on options, gold mine leases, oil wells, and tree farms. With ingenuity, even complex real options can be evaluated by constructing two or more interrelated binomial lattices.

EXERCISES

1. (Bull spread)   An investor who is bullish about a stock (believing that it will rise) may wish to construct a *bull spread* for that stock. One way to construct such a spread is to buy a call with strike price K_1 and sell a call with the same expiration date but with a strike price of $K_2 > K_1$. Draw the payoff curve for such a spread. Is the initial cost of the spread positive or negative?

2. (Put–call parity)   Suppose over the period $[0, T]$ a certain stock pays a dividend whose present value at interest rate r is D. Show that the put–call parity relation for European options at $t = 0$, expiring at T, is

$$C + D + Kd = P + S$$

where d is the discount factor from 0 to T.

3. (Parity formula) To derive the put–call parity formula, the payoff associated with buying one call option, selling one put option, and lending dK is $Q = \max(0, S - K) - \max(0, K - S) + K$. Show that $Q = S$, and hence derive the put–call parity formula.

4. (Call strikes ◊) Consider a family of call options on a non-dividend-paying stock, each option being identical except for its strike price. The value of the call with strike price K is denoted by $C(K)$. Prove the following three general relations using arbitrage arguments:

(a) $K_2 > K_1$ implies $C(K_1) \geq C(K_2)$.

(b) $K_2 > K_1$ implies $K_2 - K_1 \geq C(K_1) - C(K_2)$.

(c) $K_3 > K_2 > K_1$ implies

$$C(K_2) \leq \left(\frac{K_3 - K_2}{K_3 - K_1} \right) C(K_1) + \left(\frac{K_2 - K_1}{K_3 - K_1} \right) C(K_3).$$

5. (Fixed dividend ⊕) Suppose that a stock will pay a dividend of amount D at time τ. We wish to determine the price of a European call option on this stock using the lattice method. Accordingly, the time interval $[0, T]$ covering the life of the option is divided into N intervals, and hence $N + 1$ time periods are assigned. Assume that the dividend date τ occurs somewhere between periods k and $k + 1$. One approach to the problem would be to establish a lattice of stock prices in the usual way, but subtract D from the nodes at period k. This produces a tree with nodes that do not recombine, as shown in Figure 12.15.

The problem can be solved this way, but there is another representation that does recombine. Since the dividend amount is known, we regard it as a nonrandom component of the stock price. At any time before the dividend we regard the price as having two components: a random component S^* and a deterministic component equal to the present value of the future dividend. The random component S^* is described by a lattice with initial value $S(0) - De^{-r\tau}$ and with u and d determined by the volatility σ of the stock. The option is evaluated on this lattice. The only modification that must be made in the computation is that when valuing the option at a node, the stock price used in the valuation formula is not just S^* at that node, but rather $S = S^* + De^{-r(\tau-t)}$ for $t < \tau$. Use this technique to find the value of a 6-month call option with $S(0) = 50$, $K = 50$, $\sigma = 20\%$, $R = 10\%$, and $D = \$3$ to be paid in $3\frac{1}{2}$ months.

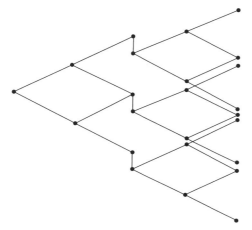

FIGURE 12.15 Nonrecombining dividend tree.

6. (Call inequality)   Consider a European call option on a non-dividend-paying stock. The strike price is K, the time to expiration is T, and the price of one unit of a zero-coupon bond maturing at T is $B(T)$. Denote the price of the call by $C(S, T)$. Show that

$$C(S, T) \geq \max [0, S - K B(T)].$$

[*Hint:* Consider two portfolios: (*a*) purchase one call, (*b*) purchase one share of stock and sell K bonds.]

7. (Perpetual call)   A perpetual option is one that never expires. (Such an option must be of American style.) Use Exercise 6 to show that the value of a perpetual call on a non-dividend-paying stock is $C = S$.

8. (A surprise ⊕)   Consider a deterministic cash flow stream $(x_0, x_1, x_2, \ldots, x_n)$ with all positive flows. Let $\mathrm{PV}(r)$ denote the present value of this stream at an interest rate r.

(*a*) If r decreases, does $\mathrm{PV}(r)$ increase or decrease?

(*b*) Solve the Simplico gold mine problem with $r = 4\%$ and find that the value of the lease is $22.1 million. Can you explain why the value decreased relative to its value with $r = 10\%$?

9. (My coin)   There are two propositions: (*a*) I flip a coin. If it is heads, you are paid $3; if it is tails, you are paid $0. It costs you $1 to participate in this proposition. You may do so at any level, or repeatedly, and the payoffs scale accordingly. (*b*) You may keep your money in your pocket (earning no interest). Here is a third proposition: (*c*) I flip the coin three times. If at least two of the flips are heads, you are paid $27; otherwise zero. How much is this proposition worth?

10. (The happy call)   A New York firm is offering a new financial instrument called a "happy call." It has a payoff function at time T equal to $\max(.5S, S - K)$, where S is the price of a stock and K is a fixed strike price. You always get something with a happy call. Let P be the price of the stock at time $t = 0$ and let C_1 and C_2 be the prices of ordinary calls with strike prices K and $2K$, respectively. The fair price of the happy call is of the form

$$C_H = \alpha P + \beta C_1 + \gamma C_2.$$

Find the constants α, β, and γ.

11. (You are a president)   It is August 6. You are the president of a small electronics company. The company has some cash reserves that will not be needed for about 3 months, but interest rates are very low. Your chief financial officer (CFO) tells you that a progressive securities firm has an investment that guarantees no losses and allows participation in upward movements of the stock market. In fact, the total rate of return until the third week of November is to be determined by the formula $\max(0, .25r)$, where r is the rate of return on the S&P 100 stock index during the 3-month period (ignoring dividends). The CFO suggests that this conservative investment might be an ideal alternative to participation in the interest rate market and asks for your opinion. You pick up *The Wall Street Journal* and make a few simple calculations to check whether it is, in fact, a good deal. Show these calculations and the conclusion. Use the data in Table 12.1. (Note that 410c denotes a call with strike price 410.)

TABLE 12.1
Data for the President

S&P 100 index	Options		S&P index = 414.74
Nov	410c	13	Treasury bills
Nov	410p	$8\frac{1}{4}$	Nov 12: yield = 3.11
Nov	420c	$7\frac{1}{2}$	
Nov	420p	$11\frac{1}{4}$	

Source: Standard & Poor's, a division of the McGraw-Hill Companies. Reprinted with permission.

12. (Simplico invariance)   If the Simplico mine is solved with all parameters remaining the same except that $u = 1.2$ is changed to $u = 1.3$, the value of the lease remains unchanged to within three decimal places. Indeed, quite wide variations in u and d have almost no influence on the lease price. Give an intuitive explanation for this.

13. (Change of period length ⊕)   A stock has volatility $\sigma = .30$ and a current value of $36. A put option on this stock has a strike price of $40 and expiration is in 5 months. The interest rate is 8%. Find the value of this put using a binomial lattice with 1-month intervals. Repeat using a lattice with half-month intervals.

14. (Average value Complexico ⊕)   Suppose that the price received for gold extracted from time k to $k+1$ is the average of the price of gold at these two times; that is, $(g_k + g_{k+1})/2$. However, costs are incurred at the beginning of the period whereas revenues are received at the end of the period. Find the value of the Complexico mine in this case.

15. ("As you like it" option)   Consider the stock of Examples 12.3 and 12.4, which has $\sigma = .20$ and an initial price of $62. The interest rate is 10%, compounded monthly. Consider a 5-month option with a strike price of $60. This option can be declared, after exactly 3 months, by the purchaser to be either a European call or a European put. Find the value of this "as you like it" option.

16. (Tree harvesting ⊕)   You are considering an investment in a tree farm. Trees grow each year by the following factors:

Year	1	2	3	4	5	6	7	8	9	10
Growth	1.6	1.5	1.4	1.3	1.2	1.15	1.1	1.05	1.02	1.01

The price of lumber follows a binomial lattice with $u = 1.20$ and $d = .9$. The interest rate is constant at 10%. It costs $2 million each year, payable at the beginning of the year, to lease the forest land. The initial value of the trees is $5 million (assuming they were harvested immediately). You can cut the trees at the end of any year and then not pay rent after that. (For those readers who care, we assume that cut lumber can be stored at no cost.)

(a) Argue that if the rent were zero, you would never cut the trees as long as they were growing.

(b) With rent of $2 million per year, find the best cutting policy and the value of the investment opportunity.

REFERENCES

For general background material on options, see [1–3]. The pricing of options was originally addressed mathematically by Bachelier [4] using a statistical approach. The analysis of put–call parity and various price inequalities that hold independently of the underlying stock process was systematically developed in [5]. The rational option price based on the no-arbitrage principle was first discovered by Black and Scholes [6] when the price of the underlying asset was governed by geometric Brownian motion. The simplified approach using a binomial lattice was first presented in [7] and later developed in [8, 9]. The risk-neutral formulation of option evaluation was generalized to other derivatives in [10]. Exercise 4 is adopted from [2].

1. Gastineau, G. L. (1975), *The Stock Options Manual*, McGraw-Hill, New York.
2. Cox, J. C., and M. Rubinstein (1985), *Options Markets*, Prentice Hall, Englewood Cliffs, NJ.
3. Hull, J. C. (1993), *Options, Futures, and Other Derivative Securities*, 2nd ed., Prentice Hall, Englewood Cliffs, NJ.
4. Bachelier, L. (1900), "Théorie de la Spéculation," *Annals de l'Ecole Normale Superieure,* **17,** 21–86. English translation by A. J. Boness (1967) in *The Random Character of Stock Market Prices*, P. H. Cootner, Ed., M.I.T. Press, Cambridge, MA, 17–78.
5. Merton, R. C. (1973), "Theory of Rational Option Pricing," *Bell Journal of Economics and Management Science,* **4,** 141–183.
6. Black, F., and M. Scholes (1973), "The Pricing of Options and Corporate Liabilities," *Journal of Political Economy,* **81,** 637–654.
7. Sharpe, W. F. (1978), *Investments,* Prentice Hall, Englewood Cliffs, NJ.
8. Cox, J. C., S. A. Ross, and M. Rubinstein (1979), "Option Pricing: A Simplified Approach," *Journal of Financial Economics,* **7,** 229–263.
9. Rendleman, R. J., Jr., and B. J. Bartter (1979), "Two-State Option Pricing," *Journal of Finance,* **34,** 1093–1110.
10. Harrison, J. M., and D. M. Kreps (1979), "Martingales and Arbitrage in Multiperiod Securities Markets," *Journal of Economic Theory,* **20,** 381–408.

Appendix A

BASIC PROBABILITY THEORY

A.1 GENERAL CONCEPTS

As discussed in Chapter 6, a random variable x is described by its **probability density function.** If x can take on only a finite number of values, say, $x_1, x_2, \ldots, x_m$, then the density function gives the probability of each of those outcome values. We may express the probability density function as $p(\xi)$, and it has nonzero values only at values of ξ equal to $x_1, x_2, \ldots, x_m$. Specifically,

$$p(x_i) = \text{prob}(x_i);$$

that is, $p(x_i)$ is the probability that x takes on the value x_i. We always have $p(\xi) \geq 0$ for all x. Also, $\sum_i p(x_i) = 1$.

If the random variable x can take on a continuum of values, such as all real numbers, then the probability density function $p(\xi)$ is also defined for all these values. The interpretation in this case is, roughly, that

$$p(\xi)\, d\xi = \text{prob}(\xi \leq x \leq \xi + d\xi).$$

The **probability distribution** of the random variable x is the function $F(\xi)$ defined as

$$F(\xi) = \text{prob}(x \leq \xi).$$

It follows that $F(-\infty) = 0$ and $F(\infty) = 1$. In the case of a continuum of values, if F is differentiable at ξ, then $dF(\xi)/d\xi = p(\xi)$.

Two random variables x and y are described by their **joint probability density** or **joint probability distribution.** The joint distribution is the function F defined as

$$F(\xi, \eta) = \text{prob}(x \leq \xi, y \leq \eta).$$

The joint density is defined in terms of derivatives, or if there are only a finite number of possible outcomes, the joint density at a pair x_i, y_j is $p(x_i, y_j)$ equal to the probability of that pair occurring. In general, n random variables are defined by their joint probability distribution defined with respect to n variables.

From a joint distribution the distribution of any one of the random variables can be easily recovered. For example, given the distribution $F(\xi, \eta)$ of x and y, the distribution of x is

$$F_x(\xi) = F(\xi, \infty).$$

The random variables x and y are **independent** if the density function factors into the form

$$p(\xi, \eta) = p_x(\xi) p_y(\eta).$$

This is the case for the pair of random variables defined as the outcomes on two fair tosses of a die. For example, the probability of obtaining the pair (3, 5) is $\frac{1}{6} \times \frac{1}{6}$.

The **expected value** of a random variable x with density function p is

$$E(x) = \int_{-\infty}^{\infty} \xi \, p(\xi) \, d\xi.$$

If $E(x)$ is denoted by $\overline{x}$, the **variance** of x is

$$\mathrm{var}(x) = \int_{-\infty}^{\infty} (\xi - \overline{x})^2 p(\xi) \, d\xi.$$

Likewise the **covariance** of x and y is

$$\mathrm{cov}(x, y) = \int_{-\infty}^{\infty} \int_{-\infty}^{\infty} (\xi - \overline{x})(\eta - \overline{y}) p(\xi, \eta) \, d\xi \, d\eta.$$

It is easy to show that if x and y are independent, then they have zero covariance.

A.2 NORMAL RANDOM VARIABLES

A random variable x is said to be **normal** or **Gaussian** if its probability density function is of the form

$$p(\xi) = \frac{1}{\sqrt{2\pi}\sigma} e^{-\frac{1}{2\sigma^2}(\xi - \mu)^2}.$$

In this case the expected value of x is $\overline{x} = \mu$ and the variance of x is σ^2. This density function is the characteristic "bell-shaped" curve, illustrated in Figure A.1.

A normal random variable is **normalized** or **standard** if $\overline{x} = 0$ and $\sigma^2 = 1$. Thus a standard normal random variable has the density function (written in terms of the variable x)

$$p(x) = \frac{1}{\overline{2\pi}} e^{-\frac{1}{2}x^2}.$$

The corresponding standard distribution is denoted by N and given by the expression

$$N(x) = \frac{1}{\overline{2\pi}} \int_{-\infty}^{x} e^{-\frac{1}{2}\xi^2} \, d\xi.$$

There is no analytic expression for $N(x)$, but because of its importance, tables of its values and analytic approximations are available.

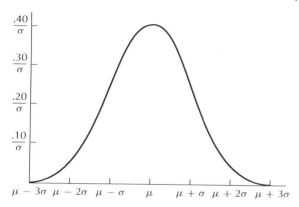

To work with more than one normal random variable it is convenient to use matrix notation. We let $\mathbf{x} = (x_1, x_2, \ldots, x_n)$ be a vector of n random variables. The expected value of this vector is the vector $\overline{\mathbf{x}}$, whose components are the expected values of the components of $\mathbf{x}$. The **covariance matrix** associated with $\mathbf{x}$ is the $n \times n$ matrix $\mathbf{Q}$ with components $[\mathbf{Q}]_{ij} = \mathrm{cov}(x_i, x_j)$. If $\mathbf{x}$ is regarded as a column vector and $\mathbf{x}^T$ is the corresponding row vector, then $\mathbf{Q}$ can be expressed as

$$\mathbf{Q} = \mathrm{E}[(\mathbf{x} - \overline{\mathbf{x}})(\mathbf{x} - \overline{\mathbf{x}})^T].$$

If the n variables are jointly normal, the distribution of $\mathbf{x}$ is

$$p(\mathbf{x}) = \frac{1}{(2\pi)^{n/2}|\mathbf{Q}|^{1/2}} e^{-\frac{1}{2}(\mathbf{x} - \overline{\mathbf{x}})^T \mathbf{Q}^{-1}(\mathbf{x} - \overline{\mathbf{x}})}.$$

If two jointly normal random variables are uncorrelated, then it is easy to see that the joint density function factors into a product of densities for the two separate variables. Hence if two jointly normal random variables are uncorrelated, they are independent.

A most important property of jointly normal random variables is the summation property. Specifically, if x and y are jointly normal, then all random variables of the form $\alpha x + \beta y$, where α and β are constants, are also normal. This result is easily extended to higher order sums. In fact if $\mathbf{x}$ is a column vector of jointly normal random variables and $\mathbf{T}$ is an $m \times n$ matrix, then the vector $\mathbf{Tx}$ is an m-dimensional vector of jointly normal random variables.

A.3 LOGNORMAL RANDOM VARIABLES

A random variable z is lognormal if the random variable $\ln z$ is normal. Equivalently, if x is normal, then $z = e^x$ is lognormal. In concrete terms this means that the density function for z has the form

$$p(\zeta) = \frac{1}{\sqrt{2\pi}\,\sigma\zeta} e^{-\frac{1}{2\sigma^2}(\ln \zeta - \nu)^2}.$$

We have the following values:

$$E(z) = e^{(\nu + \sigma^2/2)} \tag{A.1}$$

$$E(\ln z) = \nu \tag{A.2}$$

$$\text{var}(z) = e^{(2\nu + \sigma^2)} (e^{\sigma^2} - 1) \tag{A.3}$$

$$\text{var}(\ln z) = \sigma^2. \tag{A.4}$$

It follows from the summation result for jointly normal random variables that products and powers of jointly lognormal variables are again lognormal. For example, if u and v are lognormal, then $z = u^\alpha v^\beta$ is also lognormal.

Appendix B

CALCULUS AND OPTIMIZATION

This appendix reviews the essential elements of calculus and optimization mathematics used in the text.

B.1 FUNCTIONS

A function assigns a value that depends on its independent variables. Usually a function is denoted by a single letter, such as f. If the value of f depends on a single variable x, the corresponding function value is denoted by $f(x)$. An example is the function $f(x) = x^2 - 3x$. We can evaluate this function at $x = 2$ as $f(2) = 2^2 - 3 \times 2 = -2$. Although a function is most properly called by its name, such as f, it is sometimes convenient, and quite common, to refer to $f(x)$ as a function, even though $f(x)$ really is the value of f at x.

A function may be defined only for certain numerical values. In many cases, for example, a function is defined only for integer values, in which case the independent variable is usually denoted by i, j, k, m, or n. An example is the function $d(n) = 1/(1 + r)^n$, which is the discount function.

Functions of several variables are also important. For example, a function g may depend on two variables x and y, in which case the value of g at x and y is $g(x, y)$. An example is $g(x, y) = x^2 + 3xy - y^2$.

Certain types of functions are commonly used in investment science. These include:

1. **Exponential functions** An exponential function is a function of a single variable of the form

$$f(t) = ac^{bt}$$

where a, b, and c are constants. Very often the constant c is $e = 2.7182818\ldots$, the base of the natural logarithm.

The exponential function also arises when the variable is restricted to be an integer, such as the function $k(n) = (1+r)^n$, which shows how capital grows under compound interest. In this case the function is said to exhibit geometric growth, or to be a geometric growth function.

2. **Logarithmic functions**   The natural logarithm is the function denoted by ln, which satisfies the relation

$$e^{\ln(x)} = x.$$

Some important values are $\ln(1) = 0$, $\ln(e) = 1$, and $\ln(0) = -\infty$.

3. **Linear functions**   A linear function of a single variable x has the form $f(x) = ax$, where a is a constant. A function f of several variables $x_1, x_2, \ldots, x_n$ is linear if it has the form

$$f(x_1, x_2, \ldots, x_n) = a_1 x_1 + a_2 x_2 + \cdots + a_n x_n$$

for some constants $a_1, a_2, \ldots, a_n$.

4. **Inverse functions**   A function f has an inverse function g if for every x there holds $g(f(x)) = x$. Often the inverse function is denoted by f^{-1}.

   As an example consider the function $f(x) = x^2$. This function has the inverse $f^{-1}(y) = \sqrt{y}$. Clearly $f^{-1}(f(x)) = \sqrt{x^2} = x$. As another example, if f is the logarithmic function $f(x) = \ln(x)$, then the inverse function is $f^{-1}(y) = e^y$ because $e^{\ln(x)} = x$. It is also true that if g is the inverse of f, then f is the inverse of g. For example, we know that $\ln(e^x) = x$.

5. **Vector notation**   When working with several variables it is convenient to regard them as a vector and write, for example, $\mathbf{x} = (x_1, x_2, \ldots, x_n)$. We then write the value of a function of these variables as $f(\mathbf{x})$.

B.2 DIFFERENTIAL CALCULUS

It is assumed that the reader is familiar with differential calculus. We shall review a certain number of concepts that are used in the text.

1. **Limits**   Differential calculus is based on the notion of a limit of a function. If the function value $f(x)$ approaches the value L as x approaches x_0, we write

$$L = \lim_{x \to x_0} f(x).$$

An example is $\lim_{x \to \infty} 1/x = 0$.

2. **Derivatives**   Given a function f, the derivative of f at x is

$$\frac{df(x)}{dx} = \lim_{\Delta x \to 0} \frac{f(x + \Delta x) - f(x)}{\Delta x}.$$

Sometimes we write $f'(x)$ for the derivative of f at x. It is important to know these common derivatives:

   (a) If $f(x) = x^n$, then $f'(x) = nx^{n-1}$.
   (b) If $f(x) = e^{ax}$, then $f'(x) = ae^{ax}$.
   (c) If $f(x) = \ln(x)$, then $f'(x) = 1/x$.

3. **Higher order derivatives**   Higher order derivatives are formed by taking derivatives of derivatives. For example, the second derivative of f is the derivative of the function f'. We denote the nth derivative of f by $d^n f/dx^n$. In the special case of the second derivative we often use the alternative notation f''.

As an example, consider the function $f(x) = \ln(x)$. The first derivative is $f'(x) = 1/x$; the second derivative is $f''(x) = -1/x^2$.

4. **Partial derivatives**   A function of several variables can be differentiated partially with respect to each of its arguments. We define

$$\frac{\partial f(x_1, x_2, \ldots, x_n)}{\partial x_i} = \lim_{\Delta x \to 0} \frac{f(x_1, x_2, \ldots, x_i + \Delta x, x_{i+1}, \ldots, x_n) - f(x_1, x_2, \ldots, x_n)}{\Delta x}.$$

For example, suppose $f(x, y) = x^2 + 3xy - y^2$. Then $\partial f(x, y)/\partial x = 2x + 3y$ and $\partial f(x, y)/\partial y = 3x - 2y$.

We write the total differential of f as

$$df = \frac{\partial f}{\partial x_1}dx_1 + \frac{\partial f}{\partial x_2}dx_2 + \cdots + \frac{\partial f}{\partial x_n}dx_n.$$

5. **Approximation**   A function f can be approximated in a region near a given point x_0 by using its derivatives. The following two approximations are especially useful:

(*a*) $f(x_0 + \Delta x) = f'(x_0)\Delta x + O(\Delta x)^2$
(*b*) $f(x_0 + \Delta x) = f(x_0)\Delta x + \frac{1}{2}f''(x_0)(\Delta x)^2 + O(\Delta x)^3$

where $O(\Delta x)^2$ and $O(\Delta x)^3$ denote terms of order $(\Delta x)^2$ and $(\Delta x)^3$, respectively. These approximations apply only to ordinary functions with well-defined derivatives. They do not apply to functions that contain Wiener processes. (See Chapter 11.)

B.3 OPTIMIZATION

Optimization is a very useful tool for investment problems. This section reviews only the barest essentials; but these are sufficient for most of the work in the text.

1. **Necessary conditions**   A function f of a single variable x is said to have a maximum at a point x_0 if $f(x_0) \geq f(x)$ for all x. If the point x_0 is not at a boundary point of an interval over which f is defined, then if x_0 is a maximum point, it is necessary that the derivative of f be zero at x_0; that is,

$$f'(x_0) = 0.$$

This equation can be used to find the maximum point x_0.

For example, consider the function $f(x) = -x^2 + 12x$. To find the maximum, we set the derivative equal to zero to obtain the equation $-2x + 12 = 0$. This has solution $x = 6$, which is the maximum point.

A similar result holds when the function f depends on several variables. At a maximum point (with none of the variables at a boundary point) each of the partial derivatives of f must be zero. In other words, at the maximum point,

$$\frac{\partial f(x_1, x_2, \ldots, x_n)}{\partial x_1} = 0$$

$$\frac{\partial f(x_1, x_2, \ldots, x_n)}{\partial x_2} = 0$$

$$\vdots$$

$$\frac{\partial f(x_1, x_2, \ldots, x_n)}{\partial x_2} = 0.$$

This is a system of n equations for the n unknowns $x_1, x_2, \ldots, x_n$.

2. **Lagrange multipliers**   Consider the problem of maximizing the function f of several variables when there is a constraint that the point x must satisfy the auxiliary condition $g(x_1, x_2, \ldots, x_n) = 0$. We say that we are looking for a solution to the following maximization problem:

$$\underset{\mathbf{x}}{\text{maximize }} f(x_1, x_2, \ldots, x_n)$$

$$\text{subject to } g(x_1, x_2, \ldots, x_n) = 0.$$

The condition for a maximum can be found by introducing a Lagrange multiplier λ. We form the Lagrangian

$$L = f(x_1, x_2, \ldots, x_n) - \lambda g(x_1, x_2, \ldots, x_n).$$

We can then treat this Lagrangian function as if it were unconstrained to find the necessary conditions for a maximum. Specifically, we set the partial derivatives of L with respect to each of the variables equal to zero. This gives a system of n equations, but there are now $n+1$ unknowns, consisting of $x_1, x_2, \ldots, x_n$ and λ. We obtain an additional equation from the original constraint $g(x_1, x_2, \ldots, x_n) = 0$. Therefore we have a system of $n + 1$ equations and $n + 1$ unknowns.

If there are additional constraints, we define additional Lagrange multipliers—one for each constraint. For example, the problem

$$\underset{\mathbf{x}}{\text{maximize }} f(x_1, x_2, \ldots, x_n)$$

$$\text{subject to } g(x_1, x_2, \ldots, x_n) = 0$$

$$h(x_1, x_2, \ldots, x_n) = 0$$

can be solved by introducing the two Lagrange multipliers λ and μ. The Lagrangian is

$$L = f(x_1, x_2, \ldots, x_n) - \lambda g(x_1, x_2, \ldots, x_n) - \mu h(x_1, x_2, \ldots, x_n).$$

The partial derivatives of this Lagrangian are all set equal to zero, giving n equations. Two additional equations are obtained from the original constraints. Therefore there are $n + 2$ equations and $n + 2$ unknowns.

Some problems have inequality constraints of the form $g(x_1, x_2, \ldots, x_n) \leq 0$. If it is known that they are satisfied by strict inequality at the solution [with $g(x_1, x_2, \ldots, x_n) < 0$], then the constraint is not active and can be dropped from consideration; no Lagrange multiplier is needed. If it is known that the constraint is satisfied with equality at the solution, then a Lagrange multiplier can be introduced, as before. In this case the Lagrange multiplier is nonnegative (that is, $\lambda \geq 0$).

ANSWERS TO EXERCISES

T he answers to all odd-numbered exercises are given here.[1] If the exercise involves a proof, a very brief outline or hint is given.

CHAPTER 2

1. (*a*) \$1,000; (*b*) \$1,000,000.
3. (*a*) 3.04%; (*b*) 19.56%; (*c*) 19.25%.
5. PV = \$4,682,460.
7. $x < 3.3$.
9. \$6,948.
11. $NPV_1 = 29.88$ and $NPV_2 = 31.84$; hence recommend 2.
    $IRR_1 = 15.2\%$ and $IRR_2 = 12.4\%$; hence recommend 1.
13. (*b*) $c = .946$, $r = 5.7\%$.
15. No inflation applied: NPV = −\$435,000; inflation applied: NPV = \$89,000.

CHAPTER 3

1. \$4,638.83.
3. (*a*) 95.13 years; (*b*) \$40,746; (*c*) \$38,387.
5. YTM < 9.366%.
7. The annual worths are $A_A = \$6,449$ and $A_B = \$7,845$.
9. 91.17.
11. $D = \dfrac{1+r}{r}$, $D_M = 1/r$.
13. $dP/d\lambda = -DP$.
15. $C = T^2$.

---

[1]Compilation of these answers was the result of a massive project by a number of devoted individuals. We do not guarantee that they are free from errors. Please report errors to the author.

CHAPTER 4

1. 7.5%.

3. $P = 65.9$.

5. (a) $f_{t_1,t_2} = [s(t_2)t_2 - s(t_1)t_1]/(t_2 - t_1)$; (c) $x(t) = x(0)e^{s(t)t}$.

7. $P = 37.64$.

9. $(1 + r)^i(1 + f_{i,j})^{j-i} = (1 + r)^j$ implies $(1 + f_{i,j})^{j-i} = (1 + r)^{j-i}$, which implies $f_{i,j} = r$.

11. PV = 9.497.

13. $x_1 \approx -13.835$, $x_2 \approx 30.995$.

15. $a_k = 1/(1 + r_{k-1})^2$, $b_k = 1/(1 + r_{k-1})$.

CHAPTER 5

1. Approximate: projects 1, 2, 5; optimal: projects 1, 2, 3.

3. NPV = \$610,000 achieved by projects 4, 5, 6, 7 or 1, 4, 5, 7.

5. 16 in lattice, 40 in tree.

7. Critical $d^* = \frac{1}{2}(\sqrt{5} - 1) \approx .618$. Values $r = .33$ and $r = .25$ give $d = .75$ and $d = .8$, so solutions are the same.

9. (b) PV = \$366,740; enhance 2 years, then normal.

11. Use hint and solve for S.

CHAPTER 6

1. $R = (2X_0 - X_1)/X_0$.

3. (a) $\alpha = 19/23$; (b) 13.7%; (c) 11.4%.

5. (a) $(1.5 \times 10^6 + .5u)/(10^6 + .5u)$; (b) 3 million units, 0 variance, 20% return.

7. (a) $\mathbf{w} = (.5, 0, .5)$; (b) $\mathbf{w} = \left(\frac{1}{3}, \frac{1}{6}, \frac{1}{2}\right)$; (c) $\mathbf{w} = (0, .5, .5)$.

9. $r = \left[\sum_{i=1}^{n}(1/A_i)\right]^{-1} - 1$.

CHAPTER 7

1. (a) $\bar{r} = .07 + .5\sigma$; (b) $\sigma = .64$, borrow \$1,000 and invest \$2,000; (c) \$1,182.

3. (a) $.1 \le \bar{r}_M \le .16$; (b) $.12 \le \bar{r}_M \le .16$.

5. $\beta_i = x_i\sigma_i^2 \left(\sum_{j=1}^{n} x_j\sigma_j^2\right)^{-1}$.

7. (a) $A = 1$; (b) $\alpha = \sigma_0^2/(\sigma_0^2 - \sigma_i^2)$; (c) zero-beta point is efficient but below MVP; (d) $\bar{r}_i = 10\%$.

9. The identities require simple algebra.

CHAPTER 8

1. (a) 11.44%; (b) $\sigma = 16.7\%$.

3. Normalized $\mathbf{v} = (.217, .263, .360, .153)$; eigenvalue $= 311.16$; principal component follows market well.

5. (a) $\sigma(\hat{\bar{r}}) = \sigma$; (b) $\sigma(\hat{\sigma}^2) = \sqrt{2}\sigma^2/\sqrt{n-1}$.

7. *Method:* Index half-monthly points by i. Let r_i and ρ_i be returns for full month and half month starting at i. Assume ρ_i's uncorrelated. Then $r_i = \rho_i + \rho_{i+1}$. Show that $\operatorname{cov}(r_i, r_{i+1}) = \frac{1}{2}\sigma^2$. Find error in $\hat{\bar{r}} = \frac{1}{24}\sum_{i=1}^{24} r_i$. Ignoring missing half-month terms at the ends of the year, the method gives same result as the ordinary method.

CHAPTER 9

1. $108,610.

3. $a(x)$.

5. $a = (A' - B')/[U(A') - U(B')]$, $b = [B'U(A') - A'U(B')]/[U(A') - U(B')]$.

7. $C = (3 + e)^2/16$, $e = 4\sqrt{C} - 3$.

9. $b' = b/W$.

11. $1,500.

13. From hint: $\bar{R}_i - R = cW[\operatorname{E}(R_M, R_i) - \bar{R}_M R] = cW[\operatorname{cov}(R_M, R_i) + \bar{R}_M(\bar{R}_i - R)]$. This implies $\bar{R}_i - R = \gamma \operatorname{cov}(R_M, R_i)$ for some γ. Apply to R_M to solve for γ.

15. $P = \operatorname{E}\left(\dfrac{d}{R^*}\right) = \operatorname{E}\left(\dfrac{Rd}{RR^*}\right) = \dfrac{1}{R}\operatorname{E}\left(\dfrac{Rd}{R^*}\right) = \dfrac{\hat{\operatorname{E}}(d)}{R}$.

CHAPTER 10

1. $442.02.

3. 5%.

5. There is no cash flow at $t = 0$. At T the flow is $S/d(0, M) + \sum_{k=0}^{M-1} c(k)/d(k, M) - F$, which must be zero.

7. $-$100.34.

9. (a) $V_{i-1}(r_i) = 1 - d(i-1, i)$; (b) $V_0(r_i) = d(0, i-1) - d(0, i)$; (c) $1 - d(0, M)$.

11. (a) $3.971 million; (b) 8.64%.

13. $-131,250$ lb orange juice; $\sigma_{\text{new}} = .714\sigma_{\text{old}}$.

15. Short \$163,200 Treasury futures.

17. Proof based on $\text{cov}(x, y^2) = E(xy^2) - E(xy)E(y) = 0$. Both $E(xy^2)$ and $E(y)$ are zero by symmetry.

CHAPTER 11

1. Assuming Δt small, $p = .65$, $u = 1.106$, $d = .905$; without small Δt approximation, $p = .64367$, $u = 1.11005$, $d = .90086$. Probabilities of nodes (from the top with small approximation) are .179, .384, .311, .111, .015.

3. (a) Use $(v_1 - v_2)^2 \geq 0$; (b) 15% and 9.54%; (c) arithmetic for simple interest, geometric for compound. Usually geometric is best.

5. $\text{var}(u) = e^{2\overline{w}+\sigma^2}(e^{\sigma^2} - 1)$.

7. $dG = (\frac{1}{2}a - \frac{1}{8}b^2)G\,dt + \frac{1}{2}bG\,dz$.

9. To first order both have expected value $S(t_{k+1}) = (1 + \mu\Delta t)S(t_k)$.

CHAPTER 12

1. Cost is nonnegative.

3. $Q = (S - K) - 0 + K = S$ if $S \geq K$. Likewise $Q = 0 - (K - S) + K = S$ if $S \leq K$.

5. \$3.01.

7. $C(S, T) \geq \max[0, S - KB(T)] \to S$ as $T \to \infty$. Clearly $C(S, T) \leq S$. Hence in the limit $C = S$.

9. \$7.

11. Offer is close: low by about .3%.

13. Almost identical! One-month interval: \$4.801; half-month: \$4.796.

15. \$6.73.

CHAPTER 13

1. \$2.57.

3. $\sigma = .251$.

5. $C(63) = \$6.557$, $\Delta = .759$, $\Theta = 6.02$.

7. $\Gamma = \dfrac{\partial\Delta}{\partial S} = \dfrac{\partial N(d_1)}{\partial S} = N'(d_1)\dfrac{\partial d_1}{\partial S} = \dfrac{N'(d_1)}{\overline{T}}$. For Θ use Γ and Exercise 6.

9. $a = -\text{cov}(x, y)/\text{var}(y)$.

11. (a) \$.53; (b) \$2.04.

13. \$42.42 million.

CHAPTER 14

1. (*a*) 91.72; (*b*) 90.95.

3. Do backward evaluation on futures price lattice.

5. 6.00, 6.15, 6.29, 6.44, 6.59, 6.74, 6.89, 7.05, 7.19, 7.35 percent.

7. 7.67, 8.829, 9.799, 10.66, 11.3, 11.93 are a_0 through a_5.

9. $162,800.

11. $F(t) = r - \frac{1}{2}at + \frac{1}{6}\sigma^2 t^2$.

CHAPTER 15

1. $\gamma = \frac{1}{4}$.

3. $\max \left\{ \frac{1}{2} \ln \left[2\alpha + (1 - \alpha) \right] + \frac{1}{2} \ln \left[\alpha/2 + (1 - \alpha) \right] \right\}$ gives $\alpha = \frac{1}{2}$.

5. (*a*) $\alpha_k = p_k - p_n r_n / r_k$ for $k < n$; (*b*) $\alpha_1 = \frac{5}{18}$, $\alpha_2 = 0$, $\alpha_3 = \frac{1}{18}$.

7. Dow Jones average outperforms Mr. Jones.

9. (*a*) Conditions are

$$E \left(\frac{r_i - r_f}{1 + r_0} \right) = 0, \quad \text{or } E(r_i P_0) - r_f E(P_0) = 0,$$

$$\text{or} \quad \text{cov}(r_i, P_0) + \bar{r}_i E(P_0) = 0,$$

$$\text{or} \quad \bar{r}_i - r_f = -\frac{\text{cov}(r_i, P_0)}{E(P_0)}.$$

(*b*) We have

$$(\mu_i - r_f)\Delta t = -\frac{\text{cov}\left[n_i \sqrt{\Delta t}, 1/(1 + \mu_0 \Delta t + n_0 \sqrt{\Delta t}) \right]}{E[1/(1 + \mu_0 \Delta t + n_0 \sqrt{\Delta t})]}.$$

To first order $(\mu_i - r_f)\Delta t = \sigma_{i,0} \Delta t$.

CHAPTER 16

1. (*a*) Yes, use portfolio weights $\frac{1}{3}$, $\frac{2}{3}$ to get 1.2 risk free; (*b*) yes, use weights $-\frac{1}{2}$, $\frac{1}{2}$.

3. (*a*) and (*b*) $.8678.

5. $q_{11} = .1$, $q_{12} = .36$, $q_{21} = .4$, $q_{22} = .14$.

7. $S = 16.81, $\sigma = 20.6\%$.

9. Car B preferred by certainty equivalent difference of $370.74.

11. $V_1 = \dfrac{E(x_{2|1})}{1 + r + \beta_2(\bar{r}_2 - r)}$, $\qquad \beta_2 = \dfrac{\text{cov}(x_{2|1}/V_1, r_2)}{\sigma_{r_2}^2}$

PRESENT WORTH ANALYSIS

Boeing Versus Airbus

Until December 2002, Boeing had been working on development of the Sonic Cruiser, an innovative lightweight plane that can fly near the speed of sound. This is about 15% faster than a conventional jet, so flying the Sonic Cruiser would allow airlines to cut long-haul flight times. Then Boeing shifted its focus to providing 15 to 20% better fuel efficiency at today's top commercial jet speeds. The 787 Dreamliner is now selling very well.

Meanwhile, Airbus, Boeing's rival in the passenger aircraft business, had also been working on a more efficient plane. But Airbus was betting on size rather than speed. Its new model, the A380, is known as the super-jumbo and is the largest passenger plane in the world.

By using several recently developed composite materials, Airbus hoped to reduce by 20% both the weight and the manufacturing cost. Airbus estimates that flying the composite plane will allow airlines to cut their operating costs by about 8%.

However manufacturing problems have caused significant delays in A380 deliveries, and some airlines have cancelled orders.

1. So far, Boeing has not been able to sell the Sonic Cruiser idea to airlines. Fast is good, they say, but cheap is better. Why isn't increased speed more attractive to airlines, especially over long-haul flights? Can't airlines charge more for faster flights?

2. In many cases, air travelers actually spend as much time on the ground as in the air. Going through security, changing planes, clearing customs, and picking up baggage can add hours to the travel time. How might this affect a traveler's decision about whether to pay more to fly on a faster plane like the Sonic Cruiser?

3. Initially, airlines seemed to be more interested in the advantages claimed for the new Airbus model. Can you state some reasons for this apparent preference?

4. Cutting operating costs potentially saves Airbus millions of dollars. When costs go down, profits go up. Do companies have an ethical obligation to pass savings on to customers? What are the issues involved?

After Completing This Chapter...

The student should be able to:

- Define and apply the *present worth criteria.*
- Compare two competing alternative choices using present worth (PW).
- Apply the PW model in cases with equal, unequal, and infinite project lives.
- Compare multiple alternatives using the PW criteria.
- Develop and use spreadsheets to make *present worth* calculations.

I n Chapters 3 and 4 we accomplished two important tasks. First, we presented the concept of equivalence. We can compare cash flows only if we can resolve them into equivalent values. Second, we derived a series of compound interest factors to find those equivalent values.

ASSUMPTIONS IN SOLVING ECONOMIC ANALYSIS PROBLEMS

One of the difficulties of problem solving is that most problems tend to be very complicated. It becomes apparent that *some* simplifying assumptions are needed to make complex problems manageable. The trick, of course, is to solve the simplified problem and still be satisfied that the solution is applicable to the *real* problem! In the subsections that follow, we will consider six different items and explain the customary assumptions that are made. These assumptions apply to all problems and examples, unless other assumptions are given.

End-of-Year Convention

As we indicated in Chapter 4, economic analysis textbooks and practice follow the end-of-period convention. This makes "*A*" a series of end-of-period receipts or disbursements.

A cash flow diagram of *P*, *A*, and *F* for the end-of-period convention is as follows:

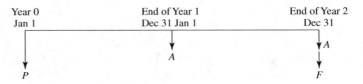

If one were to adopt a middle-of-period convention, the diagram would be:

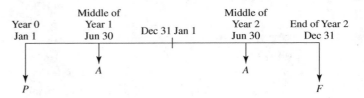

As the diagrams illustrate, only *A* shifts; *P* remains at the beginning of the period and *F* at the end of period, regardless of the convention. The compound interest tables in Appendix B are based on the end-of-period convention.

Viewpoint of Economic Analysis Studies

When we make economic analysis calculations, we must proceed from a point of reference. Generally, we will want to take the point of view of a total firm when doing industrial economic analyses. Example 1-1 vividly illustrated the problem: a firm's shipping department decided it could save money by outsourcing its printing work rather than by using the in-house printing department. An analysis from the viewpoint of the shipping department supported this, as it could get for $688.50 the same printing it was paying $793.50 for in-house. Further analysis showed, however, that its printing department costs would decline *less* than using the commercial printer would save. From the viewpoint of the firm, the net result would be an increase in total cost.

From Example 1-1 we see it *is* important that the **viewpoint of the study** be carefully considered. Selecting a narrow viewpoint, like that of the shipping department, may result in a suboptimal decision from the viewpoint of the firm. For this reason, the viewpoint of the total firm is used in industrial economic analyses. For public sector problems, the combined viewpoint of the government and the citizenry is chosen, since for many public projects the benefits of faster commuting, newer schools, and so on are received by individuals and the costs are paid by the government.

Sunk Costs

We know that it is the **differences between alternatives** that are relevant in economic analysis. Events that have occurred in the past really have no bearing on what we should do in the future. When the judge says, "$200 fine or 3 days in jail," the events that led to these unhappy alternatives really are unimportant. It is the current and future differences between the alternatives that *are* important. Past costs, like past events, have no bearing on deciding between alternatives unless the past costs somehow affect the present or future costs. In general, past costs do not affect the present or the future, so we refer to them as *sunk costs* and disregard them.

Borrowed Money Viewpoint

In most economic analyses, the proposed alternatives inevitably require money to be spent, and so it is natural to ask the source of that money. Thus, each problem has two monetary aspects: one is the **financing**—the obtaining of money; the other is the **investment**—the spending of money. Experience has shown that these two concerns should be distinguished. When separated, the problems of obtaining money and of spending it are both logical and straightforward. Failure to separate financing and investment sometimes produces confusing results and poor decision making.

The conventional assumption in economic analysis is that the money required to finance alternatives/solutions in problem solving is considered to be **obtained at interest rate i**.

Effect of Inflation and Deflation

For the present we will assume that prices are stable. This means that a machine that costs $5000 today can be expected to cost the same amount several years hence. Inflation and deflation can be serious problems for after-tax analysis and for cost and revenues whose inflation rates differ from the economy's inflation rates, but we assume stable prices for now.

Income Taxes

Income taxes, like inflation and deflation, must be considered to find the real payoff of a project. However, taxes will often affect alternatives similarly, allowing us to compare our choices without considering income taxes. We will introduce income taxes into economic analyses in a later chapter.

ECONOMIC CRITERIA

We have shown how to manipulate cash flows in a variety of ways, and we can now solve many kinds of compound interest problems. But engineering economic analysis is more than simply solving interest problems. The decision process (see Figure 1-1) requires that the outcomes of feasible alternatives be arranged so that they may be judged for **economic efficiency** in terms of the selection criterion. The economic criterion will be one of the following, depending on the situation:

Situation	**Criterion**
Neither input nor output fixed	Maximize (output−input)
For fixed input	Maximize output
For fixed output	Minimize input

We will now examine ways to resolve engineering problems, so that criteria for economic efficiency can be applied.

Equivalence provides the logic by which we may adjust the cash flow for a given alternative into some equivalent sum or series. We must still choose which comparable units to use. In this chapter we will learn how analysis can resolve alternatives into *equivalent present consequences*, referred to simply as **present worth analysis.** Chapter 6 will show how given alternatives are converted into an *equivalent uniform annual cash flow*, and Chapter 7 solves for the interest rate at which favorable consequences—that is, *benefits*—are equivalent to unfavorable consequences—or *costs*.

As a general rule, any economic analysis problem may be solved by any of these three methods. This is true because *present worth*, *annual cash flow*, and *rate of return* are exact methods that will always yield the same solution in selecting the best alternative from among a set of mutually exclusive alternatives. Remember that "mutually exclusive" means that selecting one alternative precludes selecting any other alternative. For example, constructing a gas station and constructing a drive-in restaurant on a particular piece of vacant land are mutually exclusive alternatives.

Some problems, however, may be more easily solved by one method. We now focus on problems that are most readily solved by present worth analysis.

APPLYING PRESENT WORTH TECHNIQUES

One of the easiest ways to compare mutually exclusive alternatives is to resolve their consequences to the present time. The three criteria for economic efficiency are restated in terms of present worth analysis in Table 5-1.

Present worth analysis is most frequently used to determine the present value of future money receipts and disbursements. It would help us, for example, to determine the present worth of an income-producing property, like an oil well or an apartment house. If the future income and costs are known, then we can use a suitable interest rate to calculate the present worth of the property. This should provide a good estimate of the price at which the property could be bought or sold. Another application is valuing stocks or bonds based on the anticipated future benefits of ownership.

In present worth analysis, careful consideration must be given to the time period covered by the analysis. Usually the task to be accomplished has a time period associated with it.

TABLE 5-1 Present Worth Analysis

	Situation	Criterion
Neither input nor output is fixed	Typical, general case	Maximize (present worth of benefits *minus* present worth of costs), that is, maximize net present worth
Fixed input	Amount of money or other input resources are fixed	Maximize present worth of benefits or other outputs
Fixed output	There is a fixed task, benefit, or other output to be accomplished	Minimize present worth of costs or other inputs

The consequences of each alternative must be considered for this period of time, which is usually called the **analysis period, planning horizon,** or **project life.**

The analysis period for an economy study should be determined from the situation. In some industries with rapidly changing technologies, a rather short analysis period or planning horizon might be in order. Industries with more stable technologies (like steelmaking) might use a longer period (say, 10–20 years), while government agencies frequently use analysis periods extending to 50 years or more.

Three different analysis-period situations are encountered in economic analysis problems with multiple alternatives:

1. The useful life of each alternative equals the analysis period.
2. The alternatives have useful lives different from the analysis period.
3. There is an infinite analysis period, $n = \infty$.

Useful Lives Equal the Analysis Period

Since different lives and an infinite analysis period present some complications, we will begin with four examples in which the useful life of each alternative equals the analysis period.

EXAMPLE 5-1

A firm is considering which of two mechanical devices to install to reduce costs. Both devices have useful lives of 5 years and no salvage value. Device A costs $1000 and can be expected to result in $300 savings annually. Device B costs $1350 and will provide cost savings of $300 the first year but will increase $50 annually, making the second-year savings $350, the third-year savings $400, and so forth. With interest at 7%, which device should the firm purchase?

SOLUTION

The analysis period can conveniently be selected as the useful life of the devices, or 5 years. The appropriate decision criterion is to choose the alternative that maximizes the net present worth of benefits minus costs.

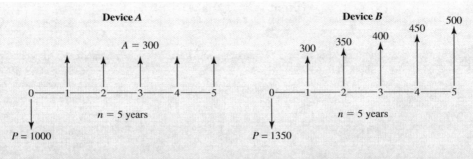

$$PW_A = 300(P/A, 7\%, 5) = -1000 + 300(4.100) = \$230$$

$$PW_B = -1350 + 300(P/A, 7\%, 5) + 50(P/G, 7\%, 5)$$

$$= -1350 + 300(4.100) + 50(7.647) = \$262.4$$

Device B has the larger present worth and is the preferred alternative.

EXAMPLE 5-2

Wayne County will build an aqueduct to bring water in from the upper part of the state. It can be built at a reduced size now for $300 million and be enlarged 25 years hence for an additional $350 million. An alternative is to construct the full-sized aqueduct now for $400 million.

Both alternatives would provide the needed capacity for the 50-year analysis period. Maintenance costs are small and may be ignored. At 6% interest, which alternative should be selected?

SOLUTION

This problem illustrates staged construction. The aqueduct may be built in a single stage, or in a smaller first stage followed many years later by a second stage to provide the additional capacity when needed.

For the Two-Stage Construction

$$\text{PW of cost} = \$300 \text{ million} + 350 \text{ million}(P/F, 6\%, 25)$$

$$= \$300 \text{ million} + 81.6 \text{ million}$$

$$= \$381.6 \text{ million}$$

For the Single-Stage Construction

$$\text{PW of cost} = \$400 \text{ million}$$

The two-stage construction has a smaller present worth of cost and is the preferred construction plan.

EXAMPLE 5-3

A purchasing agent plans to buy some new equipment for the mailroom. Two manufacturers have provided bids. An analysis shows the following:

Manufacturer	Cost	Useful Life (years)	End-of-Useful-Life Salvage Value
Speedy	$1500	5	$200
Allied	1600	5	325

The equipment of both manufacturers is expected to perform at the desired level of (fixed) output. For a 5-year analysis period, which manufacturer's equipment should be selected? Assume 7% interest and equal maintenance costs.

SOLUTION

For fixed output, the criterion is to minimize the present worth of cost.

Speedy

$$\text{PW of cost} = 1500 - 200(P/F, 7\%, 5)$$
$$= 1500 - 200(0.7130)$$
$$= 1500 - 143 = \$1357$$

Allied

$$\text{PW of cost} = 1600 - 325(P/F, 7\%, 5) = 1600 - 325(0.7130)$$
$$= 1600 - 232 = \$1368$$

Since it is only the *differences between alternatives* that are relevant, maintenance costs may be left out of the economic analysis. Although the PWs of cost for the two alternatives are nearly identical, we would still choose the one with minimum present worth of cost unless there were other tangible or intangible differences that would change the decision. Buy the Speedy equipment.

EXAMPLE 5-4

A firm is trying to decide which of two weighing scales it should install to check a package-filling operation in the plant. The ideal scale would allow better control of the filling operation, hence less overfilling. If both scales have lives equal to the 6-year analysis period, which one should be selected? Assume an 8% interest rate.

Alternatives	Cost	Uniform Annual Benefit	End-of-Useful-Life Salvage Value
Atlas scale	$2000	$450	$100
Tom Thumb scale	3000	600	700

SOLUTION

Atlas Scale

$$\text{PW of benefits} - \text{PW of cost} = 450(P/A, 8\%, 6) + 100(P/F, 8\%, 6) - 2000$$
$$= 450(4.623) + 100(0.6302) - 2000$$
$$= 2080 + 63 - 2000 = \$143$$

Tom Thumb Scale

$$\text{PW of benefits} - \text{PW of cost} = 600(P/A, 8\%, 6) + 700(P/F, 8\%, 6) - 3000$$
$$= 600(4.623) + 700(0.6302) - 3000$$
$$= 2774 + 441 - 3000 = \$215$$

The salvage value of each scale, it should be noted, is simply treated as another positive cash flow. Since the criterion is to maximize the present worth of benefits minus the present worth of cost, the preferred alternative is the Tom Thumb scale.

In Examples 5-1 and 5-4, we compared two alternatives and selected the one in which present worth of benefits *minus* present worth of cost was a maximum. The criterion is called the **net present worth criterion** and written simply as **NPW:**

$$\text{Net present worth} = \text{Present worth of benefits} - \text{Present worth of cost}$$
$$\text{NPW} = \text{PW of benefits} - \text{PW of cost} \tag{5-1}$$

The field of engineering economy and this text often use present worth (PW), present value (PV), net present worth (NPW), and net present value (NPV) as synonyms. Sometimes, as in the foregoing definition, *net* is included to emphasize that both costs and benefits have been considered.

Useful Lives Different from the Analysis Period

In present worth analysis, there always must be an identified analysis period. It follows, then, that each alternative must be considered for the entire period. In Examples 5-1 to 5-4, the useful life of each alternative was equal to the analysis period. While often this is true, in many situations at least one alternative will have a useful life different from the analysis period. This section describes one way to evaluate alternatives with lives different from the study period.

In Example 5-3, suppose that the Allied equipment was expected to have a 10-year useful life, or twice that of the Speedy equipment. Assuming the Allied salvage value would still be $325 in 10 years, which equipment should now be purchased? We can recompute the present worth of cost of the Allied equipment, starting as follows:

$$\text{PW of cost} = 1600 - 325(P/F, 7\%, 10)$$

$$= 1600 - 325(0.5083)$$

$$= 1600 - 165 = \$1435$$

The present worth of cost has increased. This, of course, is because of the more distant recovery of the salvage value. More importantly, we now find ourselves attempting to compare Speedy equipment, with its 5-year life, against the Allied equipment with a 10-year life. Because of the variation in the useful life of the equipment, we no longer have a situation of *fixed output*. Speedy equipment in the mailroom for 5 years is certainly not the same as 10 years of service with Allied equipment.

For present worth calculations, it is important that we select an analysis period and judge the consequences of each of the alternatives during that period. As such, it is not a fair comparison to compare the NPW of the Allied equipment over its 10-year life against the NPW of the Speedy equipment over its 5-year life.

The firm, its economic environment, and the specific situation are important in selecting an analysis period. If the Allied equipment (Example 5-3) has a useful life of 10 years, and the Speedy equipment will last 5 years, one method is to select an analysis period that is the **least common multiple** of their useful lives. Thus we would compare the 10-year life of Allied equipment against an initial purchase of Speedy equipment *plus* its replacement with new Speedy equipment in 5 years. The result is to judge the alternatives on the basis of a 10-year requirement in the mailroom. On this basis the economic analysis is as follows.

Assuming the replacement Speedy equipment 5 years hence will also cost $1500,

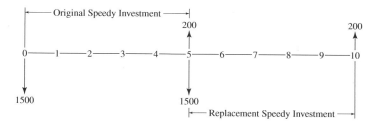

$$\text{PW of cost} = 1500 + (1500 - 200)(P/F, 7\%, 5) - 200(P/F, 7\%, 10)$$

$$= 1500 + 1300(0.7130) - 200(0.5083)$$

$$= 1500 + 927 - 102 = \$2325$$

For the Allied equipment, on the other hand, we have the following results:

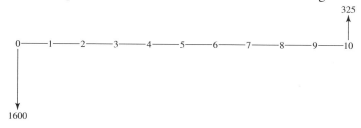

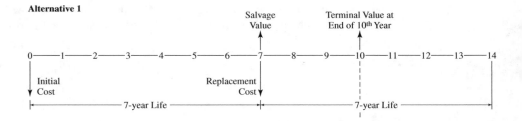

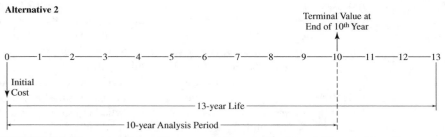

FIGURE 5-1 Superimposing a 10-year analysis period on 7- and 13-year alternatives.

$$\text{PW of cost} = 1600 - 325(P/F, 7\%, 10) = 1600 - 325(0.5083) = \$1435$$

For the fixed output of 10 years of service in the mailroom, the Allied equipment, with its smaller present worth of cost, is preferred.

We have seen that setting the analysis period equal to the least common multiple of the lives of the two alternatives seems reasonable in the revised Example 5-3. However, what if the alternatives had useful lives of 7 and 13 years? Here the least common multiple of lives is 91 years. An analysis period of 91 years hardly seems realistic. Instead, a suitable analysis period should be based on how long the equipment is likely to be needed. This may require that terminal values be estimated for the alternatives at some point prior to the end of their useful lives.

As Figure 5-1 shows, it is not necessary for the analysis period to equal the useful life of an alternative or some multiple of the useful life. To properly reflect the situation at the end of the analysis period, an estimate is required of the market value of the equipment at that time. The calculations might be easier if everything came out even, but this is not essential.

EXAMPLE 5-5

A diesel manufacturer is considering the two alternative production machines graphically depicted in Figure 5-1. Specific data are as follows:

	Alt. 1	Alt. 2
Initial cost	$50,000	$75,000
Estimated salvage value at end of useful life	$10,000	$12,000
Useful life of equipment, in years	7	13

The manufacturer uses an interest rate of 8% and wants to use the PW method to compare these alternatives over an analysis period of 10 years.

	Alt. 1	Alt. 2
Estimated market value, end of 10-year analysis period	$20,000	$15,000

SOLUTION

In this case, the decision maker is setting the analysis period at 10 years rather than accepting a common multiple of the lives of the alternatives, or assuming that the period of needed service is infinite (to be discussed in the next section). This is a legitimate approach—perhaps the diesel manufacturer will be phasing out this model at the end of the 10-year period. In any event, we need to compare the alternatives over 10 years.

As illustrated in Figure 5-1, we may assume that Alternative 1 will be replaced by an identical machine after its 7-year useful life. Alternative 2 has a 13-year useful life. The diesel manufacturer has provided an estimated market value of the equipment at the time of the analysis period. We can compare the two choices over 10 years as follows:

$$PW \text{ (Alt. 1)} = -50,000 + (10,000 - 50,000)(P/F, 8\%, 7) + 20,000(P/F, 8\%, 10)$$

$$= -50,000 - 40,000(0.5835) + 20,000(0.4632)$$

$$= -\$64,076$$

$$PW \text{ (Alt. 2)} = -75,000 + 15,000(P/F, 8\%, 10)$$

$$= -75,000 + 15,000(0.4632)$$

$$= -\$69,442$$

To minimize PW of costs the diesel manufacturer should select Alt. 1.

Infinite Analysis Period: Capitalized Cost

Another difficulty in present worth analysis arises when we encounter an infinite analysis period ($n = \infty$). In governmental analyses, a service or condition sometimes must be maintained for an infinite period. The need for roads, dams, pipelines, and so on, is sometimes considered to be permanent. In these situations a present worth of cost analysis would have an infinite analysis period. We call this particular analysis **capitalized cost.**

Infinite lives are rare in the private sector, but a similar assumption of "indefinitely long" horizons is sometimes made. This assumes that the facility will need electric motors, mechanical HVAC equipment, and forklifts as long as it operates, and that the facility will last far longer than any individual unit of equipment. So the equipment can be analyzed as though the problem horizon is *infinite* or indefinitely long.

Capitalized cost is the present sum of money that would need to be set aside now, at some interest rate, to yield the funds required to provide the service (or whatever) indefinitely. To accomplish this, the money set aside for future expenditures must not decline. The interest received on the money set aside can be spent, but not the principal. When one stops to think about an infinite analysis period (as opposed to something relatively short, like a hundred years), we see that an undiminished principal sum is essential; otherwise one will of necessity run out of money prior to infinity.

In Chapter 4 we saw that

Principal sum + Interest for the period = Amount at end of period, or

$$P \quad + \quad iP \quad = \quad P + iP$$

If we spend iP, then in the next interest period the principal sum P will again increase to $P + iP$. Thus, we can again spend iP.

This concept may be illustrated by a numerical example. Suppose you deposited $200 in a bank that paid 4% interest annually. How much money could be withdrawn each year without reducing the balance in the account below the initial $200? At the end of the first year, the $200 would have earned 4%($200) = $8 interest. If this interest were withdrawn, the $200 would remain in the account. At the end of the second year, the $200 balance would again earn 4%($200) = $8. This $8 could also be withdrawn and the account would still have $200. This procedure could be continued indefinitely and the bank account would always contain $200. If more or less than $8 is withdrawn, the account will either increase to ∞ or decrease to 0.

The year-by-year situation would be depicted like this:

$$
\begin{aligned}
&\textit{Year 1: } \$200 \text{ initial } P \rightarrow 200 + 8 = 208 \\
&\qquad\qquad\text{Withdrawal } iP = -\ 8 \\
\hline
&\textit{Year 2: } \$200 \rightarrow 200 + 8 = 208 \\
&\qquad\qquad\quad\text{Withdrawal } iP = -\ 8 \\
\hline
&\qquad\qquad\qquad\qquad\qquad\$200 \\
&\qquad\qquad\qquad\qquad\qquad\qquad\quad\text{and so on}
\end{aligned}
$$

Thus, for any initial present sum P, there can be an end-of-period withdrawal of A equal to iP each period, and these withdrawals can continue forever without diminishing the initial sum P. This gives us the basic relationship:

$$\text{For} \quad n = \infty, \quad A = Pi$$

This relationship is the key to capitalized cost calculations. Earlier we defined capitalized cost as the present sum of money that would need to be set aside at some interest rate to yield the funds to provide the desired task or service forever. Capitalized cost is therefore the P in the equation $A = iP$. It follows that:

$$\textbf{Capitalized cost} \qquad P = \frac{A}{i} \tag{5-2}$$

If we can resolve the desired task or service into an equivalent A, the capitalized cost can be computed. The following examples illustrate such computations.

EXAMPLE 5-6

How much should one set aside to pay $50 per year for maintenance on a gravesite if interest is assumed to be 4%? For perpetual maintenance, the principal sum must remain undiminished after the annual disbursement is made.

SOLUTION

$$\text{Capitalized cost } P = \frac{\text{Annual disbursement } A}{\text{Interest rate } i}$$

$$P = \frac{50}{0.04} = \$1250$$

One should set aside $1250.

EXAMPLE 5-7

A city plans a pipeline to transport water from a distant watershed area to the city. The pipeline will cost $8 million and will have an expected life of 70 years. The city expects to keep the water line in service indefinitely. Compute the capitalized cost, assuming 7% interest.

SOLUTION

The capitalized cost equation

$$P = \frac{A}{i}$$

is simple to apply when there are end-of-period disbursements A. Here we have renewals of the pipeline every 70 years. To compute the capitalized cost, it is necessary to first compute an end-of-period disbursement A that is equivalent to $8 million every 70 years.

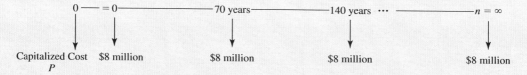

The $8 million disbursement at the end of each 70-year period may be resolved into an equivalent A.

$$A = F(A/F, i, n) = \$8 \text{ million}(A/F, 7\%, 70)$$
$$= \$8 \text{ million}(0.00062)$$
$$= \$4960$$

Each 70-year period is identical to this one, and the infinite series is shown in Figure 5-2.

$$\text{Capitalized cost } P = 8 \text{ million} + \frac{A}{i} = 8 \text{ million} + \frac{4960}{0.07}$$
$$= \$8,071,000$$

FIGURE 5-2
Using the sinking fund factor to compute an infinite series.

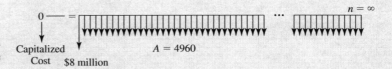

ALTERNATE SOLUTION 1

Instead of solving for an equivalent end-of-period payment A based on a *future* $8 million disbursement, we could find A, given a *present* $8 million disbursement.

$$A = P(A/P, i, n) = 8 \text{ million}(A/P, 7\%, 70)$$
$$= 8 \text{ million}(0.0706) = \$565,000$$

On this basis, the infinite series is shown in Figure 5-3. Carefully note the difference between this and Figure 5-2. Now:

$$\text{Capitalized cost } P = \frac{A}{i} = \frac{565,000}{0.07} = \$8,071,000$$

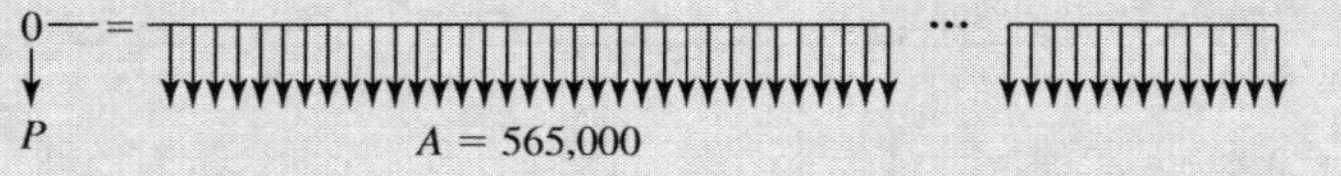

FIGURE 5-3 Using the capital recovery factor to compute an infinite series.

ALTERNATE SOLUTION 2

Another way of solving the problem is to assume the interest period is 70 years long and compute an equivalent interest rate for the 70-year period. Then the capitalized cost may be computed by using Equation 4-33 for $m = 70$

$$i_{70\,\text{yr}} = (1 + i_{1\,\text{yr}})^{70} - 1 = (1 + 0.07)^{70} - 1 = 112.989$$

$$\text{Capitalized cost} = 8 \text{ million} + \frac{8 \text{ million}}{112.989} = \$8,070,803$$

Multiple Alternatives

So far the discussion has been based on examples with only two alternatives. But multiple-alternative problems may be solved by exactly the same methods. (The only reason for avoiding multiple alternatives was to simplify the examples.) Examples 5-8 and 5-9 have multiple alternatives.

EXAMPLE 5-8

A contractor has been awarded the contract to construct a 6-mile-long tunnel in the mountains. During the 5-year construction period, the contractor will need water from a nearby stream. He will construct a pipeline to carry the water to the main construction yard. An analysis of costs for various pipe sizes is as follows:

	Pipe Sizes (in.)			
	2	3	4	6
Installed cost of pipeline and pump	$22,000	$23,000	$25,000	$30,000
Cost per hour for pumping	$1.20	$0.65	$0.50	$0.40

At the end of 5 years, the pipe and pump will have a salvage value equal to the cost of removing them. The pump will operate 2000 hours per year. The lowest interest rate at which the contractor is willing to invest money is 7%. (The minimum required interest rate for invested money is called the **minimum attractive rate of return,** or MARR.) Select the alternative with the least present worth of cost.

SOLUTION

We can compute the present worth of cost for each alternative. For each pipe size, the present worth of cost is equal to the installed cost of the pipeline and pump plus the present worth of 5 years of pumping costs.

	Pipe Size (in.)			
	2	3	4	6
Installed cost of pipeline and pump	$22,000	$23,000	$25,000	$30,000
1.20×2000 hr $\times (P/A, 7\%, 5)$	9,840			
0.65×2000 hr $\times 4.100$		5,330		
0.50×2000 hr $\times 4.100$			4,100	
0.40×2000 hr $\times 4.100$				3,280
Present worth of cost	$31,840	$28,330	$29,100	$33,280

Select the 3 in. pipe.

EXAMPLE 5-9

An investor paid $8000 to a consulting firm to analyze possible uses for a small parcel of land on the edge of town that can be bought for $30,000. In their report, the consultants suggested four alternatives:

	Alternatives	Total Investment Including Land*	Uniform Net Annual Benefit	Terminal Value at End of 20 yr
A	Do nothing	$ 0	$ 0	$ 0
B	Vegetable market	50,000	5,100	30,000
C	Gas station	95,000	10,500	30,000
D	Small motel	350,000	36,000	150,000

*Includes the land and structures but does not include the $8000 fee to the consulting firm.

Assuming 10% is the minimum attractive rate of return, what should the investor do?

SOLUTION

Alternative *A* is the "do-nothing" alternative. Generally, one feasible alternative in any situation is to remain in the present status and do nothing. In this problem, the investor could decide that the most attractive alternative is not to purchase the property and develop it. This is clearly a decision to do nothing.

We note, however, that if he does nothing, the total venture would not be a very satisfactory one. This is because the investor spent $8000 for professional advice on the possible uses of the property. But because the $8000 is a past cost, it is a **sunk cost.** The only relevant costs in an economic analysis are *present* and *future* costs. Past events and past, or sunk, costs are gone and cannot be allowed to affect future planning. (Past costs may be relevant in computing depreciation charges and income taxes, but nowhere else.) The past should not deter the investor from making the best decision now, regardless of the costs that brought him to this situation and point of time.

This problem is one of neither fixed input nor fixed output, so our criterion will be to maximize the present worth of benefits *minus* the present worth of cost; that is, to maximize net present worth.

Alternative *A*, Do Nothing

$$\text{NPW} = 0$$

Alternative *B*, Vegetable Market

$$\text{NPW} = -50,000 + 5100(P/A, 10\%, 20) + 30,000(P/F, 10\%, 20)$$
$$= -50,000 + 5100(8.514) + 30,000(0.1486)$$
$$= -50,000 + 43,420 + 4460$$
$$= -\$2120$$

Alternative C, Gas Station

$$NPW = -95,000 + 10,500(P/A, 10\%, 20) + 30,000(P/F, 10\%, 20)$$

$$= -95,000 + 89,400 + 4460$$

$$= -\$1140$$

Alternative D, Small Motel

$$NPW = -350,000 + 36,000(P/A, 10\%, 20) + 150,000(P/F, 10\%, 20)$$

$$= -350,000 + 306,500 + 22,290$$

$$= -\$21,210$$

The criterion is to maximize net present worth. In this situation, one alternative has NPW equal to zero, and three alternatives have negative values for NPW. We will select the best of the four alternatives, namely, the do-nothing Alt. *A*, with NPW equal to zero.

EXAMPLE 5-10

A piece of land may be purchased for $610,000 to be strip-mined for the underlying coal. Annual net income will be $200,000 for 10 years. At the end of the 10 years, the surface of the land will be restored as required by a federal law on strip mining. The reclamation will cost $1.5 million more than the resale value of the land after it is restored. Using a 10% interest rate, determine whether the project is desirable.

SOLUTION

The investment opportunity may be described by the following cash flow:

Year	Cash Flow (thousands)
0	−$610
1–10	+200 (per year)
10	−1500

$$NPW = -610 + 200(P/A, 10\%, 10) - 1500(P/F, 10\%, 10)$$

$$= -610 + 200(6.145) - 1500(0.3855)$$

$$= -610 + 1229 - 578$$

$$= +\$41$$

Since NPW is positive, the project is desirable. (See Appendix 7A for a more complete analysis of this type of problem. At interest rates of 4.07% and 18.29%, NPW = 0.)

EXAMPLE 5-11

Two pieces of construction equipment are being analyzed:

Year	Alt. A	Alt. B
0	−$2000	−$1500
1	+1000	+700
2	+850	+300
3	+700	+300
4	+550	+300
5	+400	+300
6	+400	+400
7	+400	+500
8	+400	+600

At an 8% interest rate, which alternative should be selected?

SOLUTION

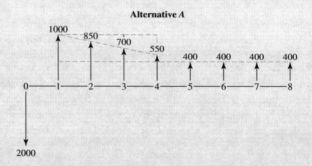

PW of benefits $= 400(P/A, 8\%, 8) + 600(P/A, 8\%, 4) - 150(P/G, 8\%, 4)$

$= 400(5.747) + 600(3.312) - 150(4.650) = 3588.50$

PW of cost $= 2000$

Net present worth $= 3588.50 - 2000 = +\$1588.50$

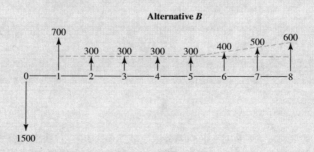

$$\text{PW of benefits} = 300(P/A, 8\%, 8) + (700 - 300)(P/F, 8\%, 1)$$
$$+ 100(P/G, 8\%, 4)(P/F, 8\%, 4)$$
$$= 300(5.747) + 400(0.9259) + 100(4.650)(0.7350)$$
$$= 2436.24$$
$$\text{PW of cost} = 1500$$
$$\text{Net present worth} = 2436.24 - 1500$$
$$= +\$936.24$$

To maximize NPW, choose Alt. *A*.

SPREADSHEETS AND PRESENT WORTH

Spreadsheets make it easy to build more accurate models with shorter time periods. When one is using factors, it is common to assume that costs and revenues are uniform for n years. With spreadsheets it is easy to use 120 months instead of 10 years, and the cash flows can be estimated for each month. For example, energy costs for air conditioning peak in the summer, and in many areas there is little construction during the winter. Cash flows that depend on population often increase at $x\%$ per year, such as for electric power and transportation costs.

In spreadsheets any interest rate is entered exactly—so no interpolation is needed. This makes it easy to calculate the monthly repayment schedule for a car loan or a house mortgage. Examples 5-12 and 5-13 illustrate using spreadsheets to calculate PWs.

EXAMPLE 5-12

NLE Construction is bidding on a project whose costs are divided into $30,000 for start-up and $240,000 for the first year. If the interest rate is 1% per month or 12.68% per year, what is the present worth with monthly compounding?

SOLUTION

Figure 5-4 illustrates the spreadsheet solution with the assumption that costs are distributed evenly throughout the year ($-20,000 = -240,000/12$).

FIGURE 5-4 Spreadsheet with monthly cash flows.

	A	B	C	D
1	1%	*i*		
2	−30,000	initial cash flow		
3	−240,000	annual amount		
4				
5	Month	Cash Flow		
6	0	−30000		
7	1	−20000		
8	2	−20000		
9	3	−20000		
10	4	−20000		
11	5	−20000		
12	6	−20000		
13	7	−20000		
14	8	−20000		
15	9	−20000		
16	10	−20000		
17	11	−20000		
18	12	−20000		
19	NPV	−$255,102	=NPV(A1,B7:B18)+B6	

Since the costs are uniform, the factor solution is:

$$\text{PW}_{mon} = -30,000 - 20,000(P/A, 1\%, 12) = -\$255,102$$

The value of monthly periods can be illustrated by computing the PW assuming an annual period. The results differ by more than $12,000, because $20,000 at the end of Months 1 through 12 is not the same as $240,000 at the end of Month 12. The timing of the cash flows makes the difference, even though the effective interest rates are the same.

$$\text{PW}_{annual} = -30,000 - 240,000(P/F, 12.68\%, 1) = -30,000 - 240,000/1.1268 = -\$242,993$$

EXAMPLE 5-13

Regina Industries has a new product whose sales are expected to be 1.2, 3.5, 7, 5, and 3 million units per year over the next 5 years. Production, distribution, and overhead costs are stable at $120 per unit. The price will be $200 per unit for the first 2 years, and then $180, $160, and $140 for the next 3 years. The remaining R&D and production costs are $300 million. If *i* is 15%, what is the present worth of the new product?

SOLUTION

It is easiest to calculate the yearly net revenue per unit before building the spreadsheet shown in Figure 5-5. Those values are the yearly price minus the $120 of costs, which equals $80, $80, $60, $40, and $20.

	A	B	C	D	E
1	12%	*i*			
2			Net Unit	Cash	
3	Year	Sales (M)	Revenue	Flow ($M)	
4	0			−300	
5	1	1.2	80	96	
6	2	3.5	80	280	
7	3	7	60	420	
8	4	5	40	200	
9	5	3	20	60	
10		D4+NPV(A1,D5:D9) =		$469	Million

FIGURE 5-5 Present worth of a new product.

SUMMARY

Present worth analysis is suitable for almost any economic analysis problem. But it is particularly desirable when we wish to know the present worth of future costs and benefits. And we frequently want to know the value today of such things as income-producing assets, stocks, and bonds.

For present worth analysis, the proper economic criteria are:

Neither input nor output is fixed	Maximize (PW of benefits − PW of costs) or, more simply stated: Maximize NPW
Fixed input	Maximize the PW of benefits
Fixed output	Minimize the PW of costs

To make valid comparisons, we need to analyze each alternative in a problem over the same **analysis period** or **planning horizon.** If the alternatives do not have equal lives, some technique must be used to achieve a common analysis period. One method is to select an analysis period equal to the least common multiple of the alternative lives. Another method is to select an analysis period and estimate end-of-analysis-period salvage values for the alternatives.

Capitalized cost is the present worth of cost for an infinite analysis period ($n = \infty$). When $n = \infty$, the fundamental relationship is $A = iP$. Some form of this equation is used whenever there is a problem with an infinite analysis period.

The numerous assumptions routinely made in solving economic analysis problems include the following.

1. Present sums P are beginning-of-period, and all series receipts or disbursements A and future sums F occur at the end of the interest period. The compound interest tables were derived on this basis.

2. In industrial economic analyses, the point of views for computing the consequences of alternatives is that of the total firm. Narrower views can result in suboptimal solutions.

3. Only the differences between the alternatives are relevant. Past costs are sunk costs and generally do not affect present or future costs. For this reason they are ignored.

4. The investment problem is isolated from the financing problem. We generally assume that all required money is borrowed at interest rate i.

5. For now, stable prices are assumed. The inflation–deflation problem is deferred to Chapter 14. Similarly, our discussion of income taxes is deferred to Chapter 12.

6. Often uniform cash flows or arithmetic gradients are reasonable assumptions. However, spreadsheets simplify the finding of PW in more complicated problems.

PROBLEMS

Present Value of One Alternative

5-1 Compute the present value, P, for the following cash flows.

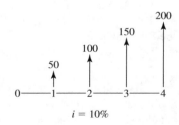

$i = 10\%$

5-2 Compute the present value, P, for the following cash flows.

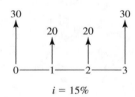

$i = 15\%$

5-3 Compute the present value, P, for the following cash flows.

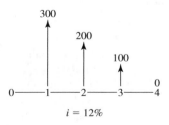

$i = 12\%$

(*Answer: P* = $498.50)

5-4 Find the value of Q so that the present value is 0.

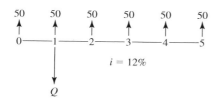

$$i = 12\%$$

5-5 Compute the present value, P, for the following cash flows.

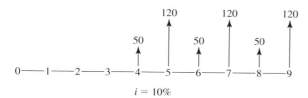

$$i = 10\%$$

5-6 Compute the present value, P, for the following cash flows.

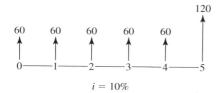

$$i = 10\%$$

(*Answer: P* = $324.71)

5-7 Use a geometric gradient formula to compute the present value, P, for the following cash flows.

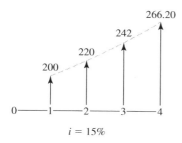

$$i = 15\%$$

5-8 If $i = 10\%$, compute the present value, P, for the following cash flows.

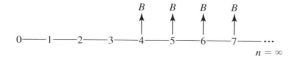

5-9 A stonecutter, assigned to carve the headstone for a well-known engineering economist, began with the following design.

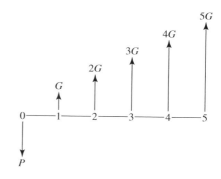

He then started the equation as follows:

$$P = G(P/G, i, 6)$$

He realized he had made a mistake. The equation should have been

$$P = G(P/G, i, 5) + G(P/A, i, 5)$$

The stonecutter does not want to discard the stone and start over. He asks you to help him with his problem. What one compound interest factor can be added to make the equation correct?

$$P = G(P/G, i, 6)(\quad, i, \quad)$$

5-10 Compute the present value, P, for the following cash flows (assume series repeats forever).

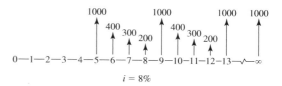

$$i = 8\%$$

5-11 A project has a net present worth of -140 as of January 1, 2010. If a 10% interest rate is used, what was the project NPW as of December 31, 2007?

5-12 The annual income from a rented house is $12,000. The annual expenses are $3000. If the house can be sold for $145,000 at the end of 10 years, how much could you afford to pay for it now, if you considered 18% to be a suitable interest rate? (*Answer:* $68,155)

5-13 Consider the following cash flow. At a 6% interest rate, what value of P at the end of Year 1 is equivalent to the benefits at the end of Years 2 through 7?

Year	Cash Flow
1	$-P$
2	$100
3	200
4	300
5	400
6	500
7	600

5-14 How much would the owner of a building be justified in paying for a sprinkler system that will save $750 a year in insurance premiums if the system has to be replaced every 20 years and has a salvage value equal to 10% of its initial cost? Assume money is worth 7%.   (*Answer:* $8156)

5-15 A manufacturer is considering purchasing equipment which will have the following financial effects:

Year	Disbursements	Receipts
0	$4400	$ 0
1	660	880
2	660	1980
3	440	2420
4	220	1760

If money is worth 6%, should he invest in the equipment?

5-16 A corporate bond has a face value of $1000 with maturity date 20 years from today. The bond pays interest semiannually at a rate of 8% per year based on the face value. The interest rate paid on similar corporate bonds has decreased to a current rate of 6%. Determine the market value of the bond.

5-17 Calculate the present worth of a 4.5%, $5000 bond with interest paid semiannually. The bond matures in 10 years, and the investor wants to make 8% per year compounded quarterly on the investment.

5-18 In a present worth analysis of certain equipment, one alternative has a net present worth of +420, based on a 6-year analysis period that equals the useful life of the alternative. A 10% interest rate was used in the computations.

The alternative device is to be replaced at the end of the 6 years by an identical item with the same cost, benefits, and useful life. Using a 10% interest rate, compute the net present worth of the alternative equipment for the 12-year analysis period. (*Answer:* NPW = +657.09)

5-19 On February 1, the Miro Company needs to purchase some office equipment. The company is short of cash and expects to be short for several months. The treasurer has said that he could pay for the equipment as follows:

Date	Payment
April 1	$150
June 1	300
Aug. 1	450
Oct. 1	600
Dec. 1	750

A local office supply firm will agree to sell the equipment to Miro now and accept payment according to the treasurer's schedule. If interest will be charged at 3% every 2 months, with compounding once every 2 months, how much office equipment can the Miro Company buy now? (*Answer:* $2020)

5-20 A machine costs $980,000 to purchase and will provide $200,000 a year in benefits. The company plans to use the machine for 13 years and then will sell the machine for scrap, receiving $20,000. The company interest rate is 12%. Should the machine be purchased?

5-21 Annual maintenance costs for a particular section of highway pavement are $2000. The placement of a new surface would reduce the annual maintenance cost to $500 per year for the first 5 years and to $1000 per year for the next 5 years. After 10 years the annual maintenance would again be $2000. If maintenance costs are the only saving, what investment can be justified for the new surface. Assume interest at 4%.

5-22 An investor is considering buying a 20-year corporate bond. The bond has a face value of $1000 and pays 6% interest per year in two semiannual payments. Thus the purchaser of the bond will receive $30 every 6 months in addition to $1000 at the end of 20 years, along with the last $30 interest payment.

If the investor wants to receive 8% interest, compounded semiannually, how much would he or she be willing to pay for the bond?

5-23 A road building contractor has received a major highway construction contract that will require 50,000 m^3 of crushed stone each year for 5 years. The stone can be obtained from a quarry for $5.80/m^3. As an alternative, the contractor has decided to try to buy the quarry. He believes that if he owned the quarry, the stone would cost him only $4.30/m^3. He thinks he could resell the quarry at the end of 5 years for $40,000. If the contractor uses a 10% interest rate, how much would he be willing to pay for the quarry?

5-24 A new office building was constructed 5 years ago by a consulting engineering firm. At that time the firm obtained a bank loan for $100,000 with a 12% annual interest rate, compounded quarterly. The terms of the loan call for equal quarterly payments to repay the loan in 10 years. The loan also allows for its prepayment at any time without penalty.

As a result of internal changes in the firm, it is now proposed to refinance the loan through an insurance company. The new loan would be for a 20-year term with an interest rate of 8% per year, compounded quarterly. The new equal quarterly payments would repay the loan in the 20-year period. The insurance company requires the payment of a 5% loan initiation charge (often described as a "5-point loan fee"), which will be added to the new loan.

(a) What is the balance due on the original mortgage if 20 payments have been made in the last five years?

(b) What is the difference between the equal quarterly payments on the present bank loan and the proposed insurance company loan?

5-25 IBP Inc. is considering establishing a new machine to automate a meatpacking process. The machine will save $50,000 in labor annually. The machine can be purchased for $200,000 today and will be used for 10 years. It has a salvage value of $10,000 at the end of its useful life. The new machine will require an annual maintenance cost of $9000. The corporation has a minimum rate of return of 10%. Do you recommend automating the process?

5-26 Argentina is considering constructing a bridge across the Rio de la Plata to connect its northern coast to the southern coast of Uruguay. If this bridge is constructed, it will reduce the travel time from Buenos Aires, Argentina, to São Paulo, Brazil, by over 10 hours, and there is the potential to significantly improve the flow of manufactured goods between the two countries. The cost of the new bridge, which will be the longest bridge in the world, spanning over 50 miles, will be $700 million. The bridge will require an annual maintenance of $10 million for repairs and upgrades and is estimated to last 80 years. It is estimated that 550,000 vehicles will use the bridge during the first year of operation, and an additional 50,000 vehicles per year until the tenth year. These data are based on a toll charge of $90 per vehicle. The annual traffic for the remainder of the life of the bridge will be 1,000,000 vehicles per year. The Argentine government requires a minimum rate of return of 9% to proceed with the project.

(a) Does this project provide sufficient revenues to offset its costs?

(b) What considerations are there besides economic factors in deciding whether to construct the bridge?

5-27 A student has a job that leaves her with $250 per month in disposable income. She decides that she will use the money to buy a car. Before looking for a car, she arranges a 100% loan whose terms are $250 per month for 36 months at 18% annual interest. What is the maximum car purchase price that she can afford with her loan?

5-28 The student in Problem 5-27 finds a car she likes and the dealer offers to arrange financing. His terms are 12% interest for 60 months and no down payment. The car's sticker price is $12,000. Can she afford to buy this car with her $250 monthly disposable income?

5-29 The student in Problem 5-28 really wants this particular car. She decides to try to negotiate a different interest rate. What is the highest interest rate that she can accept, given a 60-month term and $250 per month payments?

5-30 We know a car can be had for 60 monthly payments of $199. The dealer has set us a nominal interest rate of 4.5% compounded daily. What is the purchase price?

5-31 By installing some elaborate inspection equipment on its assembly line, the Robot Corp. can avoid hiring an extra worker who would have earned $26,000 a year in wages and an additional $7500 a year in employee benefits. The inspection equipment has a 6-year useful life and no salvage value. Use a nominal 18% interest rate in your calculations. How much can Robot afford to pay for the equipment if the wages and worker benefits would have been paid

(a) At the end of each year

(b) Monthly

Explain why the answer in (b) is larger. Assume the compounding matches the way the wages and benefits would have been paid (that is, annually and monthly).

5-32 Jerry Stans, a young industrial engineer, prepared an economic analysis for some equipment to replace one production worker. The analysis showed that the present worth of benefits (of employing one less production worker) just equaled the present worth of the equipment costs, assuming a 10-year useful life for the equipment. It was decided not to buy the equipment.

A short time later, the production workers won a new 3-year union contract that granted them an immediate 40¢-per-hour wage increase, plus an additional 25¢-per-hour wage increase in each of the two subsequent years. Assume that in each and every future year, a 25¢-per-hour wage increase will be granted.

Jerry Stans has been asked to revise his earlier economic analysis. The present worth of benefits of replacing one production employee will now increase. Assuming an interest rate of 8%, the justifiable cost of the automation equipment (with a 10-year useful life) will increase by how much? Assume the plant operates a single 8-hour shift, 250 days per year.

Lives Match

5-33 Two alternative courses of action have the following schedules of disbursements:

Year	A	B
0	−$1300	
1	0	−$100
2	0	−200
3	0	−300
4	0	−400
5	0	−500
	−$1300	−$1500

Based on a 6% interest rate, which alternative should be selected?

5-34 Dick Dickerson Construction, Inc. has asked you to help them select a new backhoe. You have a choice between a wheel-mounted version, which costs $50,000 and has an expected life of 5 years and a salvage value of $2000, and a track-mounted one, which costs $80,000, with a 5-year life and an expected salvage value of $10,000. Both machines will achieve the same productivity. Interest is 8%. Which one will you recommend? Use a present worth analysis.

5-35 Walt Wallace Construction Enterprises is investigating the purchase of a new dump truck. Interest is 9%. The cash flows for two likely models are as follows:

Model	First Cost	Annual Operating Cost	Annual Income	Salvage Value	Life (years)
A	$50,000	$2000	$9,000	$10,000	10
B	80,000	1000	12,000	30,000	10

(a) Using present worth analysis, which truck should the firm buy, and why?

(b) Before the construction company can close the deal, the dealer sells out of Model B and cannot get any more. What should the firm do now and why?

5-36 Two different companies are offering a punch press for sale. Company A charges $250,000 to deliver and install the device. Company A has estimated that the machine will have maintenance and operating costs of $4000 a year and will provide an annual benefit of $89,000. Company B charges $205,000 to deliver and install the device. Company B has estimated maintenance and operating costs of the press at $4300 a year, with an annual benefit of $86,000. Both machines will last 5 years and can be sold for $15,000 for the scrap metal. Use an interest rate of 12%. Which machine should your company buy?

5-37 A battery manufacturing plant has been ordered to cease discharging acidic waste liquids containing mercury into the city sewer system. As a result, the firm must now adjust the pH and remove the mercury from its waste liquids. Three firms have provided quotations on the necessary equipment. An analysis of the quotations provided the following table of costs.

Bidder	Installed Cost	Annual Operating Cost	Annual Income from Mercury Recovery	Salvage Value
Foxhill Instrument	$ 35,000	$8000	$2000	$20,000
Quicksilver	40,000	7000	2200	0
Almaden	100,000	2000	3500	0

If the installation can be expected to last 20 years and money is worth 7%, which equipment should be purchased? (*Answer:* Almaden)

5-38 A new tennis court complex is planned. Both alternatives will last 18 years, and the interest rate is 7%. Use present worth analysis to determine which should be selected.

	Construction Cost	Annual O&M
A	$500,000	$25,000
B	640,000	10,000

Contributed by D. P. Loucks, Cornell University

5-39   Telefono Mexico is expanding its facilities to serve a new manufacturing plant. The new plant will require 2000 telephone lines this year, and another 2000 lines after expansion in 10 years. The plant will be in operation for 30 years. The telephone company is evaluating two options to serve the demand.

Option 1 Provide one cable now with capacity to serve 4000 lines. The cable cost will be $200,000, and annual maintenance costs will be $15,000.

Option 2 Provide a cable with capacity to serve 2000 lines now and a second cable to serve the other 2000 lines in 10 years. The cost of each cable will be $150,000, and each cable will have an annual maintenance of $10,000.

The telephone cables will last at least 30 years, and the cost of removing the cables is offset by their salvage value.

(a) Which alternative should be selected, assuming a 10% interest rate?

(b) Will your answer to (*a*) change if the demand for additional lines occurs in 5 years instead of 10 years?

5-40 A consulting engineer has been engaged to advise a town how best to proceed with the construction of a 200,000 m^3 water supply reservoir. Since only 120,000 m^3 of storage will be required for the next 25 years, an alternative to building the full capacity now is to build the reservoir in two stages. Initially, the reservoir could be built with 120,000 m^3 of capacity and then, 25 years hence, the additional 80,000 m^3 of capacity could be added by increasing the height of the reservoir. Estimated costs are as follows:

	Construction Cost	Annual Maintenance Cost
Build in two stages		
First stage: 120,000 m^3 reservoir	$14,200,000	$75,000
Second stage: Add 80,000 m^3 of capacity, additional construction and maintenance costs	12,600,000	25,000
Build full capacity now 200,000 m^3 reservoir	22,400,000	100,000

If interest is computed at 4%, which construction plan is preferred?

5-41 A city has developed a plan to provide for future municipal water needs. The plan proposes an aqueduct that passes through 500 feet of tunnel in a nearby mountain. Two alternatives are being considered. The first proposes to build a full-capacity tunnel now for $556,000. The second proposes to build a half-capacity tunnel now (cost = $402,000), which should be adequate for 20 years, and then to build a second parallel half-capacity tunnel. The maintenance cost of the tunnel lining for the full-capacity tunnel is $40,000 every 10 years, and for each half-capacity tunnel it is $32,000 every 10 years.

The friction losses in the half-capacity tunnel will be greater than if the full-capacity tunnel were built. The estimated additional pumping costs in the single half-capacity tunnel will be $2000 per year, and for the two half-capacity tunnels it will be $4000 per year. Based on capitalized cost and a 7% interest rate, which alternative should be selected?

Lives Differ

5-42   Use an 8-year analysis period and a 10% interest rate to determine which alternative should be selected:

	A	B
First cost	$5300	$10,700
Uniform annual benefit	$1800	$2,100
Useful life, in years	4	8

5-43   Use capitalized cost to determine which type of road surface is preferred on a particular section of highway. Use 12% interest rate.

	A	B
Initial cost	$500,000	$700,000
Annual maintenance	35,000	25,000
Periodic resurfacing	350,000	450,000
Resurfacing interval	10 years	15 years

5-44   A man had to have the muffler replaced on his 2-year-old car. The repairman offered two alternatives. For $50 he would install a muffler guaranteed for 2 years. But for $65 he would install a muffler guaranteed "for as long as you own the car." Assuming the present owner expects to keep the car for about 3 more years, which muffler would you advise him to have installed if you thought 20% were a suitable interest rate and the less expensive muffler would only last 2 years?

5-45   An engineer has received two bids for an elevator to be installed in a new building. The bids, plus his evaluation of the elevators, are tabulated.
Given a 10% interest rate, which bid should be accepted?

Alternatives	Westinghome	Itis
Installed Cost	$45,000	$54,000
Life (years)	10	15
Annual Cost	$2700	2850
Salvage value	$3000	4500

5-46   A weekly business magazine offers a 1-year subscription for $58 and a 3-year subscription for $116. If you thought you would read the magazine for at least the next 3 years, and consider 20% as a minimum rate of return, which way would you purchase the magazine: With three 1-year subscriptions or a single 3-year subscription?   (*Answer:* Choose the 3-year subscription.)

Perpetual Life

5-47   A small dam was constructed for $2 million. The annual maintenance cost is $15,000. If interest is 5%, compute the capitalized cost of the dam, including maintenance.

5-48   A depositor puts $25,000 in a savings account that pays 5% interest, compounded semiannually. Equal annual withdrawals are to be made from the account, beginning one year from now and continuing forever. What is the maximum annual withdrawal?

5-49   What amount of money deposited 50 years ago at 8% interest would provide a perpetual payment of $10,000 a year beginning this year?

5-50   The president of the E. L. Echo Corporation thought it would be appropriate for his firm to "endow a chair" in the Department of Industrial Engineering of the local university. If the professor holding the chair will receive $67,000 per year, and the interest received on the endowment fund is expected to be 8%, what lump sum of money will the Echo Corporation need to provide to establish the endowment fund?   (*Answer:* $837,500)

5-51   Dr. Fog E. Professor is retiring and wants to endow a chair of engineering economics at his university. It is expected that he will need to cover an annual cost of $100,000 forever. What lump sum must he donate to the university today if the endowment will earn 10% interest?

5-52   The local botanical society wants to ensure that the gardens in the town park are properly cared for. The group recently spent $100,000 to plant the gardens. The members want to set up a perpetual fund to provide $100,000 for future replantings of the gardens every 10 years. If interest is 5%, how much money would be needed to forever pay the cost of replanting?

5-53   A home builder must construct a sewage treatment plant and deposit sufficient money in a perpetual trust fund to pay the $5000 per year operating cost and to replace the treatment plant every 40 years. The plant will cost $150,000, and future replacement plants will also cost $150,000 each. If the trust fund earns 8% interest, what is the builder's capitalized cost to construct the plant and future replacements, and to pay the operating costs?

5-54 A man who likes cherry blossoms very much wants an urn full of them put on his grave once each year forever after he dies. In his will, he intends to leave a certain sum of money in trust at a local bank to pay the florist's annual bill. How much money should be left for this purpose? Make whatever assumptions you feel are justified by the facts presented. State your assumptions, and compute a solution.

5-55 An elderly lady decided to distribute most of her considerable wealth to charity and to keep for herself only enough money to provide for her living. She feels that $1000 a month will amply provide for her needs. She will establish a trust fund at a bank that pays 6% interest, compounded monthly. At the end of each month she will withdraw $1000. She has arranged that, upon her death, the balance in the account is to be paid to her niece, Susan. If she opens the trust fund and deposits enough money to pay herself $1000 a month in interest as long as she lives, how much will Susan receive when her aunt dies?

5-56 A trust fund is to be established for three purposes: (1) to provide $750,000 for the construction and $250,000 for the initial equipment of a small engineering laboratory; (2) to pay the $150,000 per year laboratory operating cost; and (3) to pay for $100,000 of replacement equipment every 4 years, beginning 4 years from now.

At 6% interest, how much money is required in the trust fund to provide for the laboratory and equipment and its perpetual operation and equipment replacement?

5-57 The local Audubon Society has just put a new bird feeder in the park at a cost of $500. The feeder has a useful life of 5 years and an annual maintenance cost of $50. Our cat, Fred, was very impressed with the project. He wants to establish a fund that will maintain the feeder in perpetuity. Replacement feeders cost $500 every 5 years. If the fund earns 5% interest, what amount must Fred raise for its establishment?

5-58 We want to donate a marble birdbath to the city park as a memorial to our cat, Fred, while he can still enjoy it. We also want to set up a perpetual care fund to cover future expenses "forever." The initial cost of the bath is $5000. Routine annual operating costs are $200 per year, but every fifth year the cost will be $500 to cover major cleaning and maintenance as well as operation.

(a) What is the capitalized cost of this project if the interest rate is 8%?

(b) How much is the present worth of this project if it is to be demolished after 75 years? The final $500 payment in the 75th year will cover the year's operating cost and the site reclamation.

5-59 A local symphony association offers memberships as follows:

Continuing membership, per year	$ 15
Patron lifetime membership	375

The patron membership has been based on the symphony association's belief that it can obtain a 4% rate of return on its investment. If you believed 4% to be an appropriate rate of return, would you be willing to purchase the patron membership? Explain why or why not.

5-60 A rather wealthy man decides to arrange for his descendants to be well educated. He wants each child to have $60,000 for his or her education. He plans to set up a perpetual trust fund so that six children will receive this assistance in each generation. He estimates that there will be four generations per century, spaced 25 years apart. He expects the trust to be able to obtain a 4% rate of return, and the first recipients to receive the money 10 years hence. How much money should he now set aside in the trust? (*Answer: $389,150*)

5-61 A new bridge project is being evaluated at $i = 5\%$. Recommend an alternative based on the capitalized cost for each.

	Construction Cost	Annual O&M	Life (years)
Concrete	$50 million	$ 250,000	70
Steel	40 million	1,000,000	50

5-62 A new stadium is being evaluated at $i = 6\%$. Recommend an alternative for the main structural material based on the capitalized cost for each.

	Construction Cost	Annual O&M	Life (years)
Concrete	$25 million	$200,000	80
Steel	21 million	1,000,000	60

Multiple Alternatives

5-63 A firm is considering three mutually exclusive alternatives as part of a production improvement program. The alternatives are:

	A	B	C
Installed cost	$10,000	$15,000	$20,000
Uniform annual benefit	1,625	1,530	$1,890
Useful life, in years	10	20	20

The salvage value at the end of the useful life of each alternative is zero. At the end of 10 years, Alternative A could be replaced with another A with identical cost and benefits. The maximum attractive rate of return is 6%. Which alternative should be selected?

5-64 A steam boiler is needed as part of the design of a new plant. The boiler can be fired by natural gas, fuel oil, or coal. A decision must be made on which fuel to use. An analysis of the costs shows that the installed cost, with all controls, would be least for natural gas at $30,000; for fuel oil it would be $55,000; and for coal it would be $180,000. If natural gas is used rather than fuel oil, the annual fuel cost will increase by $7500. If coal is used rather than fuel oil, the annual fuel cost will be $15,000 per year less. Assuming 8% interest, a 20-year analysis period, and no salvage value, which is the most economical installation?

5-65 Austin General Hospital is evaluating new office equipment offered by three companies. In each case the interest rate is 15% and the useful life of the equipment is 4 years. Use NPW analysis to determine the company from which you should purchase the equipment.

	Company A	Company B	Company C
First cost	$15,000	$25,000	$20,000
Maintenance and operating costs	1,600	400	900
Annual benefit	8,000	13,000	11,000
Salvage value	3,000	6,000	4,500

5-66 The following costs are associated with three tomato-peeling machines being considered for use in a canning plant.

	Machine A	Machine B	Machine C
First cost	$52,000	$63,000	$67,000
Maintenance and operating costs	15,000	9,000	12,000
Annual benefit	38,000	31,000	37,000
Salvage value	13,000	19,000	22,000
Useful life, in years	4	6	12

If the canning company uses an interest rate of 12%, which is the best alternative? Use NPW to make your decision. (*Note:* Consider the least common multiple as the study period.)

5-67 A railroad branch line to a landfill site is to be constructed. It is expected that the railroad line will be used for 15 years, after which the landfill site will be closed and the land turned back to agricultural use. The railroad track and ties will be removed at that time.

In building the railroad line, either treated or untreated wood ties may be used. Treated ties have an installed cost of $6 and a 10-year life; untreated ties are $4.50 with a 6-year life. If at the end of 15 years the ties then in place have a remaining useful life of 4 years or more, they will be used by the railroad elsewhere and have an estimated salvage value of $3 each. Any ties that are removed at the end of their service life, or too close to the end of their service life to be used elsewhere, can be sold for 50¢ each.

Determine the most economical plan for the initial railroad ties and their replacement for the

15-year period. Make a present worth analysis assuming 8% interest.

5-68 A building contractor obtained bids for some asphalt paving, based on a specification. Three paving subcontractors quoted the following prices and terms of payment:

Paving Co.	Price	Payment Schedule
Quick	$85,000	50% payable immediately 25% payable in 6 months 25% payable at the end of one year
Tartan	82,000	Payable immediately
Faultless	84,000	25% payable immediately 75% payable in 6 months

The building contractor uses a 12% nominal interest rate, compounded monthly, in this type of bid analysis. Which paving subcontractor should be awarded the paving job?

5-69 Given the following data, use present worth analysis to find the best alternative, A, B, or C.

	A	B	C
Initial cost	$10,000	15,000	$12,000
Annual benefit	6,000	10,000	5,000
Salvage value	1,000	−2,000	3,000
Useful life	2 years	3 years	4 years

Use an analysis period of 12 years and 10% interest.

5-70 Consider the following four alternatives. Three are "do something" and one is "do nothing."

	A	B	C	D
Cost	$0	$50	$30	$40
Net annual benefit	0	12	4.5	6
Useful life, in years		5	10	10

At the end of the 5-year useful life of B, a replacement is not made. If a 10-year analysis period and a 10% interest rate are selected, which is the preferred alternative?

5-71 A cost analysis is to be made to determine what, if anything, should be done in a situation offering three "do-something" and one "do-nothing" alternatives. Estimates of the cost and benefits are as follows.

Alternatives	Cost	Uniform Annual Benefit	End-of-Useful-Life Salvage Value	Useful Life (years)
1	$500	$135	$ 0	5
2	600	100	250	5
3	700	100	180	10
4	0	0	0	0

Use a 10-year analysis period for the four mutually exclusive alternatives. At the end of 5 years, Alternatives 1 and 2 may be replaced with identical alternatives (with the same cost, benefits, salvage value, and useful life).

(a) If an 8% interest rate is used, which alternative should be selected?

(b) If a 12% interest rate is used, which alternative should be selected?

5-72 Consider A–E, five mutually exclusive alternatives:

	A	B	C	D	E
Initial cost	$600	$600	$600	$600	$600
Uniform annual benefits					
for first 5 years	100	100	100	150	150
for last 5 years	50	100	110	0	50

The interest rate is 10%. If all the alternatives have a 10-year useful life, and no salvage value, which alternative should be selected?

5-73 An investor has carefully studied a number of companies and their common stock. From his analysis, he has decided that the stocks of six firms are the best of the many he has examined. They represent about the same amount of risk, and so he would like to determine one single stock in which to invest. He plans to keep the stock for 4 years and requires a 10% minimum attractive rate of return.

Which stock from Table P5-73, if any, should the investor consider buying? (*Answer:* Spartan Products)

TABLE P5-73

Common Stock	Price per Share	Annual End-of-Year Dividend per Share	Estimated Price at End of 4 Years
Western House	$23³/₄	$1.25	$32
Fine Foods	45	4.50	45
Mobile Motors	30⁵/₈	0	42
Spartan Products	12	0	20
U.S. Tire	33³/₈	2.00	40
Wine Products	52¹/₂	3.00	60

TABLE P5-84

Year	0	1	2	3	4	5	6	7
Net cash ($)	0	−120,000	−60,000	20,000	40,000	80,000	100,000	60,000

5-74   Six mutually exclusive alternatives, *A–F*, are being examined. For an 8% interest rate, which alternative should be selected? Each alternative has a 6-year useful life.

	Initial Cost	Uniform Annual Benefit
A	$ 20.00	6.00
B	35.00	9.25
C	55.00	13.38
D	60.00	13.78
E	80.00	24.32
F	100.00	24.32

5-75   The management of an electronics manufacturing firm believes it is desirable to automate its production facility. The automated equipment would have a 10-year life with no salvage value at the end of 10 years. The plant engineering department has surveyed the plant and has suggested there are eight mutually exclusive alternatives.

Plan	Initial Cost (thousands)	Net Annual Benefit (thousands)
1	$265	$51
2	220	39
3	180	26
4	100	15
5	305	57
6	130	23
7	245	47
8	165	33

If the firm expects a 10% rate of return, which plan, if any, should it adopt?   (*Answer:* Plan 1)

Spreadsheets

5-76   Assume monthly car payments of $500 per month for 4 years and an interest rate of 1/2% per month. What initial principal or PW will this repay?

5-77   Assume annual car payments of $6000 for 4 years and an interest rate of 6% per year. What initial principal or PW will this repay?

5-78   Assume annual car payments of $6000 for 4 years and an interest rate of 6.168% per year. What initial principal or PW will this repay?

5-79   Why do the values in Problems 5-76, 5-77, and 5-78 differ?

5-80   Assume mortgage payments of $1000 per month for 30 years and an interest rate of 1/2% per month. What initial principal or PW will this repay?

5-81   Assume annual mortgage payments of $12,000 for 30 years and an interest rate of 6% per year. What initial principal or PW will this repay?

5-82   Assume annual mortgage payments of $12,000 for 30 years and an interest rate of 6.168% per year. What initial principal or PW will this repay?

5-83   Why do the values in Problems 5-80, 5-81, and 5-82 differ?

5-84   Ding Bell Imports requires a return of 15% on all projects. If Ding is planning an overseas development project with the cash flows shown in Table P5-84, what is the project's net present value?

5-85 Maverick Enterprises is planning a new product. Annual sales, unit costs, and unit revenues are as tabulated; the first cost of R&D and setting up the assembly line is $42,000. If *i* is 10%, what is the PW?

Year	Annual Sales	Cost/unit	Price/unit
1	$ 5,000	$3.50	$6
2	6,000	3.25	5.75
3	9,000	3.00	5.50
4	10,000	2.75	5.25
5	8,000	2.5	4.5
6	4,000	2.25	3

5-86 Northern Engineering is analyzing a mining project. Annual production, unit costs, and unit revenues are in the table. The first cost of the mine setup is $8 million. If *i* is 15%, what is the PW?

Year	Annual Production (tons)	Cost per ton	Price per ton
1	70,000	$25	$35
2	90,000	20	34
3	120,000	22	33
4	100,000	24	34
5	80,000	26	35
6	60,000	28	36
7	40,000	30	37

ANNUAL CASH FLOW ANALYSIS

Lowest Prices on the Net! Buy Now!

Next time you review your e-mail and scroll through the spam, take a look at how many unsolicited messages are offering cut-rate ink cartridges for your printer.

Strange, isn't it? Why would spam pests imagine they can capture your attention with ads for cheap printer ink, especially when competing spammers are advertising many other products?

The answer becomes clear when you look at the price of an ink cartridge for a typical inkjet printer. Cartridges often cost $30 or more, and they need to be replaced frequently. By contrast, a good quality inkjet printer can often be purchased for under $100.

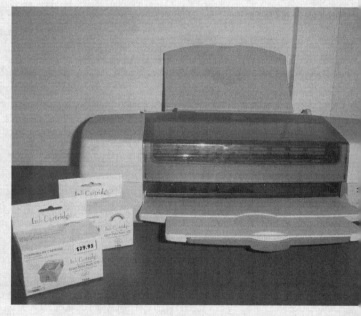

1. Retailers frequently attract buyers by advertising low sale prices for printers, but they almost never mention the cost of the ink cartridges. In analyzing the likely cost of operating a printer over its useful lifetime, how much weight should the buyer give to the price of the printer itself, and how much to the cost of the ink cartridges?

2. King Camp Gillette, inventor of the safety razor, designed his product to work with a specially crafted blade that did not need sharpening and could be disposed of after a few uses. Gillette eventually announced, to everyone's astonishment, that he would be giving his razors away. Many people couldn't imagine how he could possibly make money this way. In fact, Gillette revolutionized marketing, and his business revenue soared. Can you explain why?

3. Would Gillette's strategy work with a product such as a car? Why or why not?

4. What ethical issues do producers and marketers face in designing and selling their products? Is it true that "anything goes in business" so "caveat emptor"?

After Completing This Chapter...

The student should be able to:

- Define *equivalent uniform annual cost (EUAC)* and *equivalent uniform annual benefits (EUAB)*.
- Resolve an engineering economic analysis problem into its annual cash flow equivalent.
- Conduct an *equivalent uniform annual worth (EUAW) analysis* for a single investment.
- Use EUAW, EUAC, and EUAB to compare alternatives with equal, common multiple, or continuous lives, or over some fixed study period.
- Develop and use spreadsheets to analyze loans for purposes of building an amortization table, calculating interest versus principal, finding the balance due, and determining whether to pay off a loan early.

his chapter is devoted to annual cash flow analysis—the second of the three major analysis techniques. With present worth, analysis, we resolved an alternative into an equivalent cash sum. This might have been an equivalent net present worth, a present worth of cost, or a present worth of benefit. Here we compare alternatives based on their equivalent annual cash flows. Depending on the particular situation, we may wish to compute the equivalent uniform annual cost (EUAC), the equivalent uniform annual benefit (EUAB), or their difference, the equivalent uniform annual worth (EUAW) = (EUAB − EUAC).

To prepare for a discussion of annual cash flow analysis, we will review some annual cash flow calculations, then examine annual cash flow criteria. Following this, we will proceed with annual cash flow analysis.

ANNUAL CASH FLOW CALCULATIONS

Resolving a Present Cost to an Annual Cost

Equivalence techniques were used in prior chapters to convert money, at one point in time, to some equivalent sum or series. In annual cash flow analysis, the goal is to convert money to an equivalent uniform annual cost or benefit. The simplest case is to convert a present sum P to a series of equivalent uniform end-of-period cash flows. This is illustrated in Example 6-1.

EXAMPLE 6-1

A student bought $1000 worth of home furniture. If the items are expected to last 10 years, what will the equivalent uniform annual cost be if interest is 7%?

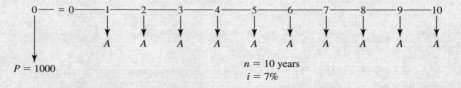

$n = 10$ years
$i = 7\%$

SOLUTION

$$\text{Equivalent uniform annual cost} = P(A/P, i, n)$$
$$= 1000(A/P, 7\%, 10)$$
$$= \$142.40$$

Equivalent uniform annual cost is $142.40.

Treatment of Salvage Value

When there is a salvage value at the end of an asset's useful life, this decreases the equivalent uniform annual cost.

EXAMPLE 6-2

The student in Example 6-1 now believes the furniture can be sold at the end of 10 years for $200. Under these circumstances, what is the equivalent uniform annual cost?

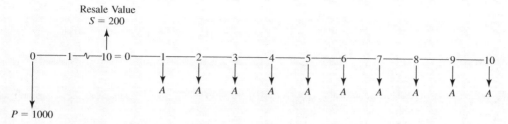

SOLUTION

For this situation, the problem may be solved by means of three different calculations.

SOLUTION 1

$$\text{EUAC} = P(A/P, i, n) - S(A/F, i, n) \tag{6-1}$$
$$= 1000(A/P, 7\%, 10) - 200(A/F, 7\%, 10)$$
$$= 1000(0.1424) - 200(0.0724)$$
$$= 142.40 - 14.48 = \$127.92$$

This method reflects the annual cost of the cash disbursement minus the annual benefit of the future resale value.

SOLUTION 2

Equation 6-1 describes a relationship that may be modified by an identity presented in Chapter 4:

$$(A/P, i, n) = (A/F, i, n) + i \tag{6-2}$$

Substituting this into Equation 6-1 gives:

$$\text{EUAC} = P(A/F, i, n) + Pi - S(A/F, i, n) \tag{6-3}$$
$$= (P - S)(A/F, i, n) + Pi$$
$$= (1000 - 200)(A/F, 7\%, 10) + 1000(0.07)$$
$$= 800(0.0724) + 70 = 57.92 + 70$$
$$= \$127.92$$

This method computes the equivalent annual cost due to the unrecovered $800 when the furniture is sold, and adds annual interest on the $1000 investment.

SOLUTION 3

If the value for $(A/F, i, n)$ from Equation 6-2 is substituted into Equation 6-1, we obtain:

$$\text{EUAC} = P(A/P, i, n) - S(A/P, i, n) + Si \qquad (6\text{-}4)$$
$$= (P - S)(A/P, i, n) + Si$$
$$= (1000 - 200)(A/P, 7\%, 10) + 200(0.07)$$
$$= 800(0.1424) + 14 = 113.92 + 14 = \$127.92$$

This method computes the annual cost of the $800 decline in value during the 10 years, plus interest on the $200 tied up in the furniture as the salvage value.

When there is an initial disbursement P followed by a salvage value S, the annual cost may be computed in the three different ways introduced in Example 6-2.

$$\textbf{EUAC} = P(A/P, i, n) - S(A/F, i, n) \qquad (6\text{-}1)$$

$$\textbf{EUAC} = (P - S)(A/F, i, n) + Pi \qquad (6\text{-}3)$$

$$\textbf{EUAC} = (P - S)(A/P, i, n) + Si \qquad (6\text{-}4)$$

Each of the three calculations gives the same results. In practice, the first and third methods are most commonly used. The EUAC calculated in Equations 6-1, 6-3, and 6-4 is also known as the *capital recovery cost* of a project.

EXAMPLE 6-3

Bill owned a car for 5 years. One day he wondered what his uniform annual cost for maintenance and repairs had been. He assembled the following data:

Year	Maintenance and Repair Cost for Year
1	$ 45
2	90
3	180
4	135
5	225

Compute the equivalent uniform annual cost (EUAC) assuming 7% interest and end-of-year disbursements.

The EUAC may be computed for this irregular series of payments in two steps:

1. Use single payment present worth factors to compute the present worth of cost for the 5 years.
2. With the PW of cost known, use the capital recovery factor to compute EUAC.

$$\text{PW of cost} = 45(P/F, 7\%, 1) + 90(P/F, 7\%, 2) + 180(P/F, 7\%, 3)$$
$$+ \ 135(P/F, 7\%, 4) + 225(P/F, 7\%, 5)$$
$$= 45(0.9346) + 90(0.8734) + 180(0.8163) + 135(0.7629) + 225(0.7130)$$
$$= \$531$$
$$\text{EUAC} = 531(A/P, 7\%, 5) = 531(0.2439) = \$130$$

EXAMPLE 6-4

Bill reexamined his calculations and found that in his table he had reversed the maintenance and repair costs for Years 3 and 4. The correct table is:

Year	Maintenance and Repair Cost for Year
1	$ 45
2	90
3	135
4	180
5	225

Recompute the EUAC.

This time the schedule of disbursements is an arithmetic gradient series plus a uniform annual cost, as follows:

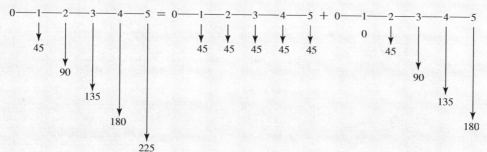

$$\text{EUAC} = 45 + 45(A/G, 7\%, 5)$$

$$= 45 + 45(1.865)$$

$$= \$129$$

Since the timing of the expenditures is different in Examples 6-3 and 6-4, we would not expect to obtain the same EUAC.

The examples have shown four essential points concerning cash flow calculations:

1. There is a direct relationship between the present worth of cost and the equivalent uniform annual cost. It is

$$\text{EUAC} = (\text{PW of cost})(A/P, i, n)$$

2. In a problem, expending money increases the EUAC, while receiving money—for example, from an item's salvage value—decreases the EUAC.
3. When there are irregular cash disbursements over the analysis period, a convenient method of solution is to first determine the PW of cost; then use the equation in Item 1 to calculate the EUAC.
4. Where there is an arithmetic gradient, EUAC may be rapidly computed by using the arithmetic gradient uniform series factor, $(A/G, i, n)$.

ANNUAL CASH FLOW ANALYSIS

The criteria for economic efficiency are presented in Table 6-1. One notices immediately that the table is quite similar to Table 5-1. It is apparent that, if you are maximizing the present worth of benefits, simultaneously you must be maximizing the equivalent uniform annual worth. This is illustrated in Example 6-5.

TABLE 6-1 Annual Cash Flow Analysis

Input/Output	Situation	Criterion
Neither input nor output is fixed	Typical, general situation	Maximize equivalent uniform annual worth (EUAW = EUAB − EUAC)
Fixed input	Amount of money or other input resources is fixed	Maximize equivalent uniform benefits (maximize EUAB)
Fixed output	There is a fixed task, benefit, or other output to be accomplished	Minimize equivalent uniform annual cost (minimize EUAC)

EXAMPLE 6-5

A firm is considering which of two devices to install to reduce costs. Both devices have useful lives of 5 years with no salvage value. Device A costs $1000 and can be expected to result in $300 savings annually. Device B costs $1350 and will provide cost savings of $300 the first year; however, savings will increase $50 annually, making the second year savings $350, the third year savings $400, and so forth. With interest at 7%, which device should the firm purchase?

SOLUTION

Device A

$$EUAW = -1000(A/P, 7\%, 5) + 300$$
$$= -1000(0.2439) + 300 = \$56.1$$

Device B

$$EUAW = -1350(A/P, 7\%, 5) + 300 + 50(A/G, 7\%, 5)$$
$$= -1350(0.2439) + 300 + 50(1.865)$$
$$= \$64.0$$

To maximize EUAW, select Device B.

Example 6-5 was presented earlier, as Example 5-1, where we found:

$$PW_A = -1000 + 300(P/A, 7\%, 5)$$
$$= -1000 + 300(4.100) = \$230$$

This is converted to EUAW by multiplying by the capital recovery factor:

$$EUAW_A = 230(A/P, 7\%, 5) = 230(0.2439) = \$56.1$$

Similarly, for machine B

$$PW_B = -1350 + 300(P/A, 7\%, 5) + 50(P/G, 7\%, 5)$$
$$= -1350 + 400(4.100) + 50(7.647) = \$262.4$$

and, hence,

$$EUAW_B = 262.4(A/P, 7\%, 5) = 262.4(0.2439)$$
$$= \$64.0$$

We see, therefore, that it is easy to convert the present worth analysis results into the annual cash flow analysis results. We could go from annual cash flow to present worth just as easily, by using the series present worth factor. And, of course, both methods show that Device *B* is the preferred alternative.

EXAMPLE 6-6

Three alternatives are being considered for improving an operation on the assembly line along with the "do-nothing" alternative. Equipment costs vary, as do the annual benefits of each in comparison to the present situation. Each of Plans *A*, *B*, and *C* has a 10-year life and a salvage value equal to 10% of its original cost.

	Plan *A*	Plan *B*	Plan *C*
Installed cost of equipment	$15,000	$25,000	$33,000
Material and labor savings per year	14,000	9,000	14,000
Annual operating expenses	8,000	6,000	6,000
End-of-useful life salvage value	1,500	2,500	3,300

If interest is 8%, which plan, if any, should be adopted?

SOLUTION

Since neither installed cost nor output benefits are fixed, the economic criterion is to maximize EUAW = EUAB − EUAC.

	Plan *A*	Plan *B*	Plan *C*
Equivalent uniform annual benefit (EUAB)			
Material and labor per year	$14,000	$9,000	$14,000
Salvage value (A/F, 8%, 10)	104	172	228
EUAB =	$14,104	$9,172	$14,228
Equivalent uniform annual cost (EUAC)			
Installed cost (A/P, 8%, 10)	$ 2,235	$3,725	$ 4,917
Annual operating expenses	8,000	6,000	6,000
EUAC =	$10,235	$9,725	$10,917
EUAW = EUAB − EUAC =	$ 3,869	−$ 553	$ 3,311

Based on our criterion of maximizing EUAW, Plan *A* is the best of the four alternatives. Since the do-nothing alternative has EUAW = 0, it is a more desirable alternative than Plan *B*.

ANALYSIS PERIOD

In Chapter 5, we saw that the analysis period is an important consideration in computing present worth comparisons. In such problems, a common analysis period must be used for all alternatives. In annual cash flow comparisons, we again have the analysis period question. Example 6-7 will help in examining the problem.

EXAMPLE 6-7

Two pumps are being considered for purchase. If interest is 7%, which pump should be bought?

	Pump A	Pump B
Initial cost	$7000	$5000
End-of-useful-life salvage value	1500	1000
Useful life, in years	12	6

SOLUTION

The annual cost for 12 years of Pump A can be found by using Equation 6-4:

$$\text{EUAC} = (P - S)(A/P, i, n) + Si$$
$$= (7000 - 1500)(A/P, 7\%, 12) + 1500(0.07)$$
$$= 5500(0.1259) + 105 = \$797$$

Now compute the annual cost for 6 years of Pump B:

$$\text{EUAC} = (5000 - 1000)(A/P, 7\%, 6) + 1000(0.07)$$
$$= 4000(0.2098) + 70 = \$909$$

For a common analysis period of 12 years, we need to replace Pump B at the end of its 6-year useful life. If we assume that another pump B′ can be obtained, having the same $5000 initial cost, $1000 salvage value, and 6-year life, the cash flow will be as follows:

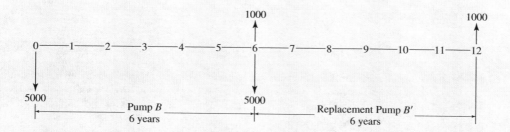

For the 12-year analysis period, the annual cost for Pump B is

$$\text{EUAC} = [5000 - 1000(P/F, 7\%, 6) + 5000(P/F, 7\%, 6)$$
$$- 1000(P/F, 7\%, 12)] \times (A/P, 7\%, 12)$$
$$= [5000 - 1000(0.6663) + 5000(0.6663) - 1000(0.4440)] \times (0.1259)$$
$$= (5000 - 666 + 3331 - 444)(0.1259)$$
$$= (7211)(0.1259) = \$909$$

The annual cost of *B* for the 6-year analysis period is the same as the annual cost for the 12-year analysis period. This is not a surprising conclusion when one recognizes that the annual cost of the first 6-year period is repeated in the second 6-year period. Thus the lengthy calculation of EUAC for 12 years of Pump *B* and *B'* was not needed. By assuming that the shorter-life equipment is replaced by equipment with identical economic consequences, we have avoided a lot of calculations. Select Pump *A*.

Analysis Period Equal to Alternative Lives

If the analysis period for an economy study coincides with the useful life for each alternative, then the economy study is based on this analysis period.

Analysis Period a Common Multiple of Alternative Lives

When the analysis period is a common multiple of the alternative lives (for example, in Example 6-7, the analysis period was 12 years with 6- and 12-year alternative lives), a "replacement with an identical item with the same costs, performance, and so forth" is frequently assumed. This means that when an alternative has reached the end of its useful life, we assume that it will be replaced with an identical item. As shown in Example 6-7, the result is that the EUAC for Pump *B* with a 6-year useful life is equal to the EUAC for the entire analysis period based on Pump *B plus* the replacement unit, Pump *B'*.

Under these circumstances of identical replacement, we can compare the annual cash flows computed for alternatives based on their own service lives. In Example 6-7, the annual cost for Pump *A*, based on its 12-year service life, was compared with the annual cost for Pump *B*, based on its 6-year service life.

Analysis Period for a Continuing Requirement

Many times an economic analysis is undertaken to determine how to provide for a more or less continuing requirement. One might need to pump water from a well as a continuing requirement. There is no distinct analysis period. In this situation, the analysis period is assumed to be long but undefined.

If, for example, we had a continuing requirement to pump water and alternative Pumps *A* and *B* had useful lives of 7 and 11 years, respectively, what should we do? The customary assumption is that Pump *A*'s annual cash flow (based on a 7-year life) may be compared to Pump *B*'s annual cash flow (based on an 11-year life). This is done without much concern that the least common multiple of the 7- and 11-year lives is 77 years. This comparison of "different-life" alternatives assumes identical replacement (with identical costs, performance, etc.) when an alternative reaches the end of its useful life.

This continuing requirement, which can also be described as an *indefinitely long horizon*, is illustrated in Example 6.8. Since this is longer than the lives of the alternatives, we can make the best decision possible given current information by minimizing EUAC or maximizing EUAW or EUAB. At a later time, we will make another replacement and there will be more information on costs *at that time*.

EXAMPLE 6-8

Pump B in Example 6-7 is now believed to have a 9-year useful life. Assuming the same initial cost and salvage value, compare it with Pump A using the same 7% interest rate.

SOLUTION

If we assume that the need for A or B will exist for some continuing period, the comparison of costs per year for the unequal lives is an acceptable technique. For 12 years of Pump A:

$$EUAC = (7000 - 1500)(A/P, 7\%, 12) + 1500(0.07) = \$797$$

For 9 years of Pump B:

$$EUAC = (5000 - 1000)(A/P, 7\%, 9) + 1000(0.07) = \$684$$

For minimum EUAC, select Pump B.

Infinite Analysis Period

At times we have an alternative with a limited (finite) useful life in an infinite analysis period situation. The equivalent uniform annual cost may be computed for the limited life. The assumption of identical replacement (replacements have identical costs, performance, etc.) is often appropriate. Based on this assumption, the same EUAC occurs for each replacement of the limited-life alternative. The EUAC for the infinite analysis period is therefore equal to the EUAC computed for the limited life. With identical replacement,

$$EUAC_{\text{infinite analysis period}} = EUAC_{\text{for limited life } n}$$

A somewhat different situation occurs when there is an alternative with an infinite life in a problem with an infinite analysis period:

$$EUAC_{\text{infinite analysis period}} = P(A/P, i, \infty) + \text{Any other annual costs}$$

When $n = \infty$, we have $A = Pi$ and, hence, $(A/P, i, \infty)$ equals i.

$$EUAC_{\text{infinite analysis period}} = Pi + \text{Any other annual costs}$$

EXAMPLE 6-9

In the construction of an aqueduct to expand the water supply of a city, there are two alternatives for a particular portion of the aqueduct. Either a tunnel can be constructed through a mountain, or a pipeline can be laid to go around the mountain. If there is a permanent need for the aqueduct, should the tunnel or the pipeline be selected for this particular portion of the aqueduct? Assume a 6% interest rate.

SOLUTION

	Tunnel Through Mountain	Pipeline Around Mountain
Initial cost	$5.5 million	$5 million
Maintenance	0	0
Useful life	Permanent	50 years
Salvage value	0	0

Tunnel

For the tunnel, with its permanent life, we want $(A/P, 6\%, \infty)$. For an infinite life, the capital recovery is simply interest on the invested capital. So $(A/P, 6\%, \infty) = i$, and we write

$$\text{EUAC} = Pi = \$5.5 \text{ million}(0.06)$$

$$= \$330,000$$

Pipeline

$$\text{EUAC} = \$5 \text{ million}(A/P, 6\%, 50)$$

$$= \$5 \text{ million}(0.0634) = \$317,000$$

For fixed output, minimize EUAC. Select the pipeline.

The difference in annual cost between a long life and an infinite life is small unless an unusually low interest rate is used. In Example 6-9 the tunnel is assumed to be permanent. For comparison, compute the annual cost if an 85-year life is assumed for the tunnel.

$$\text{EUAC} = \$5.5 \text{ million}(A/P, 6\%, 85)$$

$$= \$5.5 \text{ million}(0.0604)$$

$$= \$332,000$$

The difference in time between 85 years and infinity is great indeed; yet the difference in annual costs in Example 6-9 is very small.

Some Other Analysis Period

The analysis period in a particular problem may be something other than one of the four we have so far described. It may be equal to the life of the shorter-life alternative, the longer-life alternative, or something entirely different. One must carefully examine the consequences of each alternative throughout the analysis period and, in addition, see what differences there might be in salvage values, and so forth, at the end of the analysis period.

EXAMPLE 6-10

Suppose that Alternative 1 has a 7-year life and a salvage value at the end of that time. The replacement cost at the end of 7 years may be more or less than the original cost. If the replacement is retired prior to 7 years, it will have a terminal value that exceeds the end-of-life salvage value. Alternative 2 has a 13-year life and a terminal value whenever it is retired. If the situation indicates that 10 years is the proper analysis period, set up the equations to compute the EUAC for each alternative. Use results from Example 5-5 to compute the results.

SOLUTION

Alternative 1

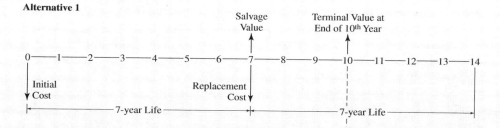

Alternative 2

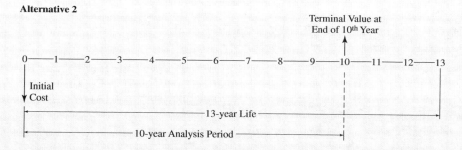

Alternative 1

$$\text{EUAC}_1 = [\text{Initial cost} + (\text{Replacement cost} - \text{Salvage value})(P/F,\ i, 7)$$
$$- (\text{Terminal value})(P/F,\ i, 10)](A/P,\ i, 10)$$
$$= 64{,}076(A/P, 8\%, 10) \quad \text{using results from Example 5-5}$$
$$= 64{,}076(8.1490) = \$9547$$

Alternative 2

$$\text{EUAC}_2 = [\text{Initial cost} - (\text{Terminal value})(P/F,\ i, 10)](A/P,\ i, 10)$$
$$= 69{,}442(A/P, 8\%, 10) \quad \text{using results from Example 5-5}$$
$$= 69{,}442(0.1490) = \$10{,}347$$

Select Alternative 1.

USING SPREADSHEETS TO ANALYZE LOANS

Loan and bond payments are made by firms, agencies, and individual engineers. Usually, the payments in each period are constant. Spreadsheets make it easy to:

- Calculate the loan's amortization schedule
- Decide how a payment is to be split between principal and interest
- Find the balance due on a loan
- Calculate the number of payments remaining on a loan.

Building an Amortization Schedule

As illustrated in previous chapters and Appendix 1, an amortization schedule lists for each payment period: the loan payment, interest paid, principal paid, and remaining balance. For each period the interest paid equals the interest rate times the balance remaining from the period before. Then the principal payment equals the payment minus the interest paid. Finally, this principal payment is applied to the balance remaining from the preceding period to calculate the new remaining balance. As a basis for comparison with spreadsheet loan functions, Figure 6-1 shows this calculation for Example 6-11.

EXAMPLE 6-11

An engineer wanted to celebrate graduating and getting a job by spending $2400 on new furniture. Luckily the store was offering 6-month financing at the low interest rate of 6% per year nominal (really $1/2\%$ per month). Calculate the amortization schedule.

SOLUTION

	A	B	C	D	E
1	2400	Initial balance			
2	0.50%	i			
3	6	N			
4	$407.03	Payment	$= -\text{PMT(A2,A3,A1)}$		
5					
6			Principal	Ending	
7	Month	Interest	Payment	Balance	
8	0			2400.00	=A1
9	1	12.00	395.03	2004.97	=D8−C9
10	2	10.02	397.00	1607.97	
11	3	8.04	398.99	1208.98	
12	4	6.04	400.98	807.99	
13	5	4.04	402.99	405.00	
14	6	2.03	405.00	0.00	
15				=$A$4−B14	
16				=Payment−Interest	
17			=$A$2*D13		
18			=rate*previous balance		

FIGURE 6-1 Amortization schedule for furniture loan.

The first step is to calculate the monthly payment:

$$A = 2400(A/P, \tfrac{1}{2}\%, 6) = 2400(0.1696) = \$407.0$$
$$= \mathrm{PMT}(0.005, 6, -2400) = \$407.03$$

With this information the engineer can use the spreadsheet of Figure 6-1 to obtain the amortization schedule.

How Much to Interest? How Much to Principal?

For a loan with constant payments, we can answer these questions for any period without the full amortization schedule. For a loan with constant payments, the functions IPMT and PPMT directly answer these questions. For simple problems, both functions have four arguments $(i, t, n, -P)$, where t is the time period being calculated. Both functions have optional arguments that permit adding a balloon payment (an F) and changing from end-of-period payments to beginning-of-period payments.

For example, consider Period 4 of Example 6-11. The spreadsheet formulas give the same answer as shown in Figure 6-1.

$$\mathrm{Interest}_4 = \mathrm{IPMT}(0.5\%, 4, 6, -2400) = \$6.04$$
$$\mathrm{Principal\ payment}_4 = \mathrm{PPMT}(0.5\%, 4, 6, -2400) = \$400.98$$

Finding the Balance Due on a Loan

An amortization schedule is one used to calculate the balance due on a loan. A second, easier way is to remember that the balance due equals the present worth of the remaining payments. Interest is paid in full after each payment, so later payments are simply based on the balance due.

EXAMPLE 6-12

A car is purchased with a 48-month, 9% nominal loan with an initial balance of $15,000. What is the balance due halfway through the 4 years?

SOLUTION

The first step is to calculate the monthly payment, at a monthly interest rate of $\tfrac{3}{4}\%$. This equals

$$\mathrm{Payment} = 15,000(A/P, 0.75\%, 48) \quad \text{or} \quad = \mathrm{PMT}(0.75\%, 48, -15000)$$
$$= (15,000)(0.0249) = \$373.50 \quad \text{or} \quad = \$373.28$$

The next step will use the spreadsheet answer, because it is more accurate (there are only three significant digits in the tabulated factor).

After 24 payments and with 24 left, the remaining balance equals $(P/A, i, N_{remaining})$ payment

$$Balance = (P/A, 0.75\%, 24)\$373.28 \quad\quad or \quad = PV(0.75\%, 24, 373.28)$$
$$= (21.889)(373.28) = \$8170.73 \quad or \quad = \$8170.78$$

Thus halfway through the repayment schedule, 54.5% of the original balance is still owed.

Pay Off Debt Sooner by Increasing Payments

Paying off debt can be a good investment because the investment earns the rate of interest on the loan. For example, this could be 8% for a mortgage, 10% for a car loan, or 19% for a credit card. When one is making extra payments on a loan, the common question is: How much sooner will the debt be paid off? Until the debt is paid off, any early payments are essentially locked up, since the same payment amount is owed each month.

The first reason that spreadsheets are convenient is fractional interest rates. For example, an auto loan might be at a nominal rate of 13% with monthly compounding or 1.08333% per month. The second reason is that the function NPER calculates the number of periods remaining on a loan.

NPER can be used to calculate how much difference is made by one extra payment or by increasing all payments by $x\%$. Extra payments are applied entirely to principal, so the interest rate, remaining balance, and payment amounts are all known. $N_{remaining}$ equals NPER(i, payment, remaining balance) with optional arguments for beginning-of-period cash flows and balloon payments. The signs of the payment and the remaining balance must be different.

EXAMPLE 6-13

Maria has a 7.5% mortgage with monthly payments for 30 years. Her original balance was $100,000, and she just made her twelfth payment. Each month she also pays into a reserve account, which the bank uses to pay her fire and liability insurance ($900 annually) and property taxes ($1500 annually). By how much does she shorten the loan if she makes an extra *loan* payment today? If she makes an extra *total* payment? If she increases each total payment to 110% of her current total payment?

SOLUTION

The first step is to calculate Maria's *loan* payment for the 360 months. Rather than calculating a six-significant digit monthly interest rate, it is easier to use 0.075/12 in the spreadsheet formulas.

$$Payment = PMT(0.075/12, 360, -100000) = \$699.21$$

The remaining balance after 12 such payments is the present worth of the remaining 348 payments.

$$Balance_{12} = PV(0.075/12, 348, 699.21) = \$99,077.53$$
$$\text{(after 12 payments, she has paid off \$922!)}$$

If she pays an extra \$699.21, then the number of periods remaining is

$$\text{NPER}(0.075/12, -699.21, 99077.53 - 699.21) = 339.5$$

This is 8.5 payments less than the 348 periods left before the extra payment. If she makes an extra total payment, then

$$\text{Total payment} = 699.21 + 900/12 + 1500/12 = \$899.21/\text{month}$$

$$\text{NPER}(0.075/12, -699.21, 99244 - 899.21) = 337.1$$

or 2.4 more payments saved. If she makes an extra 10% payment on the total payment of \$899.21, then

$$\text{NPER}(0.075/12, -(1.1 * 899.21 - 200), 99077.53) = 246.5 \text{ payments}$$

or 101.5 payments saved.
Note that \$200 of the total payment goes to pay for insurance and taxes.

SUMMARY

Annual cash flow analysis is the second of the three major methods of resolving alternatives into comparable values. When an alternative has an initial cost P and salvage value S, there are three ways of computing the equivalent uniform annual cost:

- $\text{EUAC} = P(A/P, i, n) - S(A/F, i, n)$ (6-1)
- $\text{EUAC} = (P - S)(A/F, i, n) + Pi$ (6-3)
- $\text{EUAC} = (P - S)(A/P, i, n) + Si$ (6-4)

All three equations give the same answer. This quantity is also known as the *capital recovery cost* of the project.

The relationship between the present worth of cost and the equivalent uniform annual cost is:

- $\text{EUAC} = (\text{PW of cost})(A/P, i, n)$

The three annual cash flow criteria are:

Neither input nor output fixed	Maximize EUAW = EUAB − EUAC
For fixed input	Maximize EUAB
For fixed output	Minimize EUAC

In present worth analysis there must be a common analysis period. Annual cash flow analysis, however, allows some flexibility provided the necessary assumptions are suitable in the situation being studied. The analysis period may be different from the lives of the alternatives, and provided the following criteria are met, a valid cash flow analysis may be made.

1. When an alternative has reached the end of its useful life, it is assumed to be replaced by an identical replacement (with the same costs, performance, etc.).

2. The analysis period is a common multiple of the useful lives of the alternatives, or there is a continuing or perpetual requirement for the selected alternative.

If neither condition applies, it is necessary to make a detailed study of the consequences of the various alternatives over the entire analysis period with particular attention to the difference between the alternatives at the end of the analysis period.

There is very little numerical difference between a long-life alternative and a perpetual alternative. As the value of n increases, the capital recovery factor approaches i. At the limit, $(A/P, i, \infty) = i$.

One of the most common uniform payment series is the repayment of loans. Spreadsheets are useful in analyzing loans (balance due, interest paid, etc.) for several reasons: they have specialized functions, many periods are easy, and any interest rate can be used.

PROBLEMS

Annual Calculations

6-1   Compute the EUAB for these cash flows based on a 10% interest rate.

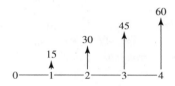

(*Answer:* EUAB= $35.72)

6-2   Compute the EUAC for these cash flows.

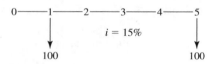

6-3   Compute the EUAB for these cash flows.

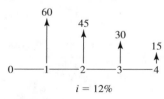

6-4   If $i = 6\%$, compute the EUAB over 6 years that is equivalent to the two receipts shown.

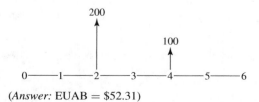

(*Answer:* EUAB = $52.31)

6-5   A loan of $100 is to be repaid in three equal semiannual (every 6 months) payments. If the annual interest rate is 7% compounded semiannually, how much is each payment?   (*Answer:* $35.69)

6-6   When he started work on his twenty-second birthday, D. B. Cooper decided to invest money each month with the objective of becoming a millionaire by the time he reaches age 65. If he expects his investments to yield 18% per annum, compounded monthly, how much should he invest each month?   (*Answer:* $6.92 a month.)

6-7   The average age of engineering students at graduation is a little over 23 years. This means that the working career of most engineers is almost exactly 500 months. How much would an engineer need to save each month to become a millionaire by the end of his working career? Assume a 15% interest rate, compounded monthly.

6-8   An engineer wishes to have $5 million by the time he retires in 40 years. Assuming 15% nominal interest, compounded continuously, what annual sum must he set aside?   (*Answer:* $2011)

6-9   Art Arfons, a K-State-educated engineer, has made a considerable fortune. He wishes to start a perpetual scholarship for engineering students at K-State. The scholarship will provide a student with an annual stipend of $2500 for each of 4 years (freshman through senior), plus an additional $5000 during the senior year to cover entertainment expenses. Assume that students graduate in 4 years, a new award is given every 4 years, and the money is paid at the beginning of each year with the first award at the beginning of Year 1. The interest rate is 8%.

(*a*) Determine the equivalent uniform annual cost (EUAC) of providing the scholarship.

(*b*) How much money must Art donate to K-State?

6-10   For the diagram, compute the value of D that results in a net equivalent uniform annual worth (EUAW) of 0.

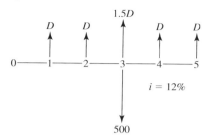

6-11   An electronics firm invested $60,000 in a precision inspection device. It cost $4000 to operate and maintain in the first year and $3000 in each of the subsequent years. At the end of 4 years, the firm changed their inspection procedure, eliminating the need for the device. The purchasing agent was very fortunate in being able to sell the inspection device for $60,000, the original price. The plant manager asks you to compute the equivalent uniform annual cost of the device during the 4 years it was used. Assume interest at 10% per year.   (*Answer:* $9287)

6-12   A firm is about to begin pilot plant operation on a process it has developed. One item of optional equipment that could be obtained is a heat exchanger unit. The company finds that a unit now available for $30,000 could be used in other company operations. It is estimated that the heat exchanger unit will be worth $35,000 at the end of 8 years. This seemingly high salvage value is due primarily to the fact that the $30,000 purchase price is really a rare bargain. If the firm believes 15% is an appropriate rate of return, what annual benefit is needed to justify the purchase of the heat exchanger unit?   (*Answer:* $4135)

6-13   A firm purchased some equipment at a very favorable price of $30,000. The equipment resulted in an annual net saving of $1000 per year during the 8 years it was used. At the end of 8 years, the equipment was sold for $40,000. Assuming interest at 8%, did the equipment purchase prove to be desirable?

6-14   A machine costs $20,000 and has a 5-year useful life. At the end of the 5 years, it can be sold for $4000. If annual interest is 8%, compounded semiannually, what is the equivalent uniform annual cost of the machine?

6-15   Mr. Wiggley wants to buy a new house. It will cost $178,000. The bank will loan 90% of the purchase price at a nominal interest rate of 10.75% compounded weekly, and Mr. Wiggley will make

monthly payments. What is the amount of the monthly payments if he intends to pay the house off in 25 years?

6-16   Steve Lowe must pay his property taxes in two equal installments on December 1 and April 1. The two payments are for taxes for the fiscal year that begins on July 1 and ends the following June 30. Steve purchased a home on September 1. Assuming the annual property taxes remain at $850 per year for the next several years, Steve plans to open a savings account and to make uniform monthly deposits the first of each month. The account is to be used to pay the taxes when they are due.

To open the account, Steve deposits a lump sum equivalent to the monthly payments that will not have been made for the first year's taxes. The savings account pays 9% interest, compounded monthly and payable quarterly (March 31, June 30, September 30, and December 31). How much money should Steve put into the account when he opens it on September 1? What uniform monthly deposit should he make from that time on?   (*Answers:* Initial deposit $350.28; monthly deposit $69.02)

6-17   A motorcycle is for sale for $2600. The dealer is willing to sell it on the following terms:

No down payment; pay $44 at the end of each of the first 4 months; pay $84 at the end of each month after that until the loan has been paid in full.

At a 12% annual interest rate compounded monthly, how many $84 payments will be required?

6-18   Your company must make a $500,000 balloon payment on a lease 2 years and 9 months from today. You have been directed to deposit an amount of money quarterly, beginning today, to provide for the $500,000 payment. The account pays 4% per year, compounded quarterly. What is the required quarterly deposit? *Note:* Lease payments are due at the beginning of the quarter.

6-19   For the diagram, compute the value of C that results in a net equivalent annual worth (EUAW) of 0.

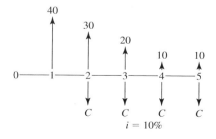

6-20 If interest is 10%, what is the EUAB?

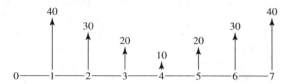

6-21 The maintenance foreman of a plant in reviewing his records found that a large press had the following maintenance cost record:

5 years ago	$ 600
4 years ago	700
3 years ago	800
2 years ago	900
Last year	1000

After consulting with a lubrication specialist, he changed the preventive maintenance schedule. He believes that maintenance will be $900 this year and will decrease by $100 a year in each of the following 4 years. If his estimate of the future is correct, what will be the equivalent uniform annual maintenance cost for the 10-year period? Assume interest at 8%. (*Answer:* $756)

6-22 Linda O'Shay deposited $30,000 in a savings account as a perpetual trust. She believes the account will earn 7% annual interest during the first 10 years and 5% interest thereafter. The trust is to provide a uniform end-of-year scholarship at the university. What uniform amount could be used for the student scholarship each year, beginning at the end of the first year and continuing forever?

6-23 An engineer has a fluctuating future budget for the maintenance of a particular machine. During each of the first 5 years, $1000 per year will be budgeted. During the second 5 years, the annual budget will be $1500 per year. In addition, $3500 will be budgeted for an overhaul of the machine at the end of the fourth year, and another $3500 for an overhaul at the end of the eighth year.

The engineer asks you to compute the uniform annual expenditure that would be equivalent to these fluctuating amounts, assuming interest at 6% per year.

6-24 A machine has a first cost of $150,000, an annual operation and maintenance cost of $2500, a life of 10 years, and a salvage value of $30,000. At the end of Years 4 and 8, it requires a major service, which costs $20,000 and $10,000, respectively. At the end of Year 5, it will need to be overhauled at a cost of $45,000. What is the equivalent uniform annual cost of owning and operating this particular machine?

6-25 There is an annual receipt of money that varies from $100 to $300 in a fixed pattern that repeats forever. If interest is 10%, compute the EUAB, also continuing forever, that is equivalent to the fluctuating disbursements.

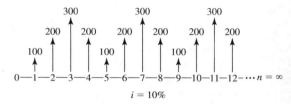

Annual Comparisons

6-26 Alice White has arranged to buy some home recording equipment. She estimates that it will have a 5-year useful life and no salvage value. The dealer has offered Alice two alternative ways to pay for the equipment:

A. Pay $2000 immediately and $500 at the end of one year.

B. Pay nothing until the end of 4 years, when a single payment of $3000 must be made.

Alice believes 12% is a suitable interest rate. Use an annual cash flow analysis to determine which method of payment she should select. (*Answer:* Select B)

6-27 The Johnson Company pays $200 a month to a trucker to haul wastepaper and cardboard to the city dump. The material could be recycled if the company were to buy a $6000 hydraulic press baler and spend $3000 a year for labor to operate the baler. The baler has an estimated useful life of 30 years and no salvage value. Strapping material would cost $200 per year for the estimated 500 bales a year that would be produced. A wastepaper company will pick up the bales at the plant and pay Johnson $2.30 per bale for them. Use an annual cash flow analysis in working this problem.

(*a*) If interest is 8%, is it economical to install and operate the baler?

(*b*) Would you recommend that the baler be installed?

6-28 Jenny McCarthy is an engineer for a municipal power plant. The plant uses natural gas, which is currently provided from an existing pipeline at an annual cost of $10,000 per year. Jenny is considering a project to construct a new pipeline. The initial cost of the new pipeline would be $35,000, but it would reduce the annual cost to $5000 per year. Assume an analysis period of 20 years and no salvage value for either the existing or new pipeline. The interest rate is 6%.

(*a*) Determine the equivalent uniform annual cost (EUAC) for the new pipeline.

(*b*) Should the new pipeline be built?

6-29 Claude James, a salesman, needs a new car for business use. He expects to be promoted to a supervisory job at the end of 3 years, and he will no longer be "on the road." The company reimburses salesmen each month at the rate of 25¢ per mile driven. Claude finds that there are three different ways of obtaining his chosen car:

A. Pay cash: the price is $13,000.

B. Lease the car: the monthly charge is $350 on a 36-month lease, payable at the end of each month; at the end of the 3-year period, the car is returned to the leasing company.

C. Lease the car with an option to buy at the end of the lease: pay $360 a month for 36 months; at the end of that time, Claude could buy the car, if he chooses, for $3500.

Claude believes he should use a 12% interest rate. If the car could be sold for $4000 at the end of 3 years, which method should he use to obtain it?

6-30 When he purchased his home, Al Silva borrowed $80,000 at 10% interest to be repaid in 25 equal annual end-of-year payments. After making 10 payments, Al found he could refinance the balance due on his loan at 9% interest for the remaining 15 years.

To refinance the loan, Al must pay the original lender the balance due on the loan, plus a penalty charge of 2% of the balance due; to the new lender he also must pay a $1000 service charge to obtain the loan. The new loan would be made equal to the balance due on the old loan, plus the 2% penalty charge, and the $1000 service charge. Should Al refinance the loan, assuming that he will keep the house for the next 15 years? Use an annual cash flow analysis in working this problem.

6-31 A firm must decide whether to provide their salespeople with firm-owned cars or to pay a mileage allowance for their own cars. New cars would cost about $18,000 each and could be resold 4 years later for about $7000 each. Annual operating costs would be $600 per year plus 12¢ per mile. If the salespeople drove their own cars, the firm would pay 30¢ per mile. How many miles must each salesperson drive each year for it to be economically

practical for the firm to provide the cars. Assume a 10% annual interest rate. Use an annual cash flow analysis.

6-32 The town of Dry Gulch needs more water from Pine Creek. The town engineer has selected two plans for comparison: a *gravity plan* (divert water at a point 10 miles up Pine Creek and pipe it by gravity to the town) and a *pumping plan* (divert water at a point closer to town). The pumping plant would be built in two stages, with half-capacity installed initially and the other half installed 10 years later.

The analysis will assume a 40-year life, 10% interest, and no salvage value. Use an annual cash flow analysis to find which plan is more economical.

	Gravity	Pumping
Initial investment	$2,800,000	$1,400,000
Additional investment in 10th year	None	200,000
Operation and maintenance	10,000/yr	25,000/yr
Power cost		
Average first 10 years	None	50,000/yr
Average next 30 years	None	100,000/yr

6-33 A manufacturer is considering replacing a production machine tool. The new machine, costing $3700, would have a life of 4 years and no salvage value, but would save the firm $500 per year in direct labor costs and $200 per year in indirect labor costs. The existing machine tool was purchased 4 years ago at a cost of $4000. It will last 4 more years and will have no salvage value. It could be sold now for $1000 cash. Assume that money is worth 8% and that differences in taxes, insurance, and so forth are negligible. Use an annual cash flow analysis to determine whether the new machine should be purchased.

6-34 Two possible routes for a power line are under study. Data on the routes are as follows:

	Around the Lake	Under the Lake
Length	15 km	5 km
First cost	$5000/km	$25,000/km
Maintenance	$200/km/yr	$400/km/yr
Useful life, in years	15	15
Salvage value	$3000/km	$5000/km
Yearly power loss	$500/km	$500/km
Annual property taxes	2% of first cost	2% of first cost

If 7% interest is used, should the power line be routed around the lake or under the lake?   (*Answer:* Around the lake.)

6-35   An oil refinery must now begin sending its waste liquids through a costly treatment process before discharging them into a nearby stream. The engineering department estimates costs at $30,000 for the first year. It is estimated that if process and plant alterations are made, the waste treatment cost will decline $3000 each year. As an alternate, a specialized firm, Hydro-Clean, has offered a contract to process the waste liquids for 10 years for a fixed price of $15,000 per year, payable at the end of each year. Either way, there should be no need for waste treatment after 10 years. The refinery manager considers 8% to be a suitable interest rate. Use an annual cash flow analysis to determine whether the Hydro-Clean offer should be accepted.

6-36   Bill Anderson buys a car every 2 years as follows: initially he makes a down payment of $6000 on a $15,000 car. The balance is paid in 24 equal monthly payments with annual interest at 12%. When he has made the last payment on the loan, he trades in the 2-year-old car for $6000 on a new $15,000 car, and the cycle begins over again.

   Doug Jones decided on a different purchase plan. He thought he would be better off if he paid $15,000 cash for a new car. Then he would make a monthly deposit in a savings account so that, at the end of 2 years, he would have $9000 in the account. The $9000 plus the $6000 trade-in value of the car will allow Doug to replace his 2-year-old car by paying $9000 for a new one. The bank pays 6% interest, compounded quarterly.

(*a*) What is Bill Anderson's monthly payment to pay off the loan on the car?

(*b*) After he purchased the new car for cash, how much per month should Doug Jones deposit in his savings account to have enough money for the next car 2 years hence?

(*c*) Why is Doug's monthly savings account deposit smaller than Bill's payment?

6-37   Two mutually exclusive alternatives are being considered.

Year	A	B
0	−$3000	−$5000
1	+845	+1400
2	+845	+1400
3	+845	+1400
4	+845	+1400
5	+845	+1400

One of the alternatives must be selected. Using a 15% nominal interest rate, compounded continuously, determine which one. Solve by annual cash flow analysis.

Different Lives

6-38   A certain industrial firm desires an economic analysis to determine which of two different machines should be purchased. Each machine is capable of performing the same task in a given amount of time. Assume the minimum attractive return is 8%.

	Machine *X*	Machine *Y*
First cost	$5000	$8000
Estimated life, in years	5	12
Salvage value	0	$2000
Annual maintenance cost	0	150

Which machine would you choose? Base your answer on annual cost. (*Answers:* $X = 1252; $Y = 1106)

6-39   A company must decide whether to buy Machine *A* or Machine *B*:

	Machine *A*	Machine *B*
Initial cost	$10,000	$20,000
Useful life, in years	4	10
End-of-useful-life salvage value	$10,000	$10,000
Annual maintenance	1,000	0

At a 10% interest rate, which machine should be installed? Use an annual cash flow analysis in working this problem.   (*Answer:* Machine *A*)

6-40   Consider the following two mutually exclusive alternatives:

	A	*B*
Cost	$100	$150
Uniform annual benefit	16	24
Useful life, in years	∞	20

Alternative *B* may be replaced with an identical item every 20 years at the same $150 cost
and will have the same $24 uniform annual ben-
efit. Using a 10% interest rate and an annual
cash flow analysis, which alternative should be
selected?

6-41   A pump is needed for 10 years at a remote location.
The pump can be driven by an electric motor if a
power line is extended to the site. Otherwise, a gasoline engine will be used. Use an annual cash flow analysis and a 10% interest rate. How should the pump be
powered?

	Gasoline	Electric
First cost	$2400	$6000
Annual operating cost	1200	750
Annual maintenance	300	50
Salvage value	300	600
Life, in years	5	10

6-42   A suburban taxi company is considering buying taxis
with diesel engines instead of gasoline engines. The
cars average 50,000 km a year.

	Diesel	Gasoline
Vehicle cost	$13,000	$12,000
Useful life, in years	3	4
Fuel cost per liter	48¢	51¢
Mileage, in km/liter	35	28
Annual repairs	$ 300	$ 200
Annual insurance premium	500	500
End-of-useful-life resale value	2,000	3,000

Use an annual cash flow analysis to determine the
more economical choice if interest is 6%.

6-43   The manager in a canned food processing
plant is trying to decide between two labeling
machines.

	Machine A	Machine B
First cost	$15,000	$25,000
Maintenance and operating costs	1,600	400
Annual benefit	8,000	13,000
Salvage value	3,000	6,000
Useful life, in years	7	10

Assume an interest rate of 12%. Use annual cash
flow analysis to determine which machine should be
chosen.

6-44   Consider the following three mutually exclusive
alternatives:

	A	B	C
Cost	$100	$150.00	$200.00
Uniform annual benefit	10	17.62	55.48
Useful life, in years	∞	20	5

Assuming that Alternatives *B* and *C* are replaced with
identical units at the end of their useful lives, and an
8% interest rate, which alternative should be selected?
Use an annual cash flow analysis in working this
problem.   (*Answer:* Select *C*)

6-45   Carp, Inc. wants to evaluate two methods of shipping their products. Use an interest rate of 15% and
annual cash flow analysis to decide which is the most
desirable alternative.

	A	B
First cost	$700,000	$1,700,000
Maintenance and operating costs	18,000	29,000
+ Cost gradient (begin Year 1)	+900/yr	+750/yr
Annual benefit	154,000	303,000
Salvage value	142,000	210,000
Useful life, in years	10	20

6-46   A college student has been looking for new tires and
has found the following alternatives:

Tire Warranty (months)	Price per Tire
12	$39.95
24	59.95
36	69.95
48	90.00

The student feels that the warranty period is a good
estimate of the tire life and that a 10% interest rate
is appropriate. Using an annual cash flow analysis,
which tire should be purchased?

6-47   Consider the following alternatives:

	A	B
Cost	$50	$180
Uniform annual benefit	15	60
Useful life, in years	10	5

The analysis period is 10 years, but there will be no replacement for Alternative *B* after 5 years. Based on a 15% interest rate, which alternative should be selected? Use an annual cash flow analysis.

6-48 Some equipment will be installed in a warehouse that a firm has leased for 7 years. There are two alternatives:

	A	*B*
Cost	$100	$150
Uniform annual benefit	55	61
Useful life, in years	3	4

At any time after the equipment is installed, it has no salvage value. Assume that Alternatives *A* and *B* will be replaced at the end of their useful lives by identical equipment with the same costs and benefits. For a 7-year analysis period and a 10% interest rate, use an annual cash flow analysis to determine which alternative should be selected.

6-49 Uncle Elmo needs to replace the family privy. The local sanitary engineering firm has submitted two alternative structural proposals with respective cost estimates as shown. Which construction should Uncle Elmo choose if his minimum attractive rate of return is 6%? Use both a present worth and annual cost approach in your comparison.

	Masonite	**Brick**
First cost	$250	$1000
Annual maintenance	20	10
Salvage value	10	100
Service life, in years	4	20

Spreadsheets and Loans

6-50 A student loan totals $18,000 at graduation. The interest rate is 6%, and there will be 60 payments beginning 1 month after graduation. What is the monthly payment? What is owed after the first 2 years of payments? (*Answer*: Payment = $347.99, balance due = $11,439)

6-51 The student in Problem 6-50 received $1500 as a graduation present. If an extra $1500 is paid at Month 1, when is the final payment made? How much is it. (*Answer*: $98 in Month 55)

6-52 A new car is purchased for $12,000 with a 0% down, 9% loan. The loan is for 4 years. After making 30 payments, the owner wants to pay off the loan's remaining balance. How much is owed?

6-53 A year after buying her car, Anita has been offered a job in Europe. Her car loan is for $15,000 at a 9% nominal interest rate for 60 months. If she can sell the car for $12,000, how much does she get to keep after paying off the loan?

6-54 A $78,000 mortgage has a 30-year term and a 9% nominal interest rate.

(*a*) What is the monthly payment?

(*b*) After the first year of payments, what is the outstanding balance?

(*c*) How much interest is paid in Month 13? How much principal?

6-55 A $92,000 mortgage has a 30-year term and a 9% nominal interest rate.

(*a*) What is the monthly payment?

(*b*) After the first year of payments, what fraction of the loan has been repaid?

(*c*) After the first 10 years of payments, what is the outstanding balance?

(*d*) How much interest is paid in Month 25? How much principal?

6-56 A 30-year mortgage for $95,000 is issued at a 9% nominal interest rate.

(*a*) What is the monthly payment?

(*b*) How long does it take to pay off the mortgage, if $1000 per month is paid?

(*c*) How long does it take to pay off the mortgage, if double payments are made?

6-57 A 30-year mortgage for $145,000 is issued at a 6% nominal interest rate.

(*a*) What is the monthly payment?

(*b*) How long does it take to pay off the mortgage, if $1000 per month is paid?

(*c*) How long does it take to pay off the mortgage, if 20% extra is paid each month?

6-58 Solve Problem 6-34 for the breakeven first cost per kilometer of going under the lake.

6-59 Redo Problem 6-42 to calculate the EUAW of the alternatives as a function of miles driven per year to see if there is a crossover point in the decision process. Graph your results.

6-60 Set up Problem 6-27 on a spreadsheet to make all the input data variable and determine various scenarios which would make the baler economical.

 6-61 Develop a spreadsheet to solve Problem 6-32. What is the breakeven cost of the additional pumping investment in Year 10?

OTHER ANALYSIS TECHNIQUES

Clean, Green, and Far Between

Designers and engineers have made great progress in developing environment-friendly construction materials and building techniques. And "green" office buildings offer numerous advantages. They can improve worker productivity, reduce health and safety costs, improve the indoor environmental quality, and reduce energy and maintenance costs.

There is a widely held belief, however, that green structures cost more to build, especially with respect to first costs. In the commercial sector, barely 1% of office construction projects have bothered to apply for certification as green buildings because managers believe that the application process is too complicated and requires too much paperwork. Despite this, the U.S. Green Building Council reports that the number of square feet of LEED projects has increased eight-fold, from 80 million in 2002 to 642 million in 2006. LEED, or Leadership in Energy and Environmental Design, is the nationally accepted benchmark for design, construction, and operation of high-performance green buildings.

Commercial developers have found that environment-friendly features can add to the expense of construction. Even though additional costs may increase overall construction expenses by only 1 or 2%, they can make it harder for the builder to recoup its investment and break even on the project in a timely manner. Furthermore, there is a general reluctance by many in this industry to embrace new ideas or new technologies.

Renters may like the idea of being cleaner and greener—but they may be unwilling to pay extra for it unless they can see a tangible impact to their bottom line.

Revised by Kim Lascola Needy, University of Pittsburgh

1. Office leases frequently require building owners, rather than tenants, to pay heating and cooling costs. What effect might this have on the decision making of potential tenants who are considering renting space in green buildings?
2. The green building movement has had more success among developers who hold onto their buildings for years and rent them out, rather than selling them as soon as they are constructed. What factors might influence their views?
3. Many environment-friendly buildings are architecturally distinctive and feature better-quality materials and workmanship than traditional commercial structures. Advocates for the environment hope these characteristics will help green buildings attract a rent "premium." How might these features make the buildings more attractive to tenants? Is it the green features or the higher-quality materials and workmanship that add significantly to the perceived higher first costs of green buildings?
4. How can the costs and benefits of green buildings be economically validated by an independent party so that designers and engineers can make a fair assessment?
5. Does the economic attractiveness of green buildings depend on which measure is used for evaluation?
6. What ethical questions arise from state or municipal regulations intended to promote or require green building practices?

After Completing This Chapter...

You should be able to:

- Use future worth, benefit–cost ratio, payback period, and sensitivity analysis methods to solve engineering economy problems.
- Link the use of the *future worth* analysis to the present worth and annual worth methods developed earlier.
- Mathematically develop the *benefit–cost ratio,* and use this model to select alternatives and make economic choices.
- Understand the concept of the *payback period* of an investment, and be able to calculate this quantity for prospective projects.
- Demonstrate a basic understanding of *sensitivity* and *breakeven analyses* and the use of these tools in an engineering economic analysis.
- Use a spreadsheet to perform *sensitivity* and *breakeven analyses*.

Chapter 9 examines four topics:

- Future worth analysis
- Benefit–cost ratio or present worth index analysis
- Payback period
- Sensitivity, breakeven, and what-if analysis

Future worth analysis is very much like present worth analysis, dealing with *then* (future worth) rather than with *now* (present worth) situations.

Previously, we have written economic analysis relationships based on either:

$$PW \text{ of cost} = PW \text{ of benefit} \quad \text{or} \quad EUAC = EUAB$$

Instead of writing it in this form, we could define these relationships as

$$\frac{PW \text{ of benefit}}{PW \text{ of cost}} = 1 \quad \text{or} \quad \frac{EUAB}{EUAC} = 1$$

When economic analysis is based on these ratios, the calculations are called benefit–cost ratio analysis. The PW ratio is also known as a present worth index.

Payback period is an approximate analysis technique, generally defined as the time required for cumulative benefits to equal cumulative costs.

Sensitivity describes how much a problem element must change to change a particular decision. Closely related is breakeven analysis, which determines the conditions under which two alternatives are equivalent. What-if analysis changes one or all variables to see how the economic value and recommended decision change. Thus, breakeven and what-if analysis are forms of sensitivity analysis.

FUTURE WORTH ANALYSIS

In present worth analysis, alternatives are compared in terms of their present consequences. In annual cash flow analysis, the comparison was in terms of equivalent uniform annual costs (or benefits). But the concept of resolving alternatives into comparable units is not restricted to a present or annual comparison. The comparison may be made at any point in time. In many situations we would like to know what the *future* situation will be, if we take some particular course of action *now*. This is called **future worth analysis.**

EXAMPLE 9-1

Ron Jamison, a 20-year-old college student, smokes about a carton of cigarettes a week. He wonders how much money he could accumulate by age 65 if he quit smoking now and put his cigarette money into a savings account. Cigarettes cost $35 per carton. Ron expects that a savings account would earn 5% interest, compounded semiannually. Compute Ron's future worth at age 65.

$$\text{Semiannual saving } \$35/\text{carton} \times 26 \text{ weeks} = \$910$$

$$\text{Future worth (FW)} = A(F/A, 2^{1}/2\%, 90) = 910(329.2) = \$299{,}572$$

EXAMPLE 9-2

An east coast firm has decided to establish a second plant in Kansas City. There is a factory for sale for $850,000 that could be remodeled and used. As an alternative, the firm could buy vacant land for $85,000 and have a new plant constructed there. Either way, it will be 3 years before the firm will be able to get a plant into production. The timing and cost of the various components for the factory are:

Year	Construct New Plant		Remodel Available Factory	
0	Buy land	$ 85,000	Purchase factory	$850,000
1	Design and initial construction costs	200,000	Design and remodeling costs	250,000
2	Balance of construction costs	1,200,000	Additional remodeling costs	250,000
3	Setup of production equipment	200,000	Setup of production equipment	250,000

If interest is 8%, which alternative has the lower equivalent cost when the firm begins production at the end of Year 3?

New Plant

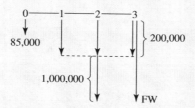

$$\text{Future worth of cost (FW)} = 85{,}000(F/P, 8\%, 3) + 200{,}000(F/A, 8\%, 3)$$

$$+ 1{,}000{,}000(F/P, 8\%, 1) = \$1{,}836{,}000$$

Remodel Available Factory

$$\text{Future worth of cost (FW)} = 850{,}000(F/P, 8\%, 3) + 250{,}000(F/A, 8\%, 3)$$
$$= \$1{,}882{,}000$$

The total cost of remodeling the available factory ($1,600,000) is smaller than the total cost of a new plant ($1,685,000). However, the timing of the expenditures, is better with the new plant. The new plant is projected to have the smaller future worth of cost and thus is the preferred alternative.

BENEFIT–COST RATIO ANALYSIS

At a given minimum attractive rate of return (MARR), we would consider an alternative acceptable, provided

$$\text{PW of benefits} - \text{PW of costs} \geq 0 \qquad \text{or} \qquad \text{EUAB} - \text{EUAC} \geq 0$$

These could also be stated as a ratio of benefits to costs, or

$$\text{Benefit–cost ratio } \frac{B}{C} = \frac{\text{PW of benefit}}{\text{PW of costs}} = \frac{\text{EUAB}}{\text{EUAC}} \geq 1$$

Rather than using present worth or annual cash flow analysis to solve problems, we can base the calculations on the benefit–cost ratio, B/C. The criteria are presented in Table 9-1. In Table 9-1 the two special cases where maximizing the B/C ratio is correct are listed below the more common situation where incremental analysis is required. In Chapter 16 we will detail how this measure is applied in the public sector. Its use there is so pervasive, that the term *present worth index* is sometimes used to distinguish private sector applications.

TABLE 9-1 **Benefit–Cost Ratio Analysis**

	Situation	Criterion
Neither input nor output fixed	Neither amount of money or other inputs nor amount of benefits or other outputs are fixed	*Two alternatives:* Compute incremental benefit–cost ratio ($\Delta B/\Delta C$) on the increment of investment between the alternatives. If $\Delta B/\Delta C \geq 1$, choose higher-cost alternative; otherwise, choose lower-cost alternative. *Three or more alternatives:* Solve by benefit–cost ratio incremental analysis
Fixed input	Amount of money or other input resources are fixed	Maximize B/C
Fixed output	Fixed task, benefit, or other output to be accomplished	Maximize B/C

EXAMPLE 9-3

A firm is trying to decide which of two devices to install to reduce costs. Both devices have useful lives of 5 years and no salvage value. Device A costs $1000 and can be expected to result in $300 savings annually. Device B costs $1350 and will provide cost savings of $300 the first year, but savings will increase by $50 annually, making the second-year savings $350, the third-year savings $400, and so forth. With interest at 7%, which device should the firm purchase?

SOLUTION

We have used three types of analysis thus far to solve this problem: present worth in Example 5-1, annual cash flow in Example 6-5, and rate of return in Example 7-14. First we correctly analyze this incrementally, then we look at each device's benefit–cost ratio.

Incremental B–A

$$\text{PW of cost} = \$350$$

$$\text{PW of benefits} = 50(P/G, 7\%, 5)$$

$$= 50(7.647) = \$382$$

$$\frac{B}{C} = \frac{\text{PW of benefit}}{\text{PW of costs}} = \frac{382}{350} = 1.09$$

The increment is justified at the MARR of 7%. Device B should be purchased.

Device A

$$\text{PW of cost} = \$1000$$

$$\text{PW of benefits} = 300(P/A, 7\%, 5)$$

$$= 300(4.100) = \$1230$$

$$\frac{B}{C} = \frac{\text{PW of benefit}}{\text{PW of costs}} = \frac{1230}{1000} = 1.23$$

Device B

$$\text{PW of cost} = \$1350$$

$$\text{PW of benefit} = 300(P/A, 7\%, 5) + 50(P/G, 7\%, 5)$$

$$= 300(4.100) + 50(7.647) = 1230 + 382 = 1612$$

$$\frac{B}{C} = \frac{\text{PW of benefit}}{\text{PW of costs}} = \frac{1612}{1350} = 1.19$$

Maximizing the benefit–cost ratio indicates the wrong choice, Device A. Incremental analysis must be used.

EXAMPLE 9-4

In Example 7-15 we analyzed two machines that were being considered for purchase. Assuming 10% interest, which machine should be bought?

	Machine X	Machine Y
Initial cost	$200	$700
Uniform, annual benefit	95	120
End-of-useful-life salvage value	50	150
Useful life, in years	6	12

SOLUTION

Assuming a 12-year analysis period, the cash flow table is:

Year	Machine X	Machine Y
0	−$200	−$700
1–5	+95	+120
6	$\begin{cases} +95 \\ -200 \\ +50 \end{cases}$	+120
7–11	+95	+120
12	$\begin{cases} +95 \\ +50 \end{cases}$	$\begin{cases} +120 \\ +150 \end{cases}$

We will solve the problem using

$$\frac{B}{C} = \frac{EUAB}{EUAC}$$

and considering the salvage value of the machines to be reductions in cost, rather than increases in benefits. This choice affects the ratio value, but not the decision.

Machine X

$$EUAC = 200(A/P, 10\%, 6) - 50(A/F, 10\%, 6)$$

$$= 200(0.2296) - 50(0.1296) = 46 - 6 = \$40$$

$$EUAB = \$95$$

Note that this assumes the replacement for the last 6 years has identical costs. Under these circumstances, the EUAC for the first 6 years equals the EUAC for all 12 years.

Machine Y

$$EUAC = 700(A/P, 10\%, 12) - 150(A/F, 10\%, 12)$$

$$= 700(0.1468) - 150(0.0468) = 103 - 7 = \$96$$

$$EUAB = \$120$$

Machine Y − Machine X

$$\frac{\Delta B}{\Delta C} = \frac{120 - 95}{96 - 40} = \frac{25}{56} = 0.45$$

The incremental benefit–cost ratio of less than 1 represents an undesirable increment of investment. We therefore choose the lower-cost alternative—Machine X. If we had computed benefit–cost ratios for each machine, they would have been:

Machine X　　　　**Machine Y**

$$\frac{B}{C} = \frac{95}{40} = 2.38 \qquad \frac{B}{C} = \frac{120}{96} = 1.25$$

Although $B/C = 1.25$ for Machine Y (the higher-cost alternative), we must not use this fact as the basis for selecting the more expensive alternative. It only indicates that Y would be acceptable if X were unavailable. The incremental benefit–cost ratio, $\Delta B/\Delta C$, clearly shows that Y is a less desirable alternative than X. Also, we must not jump to the conclusion that the best alternative is always the one with the largest B/C ratio. This, too, may lead to incorrect decisions—as we saw in Example 9-3, and we shall see again when we examine problems with three or more alternatives.

EXAMPLE 9-5

Consider the five mutually exclusive alternatives from Examples 8-6 and 8-7 plus an additional alternative, F. They have 20-year useful lives and no salvage value. If the minimum attractive rate of return is 6%, which alternative should be selected?

	A	B	C	D	E	F
Cost	$4000	$2000	$6000	$1000	$9000	$10,000
PW of benefit	7330	4700	8730	1340	9000	9,500
$\dfrac{B}{C} = \dfrac{\text{PW of benefits}}{\text{PW of cost}}$	1.83	2.35	1.46	1.34	1.00	0.95

SOLUTION

Incremental analysis is needed to solve the problem. The steps in the solution are the same as the ones presented in Example 8-7 for incremental rate of return, except here the criterion is $\Delta B/\Delta C$, and the cutoff is 1, rather than ΔIRR with a cutoff of MARR.

1. Be sure all the alternatives are identified.
2. (Optional) Compute the B/C ratio for each alternative. Since there are alternatives for which $B/C \geq 1$, we will discard any with $B/C < 1$. Discard Alt. F.

3. Arrange the remaining alternatives in ascending order of investment.

	D	**B**	**A**	**C**	**E**
Cost (= PW of cost)	$1000	$2000	$4000	$6000	$9000
PW of benefits	1340	4700	7330	8730	9000
B/C	1.34	2.35	1.83	1.46	1.00

	Increment B − D	**Increment A − B**	**Increment C − A**
ΔCost	$1000	$2000	$2000
ΔBenefit	3360	2630	1400
ΔB/ΔC	3.36	1.32	0.70

4. For each increment of investment, if $\Delta B/\Delta C \geq 1$ the increment is attractive. If $\Delta B/\Delta C < 1$ the increment of investment is not desirable. The increment $B - D$ is desirable, so B is preferred to D. The increment $A - B$ is desirable. Thus, Alt. A is preferred. Increment $C - A$ is not attractive since $\Delta B/\Delta C = 0.70$. Now we compare A and E:

	Increment E − A
ΔCost	$5000
ΔBenefit	1670
ΔB/ΔC	0.33

The increment is undesirable. We choose Alt. A as the best of the six alternatives. *Note:* The best alternative does not have the highest B/C ratio.

Benefit–cost ratio analysis may be graphically represented. Figure 9-1 is a graph of Example 9-5. We see that F has a B/C < 1 and can be discarded. Alternative D is the starting point for examining the separable increments of investment. The slope of line $B - D$ indicates a $\Delta B/\Delta C$ ratio of >1. This is also true for line $A - B$. Increment $C - A$ has a slope much flatter than B/C = 1, indicating an undesirable increment of investment. Alternative C is therefore discarded and A retained. Increment $E - A$ is similarly unattractive. Alternative A is therefore the best of the six alternatives.

FIGURE 9-1 Benefit–cost ratio graph of Example 9-5.

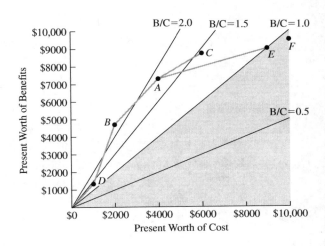

Note two additional things about Figure 9-1: first, even if alternatives with B/C ratio < 1 had not been initially excluded, they would have been systematically eliminated in the incremental analysis. Second, Alt. *B* had the highest B/C ratio (B/C = 2.35), but it is not the best of the six alternatives. We saw the same situation in rate of return analysis of three or more alternatives. The reason is the same in both analysis situations. We seek to maximize the *total* profit, not the profit rate.

Variations on the Theme of the Benefit–Cost Ratio

Two of the most common applications of the benefit–cost ratio typically use modified versions of the ratio. The basic ratio has been defined as placing *all* benefits in the numerator of the ratio and *all* costs in the denominator. Example 9-4 modified this slightly by considering the salvage values as reducing the costs rather than as increasing the benefits.

In the public sector, it is common to define the benefit–cost ratio so that the numerator includes all consequences to the users or the public and the denominator includes all consequences to the sponsor or government. For example, the numerator might include the positive benefits of improved highway traffic flow and the disbenefits of congestion during construction, since both accrue to the public or users. The denominator in this case includes consequences to the government, such as the costs of construction and the reduced maintenance cost for the new highway.

Example 9-6 illustrates this for a public project. Then in Example 9-7 the same numbers are put in a private context. Here the benefit–cost ratio is typically called a present worth index. The calculation is modified so that the denominator is the project's first cost, and all other consequences are placed in the numerator. This formulation of the benefit–cost ratio emphasizes the "bang for buck" of how much return for each dollar of investment.

We will examine the public sector application of the benefit–cost ratio in more detail in Chapter 16, and the present worth index will be used in Chapter 15. Here and in those chapters, the same standard applies for all versions of the ratio. Is the ratio ≥ 1? More importantly, if one version of the ratio is ≥ 1, then all versions are ≥ 1. As shown in Examples 9-6 and 9-7, the values of the ratios may differ, but whether they are above or below 1 and the recommended decisions do not change.

EXAMPLE 9-6

Traffic congestion on Riverview Boulevard has reached a point where something must be done. Two suggested plans have a life of 15 years, because that is the scheduled time for completion of the new Skyway Highway. After that time traffic will fall well below current levels.

Adding right-turn lanes at key intersections will cost $8.9M (million) with annual maintenance costs for signals and lane painting of $150,000. Added congestion during construction is a disbenefit of $900,000, but the reduced congestion after construction is an annual benefit of $1.6M. This benefit actually starts lower and increases over time, but for a simple initial analysis we are assuming a uniform annual benefit.

Adding a second left-turn lane at a few key intersections will cost an additional $3M with an added annual maintenance cost of $75,000. This construction is more disruptive, and the total disbenefit for congestion during construction is $2.1M. Upon completion, the total benefit for reduced congestion will be $2.2M annually.

Which alternatives is preferred if the interest rate is 10%? Analyze using a government B/C ratio (public in numerator and government in denominator).

SOLUTION

Since something *must* be done and we have only two identified alternatives, we could simply analyze the difference between the alternatives to see which is better. But we are going to start by analyzing the less expensive "right-turns" alternative to check that this is a reasonable choice for what *must* be done.

The user consequences include an annual benefit for reduced congestion and a first "cost" that is the disbenefit of increased congestion during construction.

$$PW_{right\ turns} = -900,000 + 1,600,000(P/A, 10\%, 15)$$
$$= -900,000 + 1,600,000(7.606) = \$11.27M$$

The government costs include a first cost for construction and annual maintenance costs. Note that these are calculated as present *costs*.

$$PC_{right\ turns} = 8,900,000 + 150,000(P/A, 10\%, 15)$$
$$= 8,900,000 + 150,000(7.606) = \$10.04M$$

The benefit–cost ratio for public divided by government consequences is:

$$B/C\ ratio = \$11.27M/\$10.04M = 1.122$$

Thus, the right-turns-only alternative is better than doing nothing.

Now we evaluate the incremental investment for also doing the left-turn improvements. Because we are using a benefit–cost ratio, this evaluation must be done incrementally. The user consequences include an incremental annual benefit for reduced congestion and an incremental first "cost" that is the disbenefit of increased congestion during construction.

$$PW_{left\ turns\ -\ right\ turns} = -1,200,000 + 600,000(P/A, 10\%, 15)$$
$$= -1,200,000 + 600,000(7.606) = \$3.364M$$

The government costs include a first cost for construction and annual maintenance costs.

$$PC_{left\ turns\ -\ right\ turns} = 3,000,000 + 75,000(P/A, 10\%, 15)$$
$$= 3,000,000 + 75,000(7.606) = \$3.570M$$

The benefit–cost ratio for public divided by government consequences is:

$$B/C\ ratio = \$3.364M/\$3.570M = 0.942$$

Thus, the right-turns-only alternative is better than adding the left-turn increment.

EXAMPLE 9-7

The industrial engineering department of Amalgamated Widgets is considering two alternatives for improving material flow in its factory. Both plans have a life of 15 years, because that is the estimated remaining life for the factory.

A minimal reconfiguration will cost $8.9M (million) with annual maintenance costs of $150,000. During construction there is a cost of $900,000 for extra material movements and overtime, but more efficient movement of materials will save $1.6M annually. The cost savings actually start lower and increase over time, but for a simple initial analysis we are assuming a uniform annual cost savings.

Reconfiguring a second part of the plant will cost an additional $3M with an added annual maintenance cost of $75,000. This construction is more disruptive, and the total cost for material movement and overtime congestion during construction is $2.1M. Once complete the total cost savings for more efficient movement of materials is $2.2M annually.

Which alternatives is preferred if the interest rate is 10%? Analyze using a present worth index (all consequences in Years 1 to n in numerator and all first costs in denominator).

SOLUTION

Since something *must* be done and we have only two identified alternatives, we could simply analyze the difference between the alternatives to see which is better. But we are going to start by analyzing the less expensive minimal reconfiguration alternative to check that this is a reasonable choice for what *must* be done.

The consequences in Years 1 to n include an annual cost savings for more efficient flow and annual maintenance costs.

$$PW_{\text{Years 1 to } n} = (1,600,000 - 150,000)(P/A, 10\%, 15)$$
$$= (1,600,000 - 150,000)(7.606) = \$11.03\text{M}$$

The first costs include a first cost for construction and the cost for disruption during construction.

$$PC = 8,900,000 + 900,000 = \$9.8\text{M}$$

The present worth index is:

$$PW \text{ index} = \$11.03\text{M}/\$9.8\text{M} = 1.125$$

Thus, the minimal reconfiguration is better than doing nothing.

Now we evaluate the incremental investment for also reconfiguring the second part of the plant. Because we are using a present worth index, this evaluation must be done incrementally. The annual consequences include an incremental annual cost savings and incremental maintenance costs.

$$PW_{\text{Years 1 to } n} = (600,000 - 75,000)(P/A, 10\%, 15)$$
$$= 525,000(7.606) = \$3.993\text{M}$$

There is a first cost for construction and for the associated disruption.

$$PC = 3,000,000 + 1,200,000 = \$4.2M$$

The present worth index is:

$$PW \text{ index} = \$3.993M/\$4.2M = 0.951$$

Thus, the minimal reconfiguration is better than also reconfiguring the second part of the plant.

In Examples 9-6 and 9-7, numbers in the numerator and denominator were changed, and so did the exact values of the B/C ratio and present worth index. However, the conclusions did not. The ratios were above 1.0 for the minimal investment choice. The ratios were below 1.0 for the incremental investment. It was always best to make the minimal investment.

These examples demonstrate that present worth analysis and incremental benefit–cost ratio analysis lead to the same optimal decision. We saw in Chapter 8 that rate of return and present worth analysis led to identical decisions. Any of the exact analysis methods— present worth, annual cash flow, rate of return, or benefit–cost ratio—will lead to the same decision. Benefit–cost ratio analysis is extensively used in economic analysis at all levels of government.

PAYBACK PERIOD

Payback period is the period of time required for the profit or other benefits from an investment to equal the cost of the investment. This is the general definition for payback period. Other definitions consider depreciation of the investment, interest, and income taxes; they, too, are simply called "payback period." We will limit our discussion to the simplest form.

> **Payback period** is the period of time required for the project's profit or other benefits to equal the project's cost.

The criterion in all situations is to minimize the payback period. The computation of payback period is illustrated in Examples 9-8 and 9-9.

EXAMPLE 9-8

The cash flows for two alternatives are as follows:

Year	A	B
0	−$1000	−$2783
1	+200	+1200
2	+200	+1200
3	+1200	+1200
4	+1200	+1200
5	+1200	+1200

You may assume the benefits occur throughout the year rather than just at the end of the year. Based on payback period, which alternative should be selected?

SOLUTION

Alternative A

Payback period is how long it takes for the profit or other benefits to equal the cost of the investment. In the first 2 years, only $400 of the $1000 cost is recovered. The remaining $600 cost is recovered in the first half of Year 3. Thus the payback period for Alt. A is 2.5 years.

Alternative B

Since the annual benefits are uniform, the payback period is simply

$$\$2783/\$1200 \text{ per year} = 2.3 \text{ years}$$

To minimize the payback period, choose Alt. B.

EXAMPLE 9-9   (Example 5-4 revisited)

A firm is trying to decide which of two weighing scales it should install to check a package-filling operation in the plant. If both scales have a 6-year life, which one should be selected? Assume an 8% interest rate.

Alternative	Cost	Uniform Annual Benefit	End-of-Useful-Life Salvage Value
Atlas scale	$2000	$450	$100
Tom Thumb scale	3000	600	700

SOLUTION

Atlas Scale

$$\text{Payback period} = \frac{\text{Cost}}{\text{Uniform annual benefit}}$$

$$= \frac{2000}{450} = 4.4 \text{ years}$$

Tom Thumb Scale

$$\text{Payback period} = \frac{\text{Cost}}{\text{Uniform annual benefit}}$$

$$= \frac{3000}{600} = 5 \text{ years}$$

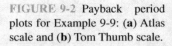

FIGURE 9-2 Payback period plots for Example 9-9: (**a**) Atlas scale and (**b**) Tom Thumb scale.

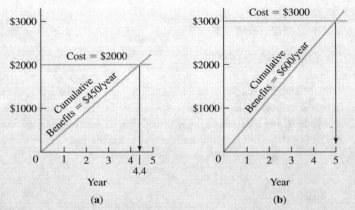

Figure 9-2 illustrates the situation. To minimize payback period, select the Atlas scale.

There are four important points to be understood about payback period calculations:

1. This is an approximate, rather than an exact, economic analysis calculation.
2. All costs and all profits, or savings of the investment before payback are included *without* considering differences in their timing.
3. All the economic consequences beyond the payback period are completely ignored.
4. Being an approximate calculation, payback period may or may not select the correct alternative.

This last point—that payback period may select the *wrong* alternative—was illustrated by Example 9-9. When payback period is used, the Atlas scale appears to be the more attractive alternative. Yet, when the same problem was solved earlier by the present worth method (Example 5-4), the Tom Thumb scale was the chosen alternative. The reason for the different conclusions is the $700 salvage value at the end of 6 years. The salvage value occurs after the payback period; so it was ignored in the payback calculation. It *was* considered in the present worth analysis, which correctly showed that the Tom Thumb scale was in fact more desirable.

But if payback period calculations are approximate and may lead to selecting the wrong alternative, why are they used? First, the calculations can be readily made by people unfamiliar with economic analysis. Second, payback period is easily understood. Earlier we pointed out that this is also an advantage to rate of return.

Moreover, payback period *does* measure how long it will take for the cost of the investment to be recovered from its benefits. Firms are often very interested in this time period: a rapid return of invested capital means that the funds can be reused sooner for other purposes. But one must not confuse the *speed* of the return of the investment, as measured by the payback period, with economic *efficiency*. They are two distinctly separate concepts. The former emphasizes the quickness with which invested funds return to a firm; the latter considers the overall profitability of the investment.

Example 9-10 illustrates how using the payback period criterion may result in an unwise decision.

EXAMPLE 9-10

A firm is buying production equipment for a new plant. Two alternative machines are being considered for a particular operation.

	Tempo Machine	**Dura Machine**
Installed cost	$30,000	$35,000
Net annual benefit after all annual expenses have been deducted	12,000 the first year, *declining* $3000 per year thereafter	1000 the first year, increasing $3000 per year thereafter
Useful life, in years	4	8

Neither machine has any salvage value. Compute the payback period for each machine.

SOLUTION BASED ON PAYBACK PERIOD

FIGURE 9-3 Payback period plots for Example 9-10: **(a)** Tempo machine and **(b)** Dura machine.

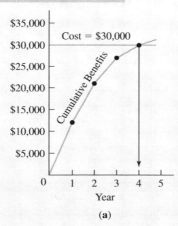

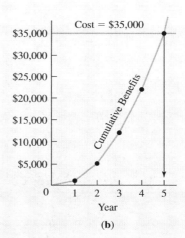

The Tempo machine has a declining annual benefit, while the Dura has an increasing annual benefit. Figure 9-3 shows the Tempo has a 4-year payback period and the Dura has a 5-year payback period. To minimize the payback period, the Tempo is selected.

Now, as a check on the payback period analysis, compute the rate of return for each alternative. Assume the minimum attractive rate of return is 10%.

SOLUTION BASED ON RATE OF RETURN

The cash flows for the two alternatives are as follows:

Year	Tempo Machine	Dura Machine
0	−$30,000	−$35,000
1	+12,000	+1,000
2	+9,000	+4,000

3	+6,000	+7,000
4	+3,000	+10,000
5	0	+13,000
6	0	+16,000
7	0	+19,000
8	0	+22,000
	0	+57,000

Tempo Machine

Since the sum of the cash flows for the Tempo machine is zero, we see immediately that the $30,000 investment just equals the subsequent benefits. The resulting rate of return is 0%.

Dura Machine

$$PW(i) = -35,000 + 1000(P/A, i, 8) + 3000(P/G, i, 8)$$

$$PW(20\%) = -35,000 + 1000(3.837) + 3000(9.883) = -1514$$

The 20% interest rate has discounted future benefits too much; it is too high. Try $i = 15\%$:

$$PW(15\%) = -35,000 + 1000(4.487) + 3000(12.481) = 6930$$

This time, the interest rate is too low. Linear interpolation would show that the rate of return is approximately 19%; and a spreadsheet gives the exact answer.

Using an exact calculation—rate of return—it is clear that the Dura machine is far superior to the Tempo. On the other hand, the shorter payback period for the Tempo does measure the speed of the return of the investment. The conclusion to be drawn is that **liquidity** and **profitability** may be two quite different criteria.

From the discussion and the examples, we see that payback period can measure the speed of the return of the investment. This might be quite important, for example, for a company that is short of working capital or for a firm in an industry experiencing rapid changes in technology. Calculation of payback period alone, however, must not be confused with a careful economic analysis. Ignoring all cash flows after the payback period is seldom wise. We have shown that a short payback period does not always mean that the associated investment is desirable. Thus, payback period is not a suitable replacement for accurate economic analysis calculations.

SENSITIVITY AND BREAKEVEN ANALYSIS

Since many data gathered in solving a problem represent *projections* of future consequences, there may be considerable uncertainty regarding the data's accuracy. Since the goal is to make good decisions, an appropriate question is: To what extent do variations in the data affect my decision? When small variations in a particular estimate would change which alternative is selected, the decision is said to be **sensitive to the estimate.** To better evaluate the impact of any particular estimate, we compute "how much a particular estimate would need to change in order to change a particular decision." This is called **sensitivity analysis.**

An analysis of the sensitivity of a problem's decision to its various parameters highlights the important aspects of that problem. For example, estimated annual maintenance and salvage values may vary substantially. Sensitivity analysis might indicate that a certain decision is insensitive to the salvage-value estimate over the full range of possible values. But, at the same time, we might find that the decision is sensitive to changes in the annual maintenance estimate. Under these circumstances, one should place greater emphasis on improving the annual maintenance estimate and less on the salvage-value estimate.

As indicated at the beginning of this chapter, breakeven analysis is a form of sensitivity analysis that is often presented as a **breakeven chart**. Another nomenclature that is sometimes used for the breakeven point is *point of indifference*. One application of these tools is **staged construction.** Should a facility be constructed now to meet its future full-scale requirement, Or should it be constructed in stages as the need for the increased capacity arises? Three examples are:

- Should we install a cable with 400 circuits now or a 200-circuit cable now and another 200-circuit cable later?
- A 10 cm water main is needed to serve a new area of homes. Should it be installed now, or should a 15 cm main be installed to ensure an adequate water supply to adjoining areas later, when other homes have been built?
- An industrial firm needs a new warehouse now and estimates that it will need to double its size in 4 years. The firm could have a warehouse built now and later enlarged, or have the warehouse with capacity for expanded operations built right away.

Examples 9-11 and 9-13 illustrate sensitivity and breakeven analysis.

EXAMPLE 9-11

Consider a project that may be constructed to full capacity now or may be constructed in two stages.

Construction Alternative	Costs
Two-stage construction	
Construct first stage now	$100,000
Construct second stage	120,000
n years from now	
Full-capacity construction	
Construct full capacity now	140,000

Other Factors

1. All facilities will last for 40 years regardless of when they are installed; after 40 years, they will have zero salvage value.

2. The annual cost of operation and maintenance is the same for both two-stage construction and full-capacity construction.
3. Assume an 8% interest rate.

Plot "age when second stage is constructed" versus "costs for both alternatives." Mark the breakeven point on your graph. What is the sensitivity of the decision to second-stage construction 16 or more years in the future?

SOLUTION

Since we are dealing with a common analysis period, the calculations may be either annual cost or present worth. Present worth calculations appear simpler and are used here.

Construct Full Capacity Now

$$\text{PW of cost} = \$140,000$$

Two-Stage Construction

If the first stage is to be constructed now and the second stage n years hence, compute the PW of cost for several values of n (years).

$$\text{PW of cost} = 100,000 + 120,000(P/F, 8\%, n)$$

$$n = 5 \quad \text{PW} = 100,000 + 120,000(0.6806) = \$181,700$$
$$n = 10 \quad \text{PW} = 100,000 + 120,000(0.4632) = 155,600$$
$$n = 20 \quad \text{PW} = 100,000 + 120,000(0.2145) = 125,700$$
$$n = 30 \quad \text{PW} = 100,000 + 120,000(0.0994) = 111,900$$

These data are plotted in the form of a breakeven chart in Figure 9-4.

FIGURE 9-4 Breakeven chart for Example 9-11.

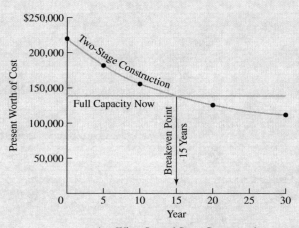

In Figure 9-4 we see that the PW of cost for two-stage construction naturally decreases as the second stage is deferred. The one-stage construction (full capacity now) is unaffected by the x-axis variable and, hence, is a horizontal line.

The breakeven point on the graph is where both alternatives have the same PW. We see that if the second stage is deferred for 15 years, then the PW of cost of two-stage construction is equal to one-stage construction; Year 15 is the breakeven point. The graph also shows that if the second stage were to be needed prior to Year 15, then one-stage construction, with its smaller PW of cost, would be preferred. On the other hand, if the second stage would not be required until after 15 years, two-stage construction is preferred.

This breakeven point can also be calculated by setting the two alternatives equal to each other.

$$PW = 140,000 = 100,000 + 120,000(P/F, 8\%, n)$$

$$(P/F, 8\%, n) = \frac{40,000}{120,000} = 0.3333$$

From the tables

$$n = 14 + (15 - 14)(0.3405 - 0.3333)/(0.3405 - 0.3152)$$

$$n = 14.3 \text{ years}$$

From Excel's NPER function or GOAL SEEK, we find that the answer is 14.27 years.

The decision on how to construct the project is sensitive to the age at which the second stage is needed *only* if the range of estimates includes 15 years. For example, if one estimated that the second-stage capacity would be needed between 5 and 10 years hence, the decision is insensitive to that estimate. For any value within that range, the decision does not change. But, if the second-stage capacity were to be needed sometime between, say, 12 and 18 years, the decision would be sensitive to the estimate of when the full capacity would be needed.

One question posed by this example is *how* sensitive the decision is to the need for the second stage at 16 years or beyond. The graph shows that the decision is insensitive. In all cases for construction on or after 16 years, two-stage construction has a lower PW of cost.

EXAMPLE 9-12

Example 8-3 posed the following situation. Three mutually exclusive alternatives are given, each with a 20-year life and no salvage value. The minimum attractive rate of return is 6%.

	A	B	C
Initial cost	$2000	$4000	$5000
Uniform annual benefit	410	639	700

In Example 8-3 we found that Alt. *B* was the preferred alternative at 6%. Here we would like to know how sensitive the decision is to our estimate of the initial cost of *B*. If *B* is preferred at an initial cost of $4000, it will continue to be preferred at any smaller initial cost. But *how much* higher than $4000 can the initial cost be and still have *B* the preferred alternative? With neither input nor output fixed, maximizing net present worth is a suitable criterion.

Alternative A

$$NPW_A = 410(P/A, 6\%, 20) - 2000$$

$$= 410(11.470) - 2000 = \$2703$$

Alternative B

Let $x =$ initial cost of B.

$$NPW_B = 639(P/A, 6\%, 20) - x$$

$$= 639(11.470) - x$$

$$= 7329 - x$$

Alternative C

$$NPW_C = 700(P/A, 6\%, 20) - 5000$$

$$= 700(11.470) - 5000 = \$3029$$

For the three alternatives, we see that B will only maximize NPW as long as its NPW is greater than 3029.

$$3029 = 7329 - x$$

$$x = 7329 - 3029 = \$4300$$

Therefore, B is the preferred alternative if its initial cost does not exceed \$4300.

Figure 9-5 is a breakeven chart for the three alternatives. Here the criterion is to maximize NPW; as a result, the graph shows that B is preferred if its initial cost is less than \$4300. At an initial cost above \$4300, C is preferred. We have a breakeven point at \$4300. When B has an initial cost of \$4300, B and C are equally desirable.

FIGURE 9-5 Breakeven chart for Example 9-12.

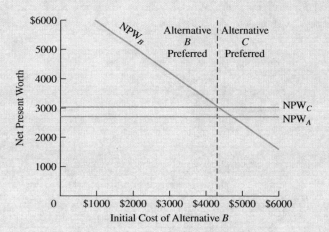

EXAMPLE 9-13

In both Examples 9-6 (traffic congestion on Riverview Boulevard) and 9-7 (reconfiguring the plant of Amalgamated Widgets), the life of 15 years is clearly subject to some uncertainty. While holding the other data constant, analyze the sensitivity of the recommended decisions to the project life. Use the present worth measure since it is the same for both examples.

SOLUTION

The two alternatives have the following present worth values.

$$\text{PW}_{\text{right turns or minimal}} = -900{,}000 - 8{,}900{,}000 + (1{,}600{,}000 - 150{,}000)(P/A, 10\%, n)$$
$$= -9{,}800{,}000 + 1{,}450{,}000(P/A, 10\%, n)$$

$$\text{PW}_{\text{left turns or 2}^{\text{nd}}\text{ part of plant}} = -2{,}100{,}000 - 8{,}900{,}000 - 3{,}000{,}000$$
$$+ (2{,}200{,}000 - 225{,}000)(P/A, 10\%, n)$$
$$= -14{,}000{,}000 + 1{,}975{,}000(P/A, 10\%, n)$$

These could be analyzed for breakeven values of n. However, it is easier to use the graphing technique for multiple alternatives that was presented in Chapter 8. Instead of using the interest rate for the x axis, use n.

As shown in Figure 9-6, the right-turn or minimal alternative is the best one for lives of 12 to 16 years. The left-turn increment or 2nd part of plant, is the best choice for lives of 17 or more years. If the life is 11 years or less, doing nothing is better. To keep the graph readable, Figure 9-6 includes only years 10 through 20.

FIGURE 9-6 Breakeven chart for Example 9-13.

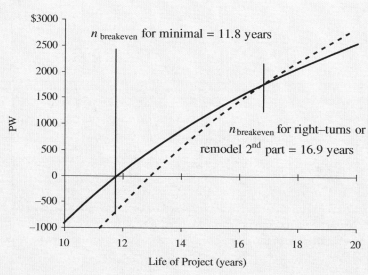

Breakeven points can be estimated from graphs or calculated with formulas or GOAL SEEK. Sensitivity analysis and breakeven point calculations can be very useful in identifying how different estimates affect the calculations. It must be recognized that these calculations assume that all parameters except one are held constant, and the sensitivity of the decision to that one variable is evaluated. The next section presents ways to modify your Excel chart to make it more effective.

GRAPHING WITH SPREADSHEETS FOR SENSITIVITY AND BREAKEVEN ANALYSIS

Chapter 4 introduced drawing xy plots with spreadsheets, and Chapter 7 reviewed this procedure for plotting present worth versus i. The Chapter 7 plot (Figure 7-6) is an example of breakeven analysis, because it is used to determine at what interest rate does the project break even or have a present worth of 0. This section will present some of the spreadsheet tools and options that can make the xy plots more effective and attractive.

The spreadsheet tools and options can be used to:

* Modify the x or y axes

    Specify the minimum or maximum value
    Specify at what value the other axis intersects (default is 0)

* Match line types to data

    Use line types to distinguish one curve from another
    Use markers to show real data
    Use lines without markers to plot curves (straight segments or smooth curves)

* Match chart colors to how displayed

    Color defaults are fine for color computer screen
    Color defaults are OK for color printers
    Black-and-white printing is better with editing (use line types not colors)

* Annotate the graph

    Add text, arrows, and lines to graphs
    Add data labels

In most cases the menus of Excel are self-explanatory, so the main step is deciding what you want to achieve. Then you just look for the way to do it. Left clicks are used to select the item to modify, and right clicks are used to bring up the options for that item. Example 9-14 illustrates this process.

EXAMPLE 9-14

The staged construction choice described in Example 9-11 used a broad range of x values for the x axis. Create a graph that focuses on the 10- to 20-year period and is designed for printing in a report. The costs are:

Year	Full Capacity	Two Stages
0	$140,000	$100,000
n	0	120,000

The first step is to create a table of values that shows the present worth of the costs for different values of n — the length of time until the second stage or full capacity is needed. Notice that the full capacity is calculated at $n = 0$. The only reason to calculate the corresponding value for staged construction is to see if the formula is properly entered, since building both stages at the same time will not really cost $220,000. The values for staged construction at 5, 10, 20, and 30 years check with the values in Example 9-11.

The next step is to select cells A8:C13, which includes the x values and two series of y values. Then the ChartWizard tool is selected. In the first step, the xy (scatter) plot is selected with the option of smoothed lines without markers. In Step 2 no action is required, since the cells A8:C13 were selected first. In Step 3 labels are added for the x and y axes. In Step 4 the chart is moved around on the worksheet page, so that it does not overlap with the data. The result is shown in Figure 9-7 (except that this is the color screen version printed to a black-and-white printer).

Our first step in cleaning up the graph is to delete the formula in cell C9, since two-stage construction will not be done at Time 0. We also delete the label in the adjacent cell, which explains the formula. Then we create a new label for cell C10. As shown in Appendix A, the easy way to create that label is to insert an apostrophe, or space, as the first entry in cell C10. This converts the formula to a label which we can copy to D10. Then we delete the apostrophe in cell C10.

FIGURE 9-7 Automatic graph from spreadsheet.

	A	B	C	D
1	Time	Full Capacity	Two Stage	
2	0	140,000	100,000	
3	n		120,000	
4				
5	Life	40		
6	i	8%		
7			Present Worth of	
8	n	Full Capacity	Two Stage	
9	0	140,000	220,000	=$C$2+PV($B$6,A9,0,−$C$3)
10	5	140,000	181,670	
11	10	140,000	155,583	
12	20	140,000	125,746	
13	30	140,000	111,925	

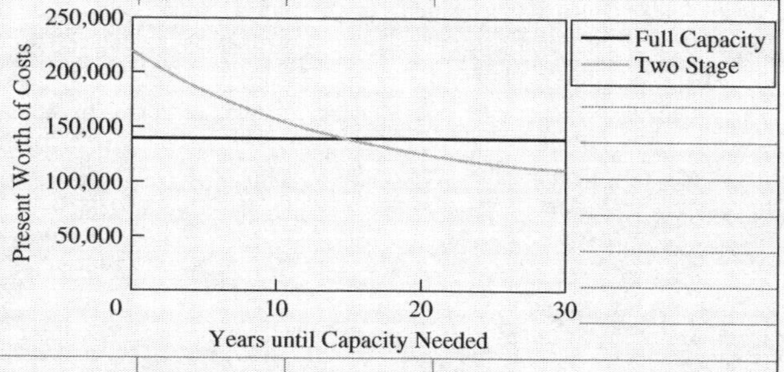

The axis scales must be modified to focus on the area of concern. Select the x axis and change the minimum from automatic to 10 and the maximum to 20. Select the y axis and change the minimum to 125,000 and the maximum to 160,000.

Left-click on the plot area to select it. Then right-click to bring up the options. Select Format Plot Area and change the area pattern to "none." This will eliminate the gray fill that made Figure 9-7 difficult to read.

Left-click on the two-stage curve to select it. Then right-click for the options. Format the data series using the "patterns" tab. Change the line style from solid to dashed, the line color from automatic to black, and increase the line weight. Similarly, increase the line weight for the full-capacity line. Finally, select a grid line and change the line style to dotted. The result is far easier to read in black and white.

To further improve the graph, we can replace the legend with annotations on the graph. Left-click somewhere in the white area around the graph to select "chart area." Right-click and then choose the chart options on the menu. The legends tab will let us delete the legend by turning "show legend" off. Similarly, we can turn the x-axis gridlines on. The line style for these gridlines should be changed to match the y-axis gridlines. This allows us to see that the breakeven time is between 14 and 15 years.

To make the graph less busy, change the scale on the x axis so that the interval is 5 years rather than automatic. Also eliminate the gridlines for the y axis (by selecting the chart area, chart

FIGURE 9-8 Spreadsheet of Figure 9-7 with improved graph.

	A	B	C	D
1	Time	Full Capacity	Two Stage	
2	0	140,000	100,000	
3	n		120,000	
4				
5	life	40		
6	i	8%		
7			Present worth of	
8	n	Full Capacity	Two Stage	
9	0	140,000		
10	5	140,000	181,670	=$C$2+PV($B$6,A10,0,−$C$3)
11	10	140,000	155,583	
12	20	140,000	125,746	
13	30	140,000	111,925	
14				

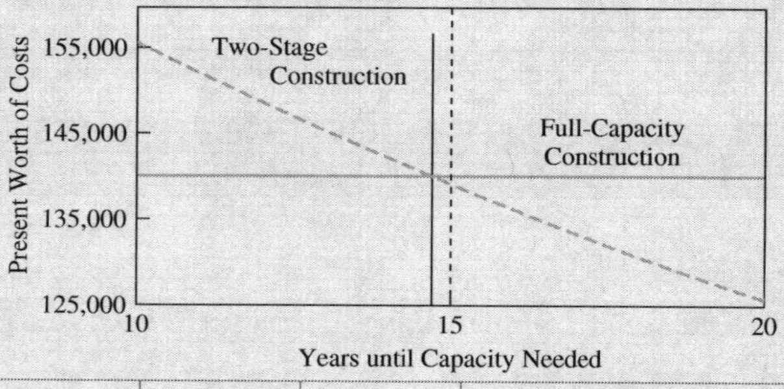

options, and gridlines tabs). The graph size can be increased for easier reading, as well. This may require specifying an interval of 10,000 for the scale of the y axis.

Finally to add the labels for the full-capacity curve and the two-stage curve, find the toolbar for graphics, which is open when the chart is selected (probably along the bottom of the spreadsheet). Select the text box icon, and click on a location close to the two-stage chart. Type in the label for two-stage construction. Notice how including a return and a few spaces can shape the label to fit the slanted line. Add the label for full construction. Figure 9-8 is the result.

DOING WHAT-IF ANALYSIS WITH SPREADSHEETS

Breakeven charts change one variable at a time, while what-if analysis may change many of the variables in a problem. However, spreadsheets remain a very powerful tool for this form of sensitivity analysis. In Example 9-15 a project appears to be very promising. However, what-if analysis indicates that a believable scenario raises some questions about whether the project should be done.

EXAMPLE 9-15

You are an assistant to the vice president for manufacturing. The staff at one of the plants has recommended approval for a new product with a new assembly line to produce it. The VP believes that the numbers presented are too optimistic, and she has added a set of adjustments to the original estimates. Analyze the project's benefit–cost ratio or present worth index as originally submitted. Reanalyze the project, asking "What if the VP's adjustments are correct?"

	Initial Estimate	Adjustment
First cost	$70,000	+10%
Units/year	1,200	−20%
Net unit revenue	$ 25	−15%
Life, in years	8	−3
Interest rate	12%	none

SOLUTION

Figure 9-9 shows that the project has a 2.13 benefit–cost ratio with the initial estimates, but only a value of 0.96 with the what-if adjustments. Thus we need to determine which set of numbers is more realistic. Real-world experience suggests that in many organizations the initial estimates are too optimistic. Auditing of past projects is the best way to develop adjustments for future projects.

FIGURE 9-9 Spread-
sheet for what-if
analysis.

	A	B	C	D
1		Initial Estimate	Adjust-ment	Adjusted Values
2	First cost	$70, 000	10%	$77, 000
3	Units/year	1,200	−20%	960
4	Net unit revenue	$25	−15%	$21
5	Life (years)	8	−3	5
6	Interest rate	12%	none	12%
7				
8	Benefits	149,029		73,537
9	Cost	70,000		77,000
10	B/C Ratio	2.13		0.96
11				
12		=PV(B6,B5-B3*B4)		

SUMMARY

In this chapter, we have looked at four new analysis techniques.

Future worth: When the comparison between alternatives will be made in the future, the calculation is called future worth. This is very similar to present worth, which is based on the present, rather than a future point in time.

Benefit–cost ratio analysis: This technique is based on the ratio of benefits to costs using either present worth or annual cash flow calculations. The method is graphically similar to present worth analysis. When neither input nor output is fixed, incremental benefit–cost ratios ($\Delta B/\Delta C$) are required. The method is similar in this respect to rate of return analysis. Benefit–cost ratio analysis is often used at the various levels of government.

Payback period: Here we define payback as the period of time required for the profit or other benefits of an investment to equal the cost of the investment. Although simple to use and understand, payback is a poor analysis technique for ranking alternatives. While it provides a measure of the speed of the return of the investment, it is not an accurate measure of the profitability of an investment.

Sensitivity, breakeven, and what-if analysis: These techniques are used to see how sensitive a decision is to estimates for the various parameters. Breakeven analysis is done to locate conditions under which the alternatives are equivalent. This is often presented in the form of breakeven charts. Sensitivity analysis is an examination of a range of values for some parameters to determine their effect on a particular decision. What-if analysis changes one to many estimates to see what the result is.

PROBLEMS

Future Worth

9-1   Compute the future worth for the following cash flows.

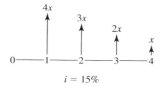

$i = 12\%$

(*Answer: F = $1199*)

9-2   For the following cash flows, compute the future worth.

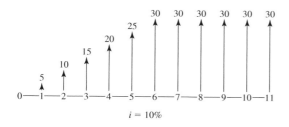

$i = 15\%$

9-3   For the following cash flows, compute the future worth.

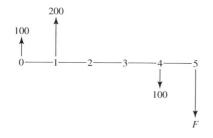

$i = 10\%$

9-4   For a 12% interest rate, compute the value of *F* so the following cash flows have a future worth of 0.

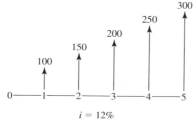

9-5   Compute *F* so the following cash flows have a future worth of 0.

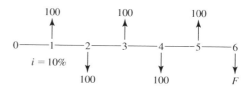

$i = 10\%$

9-6   Calculate the present worth and the future worth of a series of 10 annual cash flows with the first cash flow equal to $15,000 and each successive cash flow increasing by $1200. The interest rate is 12%.

9-7   Sally deposited $100 a month in her savings account for 24 months. For the next 5 years she made no deposits. What is the future worth in Sally's savings account at the end of the 7 years, if the account earned 6% annual interest, compounded monthly? (*Answer: $3430.78*)

9-8   A 20-year-old student decided to set aside $100 on his 21st birthday for investment. Each subsequent year through his 55th birthday, he plans to increase the investment on a $100 arithmetic gradient. He will not set aside additional money after his 55th birthday. If the student can achieve a 12% rate of return, what is the future worth of the investments on his 65th birthday? (*Answer: $1,160,700*)

9-9   You can buy a piece of vacant land for $30,000 cash. You plan to hold it for 15 years and then sell it at a profit. During this period, you would pay annual property taxes of $600. You would have no income from the property. Assuming that you want a 10% rate of return, at what net price would you have to sell the land 15 years hence? (*Answer: $144,373*)

9-10   An individual who makes $32,000 per year anticipates retiring in 30 years. If his salary is increased by $600 each year and he deposits 10% of his yearly salary into a fund that earns 7% interest, what is the future worth at retirement?

9-11   Stamp collecting has become an increasingly popular—and expensive—hobby. One favorite method is to save plate blocks (usually four stamps with the printing plate number in the margin) of each new stamp as it is issued. With rising postage rates and increased numbers of new stamps being issued, this collecting plan costs more each year.

Stamps have been a good place to invest money over the last 10 years, as the demand for stamps previously issued has caused resale prices to increase 18% each year. Suppose a collector purchased $100 worth of stamps 10 years ago, and increased his purchases by $50 per year in each subsequent year. After 10 years of stamp collecting, what is the future worth of the stamp collection?

9-12   The interest rate is 16% per year and there are 48 compounding periods per year. The principal is $50,000. What is the future worth in 5 years?

9-13   In the early 1980s, planners were examining alternate sites for a new London airport. The economic analysis included the value of structures that would need to be removed from various airport sites. At one potential site, the twelfth-century Norman church of St. Michaels, in the village of Stewkley, would have had to be demolished. The planners used the value of the fire insurance policy on the church—a few thousand pounds sterling—as the church's value.

An outraged antiquarian wrote to the London *Times* that an equally plausible computation would be to assume that the original cost of the church (estimated at 100 pounds sterling) be increased at the rate of 10% per year for 800 years. Based on his proposal, what would be the future worth of St. Michaels? (*Note:* There was great public objection to tearing down the church, and it was spared.)

9-14   Bill made a budget and planned to deposit $150 a month in a savings account, beginning September 1. He did this, but on the following January 1, he reduced the monthly deposits to $100. He made 18 deposits, four at $150 and 14 at $100. If the savings account paid 6% interest, compounded monthly, what was the future worth of his savings immediately after the last deposit?   (*Answer:* $2094.42)

9-15   A company deposits $1000 in a bank at the beginning of each year for 6 years. The account earns 8% interest, compounded every 6 months. What is in the account at the end of 6 years?

9-16   Don Ball is a 55-year-old engineer. According to mortality tables, a male at age 55 has an average life expectancy of 21 more years. Don has accumulated $48,500 toward his retirement. He is now adding $5000 per year to his retirement fund. The fund earns 12% interest. Don will retire when he can obtain an annual income from his retirement fund of $20,000, assuming he lives to age 76. He will make no provision for a retirement income after age 76. What is the youngest age at which Don can retire?

9-17   Jean invests $100 in Year 1 and doubles the amount each year after that (so the investment is $100, 200, 400, 800, ...). If she does this for 10 years, and the investment pays 10% annual interest, what is the future worth of her investment?

9-18   If you invested $2500 in a 24-month bank certificate of deposit (CD) paying 8.65%, compounded monthly, what is the future worth of the CD when it matures?

9-19   After receiving an inheritance of $25,000 on her 21st birthday, Ayn deposited the inheritance in a savings account with an effective annual interest rate of 6%. She decided to make regular deposits, beginning with $1000 on her 22nd birthday and increasing by $200 each year (i.e., $1200 on her 23rd birthday, $1400 on her 24th birthday, etc.). What was the future worth of Ayn's deposits on her 56th birthday?

9-20   The Association of General Contractors (AGC) is endowing a fund of $1 million for the Construction Engineering Technology Program at Grambling State University. The AGC established an escrow account in which 10 equal end-of-year deposits that earn 7% compound interest were to be made. After seven deposits, the Louisiana legislature revised laws relating to the licensing fees AGC can charge its members, and there was no deposit at the end of Year 8. What must the amount of the remaining equal end-of-year deposits be, to ensure that the $1 million is available on schedule for the Construction Engineering Technology Program?

9-21   A new engineer is considering investing in an individual retirement account (IRA) with a mutual fund that has an average annual return of 10%. What is the future worth of her IRA at age 65 if she makes annual investments of $2000 into the fund beginning on her 25th birthday? Assume that the fund continues to earn an annual return of 10%.

9-22   IPS Corp. will upgrade its package-labeling machinery. It costs $150,000 to buy the machinery and have it installed. Operation and maintenance costs, which are $1500 per year for the first 3 years, increase by 500 per year for the machine's 10-year life. The machinery has a salvage value of 5% of its initial cost. Interest is 10%. What is the future worth of cost of the machinery?

9-23   A company is considering buying a new bottle-capping machine. The initial cost of the machine is $325,000 and it has a 10-year life. Monthly maintenance costs are expected to be $1200 per month for the first 7 years and $2000 per month for the remaining years. The machine requires a major overhaul costing $55,000 at the end of the fifth year of service. Assume that all these costs occur at the end of the appropriate period. What is the future value of all the costs of owning and operating this machine if the nominal interest rate is 7.2%?

9-24 A family starts an education fund for their son Patrick when he is 8 years old, investing $150 on his eighth birthday, and increasing the yearly investment by $150 per year until Patrick is 18 years old. The fund pays 9% annual interest. What is the fund's future worth when Patrick is 18?

9-25 A bank account pays 19.2% interest with monthly compounding. A series of deposits started with a deposit of $5000 on January 1, 2007. Deposits in the series were to occur each 6 months. Each deposit in the series is for $150 less than the one before it. The last deposit in the series will be due on January 1, 2022. What is the future worth of the account on July 1, 2024, if the balance was zero before the first deposit and no withdrawals are made?

9-26 A recent college graduate got a good job and began a savings account. He authorized the bank to automatically transfer $75 each month from his checking account to the savings account. The bank made the first withdrawal on July 1, 2007 and is instructed to make the last withdrawal on January 1, 2025. The bank pays a nominal interest rate of 4.5% and compounds twice a month. What is the future worth of the account on January 1, 2025?

9-27 Bob, an engineer, decided to start a college fund for his son. Bob will deposit a series of equal, semi-annual cash flows with each deposit equal to $1500. Bob made the first deposit on July 1, 2008 and will make the last deposit on July 1, 2028. Joe, a friend of Bob's, received an inheritance on April 1, 2013, and has decided to begin a college fund for his daughter. Joe wants to send his daughter to the same college as Bob's son. Therefore, Joe needs to accumulate the same amount of money on July 1, 2028, as Bob will have accumulated from his semiannual deposits. Joe never took engineering economics and had no idea how to determine the amount that should be deposited. He decided to deposit $40,000 on July 1, 2013. Will Joe's deposit be sufficient? If not, how much should he have put in? Use a nominal interest of 7% with semiannual compounding on all accounts.

9-28 A business executive is offered a management job at Generous Electric Company, which offers him a 5-year contract that calls for a salary of $62,000 per year, plus 600 shares of GE stock at the end of the 5 years. This executive is currently employed by Fearless Bus Company, which also has offered him a 5-year contract. It calls for a salary of $65,000, plus 100 shares of Fearless stock each year. The Fearless stock is currently worth $60 per share and pays an annual dividend of $2 per share. Assume end-of-year payments of salary and stock. Stock dividends begin one year after the stock is received. The executive believes that the value of the stock and the dividend will remain constant. If the executive considers 9% a suitable rate of return in this situation, what must the Generous Electric stock be worth per share to make the two offers equally attractive? Use the future worth analysis method in your comparison. (*Answer:* $83.76)

9-29 Pick a discretionary expense that you incur on a regular basis, such as buying cigarettes weekly, buying fashion items monthly, buying sports tickets monthly, or going to movies weekly. Assume that you instead place the money in an investment account that earns 9% annually. After 40 years, how much is in the account?

Benefit–Cost Ratio

9-30 Each of the three alternatives shown has a 5-year useful life. If the MARR is 10%, which alternative should be selected? Solve the problem by benefit–cost ratio analysis.

	A	*B*	*C*
Cost	$600.0	$500.0	$200.0
Uniform annual benefit	158.3	138.7	58.3

(*Answer: B*)

9-31 Consider three alternatives, each with a 10-year useful life. If the MARR is 10%, which alternative should be selected? Solve the problem by benefit–cost ratio analysis.

	A	*B*	*C*
Cost	$800	$300	$150
Uniform annual benefit	142	60	33.5

9-32 An investor is considering buying some land for $100,000 and constructing an office building on it. Three different buildings are being analyzed.

	Building Height		
	2 Stories	5 Stories	10 Stories
Cost of building (excluding cost of land)	$400,000	$800,000	$2,100,000
Resale value* of land + building after 20-year horizon	200,000	300,000	400,000
Annual net rental income	70,000	105,000	256,000

*Resale value to be considered a reduction in cost, rather than a benefit.

Using benefit–cost ratio analysis and an 8% MARR, determine which alternative, if any, should be selected.

9-33   Using benefit–cost ratio analysis, determine which one of the three mutually exclusive alternatives should be selected. Each alternative has a 6-year useful life. Assume a 10% MARR.

	A	B	C
First cost	$560	$340	$120
Uniform annual benefit	140	100	40
Salvage value	40	0	0

9-34   Consider four alternatives, each of which has an 8-year useful life:

	A	B	C	D
Cost	$100.0	$80.0	$60.0	$50.0
Uniform annual benefit	12.2	12.0	9.7	12.2
Salvage value	75.0	50.0	50.0	0

If the MARR is 8%, which alternative should be selected? Solve the problem by benefit–cost ratio analysis.

9-35   Using benefit–cost ratio analysis, a 5-year useful life, and a 15% MARR, determine which of the following alternatives should be selected.

	A	B	C	D	E
Cost	$100	$200	$300	$400	$500
Uniform annual benefit	37	69	83	126	150

9-36   Five mutually exclusive investment alternatives have been proposed. Based on benefit–cost ratio analysis, and a MARR of 15%, which alternative should be selected?

Year	A	B	C	D	E
0	−$200	−$100	−$125	−$150	−$225
1–5	+68	+25	+42	+52	+68

9-37   A project will cost $50,000. The benefits at the end of the first year are estimated to be $10,000, increasing at a 10% uniform rate in subsequent years. Using an 8-year analysis period and a 10% interest rate, compute the benefit–cost ratio.

9-38   A do-nothing and two mutually exclusive alternatives are being considered for reducing traffic congestion. User benefits come from reduced congestion once the project is complete, while user disbenefits are due to increased congestion during construction. The interest rate is 9%, and the life of each alternative is 15 years. Which alternative should be chosen?

	A	B
User benefits ($M/yr)	2.1	2.6
User disbenefits ($M)	1.2	2.1
First cost ($M)	6.9	9.9
Operations and maintenance ($M/yr)	0.75	0.825

(a) Use the benefit–cost ratio.

(b) Use the modified benefit–cost ratio.

(c) Use the public/government version of the B/C ratio.

(d) Assume these numbers apply to a private firm and use a present worth index.

(e) Are your recommendations for (a) through (d) consistent? Which measure gives the largest value? Why?

9-39   A school is overcrowded and there are three options. The do-nothing alternative corresponds to continuing to use modular classrooms. The school can be expanded, or a new school can be built to "split the load" between the schools. User benefits come from improvements in school performance for the expanded or new schools. If a new school is built, there are more benefits because more students will be able to walk to school, the average distance for those who ride the school buses will be shorter, and the schools will be smaller and more "student friendly." The disbenefits for the expanded school are due to the impact of the construction process during the school year. The interest rate is 8%, and the life of each alternative is 20 years. Which alternative should be chosen? What is the incremental ratio for the preferred alternative?

	A	*B*
User benefits ($M/yr)	2.1	3.1
User disbenefits ($M)	0.8	0
First cost ($M)	8.8	10.4
Operations and maintenance ($M/yr)	0.95	1.7

(a) Use the benefit–cost ratio.

(b) Use the modified benefit–cost ratio.

(c) Use the public/government version of the B/C ratio.

(d) Assume these numbers apply to a private firm and use a present worth index.

(e) Are your recommendations for (a) through (d) consistent? Which measure gives the largest value? Why?

Payback Period and Exact Methods

9-40 Able Plastics, an injection-molding firm, has negotiated a contract with a national chain of department stores. Plastic pencil boxes are to be produced for a 2-year period. Able Plastics has never produced the item before and requires all new dies. If the firm invests $67,000 for special removal equipment to unload the completed pencil boxes from the molding machine, one machine operator can be eliminated. This would save $26,000 per year. The removal equipment has no salvage value and is not expected to be used after the 2-year production contract is completed. The equipment, although useless to Able, would be serviceable for about 15 years. What is the payback period? Should Able Plastics buy the removal equipment?

9-41 A cannery is considering installing an automatic case-sealing machine to replace current hand methods. If they purchase the machine for $3800 in June, at the beginning of the canning season, they will save $400 per month for the 4 months each year that the plant is in operation. Maintenance costs of the case-sealing machine are expected to be negligible. The case-sealing machine is expected to be useful for five annual canning seasons and then will have no salvage value. What is the payback period? What is the nominal annual rate of return?

9-42 A project has the following costs and benefits. What is the payback period?

Year	Costs	Benefits
0	$1400	
1	500	
2	300	$400
3–10		300 in each year

9-43 A car dealer leases a small computer with software for $5000 per year. As an alternative he could buy the computer for $7000 and lease the software for $3500 per year. Any time he would decide to switch to some other computer system he could cancel the software lease and sell the computer for $500. If he buys the computer and leases the software,

(a) What is the payback period?

(b) If he kept the computer and software for 6 years, what would be the benefit–cost ratio, based on a 10% interest rate?

9-44 A large project requires an investment of $200 million. The construction will take 3 years: $30 million will be spent during the first year, $100 million during the second year, and $70 million during the third year of construction. Two project operation periods are being considered: 10 years with the expected net profit of $40 million per year and 20 years with the expected net profit of $32.5 million per year. For simplicity of calculations it is assumed that all cash flows occur at end of year. The company minimum required return on investment is 10%.

Calculate for each alternative:

(a) The payback periods

(b) The total equivalent investment cost at the end of the construction period

(c) The equivalent uniform annual worth of the project (use the operation period of each alternative)

Which operation period should be chosen?

9-45 Two alternatives with identical benefits are being considered:

	A	*B*
Initial cost	$500	$800
Uniform annual cost	200	150
Useful life, in years	8	8

(a) Compute the payback period if Alt. *B* is purchased rather than Alt. *A*.

(b) Use a MARR of 12% and benefit–cost ratio analysis to identify the alternative that should be selected.

9-46 Tom Sewel has gathered data on the relative costs of a solar water heater system and a conventional electric water heater. The data are based on statistics for a mid-American city and assume that during cloudy days an electric heating element in the solar heating system will provide the necessary heat.

The installed cost of a conventional electric water tank and heater is $200. A family of four uses an average of 300 liters of hot water a day, which takes $230 of electricity per year. The glass-lined tank has a 20-year guarantee. This is probably a reasonable estimate of its actual useful life.

The installed cost of two solar panels, a small electric pump, and a storage tank with auxiliary electric heating element is $1400. It will cost $60 a year for electricity to run the pump and heat water on cloudy days. The solar system will require $180 of maintenance work every 4 years. Neither the conventional electric water heater nor the solar water heater will have any salvage value at the end of its useful life.

Using Tom's data, what is the payback period if the solar water heater system is installed, rather than the conventional electric water heater?

9-47 Consider four mutually exclusive alternatives:

	A	B	C	D
Cost	$75.0	$50.0	$15.0	$90.0
Uniform annual benefit	18.8	13.9	4.5	23.8

Each alternative has a 5-year useful life and no salvage value. The MARR is 10%. Which alternative should be selected, based on

(a) Future worth analysis
(b) Benefit–cost ratio analysis
(c) The payback period

9-48 Consider three alternatives:

	A	B	C
First cost	$50	$150	$110
Uniform annual benefit	28.8	39.6	39.6
Useful life, in years*	2	6	4
Computed rate of return	10%	15%	16.4%

*At the end of its useful life, an identical alternative (with the same cost, benefits, and useful life) may be installed.

All the alternatives have no salvage value. If the MARR is 12%, which alternative should be selected?

(a) Solve the problem by future worth analysis.
(b) Solve the problem by benefit–cost ratio analysis.
(c) Solve the problem by payback period.

(d) If the answers in parts (a), (b), and (c) differ, explain why this is the case.

9-49 Consider three mutually exclusive alternatives. The MARR is 10%.

Year	X	Y	Z
0	−$100	−$50	−$50
1	25	16	21
2	25	16	21
3	25	16	21
4	25	16	21

(a) For Alt. X, compute the benefit–cost ratio.
(b) Based on the payback period, which alternative should be selected?
(c) Determine the preferred alternative based on an exact economic analysis method.

9-50 The cash flows for three alternatives are as follows:

Year	A	B	C
0	−$500	−$600	−$900
1	−400	−300	0
2	200	350	200
3	250	300	200
4	300	250	200
5	350	200	200
6	400	150	200

(a) Based on payback period, which alternative should be selected?
(b) Using future worth analysis, and a 12% interest rate, determine which alternative should be selected.

9-51 Three mutually exclusive alternatives are being considered:

	A	B	C
Initial cost	$500	$400	$300
Benefit at end of the first year	200	200	200
Uniform benefit at end of subsequent years	100	125	100
Useful life, in years	6	5	4

At the end of its useful life, an alternative is *not* replaced. If the MARR is 10%, which alternative should be selected

(a) Based on the payback period?
(b) Based on benefit–cost ratio analysis?

9-52

Year	E	F	G	H
0	−$90	−$110	−$100	−$120
1	20	35	0	0
2	20	35	10	0
3	20	35	20	0
4	20	35	30	0
5	20	0	40	0
6	20	0	50	180

(a) Based on future worth analysis, which of the four alternatives is preferred at 6% interest?

(b) Based on future worth analysis, which alternative is preferred at 15% interest?

(a) Based on the payback period, which alternative is preferred?

(d) At 7% interest, what is the benefit–cost ratio for Alt. G?

Sensitivity

9-53   Tom Jackson is buying a new car. Alternative A is an American-built compact. It has an initial cost of $8900 and operating costs of 9 ¢/km, excluding depreciation. From resale statistics, Tom estimates the American car can be resold at the end of 3 years for $1700. Alternative B is a foreign-built Fiasco. Its initial cost is $8000, the operating cost, also excluding depreciation, is 8 ¢/km. How low could the resale value of the Fiasco be to provide equally economical transportation? Assume Tom will drive 12,000 km/year and considers 8% as an appropriate interest rate. (*Answer:* $175)

9-54   A newspaper is considering buying locked vending machines to replace open newspaper racks in the downtown area. The vending machines cost $45 each. It is expected that the annual revenue from selling the same quantity of newspapers will increase $12 per vending machine. The useful life of the vending machine is unknown.

(a) To determine the sensitivity of rate of return to useful life, prepare a graph for rate of return versus useful life for lives up to 8 years.

(b) If the newspaper requires a 12% rate of return, what minimum useful life must it obtain from the vending machines?

(c) What would be the rate of return if the vending machines were to last indefinitely?

9-55   If the MARR is 12%, compute the value of X that makes the two alternatives equally desirable.

	A	B
Cost	$800	$1000
Uniform annual benefit	230	230
Useful life, in years	5	X

9-56   If the MARR is 12%, compute the value of X that makes the two alternatives equally desirable.

	A	B
Cost	$150	$ X
Uniform annual benefit	40	65
Salvage value	100	200
Useful life, in years	6	6

9-57   Consider two alternatives:

	A	B
Cost	$500	$300
Uniform annual benefit	75	75
Useful life, in years	Infinity	X

Assume that Alt. B is not replaced at the end of its useful life. If the MARR is 10%, what must be the useful life of B to make Alternatives A and B equally desirable?

9-58   Chris Cook studied the situation described in Problem 9-46 and decided that the solar system will *not* require the $180 of maintenance every 4 years. Chris believes future replacements of either the conventional electric water heater, or the solar water heater system can be made at the same costs and useful lives as the initial installation. Based on a 10% interest rate, what must be the useful life of the solar system to make it no more expensive than the electric water heater system?

9-59   Jane Chang is making plans for a summer vacation. She will take $1000 with her in the form of traveler's checks. From the newspaper, she finds that if she purchases the checks by May 31, she will not have to pay a service charge. That is, she will obtain $1000 worth of traveler's checks for $1000. But if she waits to buy the checks until just before starting her summer trip, she must pay a 1% service charge. (It will cost her $1010 for $1000 of traveler's checks.)

Jane can obtain a 13% interest rate, compounded weekly, on her money. How many weeks after May 31 can she begin her trip and still justify buying the traveler's checks on May 31?

9-60 Fence posts for a particular job cost $10.50 each to install, including the labor cost. They will last 10 years. If the posts are treated with a wood preservative, they can be expected to have a 15-year life. Assuming a 10% interest rate, how much could one afford to pay for the wood preservative treatment?

9-61 A piece of property is purchased for $10,000 and yields a $1000 yearly net profit. The property is sold after 5 years. What is its minimum price to breakeven with interest at 10%?

9-62 Rental equipment is for sale for $110,000. A prospective buyer estimates he would keep the equipment for 12 years and spend $6000 a year on maintaining it. Estimated annual net receipts from equipment rentals would be $14,400. It is estimated the rental equipment could be sold for $80,000 at the end of 12 years. If the buyer wants a 7% rate of return on his investment, what is the maximum price he should pay for the equipment?

9-63 *The Financial Advisor* is a weekly column in the local newspaper. Assume you must answer the following question. "I recently retired at age 65, and I have a tax-free retirement annuity coming due soon. I have three options. I can receive (A) $30,976 now, (B) $359.60 per month for the rest of my life, or (C) $513.80 per month for the next 10 years. What should I do?" Ignore the timing of the monthly cash flows and assume that the payments are received at the end of year. Assume the 10-year annuity will continue to be paid to loved heirs if the person dies before the 10-year period is over.

(a) If $i = 6\%$, develop a choice table for lives from 5 to 30 years. (You do not know how long this person or other readers may live.)

(b) If $i = 10\%$, develop a choice table for lives from 5 to 30 years. (You do not know how long this person or other readers may live.)

(c) How does increasing the interest rate change your recommendations?

Contributed by D. P. Loucks, Cornell University

9-64 A motor with a 200-horsepower output is needed in the factory for intermittent use. A Graybar motor costs $7000, and has an electrical efficiency of 89%. A Blueball motor costs $6000 and has an 85% efficiency. Neither motor would have any salvage value, since the cost to remove it would equal its scrap value. The annual maintenance cost for either motor is estimated at $300 per year. Electric power costs $0.072/kWh (1 hp = 0.746 kW). If a 10% interest rate is used in the calculations, what is the minimum number of hours the higher initial cost Graybar motor must be used each year to justify its purchase?

9-65 Plan A requires a $100,000 investment now. Plan B requires an $80,000 investment now and an additional $40,000 investment at a later time. At 8% interest, compute the breakeven point for the timing of the $40,000 investment.

9-66 A low-carbon-steel machine part, operating in a corrosive atmosphere, lasts 6 years, and costs $350 installed. If the part is treated for corrosion resistance, it will cost $500 installed. How long must the treated part last to be the preferred alternative, assuming 10% interest?

9-67 Neither of the following machines has any net salvage value.

	A	B
Original cost	$55,000	$75,000
Annual expenses		
Operation	9,500	7,200
Maintenance	5,000	3,000
Taxes and insurance	1,700	2,250

At what useful life are the machines equivalent if

(a) 10% interest is used in the computations?

(b) 0% interest is used in the computations?

9-68 A machine costs $5240 and produces benefits of $1000 at the end of each year for 8 years. Assume an annual interest rate of 10%.

(a) What is the payback period (in years)?

(b) What is the breakeven point (in years)?

(c) Since the answers in (a) and (b) are different, which one is "correct"?

9-69 Analyze Problem 9-61 again with the following changes:

(a) What if the property is purchased for $12,000?

(b) What if the yearly net profit is $925?

(c) What if it is sold after 7 years?

(d) What if (a), (b), and (c) happen simultaneously?

9-70 Analyze Problem 9-53 again with the following changes:

  (*a*) What if the Fiasco is more reliable than expected, so that its operating cost is $0.075/km?

  (*b*) What if Tom drives only 9000 km/year?

  (*c*) What if Tom's interest rate is 6% annually?

  (*d*) What if (*a*), (*b*), and (*c*) happen simultaneously?

9-71 Analyze Problem 9-55 again with the following changes:

  (*a*) What if B's first cost is $1200?

  (*b*) What if B's annual benefit is $280?

  (*c*) What if the MARR is 10% annually?

  (*d*) What if (*a*), (*b*), and (*c*) happen simultaneously?

9-72 Analyze Problem 9-66 again with the following changes:

  (*a*) What if the installed cost of the corrosion-treated part is $600?

  (*b*) What if the untreated part will last only 4 years?

  (*c*) What if the MARR is 12% annually?

  (*d*) What if (*a*), (*b*), and (*c*) happen simultaneously?

CHAPTER 10

UNCERTAINTY IN FUTURE EVENTS

They Only Thought They Were Done

Since the early 1980s, under the federal Superfund program, companies have had to clean up property sites that are contaminated by hazardous waste. So far, hundreds of sites have been cleaned up (or "remediated," in Superfund terminology), at a collective cost that runs to the billions of dollars; hundreds of other sites are still in the process of being decontaminated. Superfund cleanups usually take years to complete, and often involve expensive legal wrangling among the parties involved.

A large number of Superfund sites—including some where cleanup has been completed—have been found to contain trichloroethylene (TCE), a widely used solvent. To complicate matters further, the U.S. Environmental Protection Agency (EPA) has discovered that TCE may be far more toxic than originally thought.

Moreover, the cleanup techniques used in the past to remove the substance from groundwater may actually have made the problem worse by causing TCE to be emitted in vapor form. This vapor can concentrate in buildings and other enclosed spaces, increasing the potential toxicity even further.

EPA is now studying whether previously cleaned Superfund sites should be "reopened" for additional remediation of TCE. The decision is made more difficult by the fact that some previously cleaned sites were sold after the Superfund remediation was finished and may have had buildings constructed on them.

QUESTIONS TO CONSIDER

1. How can a company quantify the risk of an event such as discovery of TCE on its property?
2. What are some ways a company might estimate the cost of such an event, should it occur?
3. Prior to the mid-1970s, it was common (and legal) for manufacturers to landfill chemicals and other potentially hazardous materials. The Superfund program begun 1980 required companies that had disposed of these materials to clean up the landfill sites, even if disposal had taken place years before, at a time when the practice was not against the law. How can companies anticipate and prepare for future laws that might penalize activities that are legal today but may become illegal (or at least socially unacceptable) in the future?

After Completing This Chapter...

You should be able to:

- Use a range of estimated variables to evaluate a project.
- Describe possible outcomes with probability distributions.
- Combine probability distributions for individual variables into joint probability distributions.
- Use expected values for economic decision making.
- Use economic decision trees to describe and solve more complex problems.
- Measure and consider risk when making economic decisions.
- Understand how simulation can be used to evaluate economic decisions.

A n assembly line is built after the engineering economic analysis has shown that the anticipated product demand will generate profits. A new motor, heat exchanger, or filtration unit is installed after analysis has shown that future cost savings will economically justify current costs. A new road, school, or other public facility is built after analysis has shown that the future demand and benefits justify the present cost to build. However, future performance of the assembly line, motor, and so on is uncertain, and demand for the product or public facility is more uncertain.

Engineering economic analysis is used to evaluate projects with long-term consequences when the time value of money matters. Thus, it must concern itself with future consequences; but describing the future accurately is not easy. In this chapter we consider the problem of evaluating the future. The easiest way to begin is to make a careful estimate. Then we examine the possibility of predicting a range of possible outcomes. Finally, we consider what happens when the probabilities of the various outcomes are known or may be estimated. We will show that the tools of probability are quite useful for economic decision making.

ESTIMATES AND THEIR USE IN ECONOMIC ANALYSIS

Economic analysis requires evaluating the future consequences of an alternative. In practically every chapter of this book, there are cash flow tables and diagrams that describe precisely the costs and benefits for future years. We don't really believe that we can exactly foretell a future cost or benefit. Instead, our goal is to select a single value representing the *best* estimate that can be made.

We recognize that estimated future consequences are not precise and that the actual values will be somewhat different from our estimates. Even so, it is likely we have made the tacit assumption that these estimates *are* correct. We know estimates will not always turn out to be correct; yet we treat them like facts once they are *in* the economic analysis. We do the analysis as though the values were exact. This can lead to trouble. If actual costs and benefits are different from the estimates, an undesirable alternative may be selected. This is because the variability of future consequences is concealed by assuming that the best estimates will actually occur. The problem is illustrated by Example 10-1.

EXAMPLE 10-1

Two alternatives are being considered. The best estimates for the various consequences are as follows:

	A	B
Cost	$1000	$2000
Net annual benefit	$150	$250
Useful life, in years	10	10
End-of-useful-life salvage value	$100	$400

If interest is 3½%, which alternative has the better net present worth (NPW)?

Alternative A

$$NPW = -1000 + 150(P/A, 3^1/_2\%, 10) + 100(P/F, 3^1/_2\%, 10)$$
$$= -1000 + 150(8.317) + 100(0.7089)$$
$$= -1000 + 1248 + 71$$
$$= +\$319$$

Alternative B

$$NPW = -2000 + 250(P/A, 3^1/_2\%, 10) + 400(P/F, 3^1/_2\%, 10)$$
$$= -2000 + 250(8.317) + 400(0.7089)$$
$$= -2000 + 2079 + 284$$
$$= +\$363$$

Alternative B, with its larger NPW, would be selected.

Alternate Formation of Example 10-1

Suppose that at the end of 10 years, the actual salvage value for *B* were $300 instead of the $400, the best estimate. If all the other estimates were correct, is *B* still the preferred alternative?

Revised B

$$NPW = -2000 + 250(P/A, 3^1/_2\%, 10) + 300(P/F, 3^1/_2\%, 10)$$
$$= -2000 + 250(8.317) + 300(0.7089)$$
$$= -2000 + 2079 + 213$$
$$= +\$292 \rightarrow A \text{ is now the preferred alternative.}$$

Example 10-1 shows that the change in the salvage value of Alternative *B* actually results in a change of preferred alternative. Thus, a more thorough analysis of Example 10-1 would consider (1) which values are uncertain, (2) whether the uncertainty is ±5% or −50 to +80%, and (3) which uncertain values lead to different decisions. A more thorough analysis, which is done with the tools of this chapter, determines which decision is better over the range of possibilities. Explicitly considering uncertainty lets us make better decisions. The tool of breakeven analysis is illustrated in Example 10-2.

EXAMPLE 10-2

Use the data of Example 10-1 to compute the sensitivity of the decision to the Alt. B salvage value by computing the breakeven value. For Alt. A, NPW $= +319$. For breakeven between the alternatives,

$$NPW_A = NPW_B$$

$$+319 = -2000 + 250(P/A, 3^1/_2\%, 10) + \text{Salvage value}_B(P/F, 3^1/_2\%, 10)$$

$$= -2000 + 250(8.317) + \text{Salvage value}_B(0.7089)$$

At the breakeven point

$$\text{Salvage value}_B = \frac{319 + 2000 - 2079}{0.7089} = \frac{240}{0.7089} = \$339$$

When Alt. B salvage value $>\$339$, B is preferred; when $<\$339$, A is preferred.

Breakeven analysis, as shown in Example 10-2, is one means of examining the impact of the variability of some estimate on the outcome. It helps by answering the question, How much variability can a parameter have before the decision will be affected? While the preferred decision depends on whether the salvage value is above or below the breakeven value, the economic difference between the alternatives is small when the salvage value is "close" to breakeven. Breakeven analysis does not solve the basic problem of how to take the inherent variability of parameters into account in an economic analysis. This will be considered next.

A RANGE OF ESTIMATES

It is usually more realistic to describe parameters with a range of possible values, rather than a single value. A range could include an **optimistic** estimate, the **most likely** estimate, and a **pessimistic** estimate. Then, the economic analysis can determine whether the decision is sensitive to the range of projected values.

EXAMPLE 10-3

A firm is considering an investment. The most likely data values were found during the feasibility study. Analyzing past data of similar projects shows that optimistic values for the first cost and the annual benefit are 5% better than most likely values. Pessimistic values are 15% worse.

The firm's most experienced project analyst has estimated the values for the useful life and salvage value.

	Optimistic	**Most Likely**	**Pessimistic**
Cost	$950	$1000	$1150
Net annual benefit	210	200	170
Useful life, in years	12	10	8
Salvage value	100	0	0

Compute the rate of return for each estimate. If a 10% before-tax minimum attractive rate of return is required, is the investment justified under all three estimates? If it is justified only under some estimates, how can these results be used?

SOLUTION

Optimistic Estimate

$$\text{PW of cost} = \text{PW of benefit}$$

$$\$950 = 210(P/A, \text{IRR}_{opt}, 12) + 100(P/F, \text{IRR}_{opt}, 12)$$

$$\text{IRR}_{opt} = 19.8\%$$

Most Likely Estimate

$$\$1000 = 200(P/A, \text{IRR}_{most\,likely}, 10)$$

$$(P/A, \text{IRR}_{most\,likely}, 10) = 1000/200 = 5 \rightarrow \text{IRR}_{most\,likely} = 15.1\%$$

Pessimistic Estimate

$$\$1150 = 170(P/A, \text{IRR}_{pess}, 8)$$

$$(P/A, \text{IRR}_{pess}, 8) = 1150/170 = 6.76 \rightarrow \text{IRR}_{pess} = 3.9\%$$

From the calculations we conclude that the rate of return for this investment is most likely to be 15.1%, but might range from 3.9% to 19.8%. The investment meets the 10% MARR criterion for two of the estimates. These estimates can be considered to be scenarios of what may happen with this project. Since one scenario indicates that the project is not attractive, we need to have a method of weighting the scenarios or considering how likely each is.

Example 10-3 made separate calculations for the sets of optimistic, most likely, and pessimistic values. The range of scenarios is useful. However, if there are more than a few uncertain variables, it is unlikely that all will prove to be optimistic (best case) or most likely or pessimistic (worst case). It is more likely that many parameters are the most likely values, while some are optimistic and some are pessimistic.

This can be addressed by using Equation 10-1 to calculate average or mean values for each parameter. Equation 10-1 puts four times the weight on the most likely value than on the other two. This equation was developed as an approximation with the beta distribution.

$$\text{Mean value} = \frac{\text{Optimistic value} + 4(\text{Most likely value}) + \text{Pessimistic value}}{6} \quad (10\text{-}1)$$

This approach is illustrated in Example 10-4.

EXAMPLE 10-4

Solve Example 10-3 by using Equation 10-1. Compute the resulting mean rate of return.

SOLUTION

Compute the mean for each parameter:

$$\text{Mean cost} = [950 + 4 \times 1000 + 1150]/6 = 1016.7$$

$$\text{Mean net annual benefit} = [210 + 4 \times 200 + 170]/6 = 196.7$$

$$\text{Mean useful life} = [12 + 4 \times 10 + 8]/6 = 10.0$$

$$\text{Mean salvage life} = 100/6 = 16.7$$

Compute the mean rate of return:

$$\text{PW of cost} = \text{PW of benefit}$$

$$\$1016.7 = 196.7(P/A, \text{IRR}_{\text{beta}}, 10) + 16.7(P/F, \text{IRR}_{\text{beta}}, 10)$$

$$\text{IRR}_{\text{beta}} = 14.2\%$$

Example 10-3 gave a most likely rate of return (15.1%) that differed from the mean rate of return (14.2%) computed in Example 10-4. These values are different because the former is based exclusively on the most likely values and the latter takes into account the variability of the parameters.

In examining the data, we see that the pessimistic values are further away from the most likely values than are the optimistic values. This is a common occurrence. For example, a savings of 10 to 20% may be the maximum possible, but a cost overrun can be 50%, 100%, or even more. This causes the resulting weighted mean values to be less favorable than the most likely values. As a result, the mean rate of return, in this example, is less than the rate of return based on the most likely values.

PROBABILITY

We all have used probabilities. For example, what is the probability of getting a "head" when flipping a coin? Using a model that assumes that the coin is fair, both the head and tail outcomes occur with a probability of 50%, or $1/2$. This probability is the likelihood of an event in a single trial. It also describes the long-run relative frequency of getting heads in many trials (out of 50 coin flips, we expect to average 25 heads).

Probabilities can also be based on data, expert judgment, or a combination of both. Past data on weather and climate, on project completion times and costs, and on highway traffic are combined with expert judgment to forecast future events. These examples can be important in engineering economy.

Another example based on long-run relative frequency is the PW of a flood-protection dam that depends on the probabilities of different-sized floods over many years. This would be based on data about past floods and would include many years of potential flooding. An example of a single event that may be estimated by expert judgment is the probability of a successful outcome for a research and development project, which will determine its PW.

All the data in an engineering economy problem may have some level of uncertainty. However, small uncertainties may be ignored, so that more analysis can be done with the large uncertainties. For example, the price of an off-the-shelf piece of equipment may vary by only ±5%. The price could be treated as a known or deterministic value. On the other hand, demand over the next 20 years will have more uncertainty. Demand should be analyzed as a random or stochastic variable. We should establish probabilities for different values of demand.

There are also logical or mathematical rules for probabilities. If an outcome can never happen, then the probability is 0. If an outcome will certainly happen, then the probability is 1, or 100%. This means that probabilities cannot be negative or greater than 1; in other words, they must be within the interval [0, 1], as indicated shortly in Equation 10-2.

Probabilities are defined so that the sum of probabilities for all possible outcomes is 1 or 100% (Equation 10-3). Summing the probability of 0.5 for a head and 0.5 for a tail leads to a total of 1 for the possible outcomes from the coin flip. An exploration well drilled in a potential oil field will have three outcomes (dry hole, noncommercial quantities, or commercial quantities) whose probabilities will sum to one.

Equations 10-2 and 10-3 can be used to check that probabilities are valid. If the probabilities for all but one outcome are known, the equations can be used to find the unknown probability for that outcome (see Example 10-5).

$$0 \leq \text{Probability} \leq 1 \qquad (10\text{-}2)$$

$$\sum_{j=1 \text{ to } K} P(\text{outcome}_j) = 1, \quad \text{where there are } K \text{ outcomes} \qquad (10\text{-}3)$$

In a probability course many probability distributions, such as the normal, uniform, and beta are presented. These continuous distributions describe a large population of data. However, for engineering economy it is more common to use 2 to 5 outcomes with discrete probabilities—even though the 2 to 5 outcomes only represent or approximate the range of possibilities.

This is done for two reasons. First, the data often are estimated by expert judgment, so that using 7 to 10 outcomes would be false accuracy. Second, each outcome requires more analysis. In most cases the 2 to 5 outcomes represents the best trade-off between representing the range of possibilities and the amount of calculation required. Example 10-5 illustrates these calculations.

EXAMPLE 10-5

What are the probability distributions for the annual benefit and life for the following project?

The annual benefit's most likely value is $8000 with a probability of 60%. There is a 30% probability that it will be $5000, and the highest value that is likely $10,000. A life of 6 years is twice as likely as a life of 9 years.

SOLUTION

Probabilities are given for only two of the possible outcomes for the annual benefit. The third value is found from the fact that the probabilities for the three outcomes must sum to 1 (Equation 10-3).

$$1 = P(\text{Benefit is } \$5000) + P(\text{Benefit is } \$8000) + P(\text{Benefit is } \$10,000)$$

$$P(\text{Benefit is } \$10,000) = 1 - 0.6 - 0.3 = 0.1$$

The probability distribution can then be summarized in a table. The histogram or relative frequency diagram is Figure 10-1.

Annual benefit	$5000	$8000	$10,000
Probability	0.3	0.6	0.1

FIGURE 10-1 Probability distribution for annual benefit.

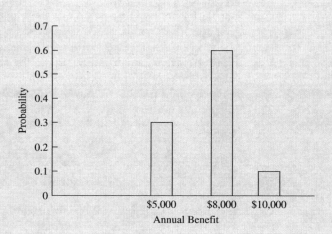

The problem statement tells us:

$$P(\text{life is 6 years}) = 2P(\text{life is 9 years})$$

Equation 10-3 can be applied to write a second equation for the two unknown probabilities:

$$P(6) + P(9) = 1$$

Combining these, we write

$$2P(9) + P(9) = 1$$
$$P(9) = 1/3$$
$$P(6) = 2/3$$

The probability distribution for the life is $P(6) = 66.7\%$ and $P(9) = 33.3\%$.

JOINT PROBABILITY DISTRIBUTIONS

Example 10-5 constructed the probability distributions for a project's annual benefit and life. These examples show how likely each value is for the input data of the problem. We would like to construct a similar probability distribution for the project's present worth. This is the distribution that we can use to evaluate the project. That present worth depends on both input probability distributions, so we need to construct the *joint* probability distribution for the different combinations of their values.

For this introductory text, we assume that two random variables such as the annual benefit and life are unrelated or statistically independent. This means that the *joint* probability of a combined event (Event A defined on the first variable and Event B on the second variable) is the product of the probabilities for the two events. This is Equation 10-4:

$$\text{If A and B are independent, then } P(A \text{ and } B) = P(A) \times P(B) \qquad (10\text{-}4)$$

For example, flipping a coin and rolling a die are statistically independent. Thus, the probability of {flipping a head and rolling a 4} equals the probability of a {heads} $= \frac{1}{2}$ times the probability of a {4} $= 1/6$, for a joint probability $= 1/12$.

The number of outcomes in the joint distribution is the product of the number of outcomes in each variable's distribution. Thus, for the coin and the die, there are 2 times 6, or 12 combinations. Each of the 2 outcomes for the coin is combined with each of the 6 outcomes for the die.

Some variables are not statistically independent, and the calculation of their joint probability distribution is more complex. For example, a project with low revenues may be terminated early and one with high revenues may be kept operating as long as possible. In these cases annual cash flow and project life are not independent. While this type of relationship can sometimes be modeled with economic decision trees (covered later in this chapter), we will limit our coverage in this text to the simpler case of independent variables.

Example 10-6 uses the three values and probabilities for the annual benefit and the two values and probabilities for the life to construct the six possible combinations. Then the values and probabilities are constructed for the project's PW.

EXAMPLE 10-6

The project described in Example 10-5 has a first cost of $25,000. The firm uses an interest rate of 10%. Assume that the probability distributions for annual benefit and life are unrelated or statistically independent. Calculate the probability distribution for the PW.

SOLUTION

Since there are three outcomes for the annual benefit and two outcomes for the life, there are six combinations. The first four columns of the following table show the six combinations of life and annual benefit. The probabilities in columns 2 and 4 are multiplied to calculate the joint probabilities in column 5. For example, the probability of a low annual benefit and a short life is $0.3 \times 2/3$, which equals 0.2 or 20%.

The PW values include the $25,000 first cost and the results of each pair of annual benefit and life. For example, the PW for the combination of high benefit and long life is:

$$\text{PW}_{\$10,000,9} = -25,000 + 10,000(P/A, 10\%, 9) = -25,000 + 10,000(5.759) = \$32,590$$

Annual Benefit	Probability	Life (years)	Probability	Joint Probability	PW
$ 5,000	30%	6	66.7%	20.0%	−$ 3,224
8,000	60	6	66.7	40.0	+9,842
10,000	10	6	66.7	6.7	18,553
5,000	30	9	33.3	10.0	3,795
8,000	60	9	33.3	20.0	21,072
10,000	10	9	33.3	3.3	32,590
				100.0%	

Figure 10-2 shows the probabilities for the PW in the form of a histogram for relative frequency distribution, or probability distribution function.

FIGURE 10-2 Probability distribution function for PW.

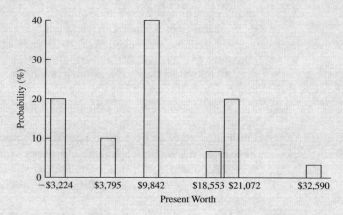

This probability distribution function shows that there is a 20% chance of having a negative PW. It also shows that there is a small (3.3%) chance of the PW being $32,590. The three values used to describe possible annual benefits for the project and the two values for life have been combined to describe the uncertainty in the project's PW.

Creating a distribution, as in Example 10-6, gives us a much better understanding of the possible PW values along with their probabilities. The three possibilities for the annual benefit and the two for the life are representative of the much broader set of possibilities that really exist. Optimistic, most likely, and pessimistic values are a good way to represent the uncertainty about a variable.

Similarly the six values for the PW represent the much broader set of possibilities. The 20% probability of a negative PW is one measure of risk that we will talk about later in the chapter.

Some problems, such as Examples 10-3 and 10-4, have so many variables or different outcomes that constructing the joint probability distribution is arithmetically burdensome. If the values in Equation 10-1 are treated as a discrete probability distribution function, the probabilities are 1/6, 2/3, 1/6. With an optimistic, most likely, and pessimistic outcome for each of 4 variables, there are $3^4 = 81$ combinations. In Examples 10-3 and 10-4, the salvage value has only two distinct values, so there are still $3 \times 3 \times 3 \times 2 = 54$ combinations.

When the problem is important enough, the effort to construct the joint probability distribution is worthwhile. It gives the analyst and the decision maker a better understanding of what may happen. It is also needed to calculate measures of a project's risk. While spreadsheets can automate the arithmetic, simulation (described at the end of the chapter) can be a better choice when there are a large number of variables and combinations.

EXPECTED VALUE

For any probability distribution we can compute the **expected value (EV)** or arithmetic average (mean). To calculate the EV, each outcome is weighted by its probability, and the results are summed. This is NOT the simple average or unweighted mean. When the class average on a test is computed, this is an unweighted mean. Each student's test has the same weight. This simple "average" is the one that is shown by the button $\bar{x}$ on many calculators.

The expected value is a weighted average, like a student's grade point average (GPA). To calculate a GPA, the grade in each class is weighted by the number of credits. For the expected value of a probability distribution, the weights are the probabilities.

This is described in Equation 10-5. We saw in Example 10-4, that these expected values can be used to compute a rate of return. They can also be used to calculate a present worth as in Example 10-7.

$$\text{Expected value} = \text{Outcome}_A \times P(A) + \text{Outcome}_B \times P(B) + \cdots \qquad (10\text{-}5)$$

EXAMPLE 10-7

The first cost of the project in Example 10-5 is $25,000. Use the expected values for annual benefits and life to estimate the present worth. Use an interest rate of 10%.

SOLUTION

$$\text{EV}_{\text{benefit}} = 5000(0.3) + 8000(0.6) + 10,000(0.1) = \$7300$$

$$\text{EV}_{\text{life}} = 6(2/3) + 9(1/3) = 7 \text{ years}$$

The PW using these values is

$$\text{PW(EV)} = -25,000 + 7300(P/A, 10\%, 7) = -25,000 + 6500(4.868) = \$10,536$$

[*Note:* This is the present worth of the expected values, PW(EV), not the expected value of the present worth, EV(PW). It is an easy value to calculate that approximates the EV(PW), which will be computed from the joint probability distribution found in Example 10-6.]

Example 10-7 is a simple way to approximate the project's expected PW. But the true expected value of the PW is somewhat different. To find it, we must use the joint probability distribution for benefit and life, and the resulting probability distribution function for PW that was derived in Example 10-6. Example 10-8 shows the expected value of the PW or the EV(PW).

EXAMPLE 10-8

Use the probability distribution function of the PW that was derived in Example 10–6 to calculate the EV(PW). Does this indicate an attractive project?

SOLUTION

The table from Example 10-6 can be reused with one additional column for the weighted values of the PW (= PW × probability). Then, the expected value of the PW is calculated by summing the column of present worth values that have been weighted by their probabilities.

Annual Benefit	Probability	Life (years)	Probability	Joint Probability	PW	PW × Joint Probability
$ 5,000	30%	6	66.7%	20.0%	−$ 3,224	−$ 645
8,000	60	6	66.7	40.0	+9,842	+3,937
10,000	10	6	66.7	6.7	18,553	1,237
5,000	30	9	33.3	10.0	3,795	380
8,000	60	9	33.3	20.0	21,072	4,214
10,000	10	9	33.3	3.3	32,590	1,086
				100.0%	EV(PW) =	$10,209

With an expected PW of $10,209, this is an attractive project. While there is a 20% chance of a negative PW, the possible positive outcomes are larger and more likely. Having analyzed the project under uncertainty, we are much more knowledgeable about the potential result of the decision to proceed.

The $10,209 value is more accurate than the approximate value calculated in Example 10-7. The values differ because PW is a nonlinear function of the life. The more accurate value of $10,209 is lower because the annual benefit values for the longer life are discounted by $1/(1 + i)$ for more years.

In Examples 10-7 and 10-8, the question was whether the project had a positive PW. With two or more alternatives, the criterion would have been to maximize the PW. With equivalent uniform annual costs (EUACs) the goal is to minimize the EUAC. Example 10-9 uses the criterion of minimizing the EV of the EUAC to choose the best height for a dam.

EXAMPLE 10-9

A dam is being considered to reduce river flooding. But if a dam is built, what height should it be? Increasing the dam's height will (1) reduce a flood's probability, (2) reduce the damage when floods occur, and (3) cost more. Which dam height minimizes the expected total annual cost? The state uses an interest rate of 5% for flood protection projects, and all the dams should last 50 years.

Dam Height (ft)	First Cost	Annual P (flood) > Height	Damages if Flood Occurs
No dam	$ 0	0.25	$800,000
20	700,000	0.05	500,000
30	800,000	0.01	300,000
40	900,000	0.002	200,000

SOLUTION

The easiest way to solve this problem is to choose the dam height with the lowest equivalent uniform annual cost (EUAC). Calculating the EUAC of the first cost requires multiplying the first cost by $(A/P, 5\%, 50)$. For example, for the dam 20 ft high, this is $700,000(A/P, 5\%, 50) = \$38,344$.

Calculating the annual expected flood damage cost for each alternative is simplified because the term for the P(no flood) is zero, because the damages for no flood are $0. Thus we need to calculate only the term for flooding. This is done by multiplying the P(flood) times the damages if a flood happens. For example, the expected annual flood damage cost with no levee is $0.25 \times \$800,000$, or $200,000.

Then the EUAC of the first cost and the expected annual flood damage are added together to find the total EUAC for each height. The 30 ft dam is somewhat cheaper than the 40 ft dam.

Dam Height (ft)	EUAC of First Cost	Expected Annual Flood Damages	Total Expected EUAC
No dam	$ 0	$200,000	$200,000
20	38,344	25,000	63,344
30	43,821	3000	46,821
40	49,299	400	49,699

ECONOMIC DECISION TREES

Some engineering projects are more complex, and evaluating them properly is correspondingly more complex. For example, consider a new product with potential sales volumes ranging from low to high. If the sales volume is low, then the product may be discontinued early in its potential life. On the other hand, if sales volume is high, additional capacity may be added to the assembly line and new product variations may be added. This can be modeled with a decision tree.

The following symbols are used to model decisions with decision trees:

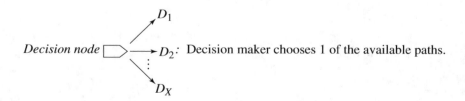

$Decision\ node$ D_2: Decision maker chooses 1 of the available paths.

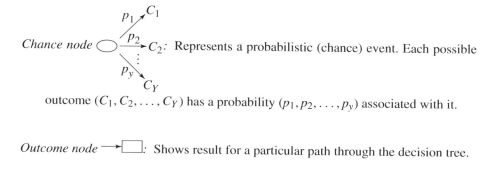

Chance node : Represents a probabilistic (chance) event. Each possible outcome $(C_1, C_2, \ldots, C_Y)$ has a probability $(p_1, p_2, \ldots, p_y)$ associated with it.

Outcome node ⟶▢: Shows result for a particular path through the decision tree.

Pruned branch ⊬➤: The double hash mark indicates that a branch has been pruned because another branch has been chosen. This can happen only at decision nodes, not at chance nodes. The term "pruned" is chosen to correspond to the gardener's practice of trimming or pruning off branches to make a tree or bush healthier.

Figure 10-3 illustrates how decision nodes ▷, chance nodes ◯, and outcome nodes ▢ can be used to describe a problem's structure. Details such as the probabilities and costs can be added on the branches that link the nodes. With the branches from decision and chance nodes, the model becomes a decision tree.

Figure 10-3 illustrates that decision trees describe the problem by starting at the decision that must be made and then adding chance and decision nodes in the proper logical sequence. Thus describing the problem starts at the first step and goes forward in time with sequences of decision and chance nodes.

To make the decision, calculations begin with the final nodes in the tree. Since they are the final nodes, enough information is available to evaluate them. At decision nodes the criterion is either to maximize PW or to minimize EUAC. At chance nodes an expected value for PW or EUAC is calculated.

Once all nodes that branch from a node have been evaluated, the originating node can be evaluated. If the originating node is a decision node, choose the branch with the best PW or EUAC and place that value in the node. If the originating node is a chance node, calculate the expected value and place that value in the node. This process "rolls back" values from the terminal nodes in the tree to the initial decision. Example 10-10 illustrates this.

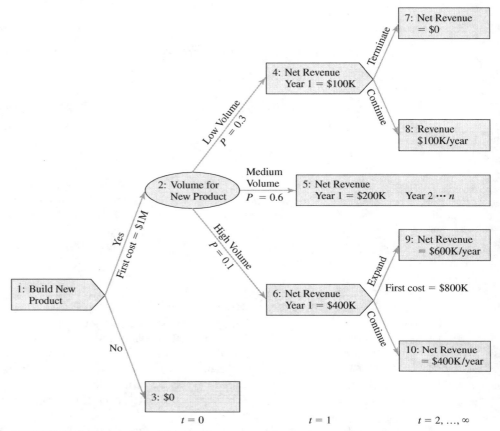

FIGURE 10-3 Economic decision tree for new product.

EXAMPLE 10-10

What decision should be made on the new product summarized in Figure 10-3? What is the expected value of the product's PW? The firm uses an interest rate of 10% to evaluate projects. If the product is terminated after one year, the capital equipment has a salvage value of $550,000 for use with other new products. If the equipment is used for 8 years, the salvage value is $0.

SOLUTION

Evaluating decision trees is done by starting with the end outcome nodes and the decisions that lead to them. In this case the decisions are whether to terminate after 1 year if sales volume is low and whether to expand after 1 year if sales volume is high.

The decision to terminate the product depends on which is more valuable, the equipment's salvage value of $550,000 or the revenue of $100,000 per year for 7 more years. The worth (PW_1) of the salvage value is $550,000. The worth (PW_1) of the revenue stream at the end of Year 1 shown in node 8 is:

$$PW_1 \text{ for node } 8 = 100,000(P/A, 10\%, 7)$$
$$= 100,000(4.868) = \$486,800$$

Thus, terminating the product and using the equipment for other products is better. We enter the two "present worth" values at the end of Year 1 in nodes 7 and 8. We make the *arc to node 7 bold* to indicate that it is our preferred choice at node 4. We use a *double hash mark* to show that we're *pruning the arc to node 8* to indicate that it has been rejected as an inferior choice at node 4.

The decision to expand at node 6 could be based on whether the $800,000 first cost for expansion can be justified based on increasing annual revenues for 7 years by $200,000 per year. However, this is difficult to show on the tree. It is easier to calculate the "present worth" values at the end of Year 1 for each of the two choices. The worth (PW_1) of node 9 (expand) is:

$$PW_1 \text{ for node } 9 = -800,000 + 600,000(P/A, 10\%, 7)$$
$$= -800,000 + 600,000(4.868)$$
$$= \$2,120,800$$

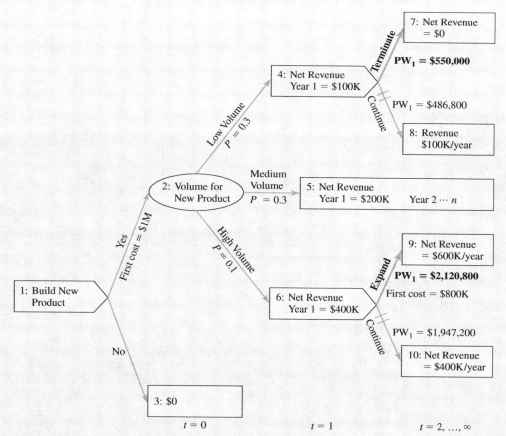

FIGURE 10-4 Partially solved decision tree for new product.

The value of node 10 (continue without expanding) is:

$$PW_1 \text{ for node } 10 = 400{,}000(P/A, 10\%, 7)$$
$$= 400{,}000(4.868)$$
$$= \$1{,}947{,}200$$

This is $173,600 less than the expansion node, so the expansion should happen if volume is high. Figure 10-4 summarizes what we know at this stage of the process.

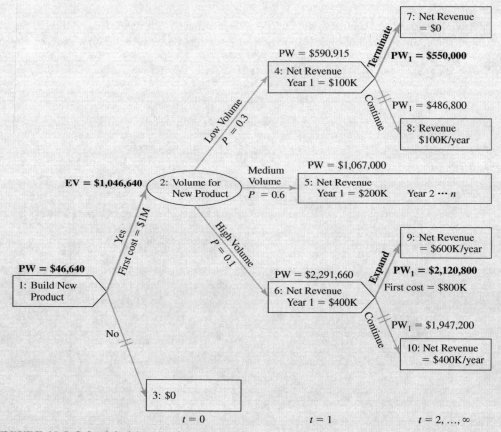

FIGURE 10-5 Solved decision tree for new product.

The next step is to calculate the PW at nodes 4, 5, and 6.

PW at node 4 = $(100{,}000 + 550{,}000)(P/F, 10\%, 1) = 650{,}000(0.9091) = \$590{,}915$

PW at node 5 = $(200{,}000)(P/A, 10\%, 8) = 200{,}000(5.335) = \$1{,}067{,}000$

PW at node 6 = $[400{,}000 - 800{,}000 + 600{,}000(P/A, 10\%, 7)](P/F, 10\%, 1)$

$\qquad = [-400{,}000 + 600{,}000(4.868)](0.9091) = \$2{,}291{,}660$

Now the expected value at node 2 can be calculated

$$\text{EV at node 2} = 0.3(590,915) + 0.6(1,067,000) + 0.1(2,291,660) = \$1,046,640$$

The cost of selecting node 2 is $1,000,000, so proceeding with the product has an expected PW of $46,640. This is greater than the $0 for not building the project. So the decision is to build. Figure 10-5 is the decision tree at the final stage.

Example 10-10 is representative of many problems in engineering economy. The main criterion is maximizing PW or minimizing EUAC. However, as shown in Example 10-11, other criteria, such as risk, are used in addition to expected value.

EXAMPLE 10-11

Consider the economic evaluation of collision and comprehensive (fire, theft, etc.) insurance for a car. This insurance is typically required by lenders, but once the car has been paid for, this insurance is not required. (Liability insurance *is* a legal requirement.)

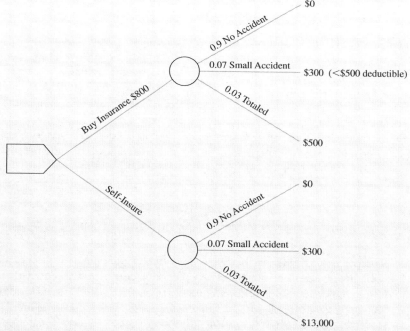

FIGURE 10-6 Decision tree for buying auto collision insurance.

Figure 10-6 begins with a decision node with two alternatives for the next year. Insurance will cost $800 per year with a $500 deductible if a loss occurs. The other option is to self-insure, which means to go without buying collision and comprehensive insurance. Then if a loss occurs, the owner must replace the vehicle with money from savings or a loan, or do without a vehicle until the owner can afford to replace it.

Three accident severities are used to represent the range of possibilities: a 90% chance of no accident, a 7% chance of a small accident (at a cost of $300, which is less than the deductible), and a 3% chance of totaling the $13,000 vehicle. Since our driving habits are likely to be the same with and without insurance, the accident probabilities are the same for both chance nodes.

Even though this is a text on engineering economy, we have simplified the problem and ignored the difference in timing of the cash flows. Insurance payments are made at the beginning of the covered period, and accident costs occur during the covered period. Since car insurance is usually paid semiannually, the results of the economic analysis are not changed significantly by the simplification. We focus on the new concepts of expected value, economic decision trees, and risk.

What are the expected values for each alternative, and what decision is recommended?

SOLUTION

The expected values are computed by using Equation 10-5. If insured, the maximum cost equals the deductible of $500. If self-insured, the cost is the cost of the accident.

$$EV_{\text{accident w/ins.}} = (0.9 \times 0) + (0.07 \times 300) + (0.03 \times 500) = \$36$$

$$EV_{\text{accident w/o ins.}} = (0.9 \times 0) + (0.07 \times 300) + (0.03 \times 13{,}000) = \$411$$

Thus, buying insurance lowers the expected cost of an accident by $375. To evaluate whether we should buy insurance, we must also account for the cost of the insurance. Thus, these expected costs are combined with the $0 for self-insuring (total $411) and the $800 for insuring (total $836). Thus self-insuring has an expected value cost that is $425 less per year ($= \$836 - \$411$). This is not surprising, since the premiums collected must cover both the costs of operating the insurance company and the expected value of the payouts.

This is also an example of *expected values alone not determining the decision*. Buying insurance has an expected cost that is $425 per year higher, but that insurance limits the maximum loss to $500 rather than $13,000. The $425 may be worth spending to avoid that risk.

RISK

Risk can be thought of as the chance of getting an outcome other than the expected value— with an emphasis on something negative. One common measure of risk is the probability of a loss (see Example 10-6). The other common measure is the **standard deviation** (σ), which measures the dispersion of outcomes about the expected value. For example, many students have used the normal distribution in other classes. The normal distribution has 68% of its probable outcomes within ± 1 standard deviation of the mean and 95% within ± 2 standard deviations of the mean.

Mathematically, the standard deviation is defined as the square root of the variance. This term is defined as the weighted average of the squared difference between the outcomes of the random variable X and its mean. Thus the larger the difference between the mean and the values, the larger are the standard deviation and the variance. This is Equation 10-6:

$$\text{Standard deviation } (\sigma) = \sqrt{[EV(X - \text{mean})^2]} \tag{10-6}$$

Squaring the differences between individual outcomes and the EV ensures that positive and negative deviations receive positive weights. Consequently, negative values for the standard deviation are impossible, and they instantly indicate arithmetic mistakes. The standard deviation equals 0 if only one outcome is possible. Otherwise, the standard deviation is positive.

This is not the standard deviation formula built into most calculators, just as the weighted average is not the simple average built into most calculators. The calculator formulas are for N equally likely data points from a randomly drawn sample, so that each probability is $1/N$. In economic analysis we will use a weighted average for the squared deviations since the outcomes are not equally likely.

The second difference is that for calculations (by hand or the calculator), it is easier to use Equation 10-7, which is shown to be equivalent to Equation 10-6 in introductory probability and statistics texts.

$$\text{Standard deviation } (\sigma) = \sqrt{\{EV(X^2) - [EV(X)]^2\}} \tag{10-7}$$

$$= \sqrt{\{\text{Outcome}_A^2 \times P(A) + \text{Outcome}_B^2 \times P(B) + \cdots - \text{expected value}^2\}} \tag{10-7'}$$

This equation is the square root of the difference between the average of the squares and the square of the average. The standard deviation is used instead of the *variance* because the standard deviation is measured in the same units as the expected value. The variance is measured in "squared dollars"—whatever they are.

The calculation of a standard deviation by itself is only a descriptive statistic of limited value. However, as shown in the next section on risk/return trade-offs, it is useful when the standard deviation of each alternative is calculated and these results are compared. But first, some examples of calculating the standard deviation.

EXAMPLE 10-12   (Example 10-11 continued)

Consider the economic evaluation of collision and comprehensive (fire, theft, etc.) insurance for an auto. One example was described in Figure 10-6. The probabilities and outcomes are summarized in the calculation of the expected values, which was done using Equation 10–5.

$$EV_{\text{accident w/ins.}} = (0.9 \times 0) + (0.07 \times 300) + (0.03 \times 500) = \$36$$

$$EV_{\text{accident w/o ins.}} = (0.9 \times 0) + (0.07 \times 300) + (0.03 \times 13{,}000) = \$411$$

Calculate the standard deviations for insuring and not insuring.

SOLUTION

The first step is to calculate the EV(outcome^2) for each.

$$EV^2_{\text{accident w/ins.}} = (0.9 \times 0^2) + (0.07 \times 300^2) + (0.03 \times 500^2) = 13,800$$

$$EV^2_{\text{accident w/o ins.}} = (0.9 \times 0^2) + (0.07 \times 300^2) + (0.03 \times 13,000^2) = 5,076,300$$

Then the standard deviations can be calculated.

$$\sigma_{\text{w/ins.}} = \sqrt{EV^2_{\text{w/ins.}} - (EV_{\text{w/ins.}})^2}$$

$$= \sqrt{(13,800 - 36^2)} = \sqrt{12,504} = \$112$$

$$\sigma_{\text{w/o ins.}} = \sqrt{EV^2_{\text{w/o ins.}} - (EV_{\text{w/o ins.}})^2}$$

$$= \sqrt{(5,076,300 - 411^2)} = \sqrt{4,907,379} = \$2215$$

As described in Example 10-11, the expected value cost of insuring is \$836 (= \$36+\$800) and the expected value cost of self-insuring is \$411. Thus the expected cost of not insuring is about half the cost of insuring. But the standard deviation of self-insuring is 20 times larger. It is clearly riskier.

Which choice is preferred depends on how much risk one is comfortable with.

As stated before, this is an example of *expected values alone not determining the decision.* Buying insurance has an expected cost that is \$425 per year higher, but that insurance limits the maximum loss to \$500 rather than \$13,000. The \$425 may be worth spending to avoid that risk.

EXAMPLE 10-13   (Example 10-6 continued)

Using the probability distribution for the PW from Example 10–6, calculate the PW's standard deviation.

SOLUTION

The following table adds a column for (PW^2) (probability) to calculate the EV(PW^2).

Annual Benefit	Probability	Life (years)	Probability	Joint Probability	PW	PW × Probability	PW^2 × Probability
\$ 5,000	30%	6	66.7%	20.0%	−\$ 3,224	−\$ 645	\$ 2,079,480
8,000	60	6	66.7	40.0	+9,842	+3,937	38,747,954
10,000	10	6	66.7	6.7	18,553	1,237	22,950,061
5,000	30	9	33.3	10.0	3,795	380	1,442,100
8,000	60	9	33.3	20.0	21,072	4,214	88,797,408
10,000	10	9	33.3	3.3	32,590	1,086	35,392,740
					EV	\$10,209	\$189,409,745

$$\text{Standard deviation} = \sqrt{\{EV(X^2) - [EV(X)]^2\}}$$

$$\sigma = \sqrt{\{189,405,745 - [10,209]^2\}} = \sqrt{85,182,064} = \$9229$$

For those with stronger backgrounds in probability than this chapter assumes, let us consider how the standard deviation in Example 10-13 depends on the assumption of independence between the variables. While exceptions exist, a positive statistical dependence between variables often increases the PW's standard deviation. Similarly, a negative statistical dependence between variables often decreases the PW's standard deviation.

RISK VERSUS RETURN

A graph of risk versus return is one way to consider these items together. Figure 10-7 in Example 10-14 illustrates the most common format. Risk measured by standard deviation is placed on the x axis, and return measured by expected value is placed on the y axis. This is usually done with the internal rates of return of the alternatives or projects.

EXAMPLE 10-14

A large firm is discontinuing an older product, so some facilities are becoming available for other uses. The following table summarizes eight new projects that would use the facilities. Considering expected return and risk, which projects are good candidates? The firm believes it can earn 4% on a risk-free investment in government securities (labeled as Project F).

Project	IRR	Standard Deviation
1	13.1%	6.5%
2	12.0	3.9
3	7.5	1.5
4	6.5	3.5
5	9.4	8.0
6	16.3	10.0
7	15.1	7.0
8	15.3	9.4
F	4.0	0.0

SOLUTION

Answering the question is far easier if we use Figure 10-7. Since a larger expected return is better, we want to select projects that are as "high up" as possible. Since a lower risk is better, we want to select projects that are as "far left" as possible. The graph lets us examine the trade-off of accepting more risk for a higher return.

FIGURE 10-7 Risk-versus-return graph.

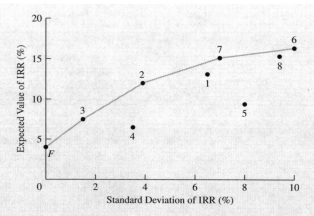

First, we can eliminate Projects 4 and 5. They are **dominated projects.** Dominated alternatives are no better than another alternative on all measures and inferior on at least one measure. Project 4 is dominated by Project 3, which has a higher expected return and a lower risk. Project 5 is dominated by Projects 1, 2, and 7. All three have a higher expected return and a lower risk.

Second, we look at the **efficient frontier.** This is the blue line in Figure 10-7 that connects Projects F, 3, 2, 7, and 6. Depending on the trade-off that we want to make between risk and return, any of these could be the best choice.

Project 1 appears to be inferior to Projects 2 and 7. Project 8 appears to be inferior to Projects 7 and 6. Projects 1 and 8 are inside and not on the efficient frontier.

There are models of risk and return that can allow us to choose between Projects F, 3, 2, 7, and 6; but those models are beyond what is covered here.

There is a simple rule of thumb for comparing a project's risk and return for which we would like to thank Joe Hartman. If the expected present worth is at least double the standard deviation of the present worth, then the project is relatively *safe*. For comparison, remember that a normal distribution has about 2.5% of its values less than 2 standard deviations below the mean.

SIMULATION

Simulation is a more advanced approach to considering risk in engineering economy problems. As such, the following discussion focuses on what it is. As the examples show, spreadsheet functions and add-in packages make simulation easier to use for economic analysis.

Economic **simulation** uses random sampling from the probability distributions of one or more variables to analyze an economic model for many iterations. For each iteration, all variables with a probability distribution are randomly sampled. These values are used to calculate the PW, IRR, or EUAC. Then the results of all iterations are combined to create a probability distribution for the PW, IRR, or EUAC.

Simulation can be done by hand, using a table of random numbers—if there are only a few random variables and iterations. However, results are more reliable as the number of iterations increases, so in practice this is usually computerized. This can be done in Excel using the RAND() function to generate random numbers, as shown in Example 10–15.

Because we were analyzing each possible outcome, the probability distributions earlier in this chapter (and in the end-of-chapter problems) used two or three discrete outcomes.

This limited the number of combinations that we needed to consider. Simulation makes it easy to use continuous probability distributions like the uniform, normal, exponential, log normal, binomial, and triangular. Examples 10-15 and 10-16 use the normal and the discrete uniform distributions.

EXAMPLE 10-15

ShipM4U is considering installing a new, more accurate scale, which will reduce the error in computing postage charges and save $250 a year. The scale's useful life is believed to be uniformly distributed over 12, 13, 14, 15, and 16 years. The initial cost of the scale is estimated to be normally distributed with a mean of $1500 and a standard deviation of $150.

FIGURE 10-8 Excel spreadsheet for simulation ($N = 25$).

	A	B	C	D
1	250	Annual Savings		
2		Life	First Cost	
3	Min	12	1500	Mean
4	Max	16	150	Std dev
5				
6	Iteration			IRR
7	1	12	1277	16.4%
8	2	15	1546	13.9%
9	3	12	1523	12.4%
10	4	16	1628	13.3%
11	5	14	1401	15.5%
12	6	12	1341	15.2%
13	7	12	1683	10.2%
14	8	14	1193	19.2%
15	9	15	1728	11.7%
16	10	12	1500	12.7%
17	11	16	1415	16.0%
18	12	12	1610	11.2%
19	13	15	1434	15.4%
20	14	12	1335	15.4%
21	15	14	1468	14.5%
22	16	13	1469	13.9%
23	17	14	1409	15.3%
24	18	15	1484	14.7%
25	19	14	1594	12.8%
26	20	15	1342	16.8%
27	21	14	1309	17.0%
28	22	12	1541	12.1%
29	23	16	1564	14.0%
30	24	13	1590	12.2%
31	25	16	1311	17.7%
32				
33	Mean	14	1468	14.4%
34	Std dev	2	135	2.2%

Use Excel to simulate 25 random samples of the problem and compute the rate of return for each sample. Construct a graph of rate of return versus frequency of occurrence.

SOLUTION

This problem is simple enough to construct a table with each iteration's values of the life and the first cost. From these values and the annual savings of $250, the IRR for each iteration can be calculated using the RATE function. These are shown in Figure 10-8. The IRR values are summarized in a relative frequency diagram in Figure 10-9.

Note: Each time Excel recalculates the spreadsheet, different values for all the random numbers are generated. Thus the results depend on the set of random numbers, and your results will be different if you create this spreadsheet.

Note for students who have had a course in probability and statistics: Creating the random values for life and first cost is done as follows. Select a random number in [0, 1) using Excel's RAND function. This is the value of the cumulative distribution function for the variable. Convert this to the variable's value by using an inverse function from Excel, or build the inverse function. For the discrete uniform life, the function is = min life + INT(range∗ RAND()). For the normally distributed first cost, the functions is = NORMINV(RAND(), mean, standard deviation).

FIGURE 10-9 Graph of IRR values.

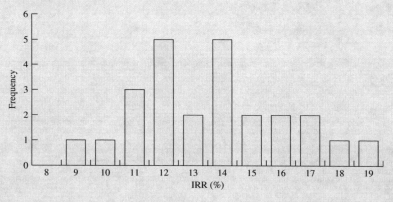

Stand-alone simulation programs and commercial spreadsheet add-in packages such as @Risk and Crystal Ball provide probability distribution functions to use for each input variable. In Example 10-16 the functions RiskUniform and RiskNormal are used. The packages also collect values for the output variables, such as the IRR for Example 10-16. In other problems the PW or EUAC could be collected. These values form a probability distribution for the PW, IRR, or EUAC. From this distribution the simulation package can calculate the expected return, P(loss), and the standard deviation of the return.

Example 10-16 uses @Risk to simulate 1000 iterations of PW for the data in Example 10-15. A simulation package makes it easy to do more iterations. More important still, since it is much easier to use different probability distributions and parameters, more accurate models can be built. Because the models are easier to build, they are less likely to contain errors.

EXAMPLE 10-16

Consider the scale described in Example 10-15. Generate 1000 iterations and construct a frequency distribution for the scale's rate of return.

SOLUTION

The first IRR (cell A8) of 14.01% that is computed in Figure 10-10 is based on the average life and the average first cost. The second IRR (cell A11) of 14.01% is computed by @Risk using the average of each distribution. The cell *content* is the RATE formula with its RiskUniform and RiskNormal function, however spreadsheets with @Risk functions *display* by default the results of using average values.

The RATE function contains two @Risk functions: RiskUniform and RiskNormal. The uniform distribution has the minimum and maximum values as parameters. The normal distribution has the average and standard deviation as parameters.

The third IRR (cell A13) is the average for 1000 iterations. It will change each time the simulation is done. The graph in Figure 10-10 with 1000 iterations is much smoother than Figure 10-9, the graph from Example 10-15, where 25 iterations were done.

FIGURE 10-10 Simulation spreadsheet for Examples 10-15 and 10-16.

	A	B	C	D	E	F
1	−1500	average first cost				
2	150	standard deviation of first cost				
3	12	minimum value of life				
4	16	maximum value of life				
5	250	annual benefit				
6						
7		IRR computed using averages				
8	14.01%	= RATE ((A3+A4)/2,A5,A1)				
9						
10		IRR for each simulation iteration				
11	14.01%	= RATE(RiskUniform(A3,A4),A5,RiskNormal(A1,A2))				
12						
13	14.15%	= average value of A11 (IRR) from 1000 iterations				
14	2.17%	= standard deviation of A11 (IRR) from 1000 iterations				
15						
16		**Distribution for IRR (cell A11)**				
17						
18						
19						
20						
21						
22						
23						
24						
25						
26						
27						
28						

REAL OPTIONS

Real-options analysis is another approach for evaluating projects with significant future uncertainties. It is derived from the theory underlying financial options in the stock market. Rather than buying or selling a share of stock, the option gives you the right to buy or sell the stock at a given price for a given period. Since the option costs less than the stock, a $1000 investment in options has more potential gain than the same investment in the stock. It also has more risk. For engineering projects, a real option is an alternative that keeps open the opportunity by delaying the decision.

For an intuitive understanding of why real options make sense, consider the example of a lease for gas and oil development rights. Many such projects are never developed because they are not "economic." Nevertheless, it may make sense to renew the lease for a noneconomic project because of the possibility that the project will *become* economically profitable. For example, prices may rise, or pipelines and facilities may be built to support a nearby tract.

The models and assumptions of real options are beyond the scope of this text. Interested readers are referred to the third edition of the advanced text *Economic Analysis of Industrial Projects* by Eschenbach, Hartman, and Bussey (2009); the chapter on real options is coauthored by Neal Lewis.

These options may include delaying, abandoning, expanding, shrinking, changing, and replicating a project—with different models for different actions. However, some suggested guidelines may help you decide when you should consider applying real options to your project analysis.

- The value of exercising an option cannot be negative, since you can choose not to exercise it.
- An option to delay a project is valuable when the project is not currently economic but may become economic. Thus, if a project's present worth is positive or very negative, a delay option is unlikely to be worthwhile.
- Unlike projects, options become more valuable as risk (described as volatility) increases. For projects, we want more return but less risk. However, options are more likely to be worthwhile and to result in action if the risk increases.
- Many published examples of real-options analysis ignore the cost of waiting, but this is rarely appropriate for engineering projects. For example, if an R&D project, a new product, or a new building is delayed, then it will later face more competition, and during the period of delay there are no revenues or cost savings since the project is not yet operating.

SUMMARY

Estimating the future is required for economic analysis, and there are several ways to do this. Precise estimates will not ordinarily be exactly correct, but they are considered to be the best single values to represent what we think will happen.

A simple way to represent uncertainty is through a range of estimates for each variable, such as optimistic, most likely, and pessimistic. The full range of prospective results may be examined by using the optimistic values to solve the problem and then using the pessimistic values. Solving the problem with the most likely values is a good single value estimate. However, the extremes with all optimistic values or all pessimistic values are less likely—it is more likely that a mix of optimistic, most likely, and pessimistic values will occur.

One approach uses weighted values instead of a range of estimates. One set of weights suggested is:

Estimate	Relative Weight
Optimistic	1
Most likely	4
Pessimistic	1

The most commonly used approach for decision making relies on **expected values.** Here, known or estimated probabilities for future events are used as weights for the corresponding outcomes.

$$\text{Expected value} = \text{Outcome}_A \times \text{Probability}_A + \text{Outcome}_B \times \text{Probability}_B + \cdots$$

Expected value is the most useful and the most frequently used technique for estimating a project's attractiveness.

However, risk as measured by standard deviation and the probability of a loss is also important in evaluating projects. Since projects with higher expected returns also frequently have higher risk, evaluating the trade-offs between risk and return is useful in decision making.

More complicated problems can be summarized and analyzed by using decision trees, which allow logical evaluation of problems with sequential chance, decision, and outcome nodes.

Where the elements of an economic analysis are stated in terms of probability distributions, a repetitive analysis of a random sample is often done. This simulation-based approach relies on the premise that a random sampling of increasing size becomes a better and better estimate of the possible outcomes. The large number of computations means that simulation is usually computerized.

PROBLEMS

Range of Estimates

10-1 Telephone poles exemplify items that have varying useful lives. Telephone poles, once installed in a location, remain in useful service until one of a variety of events occur.

(*a*) Name three reasons why a telephone pole might be removed from useful service at a particular location.

(*b*) You are to estimate the total useful life of telephone poles. If the pole is removed from an original location while it is still serviceable, it will be installed elsewhere. Estimate the optimistic life, most likely life, and pessimistic life for telephone poles. What percentage of all telephone poles would you expect to have a total useful life greater than your estimated optimistic life?

10-2 The purchase of a used pickup for $9000 is being considered. Records for other vehicles show that costs for oil, tires, and repairs about equal the cost for fuel.

Fuel costs are $990 per year if the truck is driven 10,000 miles. The salvage value after 5 years of use drops about 8¢ per mile. Find the equivalent uniform annual cost if the interest rate is 8%. How much does this change if the annual mileage is 15,000? 5000?

10-3   A heat exchanger is being installed as part of a plant modernization program. It costs $80,000, including installation, and is expected to reduce the overall plant fuel cost by $20,000 per year. Estimates of the useful life of the heat exchanger range from an optimistic 12 years to a pessimistic 4 years. The most likely value is 5 years. Assume the heat exchanger has no salvage value at the end of its useful life.

(a) Determine the pessimistic, most likely, and optimistic rates of return.

(b) Using the range of estimates to compute the mean life, determine the estimated before-tax rate of return.

10-4   For the data in Problem 10-2 assume that the 5000, 10,000, and 15,000 mileage values are, respectively, pessimistic, most likely, and optimistic estimates. Use a weighted estimate to calculate the equivalent annual cost.

10-5   A new engineer is evaluating whether to use a higher-voltage transmission line. It will cost $250,000 more initially, but it will reduce transmission losses. The optimistic, most likely, and pessimistic projections for annual savings are $20,000, $15,000, and $8,000. The interest rate is 6%, and the transmission line should have a life of 30 years.

(a) What is the present worth for each estimated value?

(b) Use the range of estimates to compute the mean annual savings, and then determine the present worth.

(c) Does the answer to (b) match the present worth for the most likely value? Why or why not?

Probabilities

10-6   When a pair of dice are tossed, the results may be any whole number from 2 through 12. In the game of craps one can win by tossing either a 7 or an 11 on the first roll. What is the probability of doing this? (*Hint:* There are 36 ways that a pair of six-sided dice can be tossed. What portion of them result in either a 7 or an 11?)   (*Answer:* $8/36$)

10-7   Over the last 10 years, the hurdle or discount rate for projects from the firm's research and development division has been 10% twice, 15% three times, and 20% the rest of the time. There is no recognizable pattern. Calculate the probability distribution for next year's discount rate.

10-8   The construction time for a bridge depends on the weather. The project is expected to take 250 days if the weather is dry and hot. If the weather is damp and cool, the project is expected to take 350 days. Otherwise, it is expected to take 300 days. Historical data suggest that the probability of cool, damp weather is 30% and that of dry, hot weather is 20%. Find the project's probability distribution.

10-9   You recently had an auto accident that was your fault. If you have another accident or receive a another moving violation within the next 3 years, you will become part of the "assigned risk" pool, and you will pay an extra $600 per year for insurance. If the probability of an accident or moving violation is 20% per year, what is the probability distribution of your "extra" insurance payments over the next 4 years? Assume that insurance is purchased annually and that violations register at the end of the year—just in time to affect next year's insurance premium.

10-10   Al took a midterm examination in physics and received a score of 65. The mean was 60 and the standard deviation was 20. Bill received a score of 14 in mathematics, where the exam mean was 12 and the standard deviation was 4. Which student ranked higher in his class? Explain.

Joint Probabilities

10-11   A project has a life of 10 years, and no salvage value. The firm uses an interest rate of 12% to evaluate engineering projects. The project has an uncertain first cost and net revenue.

First Cost	P	Net Revenue	P
$300,000	0.2	$70,000	0.3
400,000	0.5	90,000	0.5
600,000	0.3	100,000	0.2

(a) What is the joint probability distribution for first cost and net revenue?

(b) Define optimistic, most likely, and pessimistic scenarios by using both optimistic, both most likely, and both pessimistic estimates. What is the present worth for each scenario?

P
0.3
0.5
0.2

10-12 A robot has just been installed at a cost of $81,000. It will have no salvage value at the end of its useful life.

Savings per Year	Probability	Useful Life (years)	Probability
$18,000	0.2	12	1/6
20,000	0.7	5	2/3
22,000	0.1	4	1/6

(a) What is the joint probability distribution for savings per year and useful life?

(b) Define optimistic, most likely, and pessimistic scenarios by using both optimistic, both most likely, and both pessimistic estimates. What is the rate of return for each scenario?

10-13 Modifying an assembly line has a first cost of $80,000, and its salvage value is $0. The firm's interest rate is 9%. The savings shown in the table depend on whether the assembly line runs one, two, or three shifts, and on whether the product is made for 3 or 5 years.

Shifts/ day	Savings/ year	Probability	Useful Life (years)	Probability
1	$15,000	0.3	3	0.6
2	30,000	0.5	5	0.4
3	45,000	0.2		

(a) Give the joint probability distribution for savings per year and the useful life.

(b) Define optimistic, most likely, and pessimistic scenarios by using both optimistic, both most likely, and both pessimistic estimates. Use a life of 4 years as the most likely value. What is the present worth for each scenario?

Expected Value

10-14 Annual savings due to an energy efficiency project have a most likely value of $30,000. The high estimate of $40,000 has a probability of 0.2, and the low estimate of $20,000 has a probability of 0.30. What is the expected value for the annual savings? (*Answer:* $29,000)

10-15 Two instructors announced that they "grade on the curve," that is, give a fixed percentage of each of the various letter grades to each of their classes. Their curves are as follows:

Grade	Instructor A	Instructor B
A	10%	15%
B	15	15
C	45	30
D	15	20
F	15	20

If a random student came to you and said that his object was to enroll in the class in which he could expect the higher grade point average, which instructor would you recommend? (*Answer:* $GPA_B = 1.95$, Instructor A)

10-16 For the data in Problem 10-7, compute the expected value for the next year's discount rate.

10-17 For the data in Problem 10-8, compute the project's expected completion time.

10-18 A man wants to decide whether to invest $1000 in a friend's speculative venture. He will do so if he thinks he can get his money back in one year. He believes the probabilities of the various outcomes at the end of one year are as follows:

Result	Probability
$2000 (double his money)	0.3
1500	0.1
1000	0.2
500	0.3
0 (lose everything)	0.1

What would be his expected outcome if he invests the $1000?

10-19 The MSU football team has 10 games scheduled for next season. The business manager wishes to estimate how much money the team can be expected to have left over after paying the season's expenses, including any postseason "bowl game" expenses. From records for the past season and estimates by informed people, the business manager has assembled the following data:

Situation	Prob-ability	Situation	Net Income
Regular season		Regular season	
Win 3 games	0.10	Win 5 or	$250,000
Win 4 games	0.15	fewer	
Win 5 games	0.20	games	
Win 6 games	0.15	Win 6 to 8	400,000
Win 7 games	0.15	games	
Win 8 games	0.10		
Win 9 games	0.07	Win 9 or 10	600,000
Win 10 games	0.03	games	
Postseason		Postseason	Additional
Bowl game	0.10	Bowl game	income of
			$100,000

What is the expected net income for the team next season?   (*Answer:* $355,000)

10-20 In the New Jersey and Nevada gaming casinos, craps is a popular gambling game. One of the many bets available is the "Hard-way 8." A $1 bet in this fashion will win the player $4 if in the game the pair of dice come up 4 and 4 before one of the other ways of totaling 8. For a $1 bet, what is the expected result? (*Answer:* 80¢)

10-21 A man went to Atlantic City with $500 and placed 100 bets of $5 each, one after another, on the same number on the roulette wheel. There are 38 numbers on the wheel and the gaming casino pays 35 times the amount bet if the ball drops into the bettor's numbered slot in the roulette wheel. In addition, the bettor receives back the original $5 bet. Estimate how much money the man is expected to win or lose in Atlantic City.

10-22 For the data in Problems 10-2 and 10-4, assume that the optimistic probability is 20%, the most likely is 50%, and the pessimistic is 30%.

(*a*) What is the expected value of the equivalent uniform annual cost?

(*b*) Compute the expected value for the number of miles, and the corresponding equivalent uniform annual cost.

(*c*) Do the answers to (*a*) and (*b*) match? Why or why not?

10-23 For the data in Problem 10-3, assume that the optimistic probability is 15%, the most likely is 80%, and the pessimistic is 5%.

(*a*) What is the expected value of the rate of return?

(*b*) Compute the expected value for the life, and the corresponding rate of return.

(*c*) Do the answers to (*a*) and (*b*) match? Why or why not?

10-24 For the data in Problem 10-5, assume that the optimistic probability is 20%, the most likely is 50%, and the pessimistic is 30%.

(*a*) What is the expected value of the present worth?

(*b*) Compute the expected value for annual savings, and the corresponding present worth.

(*c*) Do the answers to (*a*) and (*b*) match? Why or why not?

10-25 The energy efficiency project described in Problem 10-14 has a first cost of $150,000, a life of 10 years, and no salvage value. Assume that the interest rate is 8%.

(*a*) What is the equivalent uniform annual worth for the expected annual savings?

(*b*) Compute the equivalent uniform annual worth for the pessimistic, most likely, and optimistic estimates of the annual savings. What is the expected value of the equivalent uniform annual worth?

(*c*) Do the answers to (*a*) and (*b*) match? Why or why not?

10-26 An industrial park is being planned for a tract of land near the river. To prevent flood damage to the industrial buildings that will be built on this low-lying land, an earthen embankment can be constructed. The height of the embankment will be determined by an economic analysis of the costs and benefits. The following data have been gathered.

Embankment Height Above Roadway (m)	Initial Cost
2.0	$100,000
2.5	165,000
3.0	300,000
3.5	400,000
4.0	550,000

Flood Level Above Roadway (m)	Average Frequency That Flood Level Will Exceed Height in Col. 1
2.0	Once in 3 years
2.5	Once in 8 years
3.0	Once in 25 years
3.5	Once in 50 years
4.0	Once in 100 years

The embankment can be expected to last 50 years and will require no maintenance. Whenever the flood water flows over the embankment, $300,000 of damage occurs. Should the embankment be built? If so, to which of the five heights above the roadway? A 12% rate of return is required.

10-27 If your interest rate is 8%, what is the expected value of the present worth of the "extra" insurance payments in Problem 10-9? (*Answer:* $528.7)

10-28 Should the project in problem 10-11 be undertaken, if the firm uses an expected value of present worth to evaluate engineering projects?

(*a*) Compute the PW for each combination of first cost and revenue and the corresponding expected worth.

(*b*) What are the expected first cost, expected net revenue, and corresponding present worth of the expected values?

(*c*) Do the answers for (*a*) and (*b*) match? Why or why not?

(*Answer:* (*b*) $45,900, do project).

10-29 For the data in Problem 10–12.

(*a*) What are the expected savings per year, life, and corresponding rate of return for the expected values?

(*b*) Compute the rate of return for each combination of savings per year and life. What is the expected rate of return?

(*c*) Do the answers for (*a*) and (*b*) match? Why or why not?

10-30 For the data in Problem 10-13.

(*a*) What are the expected savings per year, life, and corresponding present worth for the expected values?

(*b*) Compute the present worth for each combination of savings per year and life. What is the expected present worth?

(*c*) Do the answers for (*a*) and (*b*) match? Why or why not?

Decision Trees

10-31 A decision has been made to perform certain repairs on the outlet works of a small dam. For a particular 36-inch gate valve, there are three available alternatives:

A. Leave the valve as it is.

B. Repair the valve.

C. Replace the valve.

If the valve is left as it is, the probability of a failure of the valve seats, over the life of the project, is 60%; the probability of failure of the valve stem is 50%; and of failure of the valve body is 40%.

If the valve is repaired, the probability of a failure of the seats, over the life of the project, is 40%; of failure of the stem is 30%; and of failure of the body is 20%. If the valve is replaced, the probability of a failure of the seats, over the life of the project, is 30%; of failure of the stem is 20%; and of failure of the body is 10%.

The present worth of cost of future repairs and service disruption of a failure of the seats is $10,000; the present worth of cost of a failure of the stem is $20,000; the present worth of cost of a failure of the body is $30,000. The cost of repairing the valve now is $10,000; and of replacing it is $20,000. If the criterion is to minimize expected costs, which alternative is best?

10-32 A factory building is located in an area subject to occasional flooding by a nearby river. You have been brought in as a consultant to determine whether flood-proofing of the building is economically justified. The alternatives are as follows:

A. Do nothing. Damage in a moderate flood is $10,000 and in a severe flood, $25,000.

B. Alter the factory building at a cost of $15,000 to withstand moderate flooding without damage and to withstand severe flooding with $10,000 damages.

C. Alter the factory building at a cost of $20,000 to withstand a severe flood without damage.

In any year the probability of flooding is as follows: 0.70, no flooding of the river; 0.20, moderate flooding; and 0.10, severe flooding. If interest is 15%

and a 15-year analysis period is used, what do you recommend?

10-33 Five years ago a dam was constructed to impound irrigation water and to provide flood protection for the area below the dam. Last winter a 100-year flood caused extensive damage both to the dam and to the surrounding area. This was not surprising, since the dam was designed for a 50-year flood.

The cost to repair the dam now will be $250,000. Damage in the valley below amounts to $750,000. If the spillway is redesigned at a cost of $250,000 and the dam is repaired for another $250,000, the dam may be expected to withstand a 100-year flood without sustaining damage. However, the storage capacity of the dam will not be increased and the probability of damage to the surrounding area below the dam will be unchanged. A second dam can be constructed up the river from the existing dam for $1 million. The capacity of the second dam would be more than adequate to provide the desired flood protection. If the second dam is built, redesign of the existing dam spillway will not be necessary, but the $250,000 of repairs must be done.

The development in the area below the dam is expected to be complete in 10 years. A new 100-year flood in the meantime would cause a $1 million loss. After 10 years the loss would be $2 million. In addition, there would be $250,000 of spillway damage if the spillway is not redesigned. A 50-year flood is also likely to cause about $200,000 of damage, but the spillway would be adequate. Similarly, a 25-year flood would cause about $50,000 of damage.

There are three alternatives: (1) repair the existing dam for $250,000 but make no other alterations, (2) repair the existing dam ($250,000) and redesign the spillway to take a 100-year flood ($250,000), and (3) repair the existing dam ($250,000) and build the second dam ($1 million). Based on an expected annual cash flow analysis, and a 7% interest rate, which alternative should be selected? Draw a decision tree to clearly describe the problem.

10-34 In Problems 10-13 and 10-30, how much is it worth to the firm to be able to extend the product's life by 3 years, at a cost of $50,000, at the end of the product's initial useful life?

Risk

10-35 An engineer decided to make a careful analysis of the cost of fire insurance for his $200,000 home. From a fire rating bureau he found the following risk of fire loss in any year.

Outcome	Probability
No fire loss	0.986
$ 10,000 fire loss	0.010
40,000 fire loss	0.003
200,000 fire loss	0.001

(a) Compute his expected fire loss in any year.

(b) He finds that the expected fire loss in any year is less than the $550 annual cost of fire insurance. In fact, an insurance agent explains that this is always true. Nevertheless, the engineer buys fire insurance. Explain why this is or is not a logical decision.

10-36 The Graham Telephone Company may invest in new switching equipment. There are three possible outcomes, having net present worth of $6570, $8590, and $9730. The outcomes have probabilities of 0.3, 0.5, and 0.2, respectively. Calculate the expected return and risk associated with this proposal. (*Answer:* $E_{PW} = \$8212$, $\sigma_{PW} = \$1158$)

10-37 A new machine will cost $25,000. The machine is expected to last 4 years and have no salvage value. If the interest rate is 12%, determine the return and the risk associated with the purchase.

P	0.3	0.4	0.3
Annual savings	$7000	$8500	$9500

10-38 A new product's chief uncertainty is its annual net revenue. So far, $35,000 has been spent on development, but an additional $30,000 is required to finish development. The firm's interest rate is 10%.

(a) What is the expected PW for deciding whether to proceed?

(b) Find the $P(\text{loss})$ and the standard deviation for proceeding.

	State		
	Bad	**OK**	**Great**
Probability	0.3	0.5	0.2
Net revenue	−$15,000	$15,000	$20,000
Life, in years	5	5	10

10-39 (a) In Problem 10-38 how much is it worth to the firm to terminate the product after 1 year if the net revenues are negative?

(b) How much does the ability to terminate early change the P(loss) and the standard deviation?

10-40 What is your risk associated with Problem 10-27?

10-41 Measure the risk for Problems 10-13 and 10-28 using the P(loss), range of PW values, and standard deviation of the PWs. (*Answer:* σ_{PW} = $127,900)

10-42 (a) In Problems 10-13 and 10-30, describe the risk using the P(loss) and standard deviation of the PWs.

(b) How much do the answers change if the possible life extension in Problem 10-34 is allowed?

Risk versus Return

10-43 A firm wants to select one new research and development project. The following table summarizes six possibilities. Considering expected return and risk, which projects are good candidates? The firm believes it can earn 5% on a risk-free investment in government securities (labeled as Project F).

Project	IRR	Standard Deviation
1	15.8%	6.5%
2	12.0	4.1
3	10.4	6.3
4	12.1	5.1
5	14.2	8.0
6	18.5	10.0
F	5.0	0.0

10-44 A firm is choosing a new product. The following table summarizes six new potential products. Considering expected return and risk, which products are good candidates? The firm believes it can earn 4% on a risk-free investment in government securities (labeled as Product F).

Product	IRR	Standard Deviation
1	10.4%	3.2%
2	9.8	2.3
3	6.0	1.6
4	12.1	3.6
5	12.2	8.0
6	13.8	6.5
F	4.0	0.0

Simulation

10-45 A project's first cost is $25,000, and it has no salvage value. The interest rate for evaluation is 7%. The project's life is from a discrete uniform distribution that takes on the values 7, 8, 9, and 10. The annual benefit is normally distributed with a mean of $4400 and a standard deviation of $1000. Using Excel's RAND function simulate 25 iterations. What are the expected value and standard deviation of the present worth?

10-46 A factory's power bill is $55,000 a year. The first cost of a small geothermal power plant is normally distributed with a mean of $150,000 and a standard deviation of $50,000. The power plant has no salvage value. The interest rate for evaluation is 8%. The project's life is from a discrete uniform distribution that takes on the values 3, 4, 5, 6, and 7. (The life is relatively short due to corrosion.) The annual operating cost is expected to be about $10,000 per year. Using Excel's RAND function, simulate 25 iterations. What are the expected value and standard deviation of the present worth?

CHAPTER 11

DEPRECIATION

Depreciation and Competitiveness

Depreciation sounds like a boring accounting term, but it is part of determining how much every firm pays in taxes. Reducing taxes is a common goal. Depreciation apportions an asset's capital cost into annual deductions from taxable income. Thus, factories, bulldozers, computers, sports stadiums, and even professional baseball players are depreciated. In each case what can be depreciated, and how fast, is linked to a firm's after-tax profits and competitiveness. More and faster depreciation improves competitiveness.

Why is depreciation important to governments? The answer is that depreciation rules and regulations can be crafted to promote specific outcomes such as total revenue received, increased capital investment, and improved employment rates. In 1981 and 1986, the federal government responded to concerns about U.S. firms building plants overseas by changing the tax code to allow depreciation over shorter recovery periods. The tax code was also changed to give capital investments full depreciation, using a salvage value of $0. In 2002 the tax code was again changed by the Job Creation and Worker Assistance Act to allow an additional first year's depreciation of 30% for a 3-year period. This was later amended to increase the added depreciation in the first year to 50% for tax year 2003. This was intended to stimulate the level of investment by firms in capital assets, and thus to create new jobs in the U.S.

Courtesy of the Internal Revenue Service.

QUESTIONS TO CONSIDER

1. How can the importance of depreciation be measured?
2. What are some of the similarities and differences between depreciating a bulldozer and a ballplayer?
3. Is the added first-year depreciation still part of the tax code? How has it changed since it was legislated in 2002?
4. At times legislative bodies have been criticized for using potential changes in the depreciation and tax codes to stimulate lobbying and campaign donations. Is this truly a practical or ethical concern?

After Completing This Chapter...

The student should be able to:

- Describe depreciation, deterioration, and obsolescence.
- Distinguish various types of depreciable property and differentiate between depreciation expenses and other business expenses.
- Use *historical* depreciation methods to calculate the *annual depreciation charge* and *book value* over the asset's life.
- Explain the differences between the historical depreciation methods and the modified accelerated cost recovery system (MACRS).
- Use MACRS to calculate allowable *annual depreciation charge* and *book value* over the asset's life for various cost bases, property classes, and recovery periods.
- Fully account for *capital gains/losses, ordinary losses,* and *depreciation recapture* due to the disposal of a depreciated business asset.
- Use the *units of production* and *depletion* depreciation methods as needed in engineering economic analysis problems.
- Use spreadsheets to calculate depreciation.

W e have so far dealt with a variety of economic analysis problems and many techniques for their solution. In the process we have avoided income taxes, which are an important element in many private sector economic analyses. Now, we move to more realistic—and more complex—situations.

Our government taxes individuals and businesses to support its processes—lawmaking, domestic and foreign economic policy making, even the making and issuing of money itself. The omnipresence of taxes requires that they be included in economic analyses, which means that we must understand the *way* taxes are imposed. For capital equipment, knowledge about depreciation is required to compute income taxes. Chapter 11 examines depreciation, and Chapter 12 illustrates how depreciation and other effects are incorporated in income tax computations. The goal is to support decision making on engineering projects, not to support final tax calculations.

BASIC ASPECTS OF DEPRECIATION

The word **depreciation** is defined as a "decrease in value." This is somewhat ambiguous because *value* has several meanings. In economic analysis, value may refer to either *market value* or *value to the owner.* For example, an assembly line is far more valuable to the manufacturing firm that it was designed for, than it is to a used equipment market. Thus, we now have two definitions of depreciation: a decrease in value to the market or a decrease to the owner.

Deterioration and Obsolescence

A machine may depreciate because it is **deteriorating** or wearing out and no longer performing its function as well as when it was new. Many kinds of machinery require increased maintenance as they age, reflecting a slow but continuing failure of individual parts. In other types of equipment, the quality of output may decline due to wear on components and resulting poorer mating of parts. Anyone who has worked to maintain a car has observed deterioration due to failure of individual parts (such as fan belts, mufflers, and batteries) and the wear on components (such as bearings, piston rings, and alternator brushes).

Depreciation is also caused by **obsolescence.** A machine that is in excellent working condition, and serving a needed purpose, may still be obsolete. In the 1970s, mechanical business calculators with hundreds of gears and levers became obsolete. The advance of integrated circuits resulted in a completely different and far superior approach to calculator design. Thus, mechanical calculators rapidly declined or depreciated in value. Generations of computers have followed this pattern. The continuing stream of newer models makes older ones obsolete.

The accounting profession defines depreciation in yet another way, as allocating an asset's cost over its **useful** or **depreciable life.** Thus, we now have *three distinct definitions of depreciation:*

1. Decline in market value of an asset.
2. Decline in value of an asset to its owner.
3. Systematic allocation of an asset's cost over its depreciable life.

Depreciation and Expenses

It is the third (accountant's) definition that is used to compute depreciation for business assets. Business costs are generally either **expensed** or **depreciated. Expensed** items, such as labor, utilities, materials, and insurance, are part of regular business operations and are "consumed" over short periods of time (sometimes recurring). These costs do not lose value gradually over time. For tax purposes they are subtracted from business revenues when they occur. Expensed costs reduce income taxes because businesses are able to *write off* their full amount when they occur.

In contrast, business costs due to capital assets (buildings, forklifts, chemical plants, etc.) are not fully written off when they occur. Capital assets lose value gradually and must be written off or **depreciated** over an extended period. For instance, consider a injection-molding machine used to produce the plastic beverage cups found at sporting events. The plastic pellets melted into the cup shape lose their value as raw material directly after manufacturing. The raw material cost for production material (plastic pellets) is expensed immediately. On the other hand, the injection-molding machine itself will lose value over time, and thus its costs (purchase price and installation expenses) are written off (or depreciated) over its **depreciable life** or **recovery period.** This is often different from the asset's useful or most economic life. Depreciable life is determined by the depreciation method used to spread out the cost—depreciated assets of many types operate well beyond their depreciable life.

Depreciation is a **noncash** cost that requires no exchange of dollars. Companies do not write a check to someone to **pay** their depreciation expenses. Rather, these are business expenses that are allowed by the government to offset the loss in value of business assets. Remember, the company has paid for assets up front; depreciation is simply a way to claim these "business expenses" over time. Depreciation deductions reduce the taxable income of businesses and thus reduce the amount of taxes paid. Since taxes are cash flows, depreciation must be considered in after-tax economic analysis.

In general, business assets can be depreciated only if they meet the following basic requirements:

1. The property must be used for business purposes to produce income.
2. The property must have a useful life that can be determined, and this life must be longer than one year.
3. The property must be an asset that decays, gets used up, wears out, becomes obsolete, or loses value to the owner from natural causes.

EXAMPLE 11-1

Consider the costs that are incurred by a local pizza business. Identify each cost as either *expensed* or *depreciated* and describe why that term applies.

- Cost for pizza dough and toppings
- Cost to pay wages for janitor
- Cost of a new baking oven
- Cost of new delivery van
- Cost of furnishings in dining room
- Utility costs for soda refrigerator

Cost Item	Type of Cost	Why
Pizza dough and toppings	Expensed	Life < 1 year; lose value immediately
New delivery van	Depreciated	Meets 3 requirements for depreciation
Wages for janitor	Expensed	Life < 1 year; lose value immediately
Furnishings in dining room	Depreciated	Meet 3 requirements for depreciation
New baking oven	Depreciated	Meets 3 requirements for depreciation
Utilities for soda refrigerator	Expensed	Life < 1 year; lose value immediately

Types of Property

The rules for depreciation are linked to the classification of business property as either tangible or intangible. Tangible property is further classified as either real or personal.

Tangible property can be seen, touched, and felt.

Real property includes land, buildings, and all things growing on, built upon, constructed on, or attached to the land.

Personal property includes equipment, furnishings, vehicles, office machinery, and anything that is tangible excluding assets defined as *real property*.

Intangible property is all property that has value to the owner but cannot be directly seen or touched. Examples include patents, copyrights, trademarks, trade names, and franchises.

Many different types of property that wear out, decay, or lose value can be depreciated as business assets. This wide range includes copy machines, helicopters, buildings, interior furnishings, production equipment, and computer networks. Almost all tangible property can be depreciated.

One important and notable exception is land, which is *never* depreciated. Land does not wear out, lose value, or have a determinable useful life and thus does not qualify as a depreciable property. Rather than decreasing in value, most land becomes more valuable as time passes. In addition to the land itself, expenses for clearing, grading, preparing, planting, and landscaping are not generally depreciated because they have no fixed useful life. Other tangible property that *cannot* be depreciated includes factory inventory, containers considered as inventory, and leased property. The leased property exception highlights the fact that only the owner of property may claim depreciation expenses.

Tangible properties used in *both* business and personal activities, such as a vehicle used in a consulting engineering firm that is also used to take one's kids to school, can be depreciated, but only in proportion to the use for business purposes.

Depreciation Calculation Fundamentals

To understand the complexities of depreciation, the first step is to examine the fundamentals of depreciation calculations. Figure 11-1 illustrates the general depreciation problem of allocating the total depreciation charges over the asset's depreciable life. The vertical axis is labeled **book value.** At time zero the curve of book value starts at the cost basis (= the

FIGURE 11-1 General
depreciation.

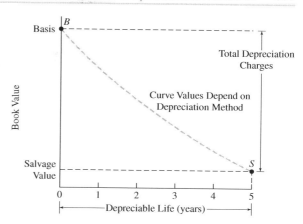

first cost plus installation cost). Over time, the book value declines to the salvage value.
Thus, at any point in time:

Book value = Asset cost − Depreciation charges made to date

Looked at another way, book value is the asset's remaining unallocated cost.

In Figure 11-1, *book value* goes from a value of B at time zero in the recovery period
to a value of S at the end of Year 5. Thus, book value is a *dynamic* variable that changes
over an asset's recovery period. The equation used to calculate an asset's book value over
time is:

$$BV_t = \text{Cost basis} - \sum_{j=1}^{t} d_j \qquad (11\text{-}1)$$

where BV_t = book value of the depreciated asset at the end of time t

Cost basis $= B =$ dollar amount that is being depreciated; this includes the asset's
purchase price as well as any other costs necessary to make the asset "ready
for use"

$\sum_{j=1}^{t} d_j =$ sum of depreciation deductions taken from time 0 to time t, where d_j is the

depreciation deduction in Year j

Equation 11-1 shows that year-to-year depreciation charges reduce an asset's book
value over its life. The following section describes methods that are or have been allowed
under federal tax law for quantifying these yearly depreciation deductions.

HISTORICAL DEPRECIATION METHODS

Allowing businesses to depreciate capital assets has long been part of the tax code. However,
over time various depreciation methods have been used to calculate these deductions. In
general, accounting depreciation methods can be categorized as follows.

Pre-1981 historical methods: These methods include the *straight-line, sum-of-the-
years'-digits,* and *declining balance* methods. Each method required estimates of

an asset's useful life and salvage value. Firms could elect to use any of these methods for assets, and thus there was little uniformity in how depreciation expenses were reported.

1981–1986 method: With the Economic Recovery Tax Act (ERTA) of 1981, Congress created the accelerated cost recovery system (ACRS). The ACRS method had three key features: (1) property class lives were created, and all depreciated assets were assigned to one particular category; (2) the need to estimate salvage values was eliminated because all assets were *fully* depreciated over their recovery period; and (3) shorter recovery periods were used to calculate annual depreciation, which *accelerated* the write-off of capital costs more quickly than did the historical methods—thus the name.

1986 to present: The modified accelerated cost recovery system (MACRS) has been in effect since the Tax Reform Act of 1986 (TRA-86). The MACRS method is similar to the ACRS system except that (1) the number of property classes was expanded and (2) the annual depreciation percentages were modified to include a half-year convention for the first and final years.

In this chapter, our primary focus is to describe the MACRS depreciation method. However, it is useful to first describe three historical depreciation methods. These methods are used in some countries, and MACRS is based on two of them.

Straight-Line Depreciation

The simplest and best known depreciation method is **straight-line depreciation.** To calculate the constant **annual depreciation charge,** the total amount to be depreciated, $B - S$, is divided by the depreciable life, in years, N:[1]

$$\textbf{Annual depreciation charge} = d_t = \frac{B - S}{N} \tag{11-2}$$

EXAMPLE 11-2

Consider the following:

Cost of the asset, B	$900
Depreciable life, in years, N	5
Salvage value, S	$70

Compute the straight-line depreciation schedule.

SOLUTION

$$\textbf{Annual depreciation charge} = d_t = \frac{B - S}{N} = \frac{900 - 70}{5} = \$166$$

---

[1]N is used for the depreciation period because it may be shorter than n, the horizon (or project life).

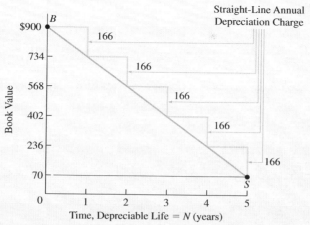

FIGURE 11-2 Straight-line depreciation.

Year,	Depreciation for Year t,	Sum of Depreciation Charges Up to Year t,	Book Value at the End of Year t,
t	d_t	$\sum_{j=1}^{t} d_j$	$BV_t = B - \sum_{j=1}^{t} d_j$
1	$166	$166	$900 - 166 = 734$
2	166	332	$900 - 332 = 568$
3	166	498	$900 - 498 = 402$
4	166	664	$900 - 664 = 236$
5	166	830	$900 - 830 = 70 = S$

This situation is illustrated in Figure 11-2. Notice the constant $166 d_t each year for 5 years, and that the asset has been depreciated down to a book value of $70, which was the estimated salvage value.

The straight-line (SL) method is often used for intangible property. For example, Veronica's firm bought a patent in April that was not acquired as part of acquiring a business. She paid $6800 for this patent and must use the straight-line method to depreciate it over 17 years with no salvage value. The annual depreciation is $400 (=$6800/17). Since the patent was purchased in April, the first year's deduction must be prorated over the 9 months of ownership. This year the deduction is $300 (=$400 × 9/12), and then next year she can begin taking the full $400 per year.

Sum-of-Years'-Digits Depreciation

Another method for allocating an asset's cost *minus* salvage value *over* its depreciable life is called **sum-of-years'-digits (SOYD) depreciation.** This method results in larger-than-straight-line depreciation charges during an asset's early years and smaller charges as the asset nears the end of its depreciable life. Each year, the depreciation charge equals a fraction of the total amount to be depreciated $(B - S)$. The denominator of the fraction is the sum of the years' digits. For example, if the depreciable life is 5 years, $1 + 2 + 3 + 4 + 5 = 15 =$ SOYD. Then $5/15, 4/15, 3/15, 2/15$, and $1/15$ are the fractions from Year 1 to Year 5. Each year the depreciation charge shrinks by $1/15$ of $B - S$. Because this change is the same every year, SOYD depreciation can be modeled as an arithmetic gradient, G. The equations can also be written as

$$\begin{pmatrix} \text{Sum-of-years'-digits} \\ \text{depreciation charge for} \\ \text{any year} \end{pmatrix} = \frac{\begin{pmatrix} \text{Remaining depreciable life} \\ \text{at beginning of year} \end{pmatrix}}{\begin{pmatrix} \text{Sum of years' digits} \\ \text{for total depreciable life} \end{pmatrix}} (\text{Total amount depreciated})$$

$$d_t = \frac{N - t + 1}{\text{SOYD}}(B - S) \tag{11-3}$$

where d_t = depreciation charge in any year t
N = number of years in depreciable life
SOYD = sum of years' digits, calculated as $N(N + 1)/2 = \text{SOYD}$
B = cost of the asset made ready for use
S = estimated salvage value after depreciable life

EXAMPLE 11-3

Compute the SOYD depreciation schedule for the situation in Example 11.2.
Cost of the asset, B	$900
Depreciable life, in years, N	5
Salvage value, S	$70

SOLUTION

$$\text{SOYD} = \frac{5 \times 6}{2} = 15$$

Thus,

$$d_1 = \frac{5 - 1 + 1}{15}(900 - 70) = 277$$

$$d_2 = \frac{5 - 2 + 1}{15}(900 - 70) = 221$$

$$d_3 = \frac{5 - 3 + 1}{15}(900 - 70) = 166$$

$$d_4 = \frac{5 - 4 + 1}{15}(900 - 70) = 111$$

$$d_5 = \frac{5 - 5 + 1}{15}(900 - 70) = 55$$

FIGURE 11-3 Sum-of-years'-digits depreciation.

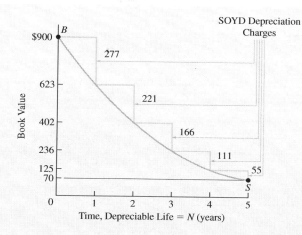

Year, t	Depreciation for Year t, d_t	Sum of Depreciation Charges Up to Year t, $\displaystyle\sum_{j=1}^{t} d_j$	Book Value at End of Year t, $BV_t = B - \displaystyle\sum_{j=1}^{t} d_j$
1	$277	$277	$900 - 277 = 623$
2	221	498	$900 - 498 = 402$
3	166	664	$900 - 664 = 236$
4	111	775	$900 - 775 = 125$
5	55	830	$900 - 830 = 70 = S$

These data are plotted in Figure 11-3.

Declining Balance Depreciation

Declining balance depreciation applies a *constant depreciation rate* to the property's declining book value. Two rates were commonly used before the 1981 and 1986 tax revisions, and they are used to compute MACRS depreciation percentages. These are 150 and 200% of the straight-line rate. Since 200% is twice the straight-line rate, it is called **double declining balance,** or DDB; the general equation is

$$\text{Double declining balance}\quad d_t = \frac{2}{N}(\text{Book value}_{t-1}) \tag{11-4a}$$

Since book value equals cost *minus* depreciation charges to date,

$$\text{DDB}\quad d_t = \frac{2}{N}(\text{Cost} - \text{Depreciation charges to date})$$

or

$$d_t = \frac{2}{N}\left(B - \sum_{j=1}^{t-1} d_j\right) \tag{11-4b}$$

EXAMPLE 11-4

Compute the DDB depreciation schedule for the situations in Examples 11-2 and 11-3.

Cost of the asset, B	$900
Depreciable life, in years, N	5
Salvage value, S	$70

SOLUTION

Year, t	Depreciation for Year t Using Equation 11-4a, d_t	Sum of Depreciation Charges Up to Year t, $\sum_{j=1}^{t} d_j$	Book Value at End of Year t, $BV_t = B - \sum_{j=1}^{t} d_j$
1	$(2/5)900 = 360$	$360	$900 - 360 = 540$
2	$(2/5)540 = 216$	576	$900 - 576 = 324$
3	$(2/5)324 = 130$	706	$900 - 706 = 194$
4	$(2/5)194 = 78$	784	$900 - 784 = 116$
5	$(2/5)116 = 46$	830	$900 - 830 = 70 = S$

Figure 11-4 illustrates the situation.

FIGURE 11-4 Declining balance depreciation.

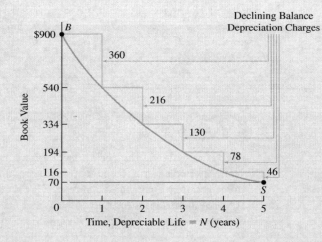

The final salvage value of $70 for Examples 11-2, 11-3, and 11-4 was chosen to match the ending value for the double declining balance method. This does not normally happen. If the final salvage value of Example 11-4 had not been $70, the double declining balance method would have had to be modified. One modification stops further depreciation once the book value has come to equal the salvage value—this prevents taking too much depreciation. The other modification would switch from declining balance depreciation to straight line—this ensures taking enough depreciation.

These modifications are not detailed here because (1) MACRS has been the legally appropriate system since 1986 and (2) MACRS incorporates the shift from declining balance to straight-line depreciation.

MODIFIED ACCELERATED COST RECOVERY SYSTEM (MACRS)

The modified accelerated cost recovery system (MACRS) depreciation method, introduced by the Tax Reform Act of 1986, was continued with the Taxpayer Relief Act of 1997. Three major advantages of MACRS are that (1) the "property class lives" are less than the "actual useful lives," (2) salvage values are assumed to be zero, and (3) tables of annual percentages simplify computations.

The definition of the MACRS classes of depreciable property is based on work by the U.S. Treasury Department. In 1971 the Treasury published guidelines for about 100 broad asset classes. For each class there was a lower limit, a midpoint, and an upper limit of useful life, called the **asset depreciation range (ADR).** The ADR midpoint lives were somewhat shorter than the actual average useful lives. These guidelines have been incorporated into MACRS so that the property class lives are again shorter than the ADR midpoint lives.

Use of MACRS focuses on the general depreciation system (GDS), which is based on declining balance with switch to straight-line depreciation. The alternative depreciation system (ADS) provides for a longer period of recovery and uses straight-line depreciation. Thus it is much less economically attractive. Under law, ADS must be used for (1) any tangible property used primarily outside the U.S., (2) any property that is tax exempt or financed by tax-exempt bonds, and (3) farming property placed in service when uniform capitalization rules are not applied. The ADS may also be *elected* for property that can be depreciated using the GDS system. However, once ADS has been elected for an asset, it is not possible to switch back to the GDS system. Because the ADS makes the depreciation deductions less valuable, unless ADS is specifically mentioned, subsequent discussion assumes the GDS system when reference is made to MACRS.

Once a property has been determined to be eligible for depreciation, the next step is to calculate its depreciation deductions over its life. The following information is required to calculate these deductions:

- The asset's cost basis.
- The asset's *property class* and *recovery period*.
- The asset's placed-in-service date.

Cost Basis and Placed-in-Service Date

The cost basis, B, is the cost to obtain and place the asset in service fit for use. However, for real property the basis may also include certain fees and charges that the buyer pays as part of the purchase. Examples of such fees include legal and recording fees, abstract fees, survey charges, transfer taxes, title insurance, and amounts that the seller owes that you pay (back taxes, interest, sales commissions, etc.).

Depreciation for a business asset begins when the asset is *placed in service* for a business purpose. If an asset is purchased and used in a personal context, depreciation may not be taken. If that asset is later used in business for income-producing activity, depreciation may begin with the change in usage.

Property Class and Recovery Period

Each depreciated asset is placed in a *MACRS property class,* which defines the **recovery period** and the depreciation percentage for each year. Historically the IRS assigned each type of depreciable asset a *class life* or an *asset depreciation range*. With MACRS, asset class lives have been pooled together in the *property classes*. Table 11-1 lists the class lives and GDS and ADS property classes for several example depreciable assets. Table 11-2 lists the MACRS GDS property classes.

The MACRS GDS property classes are described in more detail in Table 11-2. The proper MACRS property class can be found several different ways. Of the five approaches listed, the first one that works should be used.

1. Property class given in problem.
2. Asset is named in Table 11-2.
3. IRS tables or Table 11-1.
4. Class life.
5. Seven-year property for "all other property not assigned to another class."

Once the MACRS property class is known, as well as the placed-in-service date and the cost basis, the year-to-year depreciation deductions can be calculated for GDS assets

TABLE 11-1 Example Class Lives and MACRS Property Classes

IRS Asset Class	Asset Description	Class Life (years) ADR	MACRS Property Class (years) GDS	MACRS Property Class (years) ADS
00.11	Office furniture, fixtures, and equipment	10	7	10
00.12	Information systems: computers/peripheral	6	5	6
00.22	Automobiles, taxis	3	5	5
00.241	Light general-purpose trucks	4	5	5
00.25	Railroad cars and locomotives	15	7	15
00.40	Industrial steam and electric distribution	22	15	22
01.11	Cotton gin assets	12	7	12
01.21	Cattle, breeding or dairy	7	5	7
13.00	Offshore drilling assets	7.5	5	7.5
13.30	Petroleum refining assets	16	10	16
15.00	Construction assets	6	5	6
20.10	Manufacture of grain and grain mill products	17	10	17
22.2	Manufacture of yarn, thread, and woven fabric	11	7	11
24.10	Cutting of timber	6	5	6
32.20	Manufacture of cement	20	15	20
37.11	Manufacture of motor vehicles	12	7	12
48.11	Telephone communications assets and buildings	24	15	24
48.2	Radio and television broadcasting equipment	6	5	6
49.12	Electric utility nuclear production plant	20	15	20
49.13	Electric utility steam production plant	28	20	28
49.23	Natural gas production plant	14	7	14
50.00	Municipal wastewater treatment plant	24	15	24
80.00	Theme and amusement park assets	12.5	7	12.5

TABLE 11-2 **MACRS GDS Property Classes**

Property Class	Personal Property (all property except real estate)
3-year property	Special handling devices for food and beverage manufacture Special tools for the manufacture of finished plastic products, fabricated metal products, and motor vehicles Property with ADR class life of 4 years or less
5-year property	Automobiles* and trucks Aircraft (of non-air-transport companies) Equipment used in research and experimentation Computers Petroleum drilling equipment Property with ADR class life of more than 4 years and less than 10 years
7-year property	All other property not assigned to another class Office furniture, fixtures, and equipment Property with ADR class life of 10 years or more and less than 16 years
10-year property	Assets used in petroleum refining and certain food products Vessels and water transportation equipment Property with ADR class life of 16 years or more and less than 20 years
15-year property	Telephone distribution plants Municipal sewage treatment plants Property with ADR class life of 20 years or more and less than 25 years
20-year property	Municipal sewers Property with ADR class life of 25 years or more

Property Class	Real Property (real estate)
27.5 years	Residential rental property (does not include hotels and motels)
39 years	Nonresidential real property

*The depreciation deduction for most automobiles placed in service after 2005 is limited to $2960 (maximum) the first tax year, $4700 the second year, $2850 the third year, and $1675 per year in subsequent years.
Source: U.S. Department of the Treasury, Internal Revenue Service Publication 946, *How to Depreciate Property.* Washington, DC: Government Printing Office.

over their depreciable life using

$$d_t = B \times r_t \tag{11-5}$$

where d_t = depreciation deduction in year t
  B = cost basis being depreciated
  r_t = appropriate MACRS percentage rate

Percentage Tables

The IRS has prepared tables to assist in calculating depreciation charges when MACRS GDS depreciation is used. Table 11-3 gives the yearly depreciation percentages (r_t) that are used for the six personal property classes (3-, 5-, 7-, 10-, 15-, and 20-year property classes), and Table 11-4 gives the percentages for nonresidential real property. Notice that the values are given in *percentages*—thus, for example, the value of 33.33% (given in Table 11-3 for Year 1 for a 3-year MACRS GDS property) is 0.3333.

TABLE 11-3 **MACRS Depreciation for Personal Property: Half-Year Convention**

Applicable Percentage for Property Class

Recovery Year	3-Year Property	5-Year Property	7-Year Property	10-Year Property	15-Year Property	20-Year Property
1	33.33	20.00	14.29	10.00	5.00	3.750
2	44.45	32.00	24.49	18.00	9.50	7.219
3	14.81*	19.20	17.49	14.40	8.55	6.677
4	7.41	11.52*	12.49	11.52	7.70	6.177
5		11.52	8.93*	9.22	6.93	5.713
6		5.76	8.92	7.37	6.23	5.285
7			8.93	6.55*	5.90*	4.888
8			4.46	6.55	5.90	4.522
9				6.56	5.91	4.462*
10				6.55	5.90	4.461
11				3.28	5.91	4.462
12					5.90	4.461
13					5.91	4.462
14					5.90	4.461
15					5.91	4.462
16					2.95	4.461
17						4.462
18						4.461
19						4.462
20						4.461
21						2.231

Computation method

- The 3-, 5-, 7-, and 10-year classes use 200% and the 15- and 20-year classes use 150% declining balance depreciation.
- All classes convert to straight-line depreciation in the optimal year, shown with asterisk (*).
- A half-year of depreciation is allowed in the first and last recovery years.
- If more than 40% of the year's MACRS property is placed in service in the last 3 months, then a midquarter convention must be used with depreciation tables that are not shown here.

Notice in Table 11-3 that the depreciation percentages continue for *one year beyond* the property class life. For example, a MACRS 10-year property has an r_t value of 3.28% in Year 11. This is due to the *half-year convention* that also halves the percentage for the first year. The half-year convention assumes that all assets are placed in service at the midpoint of the first year.

Another characteristic of the MACRS percentage tables is that the r_t values in any column sum to 100%. This means that assets depreciated using MACRS are *fully depreciated* at the end of the recovery period. This assumes a salvage value of zero. This is a departure from the pre-1981 historical methods, where an estimated salvage value was considered.

TABLE 11-4 MACRS Depreciation for Real Property (real estate)*

Recovery Year	Recovery Percentages for Nonresidential Real Property (month placed in service)											
	1	2	3	4	5	6	7	8	9	10	11	12
1	2.461	2.247	2.033	1.819	1.605	1.391	1.177	0.963	0.749	0.535	0.321	0.107
2–39	2.564	2.564	2.564	2.564	2.564	2.564	2.564	2.564	2.564	2.564	2.564	2.564
40	0.107	0.321	0.535	0.749	0.963	1.177	1.391	1.605	1.819	2.033	2.247	2.461

*The useful life is 39 years for nonresidential real property. Depreciation is straight line using the midmonth convention. Thus a property placed in service in January would be allowed $11\frac{1}{2}$ months depreciation for recovery Year 1.

Where MACRS Percentage Rates (r_t) Come From

This section describes the connection between historical depreciation methods and the MACRS percentages that are shown in Table 11-3. Before ACRS and MACRS, the most common depreciation method was declining balance with a switch to straight line. That combined method is used for MACRS with three further assumptions.

1. Salvage values are assumed to be zero for all assets.
2. The first and last years of the recovery period are each assumed to be *half-year*.
3. The declining balance rate is 200% for 3-, 5-, 7-, and 10-year property and 150% for 15- and 20-year property.

As shown in Example 11-5, the MACRS percentage rates can be derived from these rules and the declining balance and straight-line methods. However, it is obviously much easier to simply use the r_t values from Tables 11-3 and 11-4.

EXAMPLE 11-5

Consider a 5-year MACRS property asset with an installed and "made ready for use" cost basis of $100. Develop the MACRS percentage rates (r_t) for the asset based on the underlying depreciation methods.

SOLUTION

To develop the 5-year MACRS property percentage rates, we use the 200% declining balance method, switching over to straight line at the optimal point. Since the assumed salvage value is zero, the entire cost basis of $100 is depreciated. Also the $100 basis mimics the 100% that is used in Table 11-3.

Let's explain the accompanying table year by year. In Year 1 the basis is $100 − 0, and the d_t values are halved for the initial half-year assumption. Double declining balance has a rate of 40% for 5 years (= 2/5). This is larger than straight-line for Year 1. So one-half of the 40% is used for Year 1. The rest of the declining balance computations are simply 40%×(basis minus the cumulative depreciation).

In Year 2 there are 4.5 years remaining for straight line, so 4.5 is the denominator for dividing the remaining $80 in book value. Similarly in Year 3 there are 3.5 years remaining. In Year 4 the DDB and SL calculations happen to be identical, so the switch from DDB to SL can be done in either Year 4 or Year 5. Once we know that the SL depreciation is 11.52 at the switch point, then the only further calculation is to halve that for the last year.

Notice that the DDB calculations get smaller every year, so that at some point the straight-line calculations lead to faster depreciation. This point is the optimal switch point, and it is built into Table 11-3 for MACRs.

Year	DDB Calculation	SL Calculation	MACRS r_t (%) Rates	Cumulative Depreciation (%)
1	$1/(2/5)(100 - 0) = \mathbf{20.00}$	$^1/_2(100 - 0)/5 = 10.00$	20.00 (DDB)	20.00
2	$(2/5)(100 - 20.00) = \mathbf{32.00}$	$(100 - 20)/4.5 = 17.78$	32.00 (DDB)	52.00
3	$(2/5)(100 - 52.00) = \mathbf{19.20}$	$(100 - 52)/3.5 = 13.71$	19.20 (DDB)	71.20
4	$(2/5)(100 - 71.20) = \mathbf{11.52}$	$(100 - 71.20)/2.5 = \mathbf{11.52}$	11.52 (either)	82.72
5		$\mathbf{11.52}$	11.52 (SL)	94.24
6		$(^1/_2)(11.52) = \mathbf{5.76}$	5.76 (SL)	100.00

The values given in this example match the r_t percentage rates given in Table 11-3 for a 5-year MACRS property.

MACRS Method Examples

Remember the key points in using MACRS: (1) what type of asset you have, and whether it qualifies as depreciable property, (2) the amount you are depreciating [cost basis], and (3) when you are placing the asset in service. Let's look at several examples of using MACRS to calculate both depreciation deductions and book values.

EXAMPLE 11-6

Use the MACRS GDS method to calculate the yearly depreciation allowances and book values for a firm that has purchased $150,000 worth of office equipment that qualifies as depreciable property. The equipment is estimated to have a salvage (market) value of $30,000 (20% of the original cost) after the end of its depreciable life.

SOLUTION

1. The assets qualify as depreciable property.
2. The cost basis is given as $150,000.
3. The assets are being placed in service in Year 1 of our analysis.
4. MACRS GDS applies.
5. The salvage value is not used with MACRS to calculate depreciation or book value.

Office equipment is listed in Table 11-2 as a 7-year property. We now use the MACRS GDS 7-year property percentages from Table 11-3 and Equation 11-5 to calculate the year-to-year depreciation allowances. We use Equation 11-1 to calculate the book value of the asset.

Year, t	MACRS, r_t		Cost Basis	d_t	Cumulative d_t	$BV_t = B - $ Cum. d_t
1	14.29%	×	$150,000	$ 21,435	$ 21,435	$128,565
2	24.49		150,000	36,735	58,170	91,830
3	17.49		150,000	26,235	84,405	65,595
4	12.49		150,000	18,735	103,140	46,860
5	8.93		150,000	13,395	116,535	33,465
6	8.92		150,000	13,380	129,915	20,085
7	8.93		150,000	13,395	143,310	6,690
8	4.46		150,000	6,690	150,000	0
	100.00%			$150,000		

Notice in this example several aspects of the MACRS depreciation method: (1) the sum of the r_t values is 100.00%, (2) this 7-year MACRS GDS property is depreciated over 8 years (= property class life + 1), and (3) the book value after 8 years is $0.

EXAMPLE 11-7

Investors in the JMJ Group purchased a hotel resort in April. The group paid $2.0 million for the hotel resort and $500,000 for the grounds surrounding the resort. The group sold the resort 5 years later in August. Calculate the depreciation deductions for Years 1 through 6. What was the book value at the time the resort was sold?

SOLUTION

Hotels are nonresidential real property and are depreciated over a 39-year life. Table 11-4 lists the percentages for each year. In this case the cost basis is $2.0 million, and the $500,000 paid for the land is not depreciated. JMJ's depreciation is calculated as follows:

Year 1 (obtained in April)	$d_1 = 2,000,000(1.819\%) = \$36,380$
Year 2	$d_2 = 2,000,000(2.564\%) = 51,280$
Year 3	$d_3 = 2,000,000(2.564\%) = 51,280$
Year 4	$d_4 = 2,000,000(2.564\%) = 51,280$
Year 5	$d_5 = 2,000,000(2.564\%) = 51,280$
Year 6 (disposed of in August)	$d_6 = 2,000,000(1.605\%) = 32,100$

Thus the hotel's book value when it was sold was:

$$BV_6 = B - (d_1 + d_2 + d_3 + d_4 + d_5 + d_6)$$

$$= 2,000,000 - (273,600) = \$1,726,400$$

The value of the land has not changed in terms of book value.

Comparing MACRS and Historical Methods

In Examples 11-2 through 11-4 we used the *straight-line, sum-of-the-years'-digits,* and *declining balance* depreciation methods to illustrate how the book value of an asset that cost $900 and had a salvage value of $70 changed over its 5-year depreciation life. Figures 11-2 through 11-4 provided a graphical view of book value over the 5-year depreciation period using these methods. Example 11-8 compares the MACRS GDS depreciation method directly against the historical methods.

EXAMPLE 11-8

Consider the equipment that was purchased in Example 11-6. Calculate the asset's depreciation deductions and book values over its depreciable life for MACRS and the historical methods.

SOLUTION

Table 11-5 and Figure 11-5 compare MACRS and historical depreciation methods. MACRS depreciation is the most *accelerated* or fastest depreciation method—remember its name is the modified *accelerated* cost recovery system. The book value drops fastest and furthest with MACRS, thus the present worth is the largest for the MACRS depreciation deductions.

Depreciation deductions *benefit* a firm after taxes because they reduce taxable income and taxes. The time value of money ensures that it is better to take these deductions as soon as possible. In general, MACRS, which allocates larger deductions earlier in the depreciable life, provides more economic benefits than historical methods.

TABLE 11-5 Comparison of MACRS and Historical Methods for Asset in Example 11-6

Year, t	MACRS d_t	MACRS BV_t	Straight Line d_t	Straight Line BV_t	Double Declining d_t	Double Declining BV_t	Sum-of-Years' Digits d_t	Sum-of-Years' Digits BV_t
1	21,435	128,565	12,000	138,000	30,000	120,000	21,818	128,182
2	36,735	91,830	12,000	126,000	24,000	96,000	19,636	108,545
3	26,235	65,595	12,000	114,000	19,200	76,800	17,455	91,091
4	18,735	46,860	12,000	102,000	15,360	61,440	15,273	75,818
5	13,395	33,465	12,000	90,000	12,288	49,152	13,091	62,727
6	13,380	20,085	12,000	78,000	9,830	39,322	10,909	51,818
7	13,395	6,690	12,000	66,000	7,864	31,457	8,727	43,091
8	6,690	0	12,000	54,000	1,457	30,000	6,545	36,545
9	0	0	12,000	42,000	0	30,000	4,364	32,182
10	0	0	12,000	30,000	0	30,000	2,182	30,000
PW (10%)	$108,217		$73,734		$89,918		$84,118	

DEPRECIATION AND ASSET DISPOSAL

When a depreciated asset is disposed of, the key question is, Which is larger, the asset's *book value, BV*, or the asset's *market value, MV*? If the book value is lower than the market

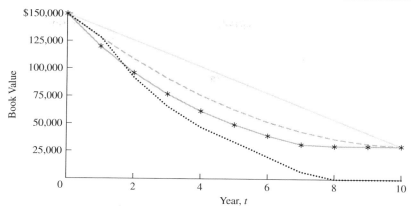

FIGURE 11-5 Comparing MACRS (┄┄┄┄) and historical depreciation methods: double declining balance (———✱———), sum of the years' digits (— — — —), and straight line (———).

value, then excess depreciation will be recaptured and taxed. On the other hand, if the book value is higher than the market value, there is a *loss* on the disposal. In either case, the level of taxes owed changes.

> *Depreciation recapture (ordinary gains):* Depreciation recapture, also called ordinary gains, is necessary when an asset is sold for more than an asset's current book value. If more than the original cost basis is received, only the amount up to the original cost basis is recaptured depreciation. Since MACRS assumes $S = 0$ for its annual calculations, MACRS often has recaptured depreciation at disposal.

> *Losses:* A *loss* occurs when less than book value is received for a depreciated asset. In the accounting records we've disposed of an asset for a dollar amount less than its book value, which is a loss.

> *Capital gains:* Capital gains occur when more than the asset's original cost basis is received for it. The excess over the original cost basis is the *capital gain*. As described in Chapter 12, the tax rate on such gains is sometimes lower than the rate on ordinary income, but this depends on how long the investment has been held ("short," ≤ 1 year; "long," ≥ 1 year). In most engineering economic analyses capital gains are very uncommon because business and production equipment and facilities almost always *lose* value over time. Capital gains are much more likely to occur for nondepreciated assets like stocks, bonds, real estate, jewelry, art, and collectibles.

The relationship between depreciation recapture, loss, and capital gain is illustrated in Figure 11-6. Each case given is at a point in time in the life of the depreciated asset, where the original cost basis is $10,000 and the book value is $5000. Case (a) represents depreciation recapture (ordinary gain), Case (b) represents a loss, and in Case (c) both recaptured depreciation and a capital gain are present.

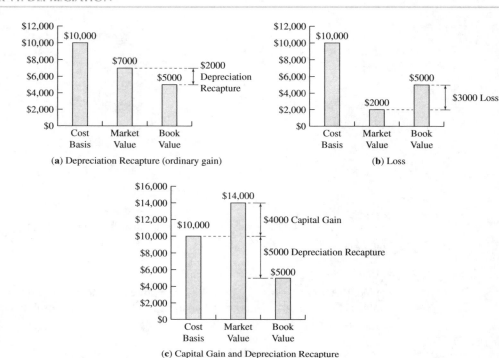

FIGURE 11-6 Recaptured depreciation, loss on sale, and capital gain.

EXAMPLE 11-9

Consider an asset with a cost basis of $10,000 that has been depreciated using the MACRS method. This asset is a 3-year MACRS property. What is the gain or loss if the asset is disposed of after 5 years of operation for **(a)** $7000, **(b)** $0, and **(c)** a cost of $2000.

SOLUTION

To find *gain* or *loss* at disposal we compare *market* and *book value*. Since MACRS depreciates to a salvage value of 0, and 5 years is greater than the recovery period, the book value equals $0.

  (a) Recaptured depreciation = $7000, since the book value is $7000 higher.
  (b) Since market value equals salvage value, there is no recaptured depreciation or loss.
  (c) Since the money is paid for disposal, this is less than the book value, and there is a loss.

This general method for calculating recaptured depreciation or loss applies to all of the depreciation methods described in this chapter.

If the asset is in the middle of its depreciable life, then recaptured depreciation and losses are calculated in a similar manner—compare the *market* and *book values* at the time of disposal. However, in computing the book value with MACRS depreciation, a special rule must be applied for assets disposed of before the end of the recovery period. The rule is to *take one half of the allowable depreciation deduction for that year.* This rule assumes that disposals take place on average halfway through the year. Thus for a 5-year asset disposed of in the middle of Year 4, the rate allowed for MACRS depreciation is half of 11.52% or 5.76%. If the asset is disposed of in Year 6, it is already past the recovery period, and a half-year assumption has already been built into the MACRS schedule. Thus, the full r_6 is taken. Example 11-10 illustrates several cases of disposal before the asset is fully depreciated.

EXAMPLE 11-10

Consider the $10,000 asset in Example 11-9. Do the following:

1. Calculate the effect of disposal if this asset is sold during Year 2 for $2500.
2. Calculate the effect of disposal if the asset is sold during Year 3 for $2500.
3. Calculate the effect of disposal if the asset is sold after Year 3 for $4000 if straight-line depreciation is used over the asset's 5-year life, and a salvage value of $5000 is assumed.

SOLUTION

1. Market value$_2$ = $2500

$$\text{Book value}_2 = 10,000 - 10,000[r_1 + r_2/2] = 10,000 - 10,000[0.3333 + 0.4445/2]$$
$$= \$4444.5$$
$$\text{Loss} = \$1944.5 \, (= 4444.5 - 2500) \qquad \text{(Loss, since BV greater than MV)}$$

Note: If the full rather than half-deduction were taken in Year 2, then the book value would be $2222.50 less and the loss would become a gain of $278. Since depreciation would increase by that $2222.50, the total of (depreciation) + (loss or gain) would be $4167 in either calculation.

2. Market value$_3$ = $2500

$$\text{Book value}_3 = 10,000 - 10,000[r_1 + r_2 + r_3/2]$$
$$= 10,000 - 10,000[0.3333 + 0.4445 + 0.1481/2] = \$1481.50$$

$$\text{Recaptured depreciation} = 2500 - 1481.50 = \$1018.50 \quad \text{(Recaptured, since MV > BV)}$$

3.   Straight-line rate $= (B - S)/N = (10,000 - 5000)/5 = \$1000$

$$\text{Market value}_4 = \$4000$$
$$\text{Book value}_4 = 10,000 - (4)(1000) = \$6000$$
$$\text{Loss} = 6000 - 4000 = \$2000$$

If the asset were disposed of *during the year rather than at year's end,* then the straight-line depreciation deduction would have to be prorated for the number of months during the year that the asset was in service. There is no half-year convention with the historical depreciation methods. For example, if disposal occurred on September 30 of Year 4, $d_4 = (9/12)(1000) = \$750$.

Note: In Case 1 it was shown that the required half-year convention did not affect the total deductions from taxable income. This is true for the other cases as well, since both recaptured depreciation and losses are treated as ordinary income.

UNIT-OF-PRODUCTION DEPRECIATION

At times the recovery of depreciation on a particular asset is more closely related to use than to time. In these few situations (and they are rare), the **unit-of-production (UOP) depreciation** in any year is

$$\text{UOP depreciation in any year} = \frac{\text{Production for year}}{\text{Total lifetime production for asset}}(B - S) \qquad (11\text{-}6)$$

This method might be useful for machinery that processes natural resources if the resources will be exhausted before the machinery wears out. Historically, this method was sometimes used for construction equipment that had very heavy use in some years and very light use in others. It is not considered an acceptable method for general use in depreciating industrial equipment.

EXAMPLE 11-11

For numerical similarity with previous examples, assume that equipment costing $900 has been purchased for use in a sand and gravel pit. The pit will operate for 5 years, while a nearby airport is being reconstructed and paved. Then the pit will be shut down, and the equipment removed and sold for $70. Compute the unit-of-production (UOP) depreciation schedule if the airport reconstruction schedule calls for 40,000 m^3 of sand and gravel as follows:

Year	Required Sand and Gravel (m^3)
1	4,000
2	8,000
3	16,000
4	8,000
5	4,000

SOLUTION

The cost basis, B, is $900. The salvage value, S, is $70. The total lifetime production for the asset is 40,000 m^3 of sand and gravel. From the airport reconstruction schedule, the first-year UOP depreciation would be:

$$\text{First-year UOP depreciation} = \frac{4000 \text{ m}^3}{40,000 \text{ m}^3}(\$900 - \$70) = \$83$$

Similar calculations for the subsequent 4 years give the complete depreciation schedule:

Year	UOP Depreciation
1	$ 83
2	166
3	332
4	166
5	83
	$830

It should be noted that the actual unit-of-production depreciation charge in any year is based on the actual production for the year rather than the scheduled production.

DEPLETION

Depletion is the exhaustion of natural resources as a result of their removal. Since depletion covers such things as mineral properties, oil and gas wells, and standing timber, removal may take the form of digging up metallic or nonmetallic minerals, producing petroleum or natural gas from wells, or cutting down trees.

Depletion is recognized for income tax purposes for the same reason depreciation is— capital investment is being consumed or used up. Thus a portion of the gross income should be considered to be a return of the capital investment. The calculation of the depletion allowance is different from depreciation because there are two distinct methods of calculating depletion: *cost depletion* and *percentage depletion*. Except for standing timber and most oil and gas wells, depletion is calculated by both methods and the larger value is taken as depletion for the year. For standing timber and most oil and gas wells, only cost depletion is permissible.

Cost Depletion

Depreciation relied on an asset's cost, depreciable life, and salvage value to apportion the cost *minus* salvage value *over* the depreciable life. In some cases, where the asset is used at fluctuating rates, we might use the unit-of-production (UOP) method of depreciation. For mines, oil wells, and standing timber, fluctuating production rates are the usual situation. Thus, *cost depletion* is computed like unit-of-production depreciation using:

1. Property cost, less cost for land.
2. Estimated number of recoverable units (tons of ore, cubic meters of gravel, barrels of oil, million cubic feet of natural gas, thousand board-feet of timber, etc.).
3. Salvage value, if any, of the property.

EXAMPLE 11-12

A small lumber company bought a tract of timber for $35,000, of which $5000 was the land's value and $30,000 was the value of the estimated 1.5 million board-feet of standing timber. The first year, the company cut 100,000 board-feet of standing timber. What was the year's depletion allowance?

SOLUTION

$$\text{Depletion allowance per 1000 board-ft} = \frac{\$35,000 - \$5000}{1500 \times 1000 \text{ board-ft}}$$

$$= \$20 \text{ per 1000 board-ft}$$

The depletion allowance for the year would be

$$100,000 \text{ board-ft} \times \$20 \text{ per 1000 board-ft} = \$2000$$

Percentage Depletion

Percentage depletion is an alternate method for mineral property. The allowance is a certain percentage of the property's gross income during the year. This is an entirely different concept from depreciation. Unlike depreciation, which allocates cost *over* useful life, the **percentage depletion** allowance (see Table 11-6) is based on the property's gross income.

Since percentage depletion is computed on the *income* rather than the property's cost, the total depletion *may exceed the cost of the property*. In computing the *allowable*

TABLE 11-6 **Percentage Depletion Allowances for Selected Deposits**

Deposits	Rate
Sulfur, uranium, and, if from deposits in the U.S., asbestos, lead ore, zinc ore, nickel ore, and mica	22%
Gold, silver, copper, iron ore, and certain oil shale, if from deposits in the U.S.	15%
Borax, granite, limestone, marble, mollusk shells, potash, slate, soapstone, and carbon dioxide produced from a well	14%
Coal, lignite, and sodium chloride	10%
Clay and shale used or sold for use in making sewer pipe or bricks or used or sold for use as sintered or burned lightweight aggregates	$7\frac{1}{2}\%$
Clay used or sold for use in making drainage and roofing tile, flower pots, and kindred products, and gravel, sand, and stone (other than stone used or sold for use by a mine owner or operator as dimension or ornamental stone)	5%

Source: Internal Revenue Service, Publication 535, Chapter 9. Section 613(b) of the Internal Revenue Code gives a complete list of minerals and their percentage depletion rates.

percentage depletion on a property in any year, the *percentage depletion allowance* cannot exceed 50% of the property's taxable income computed without the depletion deduction. The percentage depletion calculations are illustrated by Example 11-13.

EXAMPLE 11-13

A coal mine has a gross income of $250,000. Mining expenses equal $210,000. Compute the allowable percentage depletion deduction.

SOLUTION

From Table 11-6, coal has a 10% depletion allowance based on gross mining income. The allowable percentage depletion deduction is also limited to a maximum of 50% of taxable income.

Computed Percentage Depletion

Gross income from mine	$250,000
Depletion percentage	× 10%
Computed percentage depletion	$ 25,000

Taxable Income Limitation

Gross income from mine	$250,000
Less: Expenses other than depletion	−210,000
Taxable income from mine	40,000
Deduction limitation	× 50%
Taxable income limitation	$20,000

Since the taxable income limitation ($20,000) is less than the computed percentage depletion ($25,000), the allowable percentage depletion deduction is $20,000.

As previously stated, on mineral property the depletion deduction can be based on either cost or percentage depletion. Each year, depletion is computed by both methods, and the allowable depletion deduction is the larger of the two amounts.

SPREADSHEETS AND DEPRECIATION

The spreadsheet functions for straight-line, double declining balance, and sum-of-years'-digits depreciation are listed in Table 11-7. Because these techniques are simple and were

TABLE 11-7 **Spreadsheet Functions for Depreciation**

Depreciation Technique	Excel
Straight line	SLN(cost, salvage, life)
Declining balance	DDB(cost, salvage, life, period, factor)
Sum of years' digits	SYD(cost, salvage, life, period)
MACRS	VDB(cost, salvage, life, start_period, end_period, factor, no_switch)

replaced by MACRS in 1986, they are not covered in detail here. All three functions include parameters for *cost* (initial book value), *salvage* (final salvage value), and *life* (depreciation period). Both DDB and SYD change depreciation amounts every year, so they include a parameter to pick the *period* (year). Finally, DDB includes a *factor*. The default value is 2 for 200% or double declining balance, but another commonly used value is 1.5 for 150%.

Using VDB for MACRS

The Excel function VDB is a flexible or variable declining balance method. It includes the ability to specify the starting and ending periods, rather than simply a year. It also includes an optional no_switch for problems where a switch from declining balance to straight-line depreciation is NOT desired.

To use VDB to calculate MACRS depreciation, the following are true.

1. Salvage = 0, since MACRS assumes no salvage value.
2. Life = recovery period of 3, 5, 7, 10, 15, or 20 years.
3. First period runs from 0 to 0.5, 2nd period from 0.5 to 1.5, 3rd from 1.5 to 2.5, t^{th} from $t - 1.5$ to $t - 0.5$, and last period from *life* $- 0.5$ to *life*.
4. Factor $= 2$ for recovery periods of 3, 5, 7, or 10 years and $= 1.5$ for recovery periods of 15 or 20 years.
5. Since MACRS includes a switch to straight line, no_switch can be omitted.

The start_period and end_period arguments are from $t - 1.5$ to $t - 0.5$, because MACRS uses a half-year convention for the first year. Thus the first year has 0 to 0.5 year of depreciation, and the second year starts where the first year stops. When one is writing the Excel function, either the first and last periods must be edited individually, or start_period must be defined with a minimum of 0 and end_period with a maximum of life. This prevents the calculation of depreciation from -0.5 to 0 and from *life* to *life* $+0.5$.

The results of using the VDB function match Table 11-4, except that the VDB function has more significant digits rather than being rounded to 2 decimals. Example 11-14 illustrates the use of the VDB function.

EXAMPLE 11-14

Return to the data of Example 11-5 which had $150,000 of office equipment, which is 7-year MACRS property. Use VDB to compute the depreciation amounts.

SOLUTION

The spreadsheet in Figure 11-7 defines the start_period with a minimum of 0 and the end_period with a maximum of life. Remember that this is the *depreciable* life or recovery period. Thus this formula could be used for any year of any recovery schedule. Notice that the VDB formula uses the value 0 for the salvage value, rather than referring to the data cell for the salvage value. MACRS assumes a salvage value of zero—no matter what the value truly is.

	A	B	C	D	E	F	G
1	150,000	First Cost					
2	0	Salvage					
3	7	Life = recovery period					
4	200%	Factor					
5							
6	Period	Depreciation					
7	1	$21,428.57	=VDB($A$1,0,$A$3,MAX(0,A7−1.5),MIN($A$3,A7−0.5),$A$4)				
8	2	$36,734.69	or (cost, salvage, life, max(0, t−1.5), min (life, t−.5), factor)				
9	3	$26,239.07					
10	4	$18,742.19					
11	5	$13,387.28					
12	6	$13,387.28					
13	7	$13,387.28					
14	8	$6,693.64					
15		$150,000	= Sum				

FIGURE 11-7 Using VDB to calculate MACRS depreciation.

SUMMARY

Depreciation is part of computing income taxes in economic analysis. There are three distinct definitions of depreciation:

1. Decline in asset's market value.
2. Decline in asset's value to its owner.
3. Allocating the asset's cost *less* its salvage value *over* its recovery period or depreciable life.

While the first two definitions are used in everyday discussions, it is the third, or accountant's, definition that is used in tax computations and in this chapter. Book value is the remaining unallocated cost of an asset, or

Book value = Asset cost − Depreciation charges made to date

This chapter describes how depreciable assets are *written off* (or claimed as a business expense) over a period of years instead of *expensed* in a single period (like wages, material costs, etc.). The depreciation methods described include the historical pre-1981 methods: *straight line, sum of the years' digits,* and *declining balance.* These methods required estimating the asset's salvage value and depreciable life.

The current tax law specifies use of the modified accelerated capital recovery system (MACRS). This chapter has focused on the general depreciation system (GDS) with limited discussion of the less attractive alternative depreciation system (ADS). MACRS (GDS) specifies faster *recovery periods* and a salvage value of zero, so it is generally economically more attractive than the historical methods.

The MACRS system is the current tax law, and it assumes a salvage value of zero. This is in contrast with historical methods, which ensured the final book value would equal the predicted salvage value. Thus, when one is using MACRS it is often necessary to consider recaptured depreciation. This is the excess of salvage value over book value, and it is taxed as ordinary income. Similarly, losses on sale or disposal are taxed as ordinary income.

Unit-of-production (UOP) depreciation relies on usage to quantify the loss in value. UOP is appropriate for assets that lose value based on the number of units produced, the tons of gravel moved, and so on (vs. number of years in service). However, this method is not considered to be acceptable for most business assets.

Depletion is the exhaustion of natural resources like minerals, oil and gas, and standing timber. The owners of the natural resources are consuming their investments as the natural resources are removed and sold. Cost depletion is computed based on the fraction of the resource that is removed or sold. For minerals and some oil and gas wells, an alternate calculation called percentage depletion is allowed. Percentage depletion is based on income, so the total allowable depletion deductions may *exceed* the invested cost.

Integrating depreciation schedules with cash flows often involves a lot of arithmetic. Thus, the tool of spreadsheets can be quite helpful. The functions for the historical methods, straight line, sum of the years' digits, and declining balance, are straightforward. Rather than individually entering MACRS percentages into the spreadsheet, the function VDB can be used to calculate MACRS depreciation percentages.

PROBLEMS

Depreciation Schedules

11-1 A depreciable asset costs $10,000 and has an estimated salvage value of $1600 at the end of its 6-year depreciable life. Compute the depreciation schedule for this asset by both SOYD depreciation and DDB depreciation.

11-2 A million-dollar oil drilling rig has a 6-year depreciable life and a $75,000 salvage value at the end of that time. Determine which one of the following methods provides the preferred depreciation schedule: DDB or SOYD. Show the depreciation schedule for the preferred method.

11-3 A new machine tool is being purchased for $16,000 and is expected to have a zero salvage value at the end of its 5-year useful life. Compute the DDB depreciation schedule for this capital asset. Assume any remaining depreciation is claimed in the last year.

11-4 Some special handling devices can be obtained for $12,000. At the end of 4 years, they can be sold for $600. Compute the depreciation schedule for the devices using the following methods:

   (a) Straight-line depreciation

   (b) Sum-of-years'-digits depreciation

   (c) Double declining balance depreciation

   (d) MACRS depreciation

11-5 The company treasurer is uncertain which of four depreciation methods the firm should use for office furniture that costs $50,000, and has a zero salvage value at the end of a 10-year depreciable life. Compute the depreciation schedule for the office furniture using the methods listed:

   (a) Straight line

   (b) Double declining balance

   (c) Sum-of-years'-digits

   (d) Modified accelerated cost recovery system

11-6 The RX Drug Company has just purchased a capsulating machine for $76,000. The plant engineer estimates the machine has a useful life of 5 years and little or no salvage value. He will use zero salvage value in the computations.

Compute the depreciation schedule for the machine using:

(a) Straight-line depreciation

(b) Sum-of-years'-digits depreciation

(c) Double declining balance depreciation (assume any remaining depreciation is claimed in the last year)

11-7 The Acme Chemical Company paid $45,000 for research equipment, which it believes will have zero salvage value at the end of its 5-year life. Compute the depreciation schedule for the equipment by each of the following methods:

(a) Straight line

(b) Sum-of-years'-digits

(c) Double declining balance

(d) Modified accelerated cost recovery system

11-8 Consider a $6500 piece of machinery, with a 5-year depreciable life and an estimated $1200 salvage value. The projected utilization of the machinery when it was purchased, and its actual production to date, are as follows:

Year	Projected Production (tons)	Actual Production (tons)
1	3500	3000
2	4000	5000
3	4500	[Not
4	5000	yet
5	5500	known]

Compute the machinery depreciation schedule by each of the following methods:

(a) Straight line

(b) Sum-of-years'-digits

(c) Double declining balance

(d) Unit of production (for first 2 years only)

(e) Modified accelerated cost recovery system

11-9 A large profitable corporation bought a small jet plane for use by the firm's executives in January. The plane cost $1.5 million and, for depreciation purposes, is assumed to have a zero salvage value at the end of 5 years. Compute the MACRS depreciation schedule.

11-10 For an asset that fits into the MACRS "all property not assigned to another class" designation, show in a table the depreciation and book value over the asset's 10-year life of use. The cost basis of the asset is $10,000.

11-11 A company that manufactures food and beverages in the vending industry has purchased some handling equipment that cost $75,000 and will be depreciated using MACRS GDS; the class life of the asset is 4 years. Show in a table the yearly depreciation amount and book value of the asset over its depreciation life.

11-12 Consider five depreciation schedules:

Year	A	B	C	D	E
1	$45.00	$35.00	$29.00	$58.00	$43.50
2	36.00	20.00	46.40	34.80	30.45
3	27.00	30.00	27.84	20.88	21.32
4	18.00	30.00	16.70	12.53	14.92
5	9.00	20.00	16.70	7.52	10.44
6			8.36		

They are based on the same initial cost, useful life, and salvage value. Identify each schedule as one of the following

- Straight-line depreciation
- Sum-of-years'-digits depreciation
- 150% declining balance depreciation
- Double declining balance depreciation
- Unit-of-production depreciation
- Modified accelerated cost recovery system

11-13 The depreciation schedule for an asset, with a salvage value of $90 at the end of the recovery period, has been computed by several methods. Identify the depreciation method used for each schedule.

Year	A	B	C	D	E
1	$323.3	$212.0	$424.0	$194.0	$107.0
2	258.7	339.2	254.4	194.0	216.0
3	194.0	203.5	152.6	194.0	324.0
4	129.3	122.1	91.6	194.0	216.0
5	64.7	122.1	47.4	194.0	107.0
6		61.1			
	970.0	1060.0	970.0	970.0	970.0

11-14 The depreciation schedule for a microcomputer has been arrived at by several methods. The estimated salvage value of the equipment at the end of its 6-year useful life is $600. Identify the resulting depreciation schedules.

Year	A	B	C	D
1	$2114	$2000	$1600	$1233
2	1762	1500	2560	1233
3	1410	1125	1536	1233
4	1057	844	922	1233
5	705	633	922	1233
6	352	475	460	1233

11-15 A heavy construction firm has been awarded a contract to build a large concrete dam. It is expected that a total of 8 years will be required to complete the work. The firm will buy $600,000 worth of special equipment for the job. During the preparation of the job cost estimate, the following utilization schedule was computed for the special equipment:

Year	Utilization (hr/yr)	Year	Utilization (hr/yr)
1	6000	5	800
2	4000	6	800
3	4000	7	2200
4	1600	8	2200

At the end of the job, it is estimated that the equipment can be sold at auction for $60,000.

(a) Compute the sum-of-years-digits' depreciation schedule.

(b) Compute the unit-of-production depreciation schedule.

11-16 Given the data in Problem 11-22, use a spreadsheet function to compute the MACRS depreciation schedule. Show the total depreciation taken (=sum( )) as well as the PW of the depreciation charges discounted at the MARR%.

11-17 Office equipment whose initial cost is $100,000 has an estimated actual life of 6 years, with an estimated salvage value of $10,000. Prepare tables listing the annual costs of depreciation and the book value at the end of each 6 years, based on the straight-line, sum-of-years'-digits, and MACRS depreciation. Use spreadsheet functions for the depreciation methods.

11-18 You are equipping an office. The total office equipment will have a first cost of $1,750,000 and a salvage value of $200,000. You expect the equipment will last 10 years. Use a spreadsheet function to compute the MACRS depreciation schedule.

11-19 Units-of-production depreciation is being used for a machine that, based on usage, has an allowable

depreciation charge of $6500 the first year and increasing by $1000 each year until complete depreciation. If the machine's cost basis is $110,000, set up a depreciation schedule that shows depreciation charge and book value over the machine's 10-year useful life.

11-20 A custom-built production machine is being depreciated using the units-of-production method. The machine costs $65,000 and is expected to produce 1.5 million units, after which it will have a $5000 salvage value. In the first 2 years of operation the machine was used to produce 140,000 units each year. In the 3rd and 4th years, production went up to 400,000 units. After that time annual production returned to 135,000 units. Use a spreadsheet to develop a depreciation schedule showing the machine's depreciation allowance and book value over its depreciable life.

Comparing Depreciation Methods

11-21 TELCO Corp. has leased some industrial land near its plant. It is building a small warehouse on the site at a cost of $250,000. The building will be ready for use January 1. The lease will expire 15 years after the building is occupied. The warehouse will belong at that time to the landowner, with the result that there will be no salvage value to TELCO. The warehouse is to be depreciated either by MACRS or SOYD depreciation. If 10% interest is appropriate, which depreciation method should be selected?

11-22 A profitable company making earthmoving equipment is considering an investment of $100,000 on equipment that will have a 5-year useful life and a $20,000 salvage value. If money is worth 10%, which one of the following three methods of depreciation would be preferable?

(a) Straight-line method

(b) Double declining balance method

(c) MACRS method

11-23 The White Swan Talc Company paid $120,000 for mining equipment for a small talc mine. The mining engineer's report indicates the mine contains 40,000 cubic meters of commercial quality talc. The company plans to mine all the talc in the next 5 years as follows:

Year	Talc Production (m³)
1	15,000
2	11,000
3	4,000
4	6,000
5	4,000

At the end of 5 years, the mine will be exhausted and the mining equipment will be worthless. The company accountant must now decide whether to use sum-of-years'-digits depreciation or unit-of-production depreciation. The company considers 8% to be an appropriate time value of money. Compute the depreciation schedule for each of the two methods. Which method would you recommend that the company adopt? Show the computations to justify your decision.

11-24 Some equipment that costs $1000 has a 5-year depreciable life and an estimated $50 salvage value at the end of that time. You have been assigned to determine whether to use straight-line or SOYD depreciation. If a 10% interest rate is appropriate, which is the preferred depreciation method for this profitable corporation? Use a spreadsheet to show your computations of the difference in present worths.

11-25 The FOURX Corp. has purchased $12,000 of experimental equipment. The anticipated salvage value is $400 at the end of its 5-year depreciable life. This profitable corporation is considering two methods of depreciation: sum of years' digits and double declining balance. If it uses 7% interest in its comparison, which method do you recommend? Show computations to support your recommendation. Use a spreadsheet to develop your solution.

Depreciation and Book Value

11-26 For its fabricated metal products, the Able Corp. is paying $10,000 for special tools that have a 4-year useful life and no salvage value. Compute the depreciation charge for the *second* year by each of the following methods:

(a) DDB

(b) Sum-of-years'-digits

(c) Modified accelerated cost recovery system

11-27 The MACRS depreciation percentages for 7-year personal property are given in Table 11-3. Make the necessary computations to determine if the percentages shown are correct.

11-28 The MACRS depreciation percentages for 10-year personal property are given in Table 11-3. Make the necessary computations to determine if the percentages shown are correct.

11-29 Use MACRS GDS depreciation for each of the assets, 1–3, to calculate the following items, (a)–(c).

1. A light general-purpose truck used by a delivery business, cost = $17,000

2. Production equipment used by a Detroit automaker to produce vehicles, cost = $30,000

3. Cement production facilities used by a construction firm, cost $130,000

(a) The MACRS GDS property class

(b) The depreciation deduction for Year 3

(c) The book value of the asset after 6 years

11-30 On July 1, Nancy paid $600,000 for a commercial building and an additional $150,000 for the land on which it stands. Four years later, also on July 1, she sold the property for $850,000. Compute the modified accelerated cost recovery system depreciation for each of the *five* calendar years during which she had the property.

11-31 A group of investors has formed Trump Corporation to purchase a small hotel. The asking price is $150,000 for the land and $850,000 for the hotel building. If the purchase takes place in June, compute the MACRS depreciation for the first three calendar years. Then assume the hotel is sold in June of the fourth year, and compute the MACRS depreciation in that year also.

11-32 Mr. Donald Spade bought a computer in January to keep records on all the property he owns. The computer cost $70,000 and is to be depreciated using MACRS. Donald's accountant pointed out that under a special tax rule (the rule applies when the value of property placed in service in the last 3 months of the tax year exceeds 40% of all the property placed in service during the tax year), the computer and all property that year would be subject to the midquarter convention. The midquarter convention assumes that all property placed in service in any quarter-year is placed in service at the midpoint of the quarter. Use the midquarter convention to compute Donald's MACRS depreciation for the first year.

11-33 A company is considering buying a new piece of machinery. A 10% interest rate will be used in the computations. Two models of the machine are available.

	Machine I	Machine II
Initial cost	$80,000	$100,000
End-of-useful-life salvage value, S	20,000	25,000
Annual operating cost	18,000	15,000 first 10 years
		20,000 thereafter
Useful life, in years	20	25

(a) Determine which machine should be purchased, based on equivalent uniform annual cost.

(b) What is the capitalized cost of Machine I?

(c) Machine I is purchased and a fund is set up to replace Machine I at the end of 20 years. Compute the required uniform annual deposit.

(d) Machine I will produce an annual saving of material of $28,000. What is the rate of return if Machine I is installed?

(e) What will be the book value of Machine I after 2 years, based on sum-of-years'-digits depreciation?

(f) What will be the book value of Machine II after 3 years, based on double declining balance depreciation?

(g) Assuming that Machine II is in the 7-year property class, what would be the MACRS depreciation in the third year?

11-34 Explain in your own words the difference between capital gains and ordinary gains. In addition, explain why it is important to our analysis as engineering economists. Do we see capital gains much in industry-based economic analyses or in our personal lives?

Gain/Loss on Disposal

11-35 Equipment costing $20,000 that is a MACRS 3-year property is disposed of during the second year for $14,000. Calculate any depreciation recapture, ordinary losses, or capital gains associated with disposal of the equipment.

11-36 An asset with an 8-year ADR class life costs $50,000 and was purchased on January 1, 2001. Calculate any depreciation recapture, ordinary losses, or capital gains associated with selling the equipment on December 31, 2003, for $15,000, $25,000, and $60,000. Consider two cases of depreciation for the problem: if MACRS GDS is used, and if straight-line depreciation over the ADR class life is used with a $10,000 salvage value.

11-37 A $150,000 asset has been depreciated with the straight-line method over an 8-year life. The estimated salvage value was $30,000. At the end of the 5th year the asset was sold for $90,000. From a tax perspective, what is happening at the time of disposal, and what is the dollar amount?

11-38 O'Leary Engineering Corp. has been depreciating a $50,000 machine for the last 3 years. The asset was just sold for 60% of its first cost. What is the size of the recaptured depreciation or loss at disposal using the following depreciation methods?

(a) Sum of years digits with $N = 8$ and $S = 2000$

(b) Straight-line depreciation with $N = 8$ and $S = 2000$

(c) MACRS GDS depreciation, classified as a 7-year property

Depletion

11-39 When a major highway was to be constructed nearby, a farmer realized that a dry streambed running through his property might be a valuable source of sand and gravel. He shipped samples to a testing laboratory and learned that the material met the requirements for certain low-grade fill material. The farmer contacted the highway construction contractor, who offered 65¢ per cubic meter for 45,000 cubic meters of sand and gravel. The contractor would build a haul road and would use his own equipment. All activity would take place during a single summer.

The farmer hired an engineering student for $2500 to count the truckloads of material hauled away. The farmer estimated that 2 acres of streambed had been stripped of the sand and gravel. The 640-acre farm had cost him $300 per acre, and the farmer felt the property had not changed in value. He knew that there had been no use for the sand and gravel prior to the construction of the highway, and he could foresee no future use for any of the remaining 50,000 cubic meters of sand and gravel.

Determine the farmer's depletion allowance. (*Answer:* $1462.50)

11-40 Mr. H. Salt purchased an $^1/_8$ interest in a producing oil well for $45,000. Recoverable oil reserves for the well were estimated at that time at 15,000 barrels, $^1/_8$ of which represented Mr. Salt's share of the reserves. During the subsequent year, Mr. Salt received $12,000 as his $^1/_8$ share of the gross income from the sale of 1000 barrels of oil. From this amount, he had to pay $3000 as his share of the expense of producing the oil. Compute Mr. Salt's depletion allowance for the year. (*Answer:* $3000)

11-41 American Pulp Corp. (APC) has entered into a contract to harvest timber for $450,000. The total estimated available harvest is 150 million board-feet.

(a) What is the depletion allowance for Years 1 to 3, if 42, 45, and 35 million board-feet are harvested by APC in those years?

(b) After 3 years, the total available harvest for the original tract was reestimated at 180 million board-feet. Compute the depletion allowances for Years 4 and beyond.

11-42 A piece of machinery has a cost basis of $45,000. Its salvage value will be $5000 after 10,000 hours of operation. With units-of-production depreciation, what is the allowable depreciation rate per hour? What is the book value after 4000 hours of operation?

11-43 Mining recently began on a new deposit of 10 million metric tons of ore (2% nickel and 4% copper). Annual production of 350,000 metric tons begins this year. The market price of nickel is $3.75 per pound and $0.65 for copper. Mining operation costs are expected to be $0.50 per pound. XYZ Mining Company paid $600 million for the deposits. What is the maximum depletion allowance each year for the mine?

CHAPTER 12

INCOME TAXES

On with the Wind

For over three decades, environmental activists and community leaders have bemoaned American dependence on foreign oil. The war in Iraq again highlighted the precariousness of relying on an unstable region of the world for a major part of our energy requirements.

One solution to this dilemma is to rely more on renewable sources of energy, such as solar power and wind. The technology for such alternative energy sources has been around for many years, and most voters seem to favor more reliance on renewables. If good intentions were all it took, we'd be getting much of our electricity from windmills.

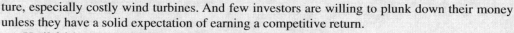

But, of course, making the transition to greater use of wind power requires a significant investment in infrastructure, especially costly wind turbines. And few investors are willing to plunk down their money unless they have a solid expectation of earning a competitive return.

Until fairly recently, cost factors kept wind energy from becoming an attractive investment. As recently as the late 1980s, wind-generated power cost roughly twice as much to produce as energy from conventional sources.

More recently, however, wind energy has decreased dramatically in price. The American Wind Energy Association (AWEA) reports that many modern, state-of-the-art wind plants can now produce power for less than 5¢ per kilowatt-hour, making them competitive with conventional sources. Unsurprisingly, investment in wind power production has also increased substantially.

How did this happen? In part, the trend was driven by advances in wind turbine technology. But it was helped significantly by a provision of the federal tax law contained in the Energy Policy Act of 1992. This statute allowed utilities and other electricity suppliers a "production tax credit" of 1.5¢ per kilowatt-hour (later adjusted to 1.9¢ to account for the effects of inflation).

This was a key incentive to the wind power industry which, like all energy producers, must expend large sums on capital assets. The tax credit had a dramatic effect on the wind energy market. During 2001, for instance, energy producers added almost 1700 megawatts of wind-generating capacity—enough to power nearly half a million homes.

But what the government giveth, the government can take away. When the production tax credit (PTC) briefly expired at the end of 2001, an estimated $3 billion worth of wind projects were suspended, and hundreds of workers were laid off. Fortunately for the industry, the credit was subsequently extended to the end of 2003. Later, the PTC was extended again, until 2008.

1. The wind energy tax credit has both advocates and opponents. One camp argues that the government should not support wind energy through tax credits—instead, let the market determine the future of alternative energy sources. Others argue that government has historically supported the oil and coal industries through subsidies, and in addition we as a society "pay" for the negative effects that these forms of energy have on health and the environment. Which side has the stronger argument in your view? Why?

2. Clearly wind energy has both costs and benefits as an alternate energy technology, and government may have some role in enabling its development and promoting investments in it. Develop a table of the costs and benefits of wind energy technology. In doing so, think about the producers and consumers of the technology as well as society in general. Think about who the winners and losers would be if we as a nation could dramatically increase the fraction of our energy from wind sources. Add a column that identifies the ethical issues that arise? Can we solve any of the ethical issues that you've identified?

3. Developing a wind power project takes many years and requires the commitment of large sums of investment capital before the project begins to return a profit. What is the effect on investment when the wind power production tax credit is allowed to expire, or is extended for periods of only a few years?

4. The federal income tax was introduced in the U.S. in 1913. Using the Internet, can you determine how tax rates changed throughout the course of the 20th century? How has this affected the value of tax credits to industry?

After Completing This Chapter...

The student should be able to:

- Calculate *taxes due* or *taxes owed* for both individuals and corporations.
- Understand the incremental nature of the individual and corporate tax rates used for calculating taxes on income.
- Calculate a combined income tax rate for state and federal income taxes and select an appropriate tax rate for engineering economic analyses.
- Utilize an *after-tax tax table* to find the after-tax cash flows for a prospective investment project.
- Calculate after-tax measures of merit, such as present worth, annual worth, payback period, internal rate of return, and benefit–cost ratio, from developed after-tax cash flows.
- Evaluate investment alternatives on an after-tax basis including asset disposal.
- Use spreadsheets for solving after-tax economic analysis problems.

As Benjamin Franklin said, two things are inevitable: death and taxes. In this chapter we will examine the structure of taxes in the U.S. These include sales taxes, gasoline taxes, property taxes, and state and federal income taxes. Here we will concentrate our attention on federal income taxes. Income taxes are part of most real problems and often have a substantial impact that must be considered.

First, we must understand the way in which taxes are imposed. Chapter 11 concerning depreciation is an integral part of this analysis, so the principles covered there must be well understood. Then, having understood the mechanism, we will see how federal income taxes affect our economic analysis.

A PARTNER IN THE BUSINESS

Probably the most straightforward way to understand the role of federal income taxes is to consider the U.S. government as a partner in every business activity. As a partner, the government shares in the profits from every successful venture. In a somewhat more complex way, the government shares in the losses of unprofitable ventures too. The tax laws are complex, and it is not our purpose to fully explain them.[1] Instead, we will examine the fundamental concepts of the federal income tax laws—and we emphasize at the start that there are exceptions and variations to almost every statement we shall make!

CALCULATION OF TAXABLE INCOME

At the mention of income taxes, one can visualize dozens of elaborate and complex calculations. There is some truth to that vision, for there can be complexities in computing income taxes. Yet incomes taxes are just another type of disbursement. Our economic analysis calculations in prior chapters have dealt with all sorts of disbursements: operating costs, maintenance, labor and materials, and so forth. Now we simply add one more prospective disbursement to the list—income taxes.

Taxable Income of Individuals

The amount of federal income taxes to be paid depends on taxable income and the income tax rates. Therefore, our first concern is the definition of **taxable income.** To begin, one must compute his or her **gross income:**

$$\text{Gross income} = \text{Wages, salary, etc.} + \text{Interest income} + \text{Dividends} + \text{Capital gains}$$
$$+ \text{Unemployment compensation} + \text{Other income}$$

From gross income, we subtract any allowable retirement plan contributions and other **adjustments.** The result is **adjusted gross income (AGI).** From adjusted gross income, individuals may deduct the following items:[2]

---

[1] Many government and private sources exist that describe detailed taxation information. These include the Internal Revenue Service (www.irs.gov), U.S. Treasury (www.treasury.gov), Commerce Clearing House (www.cch.com), and Research Institute of America (www.riahome.com).

[2] The 2007 returns itemized deductions are limited if adjusted gross income is more than $156,400 ($78,200 if married filing separately). Data given here is for 2007 returns, filed in 2008.)

1. **Personal Exemptions.** One exemption ($3400 for 2007 returns) is provided for each person who depends on the gross income for his or her living.[3]

2. **Itemized Deductions.** Some of these are:

   (*a*) Excessive medical and dental expenses (exceeding $7\frac{1}{2}\%$ of adjusted gross income)

   (*b*) State and local income, real estate and personal property tax

   (*c*) Home mortgage interest

   (*d*) Charitable contributions

   (*e*) Casualty and theft losses (exceeding $100 + 10\%$ of adjusted gross income)

   (*f*) Job expenses and certain miscellaneous deductions (some categories must exceed 2% of adjusted gross income)

3. **Standard Deduction**. Each taxpayer may either itemize his or her deductions, or instead take a standard deduction as follows:

   (*a*) Single taxpayers, $5350 (for 2007 returns)

   (*b*) Married taxpayers filing a joint return, $10,700 (for 2007 returns)

The result is **taxable income.**

For individuals, taxable income is computed as follows:

$$\text{Adjusted gross income} = \text{Gross income} - \text{Adjustments}$$

$$\textbf{Taxable income} = \text{Adjusted gross income}$$
$$- \text{ Personal exemption(s)}$$
$$- \text{ Itemized deductions or Standard deduction} \qquad (12\text{-}1)$$

Classification of Business Expenditures

When an individual or a firm operates a business, there are three distinct types of business expenditure:

1. For depreciable assets.

2. For nondepreciable assets.

3. All other business expenditures.

Expenditures for depreciable assets: When facilities or productive equipment with useful lives in excess of one year are acquired, the taxpayer will recover the investment through depreciation charges.[4] Chapter 11 detailed how to allocate an asset's cost over its useful life.

---

[3]For 2007 returns if adjusted gross income is over $117,300 and depending upon filing status, the personal exemption deduction may be reduced.

[4]There is an exception. In 2007, businesses may immediately deduct (*expense*) up to $112,000 of business equipment (via the Section 179 Business Deduction) in a year, provided their total equipment expenditure for the year does not exceed $450,000. Between $450,000 and $562,000 in qualifying Section 179 property, the dollar limit is reduced by the amount over $450,000. Above $562,000 a Section 179 deduction cannot be taken.

Expenditures for nondepreciable assets: Land is considered to be a nondepreciable asset, for there is no finite life associated with it. Other nondepreciable assets are properties *not* used either in a trade, in a business, or for the production of income. An individual's home and car are generally nondepreciable assets. The final category of nondepreciable assets comprises those subject to *depletion,* rather than *depreciation.* Since business firms generally acquire assets for use in the business, their only nondepreciable assets normally are land and assets subject to depletion.

All other business expenditures: This category is probably the largest of all, for it includes all the ordinary and necessary expenditures of operating a business. Labor costs, materials, all direct and indirect costs, and facilities and productive equipment with a useful life of one year or less are part of routine expenditures. They are charged as a business expense—*expensed*—when they occur.

Business expenditures in the first two categories—that is, for either depreciable or nondepreciable assets—are called **capital expenditures.** In the accounting records of the firm, they are **capitalized;** all ordinary and necessary expenditures in the third category are **expensed.**

Taxable Income of Business Firms

The starting point in computing a firm's taxable income is *gross income.* All ordinary and necessary expenses to conduct the business—*except* capital expenditures—are deducted from gross income. Capital expenditures may *not* be deducted from gross income. Except for land, business capital expenditures are allowed on a period by period basis through depreciation or depletion charges.

For business firms, taxable income is computed as follows:

$$\textbf{Taxable income} = \text{Gross income}$$
$$- \text{All expenditures except capital expenditures}$$
$$- \text{Depreciation and depletion charges} \qquad (12\text{-}2)$$

Because of the treatment of capital expenditures for tax purposes, the taxable income of a firm may be quite different from the actual cash flows.

EXAMPLE 12-1

During a 3-year period, a firm had the following cash flows (in millions of dollars):

	Year 1	Year 2	Year 3
Gross income from sales	$200	$200	$200
Purchase of special tooling (useful life: 3 years)	−60	0	0
All other expenditures	−140	−140	−140
Cash flows for the year	$ 0	$ 60	$ 60

Compute the taxable income for each of the 3 years.

SOLUTION

The cash flows for each year would suggest that Year 1 was a poor one, while Years 2 and 3 were very profitable. A closer look reveals that the firm's cash flows were adversely affected in Year 1 by the purchase of special tooling. Since the special tooling has a 3-year useful life, it is a capital expenditure with its cost allocated over the useful life. If we assume that straight-line depreciation applies with no salvage value, we use Equation 11-2 to find the annual charge:

$$\text{Annual depreciation charge} = \frac{B - S}{N} = \frac{60 - 0}{3} = \$20 \text{ million}$$

Applying Equation 12-2, we write

$$\text{Taxable income} = 200 - 140 - 20 = \$40 \text{ million}$$

In each of the 3 years, the taxable income is $40 million.

An examination of the cash flows and the taxable income in Example 12-1 indicates that taxable income is a better indicator of the firm's annual performance.

INCOME TAX RATES

Income tax rates for individuals changed many times between 1960 and 1995, as illustrated in Figure 12-1. Recent movements have been less dramatic. From 1995 to 2000 the maximum rate was 39.6%; it fell to 39.1% in 2001 and to 38.6% in 2002. From 2003 through 2007 it was 35%.

Individual Tax Rates

There are four schedules of federal income tax rates for individuals. Single taxpayers use the Table 12-1a schedule. Married taxpayers filing a joint return use the Table 12-1b

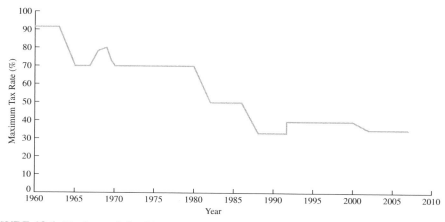

FIGURE 12-1 Maximum federal income tax rates for individuals.

TABLE 12-1a **2007 Tax Rates for Single Taxpayers**

Taxable Income		Tax		
Over	But Not Over	Base Tax	Plus	On Income Over
$ 0	$ 7,825	$ 0.00	10%	$ 0
7,825	31,850	782.50	15%	7,825
31,850	77,100	4,386.50	25%	31,850
77,100	160,850	15,698.75	28%	77,100
160,850	349,700	39,148.75	33%	160,850
Over 349,700		101,469.25	35%	349,700

TABLE 12-1b **2007 Tax Rates for Married Individuals Filing Jointly**

Taxable Income		Tax		
Over	But Not Over	Base Tax	Plus	On Income Over
$ 0	$ 15,650	$ 0.00	10%	$ 0
15,650	63,700	1,565.00	15%	15,650
63,700	128,500	8,772.50	25%	63,700
128,500	195,850	24,972.50	28%	128,500
195,850	349,700	43,830.50	33%	195,850
Over 349,700		94,601.00	35%	349,700

schedule. Two other schedules (not shown here) are applicable to unmarried individuals with dependent relatives ("head of household"), and married taxpayers filing separately.

EXAMPLE 12-2

An unmarried student earned $10,000 in the summer plus another $6000 during the rest of the year. When he files an income tax return, he will be allowed one exemption (for himself). He estimates that he spent $1000 on allowable itemized deductions. How much income tax will he pay?

$$\textbf{Adjusted gross income} = \$10,000 + \$6000 = \$16,000$$

$$\textbf{Taxable income} = \text{Adjusted gross income}$$

$$- \text{Deduction for one exemption (\$3400)}$$

$$- \text{Standard deduction (\$5350)}$$

$$= 16,000 - 3400 - 5350 = \$7250$$

$$\textbf{Federal income tax} = 10\%\ (7250) = \$725$$

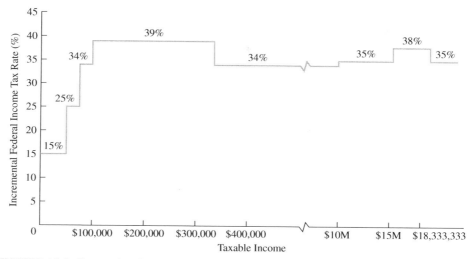

FIGURE 12-2 Corporation federal income tax rates (2006) rates. Federal corporate tax rates have been constant over the past several years.

TABLE 12-2 **Corporate Income Tax Rates**

Taxable Income	Tax Rate	Corporate Income Tax
Not over $50,000	15%	15% over $0
$50,000–75,000	25%	$7,500 + 25% over $50,000
$75,000–100,000	34%	$13,750 + 34% over $75,000
$100,000–335,000	39%*	$22,250 + 39% over $100,000
$335,000–10 million	34%	$113,900 + 34% over $335,000
$10 million–15 million	35%	$3,400,000 + 35% over $10 million
$15 million–18,333,333	38%	$5,159,000 + 38% over $15 million
≥$18,333,333	35%	$6,425,667 + 35% over $18,333,333

*The extra 5% from $100,000 to $335,000 was chosen so that firms in the $335,000 to $10 million bracket pay a flat 34% tax rate. [(0.39 − 0.34)](335,000 − 100;000) = (0.34 − 0.15)(50,000) + (0.34 − 0.25)(75,000 − 50,000)] so tax = 0.34 (tax income) in $335,000 to $10 million bracket. Similarly, for corporate incomes over $18,333,333 the tax rate schedule is equivalent to a flat tax rate of 35%.

Corporate Tax Rates

Income tax for corporations is computed in a manner similar to that for individuals. The data in Figure 12-2 can be presented in schedule form (Table 12-2).

EXAMPLE 12-3

The French Chemical Corporation was formed to produce household bleach. The firm bought land for $220,000, had a $900,000 factory building erected, and installed $650,000 worth of chemical and packaging equipment. The plant was completed and operations begun on April 1. The gross income for the calendar year was $450,000. Supplies and all operating expenses, excluding the capital expenditures, were $100,000. The firm will use modified accelerated cost recovery system (MACRS) depreciation.

    (a) What is the first-year depreciation charge?

    (b) What is the first-year taxable income?

    (c) How much will the corporation pay in federal income taxes for the year?

SOLUTION TO PART a

MACRS depreciation: Chemical equipment is personal property. From Table 11-2, it is probably in the "7-year, all other property" class.

$$\text{First-year depreciation(equipment)} = \$650,000 \times 14.29\% = \$92,885$$

The building is in the 39-year real property class. Since it was placed in service on April 1, the first-year depreciation is:

$$\text{First-year depreciation(building)} = \$900,000 \times 1.819\% = \$16,371 \quad \text{(see Table 11-4)}$$

The land is a nondepreciable asset. Thus we have

$$\text{Total first year MACRS depreciation} = \$92,885 + \$16,371 = \$109,256$$

SOLUTION TO PART b

$$
\begin{aligned}
\text{Taxable income} = {} & \text{Gross income} \\
& - \text{All expenditures except capital expenditures} \\
& - \text{Depreciation and depletion charges} \\
= {} & \$450,000 - 100,000 - 109,256 = \$240,744
\end{aligned}
$$

SOLUTION TO PART c

$$
\begin{aligned}
\text{Federal income tax} &= \$22,250 + 39\%(240,744 - 100,000) \\
&= \$77,140
\end{aligned}
$$

Combined Federal and State Income Taxes

In addition to federal income taxes, most individuals and corporations pay state income taxes. It would be convenient if we could derive a single tax rate to represent both the state and federal incremental tax rates. In the computation of taxable income for federal taxes, the amount of state taxes paid is one of the allowable itemized deductions. Federal income taxes are not, however, generally deductible in the computation of state taxable income. Therefore, the state income tax is applied to a *larger* taxable income than is the federal income tax rate. As a result, the combined incremental tax rate will not be the sum of two tax rates.

    For an increment of income (ΔIncome) and tax rate on incremental income (ΔTax rate):

$$\text{State income taxes} = (\Delta\text{State tax rate})(\Delta\text{Income})$$

$$\text{Federal taxable income} = (\Delta\text{Income})(1 - \Delta\text{State tax rate})$$

$$\text{Federal income taxes} = (\Delta\text{Federal tax rate})(\Delta\text{Income}) \times (1 - \Delta\text{State tax rate})$$

The total of state and federal income taxes is

$$[\Delta\text{State tax rate} + (\Delta\text{Federal tax rate})(1 - \Delta\text{State tax rate})](\Delta\text{Income})$$

The term in the brackets gives the combined incremental tax rate.

Combined incremental tax rate

$$= \Delta\text{State tax rate} + (\Delta\text{Federal tax rate})(1 - \Delta\text{State tax rate}) \quad (12\text{-}3)$$

EXAMPLE 12-4

An engineer has an income that puts her in the 25% federal income tax bracket and at the 10% state incremental tax rate. She has an opportunity to earn an extra $500 by doing a small consulting job. What will be her combined state and federal income tax rate on the additional income?

SOLUTION

Use Equation 12-3 to find the combined incremental tax rate: $0.10 + 0.25(1 - 0.10) = 32.5\%$.

Selecting an Income Tax Rate for Economy Studies

Since income tax rates vary with the level of taxable income for both individuals and corporations, one must decide which tax rate to use in a particular situation. The simple answer is that the tax rate to use is the incremental tax rate that applies to the change in taxable income projected in the economic analysis. If a married couple filing jointly has a taxable income of $40,000 and can increase their income by $2000, what tax rate should be used for the $2000 of incremental income? From Table 12-1b, we see the $2000 falls within the 10% tax bracket.

Now suppose this couple could increase their $40,000 income by $10,000. In this situation, Table 12-1b shows that the 10% incremental tax rate should be applied to the first $7825 and a 25% incremental tax rate to the last $2175 of extra income. The appropriate incremental tax rate for corporations is equally easy to determine. For larger corporations, the federal incremental tax rate is 35%. In addition, there may be up to a 12 to 15% state tax.

ECONOMIC ANALYSIS TAKING INCOME TAXES INTO ACCOUNT

An important step in economic analysis has been to resolve the consequences of alternatives into a cash flow. Because income taxes have been ignored, the result has been a *before-tax cash flow*. This before-tax cash flow is an essential component in economic analysis that also considers the consequences of income tax. The principal elements in an *after-tax analysis* are as follows:

- Before-tax cash flow
- Depreciation
- Taxable income (Before-tax cash flow − Depreciation)
- Income taxes (Taxable income × Incremental tax rate)
- After-tax cash flow (Before-tax cash flow − Income taxes)

These elements are usually arranged to form an after-tax *cash flow table*. This is illustrated by Example 12–5.

EXAMPLE 12-5

A medium-sized profitable corporation may buy a $3000 used pickup truck for use by the shipping and receiving department. During the truck's 5-year useful life, it is estimated the firm will save $800 per year after all the costs of owning and operating the truck have been paid. Truck salvage value is estimated at $750.

(a) What is the before-tax rate of return?

(b) What is the after-tax rate of return on this capital expenditure? Assume straight-line depreciation.

SOLUTION TO PART a

For a before-tax rate of return, we must first compute the before-tax cash flow.

Year	Before-Tax Cash Flow
0	−$3000
1	+800
2	+800
3	+800
4	+800
5	$\begin{cases} +800 \\ +750 \end{cases}$

Solve for the before-tax rate of return, IRR_{BT}:

$$3000 = 800(P/A, i, 5) + 750(P/F, i, 5)$$

Try $i = 15\%$:

$$3000 \stackrel{?}{=} 800(3.352) + 750(0.4972) \stackrel{?}{=} 2682 + 373 = 3055$$

Since i is slightly low, try $i = 18\%$:

$$3000 \stackrel{?}{=} 800(3.127) + 750(0.4371) \stackrel{?}{=} 2502 + 328 = 2830$$

$$IRR_{BT} = 15\% + 3\% \left(\frac{3055 - 3000}{3055 - 2830} \right) = 15\% + 3\%(0.15) = 15.7\%$$

SOLUTION TO PART b

For an after-tax rate of return, we must set up an after-tax cash flow table (Table 12-3). The starting point is the before-tax cash flow. Then we will need the depreciation schedule for the truck:

$$\text{Straight-line depreciation} = \frac{B - S}{N} = \frac{3000 - 750}{5} = \$450 \text{ per year}$$

TABLE 12-3 After-Tax Cash Flow Table for Example 12-5

Year	(a) Before-Tax Cash Flow	(b) Straight-Line Depreciation	(c) Δ(Taxable Income) (a)−(b)	(d) 34% Income Taxes −0.34 (c)	(e) After-Tax Cash Flow (a) + (d)†
0	−$3000				−$3000
1	800	$450	$350	−$119	681
2	800	450	350	−119	681
3	800	450	350	−119	681
4	800	450	350	−119	681
5	$\begin{cases}800\\750\end{cases}$	450	350	−119	$\begin{cases}681\\750\end{cases}$

*Sign convention for income taxes: a minus (−) represents a disbursement of money to pay income taxes; a plus (+) represents the receipt of money by a decrease in the tax liability.

†The after-tax cash flow is the before-tax cash flow minus income taxes. Based on the income tax sign convention, this is accomplished by *adding* columns (a) and (d).

Taxable income is the before-tax cash flow *minus* depreciation. For this medium-sized profitable corporation, let's assume an incremental federal income tax rate of 34%. Therefore income taxes are 34% of taxable income. Finally, the after-tax cash flow equals the before-tax cash flow *minus* income taxes. These data are used to compute Table 12-3.

The after-tax cash flow may be solved to find the after-tax rate of return, IRR_{AT}. Try $i = 10\%$:

$$3000 \overset{?}{=} 681(P/A, 10\%, 5) + 750(P/F, 10\%, 5)$$
$$\overset{?}{=} 681(3.791) + 750(0.6209) = 3047$$

Since i is slightly low, try $i = 12\%$:

$$3000 \overset{?}{=} 681(3.605) + 750(0.5674) = 2881$$

$$\text{IRR}_{AT} = 10\% + 2\%\left(\frac{3047 - 3000}{3047 - 2881}\right) = 10.6\%$$

The calculations required to compute the after-tax rate of return in Example 12-5 were certainly more elaborate than those for the before-tax rate of return. It must be emphasized, however, that often the after-tax rate of return is the key value, since income taxes are a major disbursement that cannot be ignored.

EXAMPLE 12-6

An analysis of a firm's sales activities indicates that a number of profitable sales are lost each year because the firm cannot deliver some of its products quickly enough. By investing an additional $20,000 in inventory it is believed that the firm will realize $1000 more in before-tax profits in the first year. In the second year, before-tax extra profit will be $1500. Profits for subsequent years are expected to continue to increase on a $500-per-year gradient. The investment in the additional inventory may be recovered at the end of a 4-year analysis period simply by selling it and not replenishing the inventory. Compute:

(a) The before-tax rate of return.

(b) The after-tax rate of return assuming an incremental tax rate of 39%.

SOLUTION

Inventory is not considered to be a depreciable asset. Therefore, the investment in additional inventory is not depreciated. The after-tax cash flow table for the problem is presented in Table 12-4.

SOLUTION TO PART a

Use the following equation to calculate the before-tax rate of return:

$$20,000 = 1000(P/A, i, 4) + 500(P/G, i, 4) + 20,000(P/F, i, 4)$$

Try $i = 8\%$:

$$20,000 \neq 1000(3.312) + 500(4.650) + 20,000(0.7350)$$
$$\neq 3312 + 2325 + 14,700 = 20,337$$

TABLE 12-4 After-tax Cash Flow Table for Example 12-6

Year	(a) Before-Tax Cash Flow	(b) Depreciation	(c) △(Taxable Income) (a)−(b)	(d) 39% Income Taxes (c) x−0.39	(e) After-Tax Cash Flow (a) + (d)
0	−$20,000				−$20,000
1	1,000	—	$1000	−$390	610
2	1,500	—	1500	−585	915
3	2,000	—	2000	−780	1,220
4	{ 2,500 20,000	—	2500	−975	{ 1,525 20,000

Since i is too low, try $i = 10\%$:

$$20,000 \neq 1000(3.170) + 500(4.378) + 20,000(0.6830)$$
$$\neq 3170 + 2189 + 13,660 = 19,019$$

$$\text{Before-tax rate of return } = 8\% + 2\%\left(\frac{20,337 - 20,000}{20,337 - 19,019}\right) = 8.5\%$$

SOLUTION TO PART b

For a before-tax cash flow gradient of $500, the resulting after-tax cash flow gradient is $(1 - 0.39)(500) = \$305$.

$$20,000 = 610(P/A, i, 4) + 305(P/G, i, 4) + 20,000(P/F, i, 4)$$

Try $i = 5\%$:

$$20,000 \neq 610(3.546) + 305(5.103) + 20,000(0.8227) \neq 20,173$$

Since i is too low, try $i = 6\%$:

$$20,000 \neq 610(3.465) + 300(4.4945) + 20,000(0.7921) \neq 19,304$$

$$\text{After-tax rate of return} = 5\% + 1\%\left(\frac{20,173 - 20,000}{20,173 - 19,304}\right) = 5.2\%$$

CAPITAL GAINS AND LOSSES FOR NONDEPRECIATED ASSETS

When a nondepreciated capital asset is sold or exchanged, appropriate entries are made in the firm's accounting records. If the selling price of the capital asset exceeds the original cost basis, the excess is called a **capital gain.** If the selling price is less than the original cost basis, the difference is a **capital loss.** Examples of nondepreciated assets include stocks, land, art, and collectibles.

$$\text{Capital}\begin{bmatrix}\text{Gain} \\ \text{Loss}\end{bmatrix} = \text{Selling price} - \text{Original cost basis}$$

Current tax law sets the highest net capital gains tax at 15% for most assets held by individuals for more than one year. This is in contrast to recaptured depreciation, which is taxed at the same rate as other (ordinary) income. The tax treatment of capital gains and losses for nondepreciated assets is shown in Table 12-5.

Investment Tax Credit

When the economy slows down and unemployment rises, the U.S. government frequently alters its tax laws to promote greater industrial activity. One technique used to stimulate capital investments has been the **investment tax credit (ITC).** Businesses were able to

TABLE 12-5 **Tax Treatment of Capital Gains and Losses**

For Individuals

Capital gain	For most assets held for less than 1 year, taxed as ordinary income. For most assets held for more than 1 year, taxed at 15% tax rate.*
Capital loss	Subtract capital losses from any capital gains; balance may be deducted from ordinary income, but not more than $3000 per year ($1500 if married filing separately). Excess capital losses may be carried into future taxable years indefinitely.

For Corporations

Capital gain	Taxed as ordinary income.
Capital loss	Corporations may deduct capital losses only to the extent of capital gains. Any capital loss in the current year that exceeds capital gains can be carried back 2 years, and, if not completely absorbed, is then carried forward for up to 20 years.

*Depending on tax bracket, type of asset, and duration of ownership, the capital gain tax rate can range from 5% to 28%. In addition, a special 0% capital gain tax rate applies to homeowners who treat their home as a primary residence for at least 2 years within a 5-year period before selling. In such cases, single taxpayers are allowed $250,000 in tax-free gain ($500,000 for married couples).

deduct a percentage of their new business equipment purchases as a *tax credit*. This meant that the firm's net cost of the equipment was reduced by the amount of the investment tax credit. Depending on the specific investment tax credit provisions, the credit might be subtracted from the basis for depreciation, or the basis for computing depreciation might remain the full cost of the equipment. The Tax Reform Act of 1986 eliminated the investment tax credit for most assets, although credits are allowed in some specialized cases such as historic building preservation and in the development of alternate energy sources. It is likely, however, that the general ITC will reappear at some future time.

ESTIMATING THE AFTER-TAX RATE OF RETURN

There is no shortcut method for computing the after-tax rate of return from the before-tax rate of return. One possible exception to this statement is in the situation of nondepreciable assets. In this special case, we have

After-tax rate of return = $(1 - $ Incremental tax rate$) \times ($Before-tax rate of return$)$

For Example 12-6, we could estimate the after-tax rate of return from the before-tax rate of return as follows:

$$\text{After-tax rate of return} = (1 - 0.39)(8.5\%) = 5.2\%$$

This value agrees with the value computed in Example 12-6(b).

This relationship may be helpful for selecting a trial after-tax rate of return when the before-tax rate of return is known. It must be emphasized, however, this relationship is only a rough approximation in almost all situations.

AFTER-TAX CASH FLOWS AND SPREADSHEETS

Realistic after-tax analysis requires spreadsheets. Even if costs and revenues are the same every year, MACRS depreciation percentages are not. The steps for calculating an after-tax internal rate of return are illustrated in Example 12-7. Because some cash flows are taxed and some are not, the spreadsheet is easier to build if these two types are separated. Spreadsheet construction is easier, as well, if recaptured depreciation or other gain/loss on disposal or sale is tabulated separately.

Taxes are considered even if only the costs of a project are known. The firm that does an engineering project must generate profits—or go out of business. Even if a firm has an unprofitable year, the tax law includes carry-forward and -backward provisions to transfer deductions to profitable years. The depreciation and revenues in Example 12-7 result in a negative taxable income for Year 2. Thus the *positive cash flow* due to taxes that is shown in Year 2 of Example 12-7 really represents tax savings for the firm.

EXAMPLE 12-7

Return to the data of Example 12-6, where the used truck had a first cost of $3000, a salvage value after 5 years of $750, and savings of $800 per year. Use MACRS depreciation and calculate the after-tax rate of return.

SOLUTION

Under MACRS, vehicles have a 5-year recovery period. Thus the MACRS depreciation can be calculated by using a VDB function (see "Spreadsheets and Depreciation" at the end of Chapter 11) or by lookup in Table 11-3. The depreciation in Year 5 has been halved, since it is the year of disposal.

	A	B	C	D	E	F	G	H
1	3000	First Cost						
2	800	Annual Benefit						
3	5	Recovery Period						
4	750	Salvage Value						
5	0.34	Tax Rate						
6								
7	Year	Untaxed BTCF	Taxed BTCF	MACRS	Recaptured Depreciation	Tax Income	Tax	ATCF
8	0	−3000						−3000.0
9	1		800	600.0		200.0	−68.0	732.0
10	2		800	960.0		(160.0)	54.4	854.4
11	3		800	576.0		224.0	−76.2	723.8
12	4		800	345.6		454.4	−154.5	645.5
13	5	750	800	172.8	404.4	1031.6	−350.7	1199.3
14		Cum. Depr.=		2654.4			IRR=	11.24%
15								
16						=Taxed BTCF − MACRS + Recapt.		
17					=Salvage − BookValue			

FIGURE 12-3 Spreadsheet for after-tax IRR calculation.

Note from Figure 12-3 that using MACRS rather than straight-line depreciation increases the after-tax IRR from 10.6% to 11.24%. This is due solely to the faster write-off that is allowed under MACRS.

SUMMARY

Since income taxes are part of most problems, no realistic economic analysis can ignore their consequences. Income taxes make the U.S. government a partner in every business venture. Thus the government benefits from all profitable ventures and shares in the losses of unprofitable ventures.

The first step in computing individual income taxes is to tabulate gross income. Any adjustments—for example, allowable taxpayer contributions to a retirement fund—are subtracted to yield adjusted gross income. Personal exemptions and either itemized deductions or the standard deduction are subtracted to find taxable income. This is used, together with a tax rate table, to compute the income tax liability for the year.

For corporations, taxable income equals gross income *minus* all ordinary and necessary expenditures (except capital expenditures) and depreciation and depletion charges. The income tax computation (whether for an individual or a corporation) is relatively simple, with rates ranging from 10 to 39%. The proper rate to use in an economic analysis is the incremental tax rate applicable to the increment of taxable income being considered.

Most individuals and corporations pay state income taxes in addition to federal income taxes. Since state income taxes are an allowable deduction in computing federal taxable income, it follows that the taxable income for the federal computation is lower than the state taxable income.

Combined state and federal incremental tax rate

$$= \Delta\text{State tax rate} + (\Delta\text{Federal tax rate})(1 - \Delta\text{State tax rate})$$

To introduce the effect of income taxes into an economic analysis, the starting point is a before-tax cash flow. Then the depreciation schedule is deducted from appropriate parts of the before-tax cash flow to obtain taxable income. Income taxes are obtained by multiplying taxable income by the proper tax rate. Before-tax cash flow less income taxes equals the after-tax cash flow. This data is all captured in an after-tax cash flow table.

Current tax law has decreased long-term capital gains on most nondepreciated assets for individuals to 15% when held for more than 1 year and provided an exclusion on the gain of the principal residence held for more than 2 years.

When dealing with nondepreciable assets, there is a nominal relationship between before-tax and after-tax rate of return. It is

$$\text{After-tax rate of return} = (1 - \Delta\text{Tax rate})(\text{Before-tax rate of return})$$

There is no simple relationship between before-tax and after-tax rate of return in the more usual case of investments involving depreciable assets.

PROBLEMS

These problems can be solved by hand, but most will be solved much more easily with a spreadsheet.

Individual/Joint Taxes

12-1 An unmarried taxpayer with no dependents expects an adjusted gross income of $70,000 in a given year. His nonbusiness deductions are expected to be $6000.

(*a*) What will his federal income tax be?

(*b*) He is considering an additional activity expected to increase his adjusted gross income. If this increase should be $16,000 and there should be no change in nonbusiness deductions or exemptions, what will be the increase in his federal income tax?

12-2 John Adams has a 65,000 adjusted gross income from Apple Corp. and allowable itemized deductions of $7200. Mary Eve has a $75,000 adjusted gross income and $2000 of allowable itemized deductions. Compute the total tax they would pay as unmarried individuals. Then compute their tax as a married couple filing a joint return. (*Answers:* $10,024 + 12,986.50 = 23,010.50; 23,597.50)

12-3 Bill Jackson had a total taxable income of $1800. Bill's employer wants him to work another month during the summer, but Bill had planned to spend the month hiking. If an additional month's work would increase Bill's taxable income by $1600, how much more money would he have after paying the income tax? (*Answer:* $1440)

12-4 A married couple filing jointly have a combined total adjusted gross income of $75,000. They have computed that their allowable itemized deductions are $4000. Compute their federal income tax. (*Answer:* $7,842.50)

12-5 Jane Shay operates a management consulting business. The business has been successful and now produces a taxable income of $100,000 per year after all "ordinary and necessary" expenses and depreciation have been deducted. At present the business is operated as a proprietorship; that is, Jane pays personal federal income tax on the entire $100,000. For tax purposes, it is as if she had a job that pays her a $100,000 salary per year.

As an alternative, Jane is considering incorporating the business. If she does, she will pay herself a salary of $40,000 a year from the corporation. The corporation will then pay taxes on the remaining $60,000 and retain the balance of the money as a corporate asset. Thus Jane's two alternatives are to operate the business as a proprietorship or as a corporation. Jane is single and has $3500 of itemized personal deductions. Which alternative will result in a smaller total payment of taxes to the government? (*Answer:* Incorporation, $14,296 versus $19,661)

12-6 Bill Alexander and his wife, Valerie, are both employed. Bill will have an adjusted gross income this year of $70,000. Valerie has an adjusted gross income of $2000 a month. Bill and Valerie have agreed that Valerie should continue working only until the federal income tax on their joint income tax return becomes $11,500. On what date should Valerie quit her job?

12-7 An unmarried individual in California with a taxable income of about $80,000 has a federal incremental tax rate of 28% and a state incremental tax rate of 9.3%. What is his combined incremental tax rate?

Corporate Taxes

12-8 A company wants to set up a new office in a country where the corporate tax rate is as follows: 15% of first $50,000 profits, 25% of next $25,000, 34% of next $25,000, and 39% of everything over $100,000. Executives estimate that they will have gross revenues of $500,000, total costs of $300,000, $30,000 in allowable tax deductions, and a one time business start-up credit of $8000. What is taxable income for the first year, and how much should the company expect to pay in taxes?

12-9 ARKO oil company purchased two large compressors for $125,000 each. One compressor was installed in the firm's Texas refinery and is being depreciated by MACRS depreciation. The other compressor was placed in the Oklahoma refinery, where it is being depreciated by sum-of-years'-digits depreciation with zero salvage value. Assume the company pays federal income taxes each year and the tax rate is constant. The corporate accounting department noted that the two compressors are being depreciated differently and wonders whether the corporation will wind up paying more income taxes over the life of the equipment as a result of this. What do you tell them?

12-10 Sole Brother Inc. is a shoe outlet to a major shoe manufacturing industry located in Chicago. Sole Brother uses accounts payable as one of its financing sources. Shoes are delivered to Sole Brother with a 3% discount if payment on the invoice is received within 10 days of delivery. By paying after the 10-day period, Sole is borrowing money and paying (giving up) the 3% discount. Although Sole Brother is not required to pay interest on delayed payments, the shoe manufacturers require that payments not be delayed beyond 45 days after the invoice date. To be sure of paying within 10 days, Sole Brothers decides to pay on the fifth day. Sole has a marginal corporate income tax of 40% (combined state and federal). By paying within the 10-day period, Sole is avoiding paying a fairly high price to retain the money owed shoe manufacturers. What would have been the effective annual after-tax interest rate?

12-11 A major industrialized state has a state corporate tax rate of 9.6% of taxable income. If a corporation has a state taxable income of $150,000, what is the total state and federal income tax it must pay? Also, compute its combined incremental state and federal income tax rate.   (*Answers:* $50,534; 44.86%)

12-12 To increase its market share, Sole Brother Inc. decided to borrow $5000 from its banker for the purchase of newspaper advertising for its shoe retail line. The loan is to be paid in four equal annual payments with 15% interest. The loan is discounted 6 points. The 6 "points" is an additional interest charge of 6% of the loan, deducted immediately. This additional interest 6%($5000) = $300 means the actual amount received from the $5000 loan is $4700. The $300 additional interest may be deducted as four $75 additional annual interest payments. What is the after-tax interest rate on this loan?

12-13 The Lynch Bull investment company suggests that Steven Comstock, a wealthy New York City investor (his incremental income tax rate is 35%), consider the following investment.

Buy corporate bonds on the New York Stock Exchange with a face value (par value) of $100,000 and a 5% interest rate paid annually. These bonds can be purchased at their present market value of $75,000. Each year Steve will receive the $5000 interest, and after 5 years, when the bonds mature, he will receive $100,000 plus the last $5000 of interest.

Steve will pay for the bonds by borrowing $50,000 at 10% interest for 5 years. The $5000 interest paid on the loan each year will equal the $5000

of interest income from the bonds. As a result Steve will have no net taxable income during the five years due to this bond purchase and borrowing money scheme.

At the end of 5 years, Steve will receive $100,000 plus $5000 interest from the bonds and will repay the $50,000 loan and pay the last $5000 interest. The net result is that he will have a $25,000 capital gain; that is, he will receive $100,000 from a $75,000 investment. (*Note:* This situation represents an actual recommendation of a brokerage firm.)

(*a*) Compute Steve's after-tax rate of return on this dual bond-plus-loan investment package.

(*b*) What would be Steve's after-tax rate of return if he purchased the bonds for $75,000 cash and *did not* borrow the $50,000?

Historical Depreciation

12-14 Albert Chan decided to buy an old duplex as an investment. After looking for several months, he found a desirable duplex that could be bought for $93,000 cash. He decided that he would rent both sides of the duplex, and determined that the total expected income would be $800 per month. The total annual expenses for property taxes, repairs, gardening, and so forth are estimated at $600 per year. For tax purposes, Al plans to depreciate the building by the sum-of-years'-digits method, assuming that the building has a 20-year remaining life and no salvage value. Of the total $93,000 cost of the property, $84,000 represents the value of the building and $9000 is the value of the lot. Assume that Al is in the 38% incremental income tax bracket (combined state and federal taxes) throughout the 20 years.

In this analysis Al estimates that the income and expenses will remain constant at their present levels. If he buys and holds the property for 20 years, what after-tax rate of return can he expect to receive on his investment, using the following assumptions?

A. Al believes the building and the lot can be sold at the end of 20 years for the $9000 estimated value of the lot.

B. A more optimistic estimate of the future value of the building and the lot is that the property can be sold for $100,000 at the end of 20 years.

12-15 Zeon, a large, profitable corporation, is considering adding some automatic equipment to its production facilities. An investment of $120,000 will produce an initial annual benefit of $29,000, but the benefits are expected to decline $3000 per year, making second-year benefits $26,000, third-year benefits $23,000, and so forth. If the firm uses sum-of-years'-digits depreciation, an 8-year useful life, and $12,000 salvage value, will it obtain the desired 6% after-tax rate of return? Assume that the equipment can be sold for its $12,000 salvage value at the end of the 8 years. Also assume a 46% income tax rate for state and federal taxes combined.

12-16 A group of businessmen formed a corporation to lease for 5 years a piece of land at the intersection of two busy streets. The corporation has invested $50,000 in car-washing equipment. They will depreciate the equipment by sum-of-years'-digits depreciation, assuming a $5000 salvage value at the end of the 5 year useful life. The corporation is expected to have a before-tax cash flow, after meeting all expenses of operation (except depreciation), of $20,000 the first year, declining $3000 per year in future years (second year = $17,000, third year = $14,000, etc.). The corporation has other income, so it is taxed at a combined corporate tax rate of 20%. If the projected income is correct, and the equipment can be sold for $5000 at the end of 5 years, what after-tax rate of return would the corporation receive from this venture? (*Answer:* 14%)

12-17 The effective combined tax rate in an owner-managed corporation is 40%. An outlay of $20,000 for certain new assets is under consideration. It is estimated that for the next 8 years, these assets will be responsible for annual receipts of $9000 and annual disbursements (other than for income taxes) of $4000. After this time, they will be used only for stand-by purposes, and no future excess of receipts over disbursements is estimated.

(*a*) What is the prospective rate of return before income taxes?

(*b*) What is the prospective rate of return after taxes if straight-line depreciation can be used to write off these assets for tax purposes in 8 years?

(*c*) What is the prospective rate of return after taxes if it is assumed that these assets must be written off for tax purposes over the next 20 years, using straight-line depreciation?

12-18 A firm is considering the following investment project:

Year	Before-Tax Cash Flow (thousands)
0	−$1000
1	+500
2	+340
3	+244
4	+100
5	+100 / +125 Salvage value

The project has a 5-year useful life with a $125,000 salvage value, as shown. Double declining balance depreciation will be used, assuming the $125,000 salvage value. The combined income tax rate is 34%. If the firm requires a 10% after-tax rate of return, should the project be undertaken?

12-19 The Shellout Corp. owns a piece of petroleum drilling equipment that costs $100,000 and will be depreciated in 10 years by double declining balance depreciation, with conversion to straight-line depreciation at the optimal point. Assume no salvage value in the depreciation computation and a combined 34% tax rate. Shellout will lease the equipment to others and each year receive $30,000 in rent. At the end of 5 years, the firm will sell the equipment for $35,000. (Note that this is different from the zero-salvage-value assumption used in computing the depreciation.) What is the after-tax rate of return Shellout will receive from this equipment investment?

12-20 A mining corporation purchased $120,000 of production machinery and depreciated it using SOYD depreciation, a 5-year depreciable life, and zero salvage value. The corporation is a profitable one that has a 34% combined incremental tax rate.

At the end of 5 years the mining company changed its method of operation and sold the production machinery for $40,000. During the 5 years the machinery was used, it reduced mine operating costs by $32,000 a year, before taxes. If the company MARR is 12% after taxes, was the investment in the machinery a satisfactory one?

12-21 An automaker is buying some special tools for $100,000. The tools are being depreciated by double declining balance depreciation using a 4-year depreciable life and a $6250 salvage value. It is expected the tools will actually be kept in service for 6 years and then sold for $6250. The before-tax benefit of owning the tools is as follows:

Year	Before-Tax Cash Flow
1	$30,000
2	30,000
3	35,000
4	40,000
5	10,000
6	10,000
	6,250 Selling price

Compute the after-tax rate of return for this investment situation, assuming a 46% incremental tax rate. (*Answer:* 11.6%)

12-22 This is the continuation of Problem 12-21. Instead of paying $100,000 cash for the tools, the corporation will pay $20,000 now and borrow the remaining $80,000. The depreciation schedule will remain unchanged. The loan will be repaid by 4 equal end-of-year payments of $25,240.

Prepare an expanded cash flow table that takes into account both the special tools and the loan.

(a) Compute the after-tax rate of return for the tools, taking into account the $80,000 loan.

(b) Explain why the rate of return obtained in part (a) is different from the rate of return obtained in Problem 12-21.

Hints: 1. Interest on the loan is 10%, $25,240 = 80,000 (A/P, 10%, 4). Each payment is made up of part interest and part principal. Interest portion for any year is 10% of balance due at the beginning of the year.

2. Interest payments are tax deductible (i.e., they reduce taxable income and thus taxes paid). Principal payments are not. Separate each $25,240 payment into interest and principal portions.

3. The Year-0 cash flow is −$20,000.

4. After-tax cash flow will be before-tax cash flow − interest payment − principal payment − taxes.

12-23 A project will require the investment of $108,000 in equipment (sum-of-years'-digits depreciation with a depreciable life of 8 years and zero salvage value) and $25,000 in raw materials (not depreciable). The

annual project income after all expenses except depreciation have been paid is projected to be $24,000. At the end of 8 years the project will be discontinued and the $25,000 investment in raw materials will be recovered.

Assume a 34% combined income tax rate for this corporation. The corporation wants a 15% after-tax rate of return on its investments. Determine by present worth analysis whether this project should be undertaken.

12-24 A profitable incorporated business is considering an investment in equipment having the following before-tax cash flow. The equipment will be depreciated by double declining balance depreciation with conversion, if appropriate, to straight-line depreciation at the preferred time. For depreciation purposes a $700 salvage value at the end of 6 years is assumed. But the actual value is thought to be $1000 and it is this sum that is shown in the before-tax cash flow.

Year	Before-Tax Cash Flow
0	$12,000
1	1,727
2	2,414
3	2,872
4	3,177
5	3,358
6	1,997
	1,000 Salvage value

If the firm wants a 9% after-tax rate of return and its combined incremental income tax rate is 34%, determine by annual cash flow analysis whether the investment is desirable.

12-25 A salad oil bottling plant can either buy caps for the glass bottles at 5¢ each or install $500,000 worth of plastic molding equipment and manufacture the caps at the plant. The manufacturing engineer estimates the material, labor, and other costs would be 3¢ per cap.

(a) If 12 million caps per year are needed and the molding equipment is installed, what is the payback period?

(b) The plastic molding equipment would be depreciated by straight-line depreciation using a 5-year useful life and no salvage value. Assuming a combined 40% income tax rate, what is the after-tax payback period, and what is the after-tax rate of return?

12-26 A firm has invested $14,000 in machinery with a 7-year useful life. The machinery will have no salvage value, as the cost to remove it will equal its scrap value. The uniform annual benefits from the machinery are $3600. For a combined 47% income tax rate, and sum-of-years'-digits depreciation, compute the after-tax rate of return.

12-27 A firm manufactures padded shipping bags. A cardboard carton should contain 100 bags, but machine operators fill the cardboard cartons by eye, so a carton may contain anywhere from 98 to 123 bags (average = 105.5 bags).

   Management realizes that they are giving away $5\frac{1}{2}\%$ of their output by overfilling the cartons. The solution would be to weigh each filled shipping carton. Underweight cartons would have additional shipping bags added, and overweight cartons would have some shipping bags removed. If the weighing is done, it is believed that the average quantity of bags per carton could be reduced to 102, with almost no cartons containing fewer than 100 bags.

   The weighing equipment would cost $18,600. The equipment would be depreciated by straight-line depreciation using a 10-year depreciable life and a $3600 salvage value at the end of 10 years. Assume the $18,600 worth of equipment qualifies for a 10% investment tax credit. One person, hired at a cost of $16,000 per year, would be required to operate the weighing equipment and to add or remove padded bags from the cardboard cartons. 200,000 cartons will be checked on the weighing equipment each year, with an average removal of 3.5 padded bags per carton with a manufacturing cost of 3¢ per bag. This large profitable corporation has a 50% combined federal-plus-state incremental tax rate. Assume a 10-year study period for the analysis and an after-tax MARR of 20%.

   Compute:

(*a*) The after-tax present worth.

(*b*) The after-tax internal rate of return.

(*c*) The after-tax simple payback period.

MACRS Depreciation

12-28 Mr. Sam K. Jones, a successful businessman, is considering erecting a small building on a commercial lot. A local furniture company is willing to lease the building for $9000 per year, paid at the end of each year. It is a net lease, which means the furniture company must also pay the property taxes, fire insurance, and all other annual costs. The furniture company will require a 5-year lease with an option to buy the building and land on which it stands for $125,000 after 5 years. Mr. Jones could have the building constructed for $82,000. He could sell the commercial lot now for $30,000, the same price he paid for it. Mr. Jones files a joint return and has an annual taxable income from other sources of $63,900. He would depreciate the commercial building by modified accelerated cost recovery system (MACRS) depreciation. Mr. Jones believes that at the end of the 5-year lease he could easily sell the property for $125,000. What is the after-tax present worth of this 5-year venture if Mr. Jones uses a 10% after-tax MARR?

12-29 One January Gerald Adair bought a small house and lot for $99,700. He estimated that $9700 of this amount represented the land's value. He rented the house for $6500 a year during the 4 years he owned the house. Expenses for property taxes, maintenance, and so forth were $500 per year. For tax purposes the house was depreciated by MACRS depreciation (27.5-year straight-line depreciation with a midmonth convention is used for rental property). At the end of 4 years the property was sold for $105,000. Gerald is married and works as an engineer. He estimates that his incremental state and federal combined tax rate is 24%. What after-tax rate of return did Gerald obtain on his investment?

12-30 A corporation with a 34% combined income tax rate is considering the following investment in research equipment and has projected the benefits as follows:

Year	Before-Tax Cash Flow
0	−$50,000
1	+2,000
2	8,000
3	17,600
4	13,760
5	5,760
6	2,880

Prepare an after-tax cash flow table assuming MACRS depreciation.

(*a*) What is the after-tax rate of return?

(*b*) What is the before-tax rate of return?

12-31 An engineer is working on the layout of a new research and experimentation facility. Two plant operators will be required. If, however, an additional

$100,000 of instrumentation and remote controls were added, the plant could be run by a single operator. The total before-tax cost of each plant operator is projected to be $35,000 per year. The instrumentation and controls will be depreciated by means of the modified accelerated cost recovery system (MACRS).

If this corporation (34% combined corporate tax rate) invests in the additional instrumentation and controls, how long will it take for the after-tax benefits to equal the $100,000 cost? In other words, what is the after-tax payback period? (*Answer:* 3.24 years).

12-32 A special power tool for plastic products costs $400, has a 4-year useful life, no salvage value, and a 2-year before-tax payback period. Assume uniform annual end-of-year benefits.

(*a*) Compute the before-tax rate of return.

(*b*) Compute the after-tax rate of return, based on MACRS depreciation and a 34% combined corporate income tax rate.

12-33 The Ogi Corporation, a construction company, purchased a pickup truck for $14,000 and used MACRS depreciation in the income tax return. During the time the company had the truck, they estimated that it saved $5000 a year. At the end of 4 years, Ogi sold the truck for $3000. The combined federal and state income tax rate for Ogi is 45%. Compute the after-tax rate of return for the truck. (*Answer:* 12.5%)

12-34 A profitable wood products corporation is considering buying a parcel of land for $50,000, building a small factory building at a cost of $200,000, and equipping it with $150,000 of MACRS 5-year class machinery.

If the project is undertaken, MACRS depreciation will be used. Assume the plant is put in service October 1. The before-tax net annual benefit from the project is estimated at $70,000 per year. The analysis period is to be 5 years, and planners assume the sale of the total property (land, building, and machinery) at the end of 5 years, also on October 1, for $328,000. Compute the after-tax cash flow based on a 34% combined income tax rate. If the corporation's criterion is a 15% after-tax rate of return, should it proceed with the project?

12-35 A chemical company bought a small vessel for $55,000; it is to be depreciated by MACRS depreciation. When requirements changed suddenly, the chemical company leased the vessel to an oil company for 6 years at $10,000 per year. The lease also provided that the oil company could buy the vessel at the end of 6 years for $35,000. At the end of the 6 years, the oil company exercised its option and bought the vessel. The chemical company has a 34% combined incremental tax rate. Compute its after-tax rate of return on the vessel. (*Answer:* 9.86%)

12-36 Xon, a small oil company, purchased a new petroleum drilling rig for $1,800,000. Xon will depreciate the drilling rig using MACRS depreciation. The drilling rig has been leased to a drilling company, which will pay Xon $450,000 per year for 8 years. At the end of 8 years the drilling rig will belong to the drilling company. If Xon has a 34% combined incremental tax rate and a 10% after-tax MARR, does the investment appear to be satisfactory?

12-37 The profitable Palmer Golf Cart Corp. is considering investing $300,000 in special tools for some of the plastic golf cart components. Executives of the company believe the present golf cart model will continue to be manufactured and sold for 5 years, after which a new cart design will be needed, together with a different set of special tools.

The saving in manufacturing costs, owing to the special tools, is estimated to be $150,000 per year for 5 years. Assume MACRS depreciation for the special tools and a 39% combined income tax rate.

(*a*) What is the after-tax payback period for this investment?

(*b*) If the company wants a 12% after-tax rate of return, is this a desirable investment?

12-38 Uncle Elmo is contemplating a $10,000 investment in a methane gas generator. He estimates his gross income would be $2000 the first year and increase by $200 each year over the next 10 years. His expenses of $200 the first year would increase by $200 each year over the next 10 years. He would depreciate the generator by MACRS depreciation, assuming a 7-year property class. A 10-year-old methane generator has no market value. The income tax rate is 40%. (Remember that recaptured depreciation is taxed at the same 40% rate).

(*a*) Construct the after-tax cash flow for the 10-year project life.

(*b*) Determine the after-tax rate of return on this investment. Uncle Elmo thinks it should be at least 8%.

(*c*) If Uncle Elmo could sell the generator for $7000 at the end of the fifth year, would his rate of return be better than if he kept the generator for 10 years? You don't have to actually find the rate of return, just do enough calculations to see whether it is higher than that of part (*b*).

12-39 Granny's Butter and Egg Business is such that she pays an effective tax rate of 40%. Granny is considering the purchase of a new Turbo Churn for $25,000. This churn is a special handling device for food manufacture and has an estimated life of 4 years and a salvage value of $5000. The new churn is expected to increase net income by $8000 per year for each of the 4 years of use. If Granny works with an after-tax MARR of 10% and uses MACRS depreciation, should she buy the churn?

12-40 Eric has a house and lot for sale for $70,000. It is estimated that $10,000 is the value of the land and $60,000 is the value of the house. Bonnie is purchasing the house on January 1 to rent and plans to own the house for 5 years. After 5 years, it is expected that the house and land can be sold on December 31 for $80,000. Total annual expenses (maintenance, property taxes, insurance, etc.) are expected to be $3000 per year. The house would be depreciated by MACRS depreciation using a 27.5-year straight-line rate with midmonth convention for rental property. For depreciation, a salvage value of zero was used. Bonnie wants a 15% after-tax rate of return on her investment. You may assume that Bonnie has an incremental income tax rate of 28%

in each of the 5 years. Capital gains are taxed at 15%. Determine the following:

(*a*) The annual depreciation

(*b*) The capital gain (loss) resulting from the sale of the house

(*c*) The annual rent Bonnie must charge to produce an after-tax rate of return of 15%. (*Hint:* Write an algebraic equation to solve for rent.)

12-41 Bill owns a data processing company. He plans to buy an additional computer for $20,000, use the computer for 3 years, and sell it for $10,000. He expects that use of the computer will produce a net income of $8000 per year. The combined federal and state incremental tax rate is 45%. Using MACRS depreciation, complete Table P12-41 to determine the net present worth of the after-tax cash flow using an interest rate of 12%.

12-42 Refer to Problem 12-33. To help pay for the pickup truck the Ogi Corp. obtained a $10,000 loan from the truck dealer, payable in four end-of-year payments of $2500 plus 10% interest on the loan balance each year.

(*a*) Compute the after-tax rate of return for the truck together with the loan. Note that the interest on the loan is tax deductible, but the $2500 principal payments are not.

(*b*) Why is the after-tax rate of return computed in part (*a*) so much different from the 12.5% obtained in Problem 12-33?

Solving for Unknowns

12-43 A store owner, Joe Lang, believes his business has suffered from the lack of adequate customer parking

TABLE P12-41 **Worksheet for Problem 12-41**

Year	Before-Tax Cash Flow	MACRS Depreciation	Taxable Income	Income Tax (45%)	After-Tax Cash Flow	Present Worth (12%)
0	−$20,000					
1	+8,000					
2	+8,000					
3	+8,000					
	+10,000					
				Net Present worth =		

space. Thus, when he was offered an opportunity to buy an old building and lot next to his store, he was interested. He would demolish the old building and make off-street parking for 20 customers' cars. Joe estimates that the new parking would increase his business and produce an additional before-income-tax profit of $7000 per year. It would cost $2500 to demolish the old building. Mr. Lang's accountant advised that both costs (the property and demolishing the old building) would be considered to comprise the total value of the land for tax purposes, and it would not be depreciable. Mr. Lang would spend an additional $3000 right away to put a light gravel surface on the lot. This expenditure, he believes, may be charged as an operating expense immediately and need not be capitalized. To compute the tax consequences of adding the parking lot, Joe estimates that his combined state and federal incremental income tax rate will average 40%. If Joe wants a 15% after-tax rate of return from this project, how much could he pay to purchase the adjoining land with the old building? Assume that the analysis period is 10 years and that the parking lot could always be sold to recover the costs of buying the property and demolishing the old building. (*Answer:* $23,100)

12-44 The management of a private hospital is considering the installation of an automatic telephone switchboard, which would replace a manual switchboard and eliminate the attendant operator's position. The class of service provided by the new equipment is estimated to be at least equal to the present method of operation. To provide telephone service, five operators will work three shifts per day, 365 days per year. Each operator earns $14,000 per year. Company-paid benefits and overhead are 25% of wages. Money costs 8% after income taxes. Combined federal and state income taxes are 40%. Annual property taxes and maintenance are $2^{1}/2$ and 4% of investment, respectively. Depreciation is 15-year straight line. Disregarding inflation, how large an investment in the new equipment can be economically justified by savings obtained by eliminating the present equipment and labor costs? The existing equipment has zero salvage value.

12-45 A contractor has to choose one of the following alternatives in performing earthmoving contracts:

A. Buy a heavy-duty truck for $13,000. Salvage value is expected to be $3000 at the end of the vehicle's 7-year depreciable life. Maintenance

is $1100 per year. Daily operating expenses are $35.

B. Hire a similar unit for $83 per day.

Based on a 10% after-tax rate of return, how many days per year must the truck be used to justify its purchase? Base your calculations on straight-line depreciation and a 50% income tax rate. (*Answer:* $91^{1}/2$ days)

12-46 The Able Corporation is considering the installation of a small electronic testing device for use in conjunction with a government contract the firm has just won. The testing device will cost $20,000 and will have an estimated salvage value of $5000 in 5 years when the government contract is finished. The firm will depreciate the instrument by the sum-of-years'-digits method, using 5 years as the useful life and a $5000 salvage value. Assume that Able pays 50% federal and state corporate income taxes and uses 8% *after-tax* in economic analysis. What minimum equal annual benefit must Able obtain *before taxes* in each of the 5 years to justify purchasing the electronic testing device? (*Answer:* $5150)

12-47 A house and lot are for sale for $155,000. It is estimated that $45,000 is the value of the land and $110,000 is the value of the house. If purchased, the house can be rented to provide a net income of $12,000 per year after taking all expenses, except depreciation, into account. The house would be depreciated by straight-line depreciation using a 27.5-year depreciable life and zero salvage value.

Mary Silva, the prospective purchaser, wants a 10% after-tax rate of return on her investment after considering both annual income taxes and a capital gain when she sells the house and lot. At what price would she have to sell the house at the end of 10 years to achieve her objective? You may assume that Mary has an incremental income tax rate of 28% in each of the 10 years.

12-48 A corporation is considering buying a medium-sized computer that will eliminate a task that must be performed three shifts per day, 7 days per week, except for one 8-hour shift per week when the operation is shut down for maintenance. At present four people are needed to perform the day and night tasks. Thus the computer will replace four employees. Each employee costs the company $32,000 per year ($24,000 in direct wages plus $8000 per year in other company employee costs). It will cost $18,000 per year to maintain and operate the computer.

The computer will be depreciated by sum-of-years'-digits depreciation using a 6-year depreciable life, at which time it will be assumed to have zero salvage value.

The corporation has a combined federal and state incremental tax rate of 50%. If the firm wants a 15% rate of return, after considering both state and federal income taxes, how much can it afford to pay for the computer?

12-49 A sales engineer has the following alternatives to consider in touring his sales territory.

A. Buy a new car for $14,500. Salvage value is expected to be about $5000 after 3 years. Maintenance and insurance cost is $1000 in the first year and increases at the rate of $500/year in subsequent years. Daily operating expenses are $50/day.

B. Rent a similar car for $80/day.

Based on a 12% after-tax rate of return, how many days per year must he use the car to justify its purchase? You may assume that this sales engineer is in the 28% incremental tax bracket. Use MACRS depreciation.

12-50 A large profitable company, in the 40% combined federal/state tax bracket, is considering the purchase of a new piece of equipment that will yield benefits of $10,000 in Year 1, $15,000 in Year 2, $20,000 in Year 3, and $20,000 in Year 4. The equipment is to be depreciated using 5-year MACRS depreciation starting in the year of purchase (Year 0). It is expected that the equipment will be sold at the end of Year 4 at 20% of its purchase price. What is the maximum equipment purchase price the company can pay if its after-tax MARR is 10%?

12-51 A prosperous businessman is considering two alternative investments in bonds. In both cases the first interest payment would be received at the end of the first year. If his personal taxable income is fixed at $40,000 and he is single, which investment produces the greater after-tax rate of return? Compute the after-tax rate of return for each bond to within $1/4$ of 1 percent.

Ann Arbor Municipal Bonds: A bond with a face value of $1000 pays $60 per annum. At the end of 15 years, the bond becomes due ("matures"), at which time the owner of the bond will receive $1000 plus the final $60 annual payment. The bond may be purchased for $800. Since it is a municipal bond, the annual interest is *not* subject to federal income tax. The difference between what the businessman would pay for

the bond ($800) and the $1000 face value he would receive at the end of 15 years must be included in taxable income when the $1000 is received.

Southern Coal Corporation Bonds: A thousand-dollar bond yields $100 per year in annual interest payments. When the bonds mature at the end of 20 years, the bondholder will receive $1000 plus the final $100 interest. The bonds may be purchased now for $1000. The income from corporation bonds must be included in federal taxable income.

Multiple Alternatives

12-52 Use the after-tax IRR method to evaluate the following three alternatives for MACRS 3-year property, and offer a recommendation. The after-tax MARR is 25%, the project life is 5 years, and the firm has a combined incremental tax rate of 45%.

Alt.	First Cost	Annual Costs	Salvage Value
A	$14,000	$2500	$ 5,000
B	18,000	1000	10,000
C	10,000	5000	0

12-53 A small-business corporation is considering whether to replace some equipment in the plant. An analysis indicates there are five alternatives in addition to the do-nothing option, Alt. *A*. The alternatives have a 5-year useful life with no salvage value. Straight-line depreciation would be used.

Alternatives	Cost (thousands)	Before-Tax Uniform Annual Benefits (thousands)
A	$ 0	$ 0
B	25	7.5
C	10	3
D	5	1.7
E	15	5
F	30	8.7

The corporation has a combined federal and state income tax rate of 20%. If the corporation expects a 10% after-tax rate of return for any new investments, which alternative should be selected?

12-54 A corporation with $7 million in annual taxable income is considering two alternatives:

Before-Tax Cash Flow

Year	Alt. 1	Alt. 2
0	−$10,000	−$20,000
1–10	4,500	4,500
11–20	0	4,500

Both alternatives will be depreciated by straight-line depreciation assuming a 10-year depreciable life and no salvage value. Neither alternative is to be replaced at the end of its useful life. If the corporation has a minimum attractive rate of return of 10% *after taxes,* which alternative should it choose? Solve the problem by:

(*a*) Present worth analysis

(*b*) Annual cash flow analysis

(*c*) Rate of return analysis

(*d*) Future worth analysis

(*e*) Benefit–cost ratio analysis

12-55 Two mutually exclusive alternatives are being considered by a profitable corporation with an annual taxable income between $5 million and $10 million.

Before-Tax Cash Flow

Year	Alt. *A*	Alt. *B*
0	−$3000	−$5000
1	1000	1000
2	1000	1200
3	1000	1400
4	1000	2600
5	1000	2800

Both alternatives have a 5-year useful and depreciable life and no salvage value. Alternative *A* would be depreciated by sum-of-years'-digits depreciation, and Alt. *B* by straight-line depreciation. If the MARR is 10% after taxes, which alternative should be selected? (*Answer:* Alt. *B*)

12-56 A large profitable corporation is considering two mutually exclusive capital investments:

	Alt. *A*	Alt. *B*
Initial cost	$11,000	$33,000
Uniform annual benefit	3,000	9,000
End-of-depreciable-life salvage value	2,000	3,000
Depreciation method	SL	SOYD
End-of-useful-life salvage value obtained	2,000	5,000
Depreciable life, in years	3	4
Useful life, in years	5	5

If the firm's after-tax minimum attractive rate of return is 12% and its combined incremental income tax rate is 34%, which project should be selected?

12-57 Assume that you are deciding whether to lease a car or buy one to use exclusively in business. The estimated mileage in both cases will be 12,000/year. Insurance costs will be the same in either case at $600 per year. You want to examine the tax impacts of the two options to see which is preferred. Use MACRS depreciation.

Assume that you will have leased or purchased the car on June 30, 2006, and that you intend to keep the car for 36 months. List any assumptions that you make in your analysis. Use a 12% MARR, a 40% tax rate, and assume end of year payments.

Lease option: $2250 down and $369 a month for 36 months.

Purchase option: The car that you are interested in lists for $29,188 and the dealer finance plan calls for 30 monthly payments of $973 with no money down and 0% interest. Estimated value after 36 months is $15,200. Remember that the tax law limits the depreciation on cars according to the following rule:

Depreciation Limitation on Automobiles Purchased After 2005

Tax Year	Amount
First	$2960
Second	4700
Third	2850
Fourth and later	1675

12-58 A plant can be purchased for $1,000,000 or it can be leased for $200,000 per year. The annual income is expected to be $800,000 with the annual operating cost of $200,000. The resale value of the plant is estimated to be $400,000 at the end of its 10-year life. The company's combined federal and state income tax rate is 40%. A straight-line depreciation can be used over the 10 years with the full first-year depreciation rate.

(*a*) If the company uses the after-tax minimum attractive rate of return of 10%, should it lease or purchase the plant?

(*b*) What is the breakeven rate of return of purchase versus lease?

12-59 VML Industries has need of specialized yarn man-ufacturing equipment for operations over the next 3 years. The firm could buy the machinery for $95,000 and depreciate it using MACRS. Annual mainte-nance would be $7500, and it would have a salvage value of $25,000 after 3 years. Another alternative would be to lease the same machine for $45,000 per year on an "all costs" inclusive lease (mainte-nance costs included in lease payment). These lease payments are due at the beginning of each year. VML Industries uses an after-tax MARR of 18%, and a combined tax rate of 40%. Do an after-tax present worth analysis to determine which option is preferred.

12-60 Padre Pio owns a small business and has tax-able income of $150,000. He is considering four mutually exclusive alternative models of machin-ery. Which machine should be selected on an after-tax basis? The after-tax MARR is 15%. Assume that each machine is MACRS 5-year prop-erty and can be sold for a market value that is 25% of the purchase cost, and the project life is 10 years.

Model	I	II	III	IV
First cost	$9000	$8000	$7500	$6200
Annual costs	25	200	300	600

CHAPTER 13

REPLACEMENT ANALYSIS

The $2 Billion Upgrade

In February 2003, Intel Corporation announced it was spending $2 billion to modernize and update its silicon wafer manufacturing plant in Chandler, Arizona. The upgrade allowed Intel to manufacture 300-millimeter chips rather than the 200-millimeter size it had been producing at the plant, known as Fab 12. The project was estimated to double manufacturing capacity while at the same time reducing costs. Upgrade work included remodeling the plant's interior and the purchase of new wafer fabrication tools.

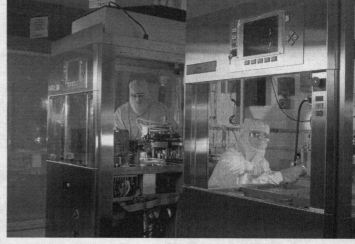

Despite the price tag for the project, Intel planned on saving money overall by upgrading the existing plant instead of designing and building a new one. The upgraded plant used newer processes that allowed chips to hold smaller and faster transistors, and the new larger wafer accommodates more chips. These all lead to lower production costs.

The company also noted that by deciding to remain in its current location it was able to retain its highly skilled workforce.

1. Intel made the decision to upgrade existing plant facilities versus building new ones. In their analysis they claimed to have saved money by doing so. Use the Internet and search for articles that discuss what new manufacturing plants cost in different type of industries. Does Intel's $2 billion upgrade decision seem in line? What issues are you not considering if you think the cost seems very high?

2. Companies that upgrade existing production assets may or may not scrap their current assets. Give a realistic scenario for each case.

3. The upgrade vs. replace decision often includes economic as well as noneconomic factors. List three economic and three noneconomic factors that may have been at the top of Intel's list in making the decision.

4. When companies build new manufacturing plants they are often sited outside the U.S. Discuss the ethical impacts that are or should be part of a firm's decision process.

After Completing This Chapter...

The student should be able to:

- Recast an equipment reinvestment decision as a *challenger vs. defender* analysis.
- Use the *replacement analysis decision map* to select the correct economic analysis technique to apply.
- Calculate the *minimum cost life* of economic challengers.
- Incorporate concepts such as *repeatability assumption for replacement analysis* and *marginal cost data for the defender* to select the correct economic analysis techniques.
- Perform replacement problems on an after-tax basis, utilizing the *defender sign change procedure* when appropriate.
- Use spreadsheets for solving before-tax and after-tax replacement analysis problems.

U p to this point in our economic analysis we have considered the evaluation and selection of *new* alternatives. Which new car or production machine should we buy? What new material handling system or ceramic grinder should we install? More frequently, however, economic analysis weighs *existing* versus *new* facilities. For most engineers the problem is less likely to be one of building a new plant; rather, the goal is more often keeping a present plant operating economically. We are not choosing between new ways to perform the desired task. Instead, we have equipment performing the task, and the question is: Should the existing equipment be retained or replaced? This adversarial situation has given rise to the terms **defender** and **challenger.** The defender is the existing equipment; the challenger is the best available replacement equipment. Economically evaluating the existing defender and its challengers is the domain of **replacement analysis.**

THE REPLACEMENT PROBLEM

Replacement of an existing asset may be appropriate due to obsolescence, depletion, and deterioration due to aging. In each of these cases, the ability of a previously implemented business asset to produce a desired output is challenged. For cases of obsolescence, depletion, and aging, it may be economical to replace the existing asset. We define each of these situations.

Obsolescence: occurs when an asset's technology is surpassed by newer and/or different technologies. As an example, today's personal computers (PCs) with more RAM, faster clock speeds, larger hard drives, and more powerful central processors have made older, less powerful PCs obsolete. Thus, obsolete assets may need to be replaced with newer, more technologically advanced ones.

Depletion: the gradual loss of market value of an asset as it is being consumed or exhausted. Oil wells and timber stands are examples of such assets. In most cases the asset will be used until it is depleted, at which time a replacement asset will be obtained. Depletion was treated in Chapter 11.

Deterioration due to aging: the general condition of loss in value of some asset due to the aging process. Production machinery and other business assets that were once new eventually become aged. To compensate for a loss in functionality due to the aging process, additional operating and maintenance expenses are usually incurred to maintain the asset at its operating efficiency.

Aging equipment often has a greater risk of breakdowns. Planned replacements can be scheduled to minimize the time and cost of disruptions. Unplanned replacements can be very costly or even, as with an airplane engine, potentially catastrophic.

There are variations of the replacement problem: an existing asset may be abandoned or retired, augmented by a new asset but kept in service, or overhauled to reduce its operating and maintenance costs. These variations are most easily considered as potential new challengers.

Replacement problems are normally analyzed by looking only at the *costs* of the existing and replacement assets. Since the assets typically perform the same function, the value of using the vehicle, machine, or other equipment can be ignored. If the new asset has new features or better performance, these can be included as a cost savings.

Alternatives in a replacement problem almost always have *different lives*, and the problem includes picking the best one. This is because an existing asset will often be kept for at most a few years longer, while the potential replacements may have lives of any length. Thus replacement problems are focused on annual marginal costs and on EUAC values. We can calculate present costs, but only as a step in calculating EUAC values.

In industry, as in government, expenditures are normally monitored by means of *annual budgets*. One important facet of a budget is the allocation of money for new capital expenditures, either new facilities or replacement and upgrading of existing facilities.

Replacement analysis may recommend that certain equipment be replaced, with the cost included in the capital expenditures budget. Even if no recommendation to replace is made, such a recommendation may be made the following year or subsequently. At *some* point, existing equipment will be replaced, either when it is no longer necessary or when better equipment is available. Thus, the question is not *if* the defender will be replaced, but *when* it will be replaced. This leads us to the first aspect of the defender–challenger comparison:

Shall we replace the defender now, or shall we keep it for one or more additional years?

If we do decide to keep the asset for another year, we will often reanalyze the problem next year. The operating environment and costs may have changed, or new challengers with lower costs or better performance may have emerged.

REPLACEMENT ANALYSIS DECISION MAP

Figure 13-1 is a basic decision map for conducting a replacement analysis.

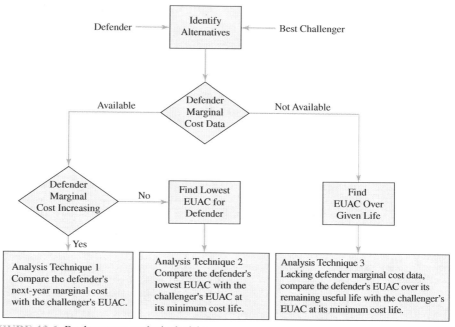

FIGURE 13-1 Replacement analysis decision map.

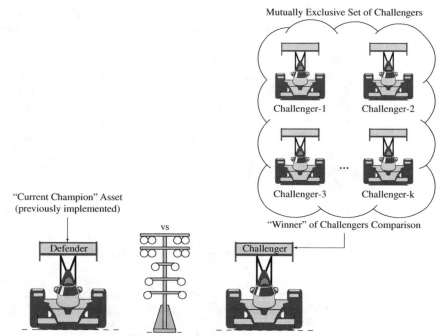

FIGURE 13-2 Defender–challenger comparison.

Looking at the map, we can see there are three *replacement analysis techniques* that are correct under different circumstances. The correct replacement analysis technique depends on the data available for the alternatives and how the data behave over time.

By looking at the replacement analysis map, we see that the first step is to identify the alternatives. Again, in replacement analysis we are interested in comparing our previously implemented asset (the *defender*) against the best current available *challenger.*

If the defender proves more economical, it will be retained. If the challenger proves more economical, it will be installed.

In this comparison the defender is being evaluated against a challenger that has been selected from a mutually exclusive set of competing challengers. Figure 13-2 illustrates this concept as a drag race between the defender and a challenger. The challenger that is competing against the defender has emerged from an earlier competition among a set of potential challengers. Any of the methods previously discussed in this text for evaluating sets of mutually exclusive alternatives could be used to identify the "best" challenger to race against the defender. However, it is important to note that the comparison of these potential challenger alternatives should be made at each alternative's respective *minimum cost life.* This concept is discussed next.

MINIMUM COST LIFE OF A NEW ASSET—THE CHALLENGER

The **minimum cost life** of any new asset is the number of years at which the equivalent uniform annual cost (EUAC) of ownership is minimized. This minimum cost life is often shorter than either the asset's physical or useful life, because of increasing operating and maintenance costs in the later years of asset ownership. The challenger asset selected to "race" against the defender (in Figure 13-2) is the one having the lowest minimum cost of all the competing mutually exclusive challengers.

To calculate the minimum cost life of an asset, we determine the EUAC for each possible life less than or equal to the useful life. As illustrated in Example 13-1, the EUAC tends to be high if the asset is kept only a few years; then it decreases to some minimum EUAC, and then increases again as the asset ages. By identifying the number of years at which the EUAC is a minimum and then keeping the asset for that number of years, we are minimizing the yearly cost of ownership.

EXAMPLE 13-1

A piece of machinery costs $7500 and has no salvage value after it is installed. The manufacturer's warranty will pay the first year's maintenance and repair costs. In the second year, maintenance costs will be $900, and this item will increase on a $900 arithmetic gradient in subsequent years. Also, operating expenses for the machinery will be $500 the first year and will increase on a $400 arithmetic gradient in the following years. If interest is 8%, compute the machinery's economic life that minimizes the EUAC. That is, find its minimum cost life.

SOLUTION

	If Retired at the End of Year n			
Year, n	EUAC of Capital Recovery Costs: $7500 $(A/P, 8\%, n)$	EUAC of Maintenance and Repair Costs: $900 $(A/G, 8\%, n)$	EUAC of Operating Costs: $500 + 400(A/G, 8\%, n)$	EUAC Total
1	$8100	$ 0	$ 500	$8600
2	4206	433	692	5331
3	2910	854	880	4644
4	2264	1264	1062	4589 ←
5	1878	1661	1238	4779
6	1622	2048	1410	5081
7	1440	2425	1578	5443
8	1305	2789	1740	5834
9	1200	3142	1896	6239
10	1117	3484	2048	6650
11	1050	3816	2196	7063
12	995	4136	2338	7470
13	948	4446	2476	7871
14	909	4746	2609	8265
15	876	5035	2738	8648

The total EUAC data are plotted in Figure 13-3. From either the tabulation or the figure, we see that the machinery's minimum cost life is 4 years, with a minimum EUAC of $4589 for each of those 4 years.

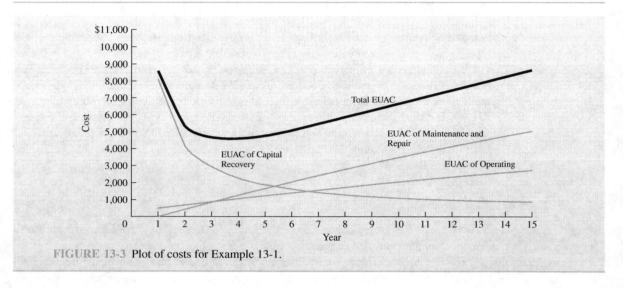

FIGURE 13-3 Plot of costs for Example 13-1.

Looking at Figure 13-3 a bit more closely, we see the effects of each of the individual cost components on total EUAC (capital recovery, maintenance/repair, and operating expense EUACs) and how they behave over time. The total EUAC curve of most assets tends to follow this concave shape—high at the beginning due to capital recovery costs, and high at the end due to increased maintenance/repair and operating expenses. The minimum EUAC occurs somewhere between these high points.

Like many pieces of installed equipment, the item considered in Example 13-1 had no salvage value. However, some assets, like your car, can easily be sold for a value than depends on the car's age and condition. Another possible complication is that repair costs may be reduced in early years by a warranty. The resulting cost curves will look like Figure 13-3, but the calculations are more work and a spreadsheet is very helpful. Example 13-11 in the last section of this chapter illustrates finding the minimum cost life for a new vehicle.

DEFENDER'S MARGINAL COST DATA

Once the basic participants in the defender–challenger comparison have been identified (see Figure 13-1), two specific questions regarding marginal costs must be answered: *Do we have marginal cost data for the defender?* and *Are the defender's marginal costs increasing on a year-to-year basis?* Let us first define marginal cost and then discuss why it is important to answer these two questions.

Marginal costs, as opposed to an EUAC, are the year-by-year costs of keeping an asset. Therefore, the "period" of any yearly marginal cost of ownership is always *1 year.* The marginal cost is compared with the EUAC, which is an end-of-year cash flow. Therefore, the marginal cost is calculated as an equivalent end-of-year cash flow.

On the other hand, an EUAC can apply to any number of consecutive years. Thus, the marginal cost of ownership for any year in an asset's life is the cost for *that year only.* In replacement problems, the total marginal cost for any year can include the capital recovery cost (loss in market value and lost interest for the year), yearly operating and maintenance costs, yearly taxes and insurance, and any other expense that occurs during that year. To calculate an asset's yearly marginal cost of ownership, it is necessary to have estimates of an asset's market value on a year-to-year basis over its useful life, as well as ordinary yearly expenses. Example 13-2 illustrates how total marginal cost can be calculated for an asset.

EXAMPLE 13-2

A new piece of production machinery has the following costs.

$$\text{Investment cost} = \$25,000$$

$$\text{Annual operating and maintenance cost} = \$2000 \text{ in Year 1 and then increasing by}$$
$$\$500 \text{ per year}$$

$$\text{Annual cost for risk of breakdown} = \$5000 \text{ per year for 3 years, then}$$
$$\text{increasing by } \$1500 \text{ per year}$$

$$\text{Useful life} = 7 \text{ years}$$

$$\text{MARR} = 15\%$$

Calculate the marginal cost of keeping this asset over its useful life.

SOLUTION

From the problem data we can easily find the marginal costs for O&M and risk of breakdowns. However, to calculate the marginal capital recovery cost, we need estimates of each year's market value.

Year	Market Value
1	$18,000
2	13,000
3	9,000
4	6,000
5	4,000
6	3,000
7	2,500

We can now calculate the machinery's *marginal cost* (year-to-year cost of ownership) over its 7-year useful life.

Year, n	Loss in Market Value in Year n	Interest in Year n	O&M Cost in Year n	Cost of Breakdown Risk in Year n	Total Marginal Cost in Year n
1	$25{,}000 - 18{,}000 = \$7000$	$25{,}000(0.15) = \$3750$	$2000	$5,000	$17,750
2	$18{,}000 - 13{,}000 = 5000$	$18{,}000(0.15) = 2700$	2500	5,000	15,200
3	$13{,}000 - 9{,}000 = 4000$	$13{,}000(0.15) = 1950$	3000	5,000	13,950
4	$9{,}000 - 6{,}000 = 3000$	$9{,}000(0.15) = 1350$	3500	6,500	14,350
5	$6{,}000 - 4{,}000 = 2000$	$6{,}000(0.15) = 900$	4000	8,000	14,900
6	$4{,}000 - 3{,}000 = 1000$	$4{,}000(0.15) = 600$	4500	9,500	15,600
7	$3{,}000 - 2{,}500 = 500$	$3{,}000(0.15) = 450$	5000	11,000	16,950

Notice that each year's total marginal cost includes loss in market value, interest, O&M cost, and cost for risk of breakdowns. For example, the Year-5 marginal cost of $14,900 is calculated as $2000 + 900 + 4000 + 8000$.

Do We Have Marginal Cost Data for the Defender?

Our decision map indicates that it is necessary to know whether marginal cost data are available for the defender asset to determine the appropriate replacement technique to use. Usually in engineering economic problems, annual savings and expenses are given for all alternatives. However, as in Example 13-2, it is also necessary to have year-to-year salvage value estimates to calculate total marginal costs. If the total marginal costs for the defender can be calculated, and if the data are increasing from year to year, then *replacement analysis technique 1* should be used to compare the defender to the challenger.

Are These Marginal Costs Increasing?

We have seen that it is important to know whether the marginal cost for the defender is increasing from year to year. This is determined by inspecting the total marginal cost of ownership of the defender over its remaining life. In most replacement analyses the defender is nearing the end of its economic life. The question usually is, Should we replace it now, next year, or perhaps the year after? In the early years of an asset's life we rarely analyze whether it is time for replacement. Thus, the defender's marginal costs are usually increasing, as shown in Example 13-3.

EXAMPLE 13-3

An asset purchased 5 years ago for $75,000 can be sold today for $15,000. Operating expenses will be $10,000 this year, but these will increase by $1500 per year. It is estimated that the asset's market value will decrease by $1000 per year over the next 5 years. If the MARR used by the company is 15%, calculate the total marginal cost of ownership of this old asset (that is, the defender) for each of the next 5 years.

SOLUTION

We calculate the total marginal cost of maintaining the old asset for the next 5-year period as follows:

Year, n	Loss in Market Value in Year n	Interest in Year n	Operating Cost in Year n	Marginal Cost in Year n
1	$15,000 - 14,000 = \$1000$	$15,000(0.15) = \$2250$	$10,000	$13,250
2	$14,000 - 13,000 = 1000$	$14,000(0.15) = 2100$	11,500	14,600
3	$13,000 - 12,000 = 1000$	$13,000(0.15) = 1950$	13,000	15,950
4	$12,000 - 11,000 = 1000$	$12,000(0.15) = 1800$	14,500	17,300
5	$11,000 - 10,000 = 1000$	$11,000(0.15) = 1650$	16,000	18,650

We can see that the marginal costs increase in each subsequent year of ownership. When the condition of increasing marginal costs for the defender has been met, then the defender–challenger comparison should be made with *replacement analysis technique 1*.

REPLACEMENT ANALYSIS TECHNIQUE 1: DEFENDER MARGINAL COSTS CAN BE COMPUTED AND ARE INCREASING

When our first method of analyzing the defender asset against the best available challenger is used, the basic comparison involves *the defender's marginal cost data and the challenger's minimum cost life data.*

When the defender's marginal cost is increasing from year to year, we will maintain that defender as long as the marginal cost of keeping it one more year is less than the challenger's minimum EUAC. Thus our decision rule is

> *Maintain the defender as long as the marginal cost of ownership for one more year is less than the challenger's minimum EUAC. When the defender's marginal cost becomes greater than the challenger's minimum EUAC, then replace the defender with the challenger.*

One can see that this technique assumes that the current best challenger, with its minimum EUAC, will be available and unchanged in the future. However, it is easy to update a replacement analysis when marginal costs for the defender change or when there is a change in the cost and/or performance of available challengers. Example 13-4 illustrates the use of this technique for comparing defender and challenger assets.

EXAMPLE 13-4

Taking the machinery in Example 13-2 as the *challenger* and the machinery in Example 13-3 as the *defender,* use *replacement analysis technique 1* to determine when, if at all, a replacement decision should be made.

SOLUTION

Replacement analysis technique 1 should be used only in the condition of increasing marginal costs for the defender. Since these marginal costs are increasing for the defender (from Example 13-3), we can proceed by comparing defender marginal costs against the minimum EUAC of the challenger asset. In Example 13-2 we calculated only the marginal costs of the challenger; thus it is necessary to calculate the challenger's minimum EUAC. The EUAC of keeping this asset for each year of its useful life is worked out as follows.

Year, n	Challenger Total Marginal Cost in Year n	Present Cost If Kept Through Year n (PC_n)	EUAC If Kept Through Year n
1	$17,750	$[17,750(P/F,15\%,1)]$	$\times (A/P,15\%,1) = \$17,750$
2	15,200	$PC_1 + 15,200(P/F,15\%,2)$	$\times (A/P,15\%,2) = 16,560$
3	13,950	$PC_2 + 13,950(P/F,15\%,3)$	$\times (A/P,15\%,3) = 15,810$
4	14,350	$PC_3 + 14,350(P/F,15\%,4)$	$\times (A/P,15\%,4) = 15,520$
5	14,900	$PC_4 + 14,900(P/F,15\%,5)$	$\times (A/P,15\%,5) = 15,430$
6	15,600	$PC_5 + 15,600(P/F,15\%,6)$	$\times (A/P,15\%,6) = 15,450$
7	16,950	$PC_6 + 16,950(P/F,15\%,7)$	$\times (A/P,15\%,7) = 15,580$

A minimum EUAC of $15,430 is attained for the challenger at Year 5, which is the challenger's *minimum cost life*. We proceed by comparing this value against the *marginal* costs of the defender from Example 13-3:

Year, n	Defender Total Marginal Cost in Year n	Challenger Minimum EUAC	Comparison Result and Recommendation
1	$13,250	$15,430	Since $13,250 is *less than* $15,430, keep defender.
2	14,600	15,430	Since $14,600 is *less than* $15,430, keep defender.
3	15,950	15,430	Since $15,950 is *greater than* $15,430, replace defender.
4	17,300		
5	18,650		

Based on the data given for the challenger and for the defender, we would keep the defender for 2 more years and then replace it with the challenger because at that point the defender's marginal cost of another year of ownership would be greater than the challenger's minimum EUAC.

REPLACEMENT REPEATABILITY ASSUMPTIONS

The decision to use the challenger's minimum EUAC reflects two assumptions: the best challenger will be available "with the same minimum EUAC" in the future; and the period of needed service is indefinitely long. In other words, we assume that once the decision has been made to replace, there will be an indefinite cycle of replacement with the current best challenger asset. These assumptions must be satisfied for our calculations to be correct into an indefinite future. However, because the near future is economically more important than the distant future, and because our analysis is done with the *best data currently available*, our results and recommendations are robust or stable for reasonable changes in the estimated data.

The repeatability assumptions together are much like the repeatability assumptions that allowed us to use the annual cost method to compare competing alternatives with different useful lives. Taken together, we call these the **replacement repeatability assumptions.** They allow us to greatly simplify comparing the defender and the challenger.

Stated formally, these two assumptions are:

1. The currently available best challenger will continue to be available in subsequent years and will be unchanged in its economic costs. When the defender is ultimately replaced, it will be replaced with this challenger. Any challengers put into service will also be replaced with the same currently available challenger.

2. The period of needed service of the asset is indefinitely long. Thus the challenger asset, once put into service, will continuously replace itself in repeating cycles.

If these two assumptions are satisfied completely, then our calculations are exact. Often, however, future challengers represent further improvements so that Assumption 1 is not satisfied. While the calculations are no longer exact, the repeatability assumptions allow us to make the best decision we can with the data we have.

If the defender's marginal cost is increasing, once it rises above the challenger's minimum EUAC, it will continue to be greater. Under the repeatability assumptions, we would never want to incur a defender's marginal cost that was greater than the challenger's minimum EUAC. Thus, we use replacement analysis technique 1 when the defender's marginal costs are increasing.

REPLACEMENT ANALYSIS TECHNIQUE 2: DEFENDER MARGINAL COSTS CAN BE COMPUTED AND ARE NOT INCREASING

If the defender's marginal costs do not increase, we have no guarantee that *replacement analysis technique 1* will produce the alternative that is of the greatest economic advantage. Consider the new asset in Example 13-2, which has marginal costs that begin at a high of $17,750, then *decrease* over the next years to a low of $13,950, and then *increase* thereafter to $16,950 in Year 7. If evaluated *one year after implementation*, the asset would not have increasing marginal costs. Defenders in their early stages typically do not fit the requirements of *replacement analysis technique 1*. In the situation graphed in Figure 13-3, such defender assets would be in the downward slope of a concave marginal cost curve.

Example 13-5 details why *replacement analysis technique 1* cannot be applied when defenders do not have consistently increasing marginal cost curves. Instead we apply *replacement analysis technique 2*. That is, we calculate the defender's minimum EUAC to see whether the replacement should occur immediately. If not, as shown in Example 13-5, the replacement occurs after the defender's minimum cost life when the marginal costs are increasing. Then *replacement analysis technique 1* applies again.

EXAMPLE 13-5

Let us look again at the defender and challenger assets in Example 13-4. This time let us arbitrarily change the defender's marginal costs for its 5-year useful life. Now when, if at all, should the defender be replaced with the challenger?

Year, n	Defender Total Marginal Cost in Year n
1	$16,000
2	14,000
3	13,500
4	15,300
5	17,500

SOLUTION

In this case the defender's total marginal costs are *not* consistently increasing from year to year. However, if we ignore this fact and apply *replacement analysis technique 1,* the recommendation would be to replace the defender now, because the defender's marginal cost for the first year ($16,000) is greater than the minimum EUAC of the challenger ($15,430). This would be the wrong choice.

Since the defender's marginal costs are below the challenger's minimum EUAC in the second through fourth years, we must calculate the EUAC of keeping the defender asset in each of its remaining 5 years, at $i = 15\%$.

Year, n	Present Cost If Kept n Years (PC_n)	EUAC If Kept n Years
1	$16,000(P/F, 15\%, 1)$	$\times (A/P, 15\%, 1) = \$16,000$
2	$PC_1 + 14,000(P/F, 15\%, 2)$	$\times (A/P, 15\%, 2) = 15,070$
3	$PC_2 + 13,500(P/F, 15\%, 3)$	$\times (A/P, 15\%, 3) = 14,618$
4	$PC_3 + 15,300(P/F, 15\%, 4)$	$\times (A/P, 15\%, 4) = 14,754$
5	$PC_4 + 17,500(P/F, 15\%, 5)$	$\times (A/P, 15\%, 5) = 15,162$

The minimum EUAC of the defender for 3 years is \$14,618, which is less than that of the challenger's minimum EUAC of \$15,430. Thus, under the replacement repeatability assumptions we will keep the defender for at least 3 years. We must still decide how much longer.

The defender's EUAC begins to rise in Year 4, because the marginal costs are increasing, and because they are above the defender's minimum EUAC. Thus, we can use *replacement analysis technique 1* for Year 4 and later. The defender's marginal cost in Year 4 is \$130 below the challenger's minimum EUAC of \$15,430. Since the defender's marginal cost is higher in Year 5, we replace it with the new challenger at the end of Year 5. Notice that we did *not* keep the defender for its minimum cost life of 3 years, we kept it for 5 years.

If the challenger's minimum EUAC were less than the defender's minimum EUAC of \$14,618, then the defender would be immediately replaced.

Example 13-5 illustrates several potentially confusing points about replacement analysis.

- If the defender's marginal cost data is not increasing, the defender's minimum EUAC must be calculated.
- If the defender's minimum EUAC exceeds the challenger's minimum EUAC, then replace immediately. If the defender's minimum EUAC is lower than the challenger's minimum EUAC, then under the replacement repeatability assumptions the defender will be kept *at least* the number of years for its minimum EUAC.
- After this number of years, then replace when the defender's increasing marginal cost exceeds the challenger's minimum EUAC.

The problem statement for Example 13-6 illustrates a second approach to calculating the defender's marginal costs for its capital costs. The value at the year's beginning is multiplied by $(1 + i)$ and the salvage value at the year's end is subtracted. Each year's total marginal cost also includes the operations and maintenance costs.

Then the solution to Example 13-6 details the calculation of the minimum EUAC when the defender's data is presented as costs and salvage values in each year rather than as marginal costs. Notice that this is calculated the same way as the minimum cost life was calculated for new assets—the challengers.

EXAMPLE 13-6

A 5-year-old machine, whose current market value is $5000, is being analyzed to determine its minimum EUAC at a 10% interest rate. Salvage value and maintenance estimates and the corresponding marginal costs are given in the following table.

	Data		Calculating Marginal Costs		
Year	Salvage Value	O&M Cost	$S_{t-1}(1+i)$	$-S_t$	Marginal Cost
0	$5000				
1	4000	$0	$5500	−4000	$1500
2	3500	100	4400	−3500	1000
3	3000	200	3850	−3000	1050
4	2500	300	3300	−2500	1100
5	2000	400	2750	−2000	1150
6	2000	500	2200	−2000	700
7	2000	600	2200	−2000	800
8	2000	700	2200	−2000	900
9	2000	800	2200	−2000	1000
10	2000	900	2200	−2000	1100
11	2000	1000	2200	−2000	1200

SOLUTION

Because the marginal costs have a complex, nonincreasing pattern, we must calculate the defender's minimum EUAC.

			If Retired at End of Year n		
Years Kept, n	Salvage Value (S) at End of Year n	Maintenance Cost for Year	EUAC of Capital Recovery $(P-S) \times (A/P, 10\%, n) + Si$	EUAC of Maintenance $100(A/G, 10\%, n)$	Total EUAC
0	$P = \$5000$				
1	4000	$ 0	$1100 + 400	$ 0	$1500
2	3500	100	864 + 350	48	1262
3	3000	200	804 + 300	94	1198
4	2500	300	789 + 250	138	1177
5	2000	400	791 + 200	181	1172
6	2000	500	689 + 200	222	1111
7	2000	600	616 + 200	262	1078
8	2000	700	562 + 200	300	1062
9	2000	800	521 + 200	337	1058 ←
10	2000	900	488 + 200	372	1060
11	2000	1000	462 + 200	406	1068

A minimum EUAC of $1058 is computed at Year 9 for the existing machine. Notice that the EUAC begins to increase with *n* when the marginal cost in Year 10 exceeds the EUAC for 9 years.

Now to apply *replacement analysis technique 2* to Example 13-6, we ask: Is the challenger's minimum EUAC higher or lower than the defender's minimum EUAC of $1058? If the challenger's minimum EUAC is lower, then we replace the defender now.

Under the repeatability assumptions, if the challenger's minimum EUAC is higher, we would keep the defender at least 9 years. Replacement would occur in Year 10 or later when the defender's marginal costs exceed the challenger's minimum EUAC. Relaxing the repeatability assumptions to allow for better challengers, we may replace the defender whenever a new challenger has an EUAC that is lower than $1058.

Example 13-7 illustrates the common situation of a current defender that may be kept if overhauled. This can also be analyzed as a potential new challenger.

EXAMPLE 13-7

We must decide whether existing (defender) equipment in an industrial plant should be replaced. A $4000 overhaul must be done now if the equipment is to be retained in service. Maintenance is $1800 in each of the next 2 years, after which it increases by $1000 each year. The defender has no present or future salvage value. The equipment described in Example 13-1 is the challenger (EUAC = $4589). Should the defender be kept or replaced if the interest rate is 8%?

FIGURE 13-4 Overhaul and maintenance costs for the defender in Example 13-7.

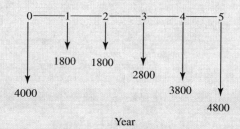

SOLUTION

The first step is to determine the defender's lowest EUAC. The pattern of overhaul and maintenance costs (Figure 13-4) suggests that if the overhaul is done, the equipment should be kept for several years. The computation is as follows:

| | If Retired at End of Year n | | |
| | EUAC of Overhaul | EUAC of Maintenance $1800 + $1000 | |
Year, n	$4000(A/P, 8%, n)$	Gradient from Year 3 on	Total EUAC
1	$4320	$1800	$6120
2	2243	1800	4043
3	1552	1800 + 308*	3660←
4	1208	1800 + 683†	3691
5	1002	1800 + 1079	3881

*For the first 3 years, the maintenance is $1800, $1800, and $2800. Thus, EUAC $=$ $1800 + 1000(A/F, 8%, 3) = 1800 + 308$.

†EUAC $= 1800 + 1000(P/G, 8%, 3)(P/F, 8%, 1)(A/P, 8%, 4) = 1800 + 683$.

The lowest EUAC of the overhauled defender is $3660. In Example 13-1, the challenger's minimum cost life was 4 years with an EUAC of $4589. If we assume the equipment is needed for at least 4 years, the overhauled defender's EUAC ($3660) is less than the challenger's EUAC ($4589). Overhaul the defender.

If the defender's and challenger's cost data do not change, we can use *replacement analysis technique 1* to determine when the overhauled defender should be replaced. We know from the minimum EUAC calculation that the defender should be kept at least 3 years. Is this the best life? The following table computes the marginal cost to answer this question.

Year, n	Overhaul Cost	Maintenance Cost	Marginal Cost to Extend Service
0	$4000	$ 0	
1	0	1800	$6120 = 4000(1.08) + 1800
2	0	1800	1800
3	0	2800	2800
4	0	3800	3800
5	0	4800	4800

Year 5 is the first year after Year 3, which has the overhauled defender's lowest EUAC (in which the $4800 marginal cost exceeds the challenger's $4589 minimum EUAC). Thus, the overhauled defender should be kept 4 more years if costs do not change. (Note that if the defender can be overhauled again after 3 or 4 years, that might be an even better choice.)

REPLACEMENT ANALYSIS TECHNIQUE 3: WHEN DEFENDER MARGINAL COST DATA ARE NOT AVAILABLE

In this case, we simply compare the defender's *EUAC over its stated useful life, and the challenger's minimum EUAC*. Pick the *EUAC* that is lower.

If the defender's marginal cost data is not known and cannot be estimated, it is impossible to apply *replacement analysis techniques 1 or 2* to decide *when* the defender should be replaced. Instead we must assume that the defender's stated useful life is the only one to consider. From a student problem-solving perspective, the defender in Example 13-7 might be described as follows.

The defender can be overhauled for $4800 to extend its life for 5 years. Maintenance costs will average $3000 per year and there will be no salvage value. In this case the only possibility is to compare the defender's EUAC for a 5-year life with the best challenger.

In the real world the most likely scenario for this approach involves a facility-wide overhaul every 3, 5, 10, etc. years. Pipelines and many process plants, such as refineries, chemical plants, and steel mills, must shut down to do major maintenance. All equipment is overhauled or replaced with a new challenger as needed, and the facility is expected to operate until the next maintenance shutdown.

The defender's EUAC over its remaining useful life is compared with the challenger's EUAC at its minimum cost life, and the lower cost is chosen. However, in making this basic comparison an often complicating factor is deciding what first cost to assign to the challenger and the defender.

COMPLICATIONS IN REPLACEMENT ANALYSIS

Defining Defender and Challenger First Costs

Because the defender is already in service, analysts often misunderstand what first cost to assign it. Example 13-8 demonstrates this problem.

EXAMPLE 13-8

A model SK-30 was purchased 2 years ago for $1600; it has been depreciated by straight-line depreciation using a 4-year life and zero salvage value. Because of recent innovations, the current price of the SK-30 is $995. An equipment firm has offered a trade-in allowance of $350 for the SK-30 on a new $1200 model EL-40. Some discussion revealed that without a trade-in, the EL-40 can be purchased for $1050. Thus, the originally quoted price of the EL-40 was overstated to allow a larger trade-in allowance. The true current market value of the SK-30 is probably only $200. In a replacement analysis, what value should be assigned to the SK-30?

SOLUTION

In the example, five different dollar amounts relating to the SK-30 have been outlined:

1. *Original cost:* It cost $1600 2 years ago.
2. *Present cost:* It now sells for $995.
3. *Book value:* The original cost less 2 years of depreciation is $1600 - \frac{2}{4}(1600 - 0) = \$800$.
4. *Trade-in value:* The offer was $350.
5. *Market value:* The estimate was $200.

We know that an economic analysis is based on the current situation, not on the past. We refer to past costs as *sunk* costs to emphasize this. These costs cannot be altered, and they are not relevant. (There is one exception: past costs may affect present or future income taxes.)

We want to use actual cash flows for each alternative. Here the question is, What value should be used in an economic analysis for the SK-30? The relevant cost is the equipment's present market value of $200. Neither the original cost, the present cost, the book value, nor the trade-in value is relevant.

At first glance, an asset's trade-in value would appear to be a suitable present value for the equipment. Often the trade-in price is inflated *along with* the price for the new item. (This practice is so common in new-car showrooms that the term *overtrade* is used to describe the excessive portion of the trade-in allowance. The buyer is also quoted a higher price for the new car.) Distorting the defender's present value, or the challenger's price can be serious because these distortions do not cancel out in an economic analysis.

Example 13-8 illustrated that of the several different values that can be assigned to the defender, the correct one is the present market value. If a trade-in value is obtained, care should be taken to ensure that it actually represents a fair market value.

Determining the value for the challenger's installed cost should be less difficult. In such cases the first cost is usually made up of purchase price, sales tax, installation costs, and other items that occur initially on a one-time basis if the challenger is selected. These values are usually rather straightforward to obtain. One aspect to consider in assigning a first cost to the challenger is the defender's potential market or salvage value. One must not arbitrarily subtract the defender's disposition value from the challenger's first cost, for this practice can lead to an incorrect analysis.

As described in Example 13-8, the correct first cost to assign to the defender SK-30 is its $200 current market value. This value represents the present economic benefit that we would be *forgoing* to keep the defender. This can be called our *opportunity first cost.* If, instead of assuming that this is the defender's *opportunity cost*, we assume it is a *cash benefit* to the challenger, a potential error arises.

The error lies in incorrect use of a *cash flow* perspective when the lives of the challenger and the defender are not equal, which is usually the case. The approach of subtracting the defender's salvage value from the challenger's first cost is called the *cash flow* perspective. From this perspective, keeping the defender in place causes $0 in cash to flow, but selecting the challenger causes the cash flow now to equal the challenger's first cost minus the defender's salvage value.

If the lives of the defender and the challenger are the same, then the cash flow perspective will lead to the correct answer. However, it is normally the case that the defender is an aging asset with a relatively short horizon of possible lives and the challenger is a new asset with a longer life. The *opportunity cost* perspective will always lead to the correct answer, so it is the one that should be used.

For example, consider the SK-30 and EL-40 from Example 13-8. It is reasonable to assume that the 2-year-old SK-30 has 3 years of life left and that the new EL-40 would have a 5-year life. Assume that neither will have any salvage value at the end of its life. Compare the difference in their annual capital costs with the correct *opportunity cost* perspective and the incorrect *cash flow* perspective.

SK-30		EL-40	
Market value	$200	First cost	$1050
Remaining life	3 years	Useful life	5 years

Looking at this from an *opportunity cost* perspective, the annual cost comparison of the first costs is:

$$\text{Annualized first cost}_{\text{SK-30}} = \$200(A/P, 10\%, 3) = \$80$$
$$\text{Annualized first cost}_{\text{EL-40}} = \$1050(A/P, 10\%, 5) = \$277$$

The *difference* in annualized first cost between the SK-30 and EL-40 is:

$$\text{AFC}_{\text{EL-40}} - \text{AFC}_{\text{SK-30}} = \$277 - \$80 = \$197$$

Now using an incorrect *cash flow* perspective to look at the first costs, we can calculate the *difference* due to first cost between the SK-30 and EL-40.

$$\text{Annualized first cost}_{\text{SK-30}} = \$0(A/P, 10\%, 3) = \$0$$
$$\text{Annualized first cost}_{\text{EL-40}} = (\$1050 - 200)(A/P, 10\%, 5) = \$224$$
$$\text{AFC}_{\text{EL-40}} - \text{AFC}_{\text{SK-30}} = \$224 - \$0 = \$224$$

When the defender's remaining life (3 years) differs from the challenger's useful life (5 years), the two perspectives yield different results. The correct difference of $197 is shown by using the *opportunity cost* approach, and an inaccurate difference of $224 is obtained if the *cash flow* perspective is used. From the opportunity cost perspective, the $200 is spread out over 3 years as a cost to the defender, and in the cash flow perspective, the opportunity cost is spread out over 5 years as a benefit to the challenger. Spreading the $200 over 3 years in one case and 5 years in the other case does not produce equivalent annualized amounts. Because of the difference in the lives of the assets, the annualized $200 opportunity cost for the defender cannot be called an equivalent benefit to the challenger.

In the case of unequal lives, the correct method is to assign the defender's current market value as its Time-0 opportunity costs, rather than subtracting this amount from the challenger's first cost. Because the cash flow approach yields an incorrect value when challenger and defender have unequal lives, the *opportunity cost* approach for assigning a first cost to the challenger and defender assets should *always* be used.

REPEATABILITY ASSUMPTIONS NOT ACCEPTABLE

Under certain circumstances, the repeatability assumptions described earlier may not apply. Then replacement analysis techniques 1, 2, and 3 may not be valid. For instance, there may be a specific study period instead of an indefinite need for the asset. For example, consider the case of phasing out production after a certain number of years—perhaps a person who is about to retire is closing down a business and selling all the assets. Another example is production equipment such as molds and dies that are no longer needed when a new model with new shapes is introduced. Yet another is a construction camp that may be needed for only a year or two or three.

This specific study period could potentially be any number of years relative to the lives of the defender and the challenger, such as equal to the defender's life, equal to the challenger's life, less than the defender's life, greater than the challenger's life, or somewhere between the lives of the defender and challenger. The analyst must be explicit about the challenger's and defender's economic costs and benefits, as well as residual or salvage values at the end of the specific study period. In this case the repeatability replacement assumptions do not apply, costs must be analyzed over the study period. The analysis techniques in the decision map also may not apply when future challengers are not assumed to be identical to the current best challenger. This concept is discussed in the next section.

A Closer Look at Future Challengers

We defined the challenger as the best available alternative to replace the defender. But in time, the best available alternative can change. And given the trend in our technological society, it seems likely that future challengers will be better than the present challenger. If so, the prospect of improved future challengers may affect the present decision between the defender and the challenger.

Figure 13-5 illustrates two possible estimates of future challengers. In many technological areas it seems likely that the equivalent uniform annual costs associated with future challengers will decrease by a constant amount each year. In other fields, however, a rapidly changing technology will produce a sudden and substantially improved challenger—with decreased costs or increased benefits. The uniform decline curve of Figure 13-5 reflects the assumption that each future challenger has a minimum EUAC that is a fixed amount less than the previous year's challenger. This assumption, of course, is only one of many possible assumptions that could be made regarding future challengers.

If future challengers will be better than the present challenger, what impact will this have on an analysis now? The prospect of better future challengers may make it more desirable to retain the defender and to reject the present challenger. By keeping the defender for now, we may be able to replace it later by a better future challenger. Or, to state it another way, the present challenger may be made less desirable by the prospect of improved future challengers.

As engineering economic analysts, we must familiarize ourselves with potential technological advances in assets targeted for replacement. This part of the decision process is much like the search for all available alternatives, from which we select the best. Upon finding out more about what alternatives and technologies are emerging, we will be better able

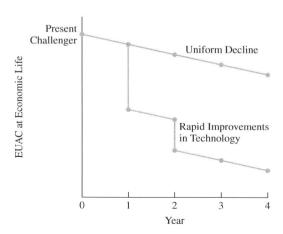

FIGURE 13-5 Two possible ways the EUAC of future challengers may decline.

to understand the repercussions of investing in the current best available challenger. Selecting the current best challenger asset can be particularly risky when (1) the costs are very high and/or (2) the challenger's useful minimum cost life is relatively long (5–10 years or more). When one or both of these conditions exist, it may be better to keep or even augment our defender asset until better future challengers emerge.

There are, of course, many assumptions that *could* be made regarding future challengers. However, if the replacement repeatability assumptions do not hold, the analysis needed becomes more complicated.

AFTER-TAX REPLACEMENT ANALYSIS

As described in Chapter 12, an after-tax analysis provides greater realism and insight. Tax effects can alter before-tax recommendations. After-tax effects may influence calculations in the defender–challenger comparisons discussed earlier. Consequently, one should always perform or check these analyses on an after-tax basis.

Marginal Costs on an After-Tax Basis

Marginal costs on an after-tax basis represent the cost that would be incurred through ownership of the defender *in each year*. On an after-tax basis we must consider the effects of ordinary taxes as well as gains and losses due to asset disposal. Consider Example 13-9.

EXAMPLE 13-9

Refer to Example 13-2, where we calculated the before-tax marginal costs for a new piece of production machinery. Calculate the asset's after-tax marginal costs considering this additional information.

- Depreciation is by the straight-line method, with $S =$ \$0 and $n = 5$ years, so $d_t = (\$25,000 -\$0)/5 = \$5000$.
- Ordinary income, recaptured depreciation, and losses on sales are taxed at a rate of 40%.
- The after-tax MARR is 10%.

Some classes skip or have not yet covered Chapter 10's explanation of expected value. Thus, the expected cost for risk of breakdowns is described here as an insurance cost.

SOLUTION

The after-tax marginal cost of ownership will involve the following elements: incurred or forgone loss or recaptured depreciation, interest on invested capital, tax savings due to depreciation, and annual after-tax operating/maintenance and insurance. Figure 13-6 shows example cash flows for the marginal cost detailed in Table 13-1.

As a refresher of the recaptured depreciation calculations in Chapter 12:

The market value in Year 0 = 25,000.
The market value decreases to \$18,000 at Year 1.
The book value at Year 1 = 25,000 − 5000 = \$20,000.
So loss on depreciation = 20,000 − 18,000 = \$2000.
This results in a tax savings of (2000)(0.4) = \$800.

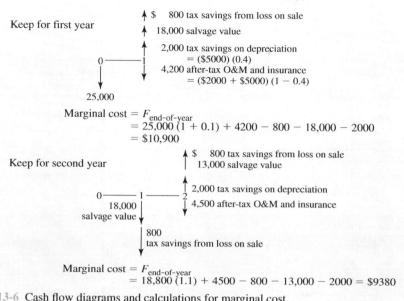

FIGURE 13-6 Cash flow diagrams and calculations for marginal cost.

TABLE 13-1 Marginal Costs of Ownership

Year	Market Value	Book Value	Recaptured Depr. or Loss	Taxes or Tax Savings	After-Tax Market Value
0	$25,000	$25,000			$25,000
1	18,000	20,000	–$2000	–$800	18,800
2	13,000	15,000	–2000	–800	13,800
3	9,000	10,000	–1000	–400	9,400
4	6,000	5,000	1000	400	5,600
5	4,000	0	4000	1600	2,400
6	3,000		3000	1200	1,800
7	2,500		2500	1000	1,500

Year	Col. B After-Tax Market Value	Col. C Beg. Yr Value × (1+i)	Col. D Tax Savings from Depr. Deduct.	O&M and Insurance Cost	Col. F After-Tax Annual Expense	= C + D + F – B Marginal Cost
0	$25,000					
1	18,800	$27,500	–$2000	$7,000	$4200	$10,900
2	13,800	20,680	–2000	7,500	4500	9,380
3	9,400	15,180	–2000	8,000	4800	8,580
4	5,600	10,340	–2000	10,000	6000	8,740
5	2,400	6,160	–2000	12,000	7200	8,960
6	1,800	2,640	0	14,000	8400	9,240
7	1,500	1,980	0	16,000	9600	10,080

The marginal cost in each year is much lower after taxes than the pretax numbers shown in Example 13-2. This is true because depreciation and expenses can be subtracted from taxable income. However, the pattern of declining and then increasing marginal costs is the same, and Year 3 is still the year of lowest marginal costs.

Minimum Cost Life Problems

Here we illustrate the effect of taxes on the calculation of the minimum cost life of the defender and the challenger. The after-tax minimum EUAC depends on both the depreciation method used and changes in the asset's market value over time. Using an accelerated depreciation method (like MACRS) tends to reduce the after-tax costs early in the asset's life. This alters the shape of the total EUAC curve—the concave shape can be shifted and the minimum EUAC changed. Example 13-10 illustrates the effect that taxes can have.

EXAMPLE 13-10

Some new production machinery has a first cost of $100,000 and a useful life of 10 years. Its estimated operating and maintenance (O&M) costs are $10,000 the first year, which will increase annually by $4000. The asset's before-tax market value will be $50,000 at the end of the first year and then will decrease by $5000 annually. This property is a 7-year MACRS property. The company uses a 6% after tax MARR and is subject to a combined federal/state tax rate of 40%.

Calculate the after-tax cash flows.

SOLUTION

To find this new production machinery's minimum cost life, we first find the after-tax cash flow (ATCF) effect of the O&M costs and depreciation (Table 13-2). Then, we find the ATCFs of disposal if the equipment is sold in each of the 10 years (Table 13-3). Finally in the closing section on spreadsheets, we combine these two ATCFs (in Figure 13-7) and choose the minimum cost life.

In Table 13-2, the O&M expense simply starts at $10,000 and increases at $4000 per year. The depreciation entries equal the 7-year r_t MACRS depreciation values given in Table 11-3 multiplied by the $100,000 first cost. The taxable income, which is simply the O&M costs minus the depreciation values, is then multiplied by minus the tax rate to determine the tax savings. The O&M expense plus the tax savings is the Table 13-2 portion of the total ATCF.

Regarding the market value data in this problem, it should be pointed out that the initial decrease of $50,000 in Year 1 is not uncommon. This is especially true for custom-built equipment for a particular and unique application at a specific plant. Such equipment would not be valuable to others in the marketplace. Also, the $100,000 first cost (cost basis) could have included costs due to installation, facility modifications, or removal of old equipment. The $50,000 is realistic for the market value of one-year-old equipment.

The next step is to determine the ATCFs that would occur in each possible year of disposal. (The ATCF for Year 0 is easy; it is −$100,000.) For example, as shown in Table 13-3, in Year 1 there is a $35,710 loss as the book value exceeds the market value. The tax savings from this loss are added to the salvage (market) value to determine the ATCF (*If the asset is disposed during Year 1*).

TABLE 13-2 **ATCF for O&M and Depreciation for Example 13-10**

Year, t	O&M Expense	MACRS Depreciation, d_t	Taxable Income	Tax Savings (at 40%)	O&M Depreciation ATCF
1	-$10,000	$14,290	-$24,290	$ 9,716	-$284
2	-14,000	24,490	-38,490	15,396	1,396
3	-18,000	17,490	-35,490	14,196	-3,804
4	-22,000	12,490	-34,490	13,796	-8,204
5	-26,000	8,930	-34,930	13,972	-12,028
6	-30,000	8,920	-38,920	15,568	-14,432
7	-34,000	8,930	-42,930	17,172	-16,828
8	-38,000	4,460	-42,460	16,984	-21,016
9	-42,000	0	-42,000	16,800	-25,200
10	-46,000	0	-46,000	18,400	-27,600

TABLE 13-3 **ATCF in Year of Disposal for Example 13-10**

Year, t	Market Value	Book Value	Gain or Loss	Gain/Loss Tax (at 40%)	ATCF if Disposed of
1	$50,000	$85,710	-$35,710	$14,284	$64,284
2	45,000	61,220	-16,220	6,488	51,488
3	40,000	43,730	-3,730	1,492	41,492
4	35,000	31,240	3,760	-1,504	33,496
5	30,000	22,310	7,690	-3,076	26,924
6	25,000	13,390	11,610	-4,644	20,356
7	20,000	4,460	15,540	-6,216	13,784
8	15,000	0	15,000	-6,000	9,000
9	10,000	0	10,000	-4,000	6,000
10	5,000	0	5,000	-2,000	3,000

These tables assume that depreciation is taken during the year of disposal and then calculates the recaptured depreciation (gain) or loss on the year-end book value.

SPREADSHEETS AND REPLACEMENT ANALYSIS

Spreadsheets are obviously useful in nearly all after-tax calculations. However, they are absolutely required for optimal life calculations in after-tax situations. Because MACRS is the tax law, the after-tax cash flows are different in every year. Thus, the NPV function and the PMT function are both needed to find the minimum EUAC after taxes. Figure 13-7 illustrates the calculation of the minimum cost life for Example 13-10.

In Figure 13-7, the NPV finds the present worth of the irregular cash flows from Period 1 through Period t for $t = 1$ to life. The PV function is used to find the PW of the salvage value. Then PMT can be used to find the EUAC over each potential life. Before-tax replacement analysis can also be done this way. The spreadsheet block function NPV is used to find the PW of cash flows from Period 1 to Period t. Note that the cell for Period 1 is an absolute address and the cell for period t is a relative address. This allows the formula to be copied.

Example 13-11 illustrates the before-tax optimal economic life of a new car.

	A	B	C	D	E	F
1		**Table 13-2**	**Table 13-3**	6%	Interest Rate	
2		O&M & Depr.	if disposed of			
3	Year	ATCF	ATCF	PW	EUAC	
4	0			−$100,000		
5	1	−$284	$64,284	−39,623	$42,000	=PMT($D$1,A5,D5)
6	2	1,396	51,488	−53,201	29,018	
7	3	−3,804	41,492	−67,382	25,208	
8	4	−8,204	33,496	−82,186	23,718	
9	5	−12,028	26,924	−97,587	23,167	
10	6	−14,432	20,356	−113,530	23,088	optimal life
11	7	−16,828	13,784	−129,904	23,270	
12	8	−21,016	9,000	−146,610	23,610	
13	9	−25,200	6,000	−163,621	24,056	
14	10	−27,600	3,000	−180,909	24,580	=PMT($D$1,A14,D14)
15						
16			=NPV($D$1,$B$5:B14)+$D$4+PV($D$1,A14,0,−C14)			
17			=NPV(*i*, B column) + year 0 + present value of a future salvage			

FIGURE 13-7 Spreadsheet for life with minimum after-tax cost.

EXAMPLE 13-11

A new vehicle costs $19,999 plus $400 in fees. Its value drops 30% the first year, 20% per year for Years 2 through 4, and 15% each additional year. When the car is sold, detailing and advertising will cost $250. Repairs on similar vehicles have averaged $50 annually in lost time (driving to/from the dealer's shop) during the 3-year warranty period. After the warranty period, the cost of repairs and the associated inconvenience climbs at $400 annually. If the MARR is 8%, what is the optimal economic life for the vehicle?

SOLUTION

Figure 13-8 is a spreadsheet that uses the same functions used in Figure 13-7. The present worth for each life is found by using the NPV function for the irregular costs from Years 1 to *n*, and the PV function for salvage value minus the cost to sell, and adding in the Time 0 costs to buy the vehicle. Then a PMT function is used to find the annual cost.

The optimal economic life is 10 years, but it is not much more expensive for lives that are 3 years shorter or 5 years longer. However, keeping a vehicle for less than 5 years is significantly more expensive.

	A	B	C	D	E	F
1	$19,999	first cost				
2	$400	cost to buy				
3	$250	cost to sell				
4	30%	salvage value drop yr 1				
5	20%	salvage value drop yr 2–4				
6	15%	salvage value drop yr 5+				
7	$50	repair during 3 yr warranty				
8	$400	gradient for repair after 3 yr warranty				
9	8%	interest rate				
10	year	cost	salvage value	PW	EUAC	
11	0	$20,399				
12	1	50	$13,999	−$7,714		=PMT($A$9,A12,D12
13	2	50	11,199	−11,101	6,225	
14	3	50	8,960	−13,614	5,283	
15	4	450	7,168	−15,774	4,762	
16	5	850	6,092	−17,461	4,373	
17	6	1250	5,179	−19,119	4,136	
18	7	1650	4,402	−20,765	3,988	
19	8	2050	3,742	−22,409	3,899	
20	9	2450	3,180	−24,055	3,851	
21	10	2850	2,703	−25,705	3,831	economic life & min cost
22	11	3250	2,298	−27,356	3,832	
23	12	3650	1,953	−29,008	3,849	
24	13	4050	1,660	−30,655	3,879	
25	14	4450	1,411	−32,293	3,917	
26	15	4850	1,199	−33,918	3,963	
27						
28	=−$B$11−NPV($A$9,$B$12:B26)+PV($A$9,A26,,−C26+$A$3)					
29	= year 0 + NPV(*i*, B column) + PV(salvage value − sale cost)					

FIGURE 13-8 Spreadsheet for vehicle's optimal economic life.

Example 13-11 shows that even with complicated cost structures, it is still relatively easy to find the minimum cost EUAC with the power of spreadsheets.

SUMMARY

The question in selecting new equipment is, Which machine will be more economical? But when there is an existing machine (called the **defender**), the question is, Shall we replace it now, or shall we keep it for one or more years? When replacement is indicated, the best available replacement equipment (called the **challenger**), will be acquired. When we already have equipment, there is a tendency to use past or sunk costs in the replacement analysis. But only present and future costs are relevant.

This chapter has presented three distinctly different **replacement analysis techniques.** All use the simplifying **replacement repeatability assumptions.** These state that the defender will ultimately be replaced by the current best challenger (as will any challengers implemented in the future), and that we have an indefinite need for the asset's service.

In the usual case, marginal cost data are both available and increasing on a year-to-year basis, and **replacement analysis technique 1** compares *the defender's marginal cost data* *against the challenger's minimum EUAC.* We keep the defender as long as its marginal cost is less than the challenger's minimum EUAC.

When marginal cost data are available for the defender but are not increasing from year to year, **replacement analysis technique 2** compares *the defender's lowest EUAC against the challenger's minimum EUAC.* If the challenger's EUAC is less, select this asset in place of the defender today. If the defender's lowest EUAC is smaller, we do not replace it yet. If the cost data for the challenger and the defender do not change, replace the defender after the life that minimizes its EUAC when its marginal cost data exceed the challenger's minimum EUAC.

In the case of no marginal cost data being available for the defender, **replacement analysis technique 3** compares *the defender's EUAC over its stated life, against the challenger's minimum EUAC.* As in the case of replacement analysis technique 2, select the alternative that has the smallest EUAC. An important concept when calculating the EUAC of both defender and challenger is the first cost to be assigned to each alternative for calculation purposes. When the lives of the two alternatives match, either an **opportunity cost** or a **cash flow approach** may be used. However, in the more common case of different useful lives, only the opportunity cost approach accurately assigns first costs to the defender and challenger.

It is important when performing engineering economic analyses to include the effects of taxes. This is much easier to do with spreadsheets. Spreadsheets also make it easy to compute the optimal economic life of vehicles and equipment—even when this includes complex patterns of declining salvage values, warranty periods, and increasing repair costs.

Replacement analyses are vastly important, yet often ignored by companies as they invest in equipment and facilities. Investments in business and personal assets should not be forgotten once an initial economic evaluation has produced a "buy" recommendation. It is important to continue to evaluate assets over their respective life cycles to ensure that invested monies continue to yield the greatest benefit. Replacement analyses help us to ensure this.

PROBLEMS

Replacement Problems

13-1 Typically there are two alternatives in a replacement analysis. One alternative is to replace the defender now. The other alternative is which one of the following?

 A. Keep the defender for its remaining useful life.

 B. Keep the defender for another year and then reexamine the situation.

 C. Keep the defender until there is an improved challenger that is better than the present challenger.

 D. The answer to this question depends on the data available for the defender and challenger as well as the assumptions made regarding the period of needed service and future challengers.

13-2 The defender's economic life can be found if certain estimates about the defender can be made. Assuming those estimates prove to be exactly correct, one can accurately predict the year when the defender should be replaced, even if nothing is known about the challenger. True or false? Explain.

13-3 A proposal has been made to replace a large heat exchanger (3 years ago, the initial cost was $85,000) with a new, more efficient unit at a cost of $120,000. The existing heat exchanger is being depreciated by the MACRS method. Its present book value is $20,400, but its scrap value just equals the cost to remove it from the plant. In preparing the before-tax economic analysis, should the $20,400 book value of the old heat exchanger be

A. *added* to the cost of the new exchanger?

B. *subtracted* from the cost of the new exchanger?

C. *ignored* in this before-tax economic analysis?

13-4 Which one of the following is the proper dollar value of defender equipment to use in replacement analysis?

A. Original cost

B. Present market value

C. Present trade-in value

D. Present book value

E. Present replacement cost, if different from original cost

13-5 Consider the following data for a defender asset. What is the correct replacement analysis technique to compare this asset against a competing challenger? How is this method used? That is, what comparison is made, and how do we choose?

Year, n	BTCF in Year n (marginal costs)
1	−$2000
2	−1750
3	−1500
4	−1250
5	−1000
6	−1000
7	−1000
8	−1500
9	−2000
10	−3000

Challenger Min EUAC

13-6 A machine has a first cost of $50,000. Its market value declines by 20% annually. The operating and maintenance costs start at $3500 per year and climb by $2000 per year. The firm's MARR is 9%. Find the minimum EUAC for this machine and its economic life.   (*Answer:* $17,240, 4 years)

13-7 A machine has a first cost of $10,000. Its market value declines by 20% annually. The repair costs are covered by the warranty in Year 1, and then they increase $600 per year. The firm's MARR is 15%. Find the minimum EUAC for this machine and its economic life.

13-8 A vehicle has a first cost of $20,000. Its market value declines by 15% annually. It is used by a firm that estimates the effect of older vehicles on the firm's image. A new car has no "image cost." But the image cost of older vehicles climbs by $700 per year. The firm's MARR is 10%. Find is the minimum EUAC for this vehicle and its economic life.

13-9 The Clap Chemical Company needs a large insulated stainless steel tank to expand its plant. Clap has located such a tank at a recently closed brewery. The brewery has offered to sell the tank for $15,000 delivered. The price is so low that Clap believes it can sell the tank at any future time and recover its $15,000 investment.

The outside of the tank is covered with heavy insulation that requires considerable maintenance.

Year	Insulation Maintenance Cost
0	$2000
1	500
2	1000
3	1500
4	2000
5	2500

(*a*) Based on a 15% before-tax MARR, what life of the insulated tank has the lowest EUAC?

(*b*) Is it likely that the insulated tank will be replaced by another tank at the end of the period with the lowest EUAC? Explain.

13-10 The plant manager may purchase a piece of unusual machinery for $10,000. Its resale value after 1 year is estimated to be $3000. Because the device is sought by antique collectors, resale value is rising $500 per year.

The maintenance cost is $300 per year for each of the first 3 years, and then it is expected to double each year. Thus the fourth-year maintenance will be $600; the fifth-year maintenance, $1200, and so on. Based on a 15% before-tax MARR, what life of this machinery has the lowest EUAC?

Replacement Technique 1

13-11 A machine tool, which has been used in a plant for 10 years, is being considered for replacement. It cost

$9500 and was depreciated by MACRS depreciation using a 5-year recovery period. An equipment dealer indicates that the machine has no resale value. Maintenance on the machine tool has been a problem, with an $800 cost this year. Future annual maintenance costs are expected to be higher. What is the economic life of this machine tool if it is kept in service?

13-12 In a replacement analysis problem, the following facts are known:

Initial cost	$12,000
Annual maintenance	Year
None	1–3
$2000	4–5
$4500	6
$7000	7
+$2500/year	

Salvage value in any year is zero. Assume a 10% interest rate and ignore income taxes. Compute the life for this challenger having the lowest EUAC. (*Answer:* 5 years)

13-13 An injection-molding machine has a first cost of $1,050,000 and a salvage value of $225,000 in any year. The maintenance and operating cost is $235,000 with an annual gradient of $75,000. The MARR is 10%. What is the most economic life?

13-14 Five years ago, Thomas Martin installed production machinery that had a first cost of $25,000. At that time initial yearly costs were estimated at $1250, increasing by $500 each year. The market value of this machinery each year would be 90% of the previous year's value. There is a new machine available now that has a first cost of $27,900 and no yearly costs over its 5 year-minimum cost life. If Thomas Martin uses an 8% before-tax MARR, when, if at all, should he replace the existing machinery with the new unit?

13-15 Consider Problem 13-14 involving Thomas Martin. When, if at all, should the old machinery be replaced with the new, given the following changes in the data. The old machine retains only 70% of its value in the market from year-to-year. The yearly costs of the old machine were $3000 in Year 1 and increase at 10% thereafter.

13-16 Mary O'Leary's company ships fine wool garments from County Cork, Ireland. Five years ago she

purchased some new automated packing equipment having a first cost of $125,000 and a MACRS class life of 7 years. The annual costs for operating, maintenance, and insurance, as well as market value data for each year of the equipment's 10-year useful life are as follows.

Year n	Annual Costs in Year n for			Market Value in Year n
	Operating	Maintenance	Insurance	
1	$16,000	$ 5,000	$17,000	$80,000
2	20,000	10,000	16,000	78,000
3	24,000	15,000	15,000	76,000
4	28,000	20,000	14,000	74,000
5	32,000	25,000	12,000	72,000
6	36,000	30,000	11,000	70,000
7	40,000	35,000	10,000	68,000
8	44,000	40,000	10,000	66,000
9	48,000	45,000	10,000	64,000
10	52,000	50,000	10,000	62,000

Now Mary is looking at the remaining 5 years of her investment in this equipment, which she had initially evaluated on the basis of an after-tax MARR of 25% and a tax rate of 35%. Assume that the replacement repeatability assumptions are valid.

(a) What is the before-tax marginal cost for the remaining 5 years?

(b) When, if at all, should Mary replace this packing equipment if a new challenger, with a minimum EUAC of $110,000, has been identified?

13-17 SHOJ Enterprises has asked you to look at the following data. The interest rate is 10%.

Year, n	Marginal Cost Data Defender	EUAC if Kept n Years Challenger
1	$3000	$4500
2	3150	4000
3	3400	3300
4	3800	4100
5	4250	4400
6	4950	6000

(*a*) What is the *defender's* lowest EUAC?

(*b*) What is the *challenger's* economic life?

(*c*) When, if at all, should we replace the *defender* with the *challenger*?

13-18 Bill's father read that each year a car's value declines by 25%. After a car is 3 years old, the rate of decline falls to 15%. Maintenance and operating costs increase as the car ages. Because of the manufacturer's warranty, first-year maintenance is very low.

Age of Car (years)	Maintenance Expense
1	$ 50
2	150
3	180
4	200
5	300
6	390
7	500

Bill's dad wants to keep his annual cost of car ownership low. The car Bill's dad prefers costs $11,200 new. Should he buy a new or a used car and, if used, when would you suggest he buy it, and how long should it be kept? Give a practical, rather than a theoretical, solution. (*Answer:* Buy a 3-year-old car and keep it 3 years.)

Replacement Technique 2

13-19 A new $40,000 bottling machine has just been installed in a plant. It will have no salvage value when it is removed. The plant manager has asked you to estimate the machine's economic service life, ignoring income taxes. He estimates that the annual maintenance cost will be constant at $2500 per year. What service life will result in the lowest equivalent uniform annual cost?

13-20 Big-J Construction Company, Inc. (Big-J CC) is conducting a routine periodic review of existing field equipment. They use a MAAR of 20%. This includes a replacement evaluation of a paving machine now in use. The machine was purchased 3 years ago for $200,000, The paver's current market value is $120,000, and yearly operating and maintenance costs are as follows.

Year, n	Operating Cost in Year n	Maintenance Cost in Year n	Market Value if Sold in Year n
1	$15,000	$ 9,000	$85,000
2	15,000	10,000	65,000
3	17,000	12,000	50,000
4	20,000	18,000	40,000
5	25,000	20,000	35,000
6	30,000	25,000	30,000
7	35,000	30,000	25,000

Data for a new paving machine have been analyzed. Its most economic life is at 8 years with a minimum EUAC of $62,000. When should the existing paving machine be replaced?

13-21 VMIC Corp. has asked you to look at the following data. The interest rate is 10%.

Year, n	Marginal Cost Data Defender	EUAC If Kept n Years Challenger
1	$2500	$4500
2	2400	3600
3	2300	3000
4	2550	2600
5	2900	2700
6	3400	3500
7	4000	4000

(*a*) What is the *defender's* lowest EUAC?

(*b*) What is the *challenger's* minimum cost life?

(*c*) When, if at all, should we replace the *defender* with the *challenger*?

Replacement Technique 3

13-22 You are considering the purchase of a new high-efficiency machine to replace older machines now. The new machine can replace four of the older machines, each with a current market value of $600. The new machine will cost $5000 and will save the equivalent of 10,000 kWh of electricity per year. After a period of 10 years, neither option (new or old) will have any market value. If you use a before-tax MARR of 25% and pay $0.075 per kilowatt-hour, would you replace the old machines today with the new one?

13-23 The Quick Manufacturing Company, a large profitable corporation, may replace a production machine tool. A new machine would cost $3700, have a 4-year useful and depreciable life, and have no salvage value. For tax purposes, sum-of-years'-digits depreciation would be used. The existing machine tool cost $4000 4 years ago and has been depreciated by straight-line depreciation assuming an 8-year life and no salvage value. The tool could be sold now to a used equipment dealer for $1000 or be kept in service for another 4 years. It would then have no salvage value. The new machine tool would save about $900 per year in operating costs compared to the existing machine. Assume a 40% combined state and federal tax rate.

Compute the before-tax rate of return on the replacement proposal of installing the new machine rather than keeping the existing machine. (*Answer: 12.6%*)

13-24 A professor of engineering economics owns a 1996 car. In the past 12 months, he has paid $2000 to replace the transmission, bought two new tires for $160, and installed a CD player for $110. He wants to keep the car for 2 more years because he invested money 3 years ago in a 5-year certificate of deposit, which is earmarked to pay for his dream machine, a red European sports car. Today the old car's engine failed. The professor has two alternatives. He can have the engine overhauled at a cost of $1800 and then most likely have to pay another $800 per year for the next 2 years for maintenance. The car will have no salvage value at that time. Alternatively, a colleague offered to make the professor a $5000 loan to buy another used car. He must pay the loan back in two equal installments of $2500 due at the end of Year 1 and Year 2, and at the end of the second year he must give the colleague the car. The "new" used car has an expected annual maintenance cost of $300. If the professor selects this alternative, he can sell his current vehicle to a junkyard for $1500. Interest is 5%. Using present worth analysis, which alternative should he select and why?

13-25 The Plant Department of the local telephone company purchased four special pole hole diggers 8 years ago for $14,000 each. They have been in constant use to the present. Owing to an increased workload, additional machines will soon be required.

Recently an improved model of the digger was announced. The new machines have a higher production rate and lower maintenance expense than the old machines but will cost $32,000 each with a service life of 8 years and salvage value of $750 each. The four original diggers have an immediate salvage of $2000 each and an estimated salvage value of $500 each 8 years hence. The average annual maintenance expense of the old machines is about $1500 each, compared with $600 each for the new machines.

A field study and trial show that the workload would require three additional new machines if the old machines continue in service. However, if the old machines were all retired from service, the workload could be carried by six new machines with an annual savings of $12,000 in operation costs. A training program to prepare employees to run the machines will be necessary at an estimated cost of $700 per new machine. If the MARR is 9% before taxes, what should the company do?

After-Tax

13-26 The Ajax Corporation purchased a railroad tank car 8 years ago for $60,000. It is being depreciated by SOYD depreciation, assuming a 10-year depreciable life and a $7000 salvage value. The tank car needs to be reconditioned now at a cost of $35,000. If this is done, it is estimated the equipment will last for 10 more years and have a $10,000 salvage value at the end of the 10 years.

On the other hand, the existing tank car could be sold now for $10,000 and a new tank car purchased for $85,000. The new tank car would be depreciated by MACRS depreciation. Its estimated actual salvage value after 10 years would be $15,000. In addition, the new tank car would save $7000 per year in maintenance costs, compared to the reconditioned tank car.

Based on a 15% before-tax rate of return, determine whether the existing tank car should be reconditioned or a new one purchased. *Note:* The problem statement provides more data than are needed, which is typical of real situations. (*Answer:* Recondition the old tank car.)

13-27 State the advantages and disadvantages with respect to after-tax benefits of the following options for a major equipment unit:

A. Buy new.

B. Trade in and buy a similar, rebuilt equipment from the manufacturer.

C. Have the manufacturer rebuild your equipment with all new available options.

D. Have the manufacturer rebuild your equipment to the original specifications.

E. Buy used equipment.

13-28 Fifteen years ago the Acme Manufacturing Company bought a propane-powered forklift truck for $4800. The company depreciated the forklift using straight-line depreciation, a 12-year life, and zero salvage value. Over the years, the forklift has been a good piece of equipment, but lately the maintenance cost has risen sharply. Estimated end-of-year maintenance costs for the next 10 years are as follows:

Year	Maintenance Cost
1	$400
2	600
3	800
4	1000
5–10	1400/year

The old forklift has no present or future net salvage value, since its scrap metal value just equals the cost to haul it away. A replacement is now being considered for the old forklift. A modern unit can be purchased for $6500. It has an economic life equal to its 10-year depreciable life. Straight-line depreciation will be employed, with zero salvage value at the end of the 10-year depreciable life. At any time the new forklift can be sold for its book value. Maintenance on the new forklift is estimated to be a constant $50 per year for the next 10 years, after which maintenance is expected to increase sharply. Should Acme Manufacturing keep its old forklift truck for the present, or replace it now with a new one? The firm expects an 8% after-tax rate of return on its investments. Assume a 40% combined state-and-federal tax rate. (*Answer:* Keep the old forklift truck.)

13-29 Machine *A* has been completely overhauled for $9000 and is expected to last another 12 years. The

$9000 was treated as an expense for tax purposes last year. Machine *A* can be sold now for $30,000 net after selling expenses, but will have no salvage value 12 years hence. It was bought new 9 years ago for $54,000 and has been depreciated since then by straight-line depreciation using a 12-year depreciable life.

Because less output is now required, Machine *A* can be replaced with a smaller machine: Machine *B* costs $42,000, has an anticipated life of 12 years, and would reduce operating costs $2500 per year. It would be depreciated by straight-line depreciation with a 12-year depreciable life and no salvage value.

The income tax rate is 40%. Compare the after-tax annual costs and decide whether Machine *A* should be retained or replaced by Machine *B*. Use a 10% after-tax rate of return.

13-30 (*a*) A new employee at CLL Engineering Consulting Inc., you are asked to join a team performing an economic analysis for a client. Your task is to find the Time-0 ATCFs. CLL Inc. has a combined federal/state tax rate of 45% on ordinary income, depreciation recapture, and losses.

Defender: This asset was placed in service 7 years ago. At that time the $50,000 cost basis was set up on a straight-line depreciation schedule with an estimated salvage value of $15,000 over its 10-year ADR life. This asset has a present market value of $30,000.

Challenger: The new asset has a first cost of $85,000 and will be depreciated by MACRS depreciation over its 10-year class life. This asset qualifies for a 10% investment tax credit.

(*b*) How would your calculations change if the present market value of the *defender* is $25,500?

(*c*) How would your calculations change if the present market value of the *defender* is $18,000?

13-31 Foghorn Leghorn may replace an old egg-sorting machine used by his business, Foggy's Farm Fresh Eggs. The old egg machine is not quite running eggs-actly the way it was originally designed and will require an additional investment now of $2500 (expensed at Time 0) to get it back in working shape. This old machine was purchased 6 years ago for $5000 and has been depreciated by the straight-line method at $500 per year. Six years ago the estimated salvage value for tax purposes was $1000. Operating expenses for the old machine are projected at $600 this next year and are increasing by $150 per year each year thereafter. Foggy projects that with refurbishing, the machine will last another 3 years. Foggy believes that he could sell the old machine as-is today for $1000 to his friend Fido to sort bones. He also believes he could sell it 3 years from now at the barnyard flea market for $500.

The new egg-sorting machine, a deluxe model, has a purchase price of $10,000 and will last 6 years, at which time it will have a salvage value of $1000. The new machine qualifies as a MACRS 7-year property and will have operating expenses of $100 the first year, increasing by $50 per year thereafter. Foghorn uses an after-tax MARR of 18% and a tax rate of 35% on original income.

(a) What was the depreciation life used with the defender asset (the old egg sorter)?

(b) Calculate the after-tax cash flows for both the defender and challenger assets.

(c) Use the annual cash flow method to offer a recommendation to Foggy. What assumptions did you make in this analysis?

13-32 A firm is concerned about the condition of some of its plant machinery. Bill James, a newly hired engineer, reviewed the situation and identified five feasible, mutually exclusive alternatives.

Alternative A: Spend $44,000 now repairing various items. The $44,000 can be charged as a current operating expense (rather than capitalized) and deducted from other taxable income immediately. These repairs will keep the plant functioning for 7 years with current operating costs.

Alternative B: Spend $49,000 to buy general-purpose equipment. Depreciation would be straight line over the equipment's 7-year useful life. The equipment has no salvage value. The new equipment will reduce annual operating costs by $6000.

Alternative C: Spend $56,000 to buy new specialized equipment. This equipment would be depreciated by sum-of-years'-digits depreciation over its 7-year useful life. This equipment would reduce annual operating costs by $12,000. It will have no salvage value.

Alternative D: This alternative is the same as Alternative *B*, except it reduces annual operating costs by $7000.

Alternative E: This is the "do-nothing" alternative, with annual operating costs $8000 above the present level.

This profitable firm pays 40% corporate income taxes and uses a 10% after-tax rate of return. Which alternative should the firm adopt?

13-33 Fred's Rodent Control Corporation has been using a low-frequency sonar device to locate subterranean pests. This device was purchased 5 years ago for $18,000. The device has been depreciated using SOYD depreciation with an 8-year depreciable life and a salvage value of $3600. Presently, it could be sold for $7000. If it is kept for the next 3 years, its market value is expected to drop to $1600.

A new lightweight subsurface heat-sensing searcher (SHSS) that is available for $10,000 would improve the annual net income by $500 for each of the next 3 years. The SHSS would be depreciated as a 5-year class property, using MACRS. At the end of 3 years, the SHSS should have a market value of $4000. Fred's Rodent Control is a profitable enterprise subject to a 40% tax rate.

(a) Construct the after-tax cash flow for the old sonar unit for the next 3 years.

(b) Construct the after-tax cash flow for the SHSS unit for the next 3 years.

(c) Construct the after-tax cash flow for the difference between the SHSS unit and the old sonar unit for the next 3 years.

(d) Should Fred buy the new SHSS unit if his MARR is 20%? You do not have to calculate the incremental rate of return; just show how you reach your decision.

13-34 Compute the after-tax rate of return on the replacement proposal for Problem 13-23.

13-35 BC Junction purchased some embroidering equipment for their Denver facility 3 years ago for $15,000. This equipment qualified as MACRS 5-year property. Maintenance costs are estimated to be $1000 this next year and will increase by $1000per year thereafter. The market (salvage) value for the equipment is $10,000 at the end of this year and declines by $1000 per year in the future. If BC Junction has an after-tax MARR of 30%, a marginal tax rate of 45% on ordinary income, depreciation recapture, and losses, what after-tax life of this previously purchased equipment has the lowest EUAC? Use a spreadsheet to develop your solution.

 13-36 Reconsider the acquisition of packing equipment for Mary O'Leary's business, as described in Problem 13-16. Given the data tabulated there, and again using an after-tax MARR of 25% and a tax rate of 35% on ordinary income to evaluate the investment, determine the after-tax lowest EUAC of the equipment. Use a spreadsheet to develop your solution.

CHAPTER 14

INFLATION AND PRICE CHANGE

The Athabasca Oil Sands

For centuries, people have known about the sticky bitumen that lines the banks of the Athabasca River in northern Alberta. Even before the coming of the European fur traders, Native people used it to seal canoes. Over the years, many people dreamed of producing usable oil from the bitumen, but the sand and oil are not easily separated, and the recovery was not viewed as economically viable. In the 1950s, the world price of oil was around $3 a barrel and the estimated cost of mining and separating oil from the sands was over $30 a barrel.

In 1964, the Sun Oil Company, with government support, formed the Great Canadian Oil Sands Company, and in 1967 it started to mine and process shallow deposits of oil sands. The target production was 31,000 barrels per day, and the initial production cost would be about $25 a barrel. The world price was then about $3.50, but the planners were predicting that production costs would decline and market prices would increase.

Forty years later, in 2004, two major oil firms together supply one-third of Canada's oil from these bitumen deposits. Other firms extract bitumen from deeper deposits by steam heating, and $40 billion worth of new oil sands projects are on the books. The successor to Great Canadian Oil Sands, Suncor Energy, has 5,500 employees and is producing 260,000 barrels of oil per day. The production costs are in the range of $22 a barrel, and the world price of oil is much higher.

Contributed by Peter Flynn, University of Alberta

1. In the 1960s, market analysts estimated that at a world price of $25 per barrel, oil sands projects could provide about a 10% rate of return. How might inflation have affected these estimates?

2. The prices of some items—for example, gas at the pumps, houses—increase over time while others, such as calculators and computers, decline in price. Given these variations, how can we know if inflation is occurring, and how could we measure it?

3. In 1967, the Canadian consumer price index was 21.5; in 2004, the CPI was 123.2. What was the 2004 production cost in 1967 dollars?

4. Use the Internet and other resources to learn more about the mining of Athabasca oil sands. Are there any environmental and ethical dimensions to this story?

After Completing This Chapter...

The student should be able to:

- Describe inflation, explain how it happens, and list its effects on purchasing power.
- Define real and actual dollars and interest rates.
- Conduct constant dollar and nominal dollar analyses.
- Define and use composite and commodity-specific price indexes.
- Develop and use cash flows that inflate at different interest rates and cash flows subject to different interest rates per period.
- Incorporate the effects of inflation in before-tax and after-tax calculations.
- Develop spreadsheets to incorporate the effects of inflation and price change.

T hus far we have assumed that the dollars in our analyses were unaffected by inflation or price change. However, this assumption is not always valid or realistic. If inflation occurs in the general economy, or if there are price changes in economic costs and benefits, the impact can be substantial on both before- and after-tax analyses. In this chapter we develop several key concepts and illustrate how inflation and price changes may be incorporated.

MEANING AND EFFECT OF INFLATION

Inflation is an important concept because the purchasing power of money used in most world economies rarely stays constant. Rather, over time the amount of goods and services that can be bought with a fixed amount of money tends to change. Inflation causes money to lose **purchasing power.** That is, when prices inflate we can buy less with the same amount of money. **Inflation makes future dollars less valuable than present dollars.** Think about examples in your own life, or for an even starker comparison, ask your grandparents how much a loaf of bread or a new car cost 50 years ago. Then compare these prices with what you would pay today for the same items. This exercise will reveal the effect of inflation: as time passes, goods and services cost more, and more monetary units are needed to buy the same goods and services.

Because of inflation, dollars in one period of time are not equivalent to dollars in another. We know that engineering economic analysis requires that comparisons be made on an **equivalent** basis. So, it is important for us to be able to incorporate the effects of inflation.

When the purchasing power of a monetary unit *increases* rather than decreases as time passes, the result is **deflation.** Deflation, very rare in the modern world, nonetheless can exist. Deflation has the opposite effect of inflation—one can buy **more** with money in future years than can be bought today. Thus, deflation makes future dollars more valuable than current dollars.

How Does Inflation Happen?

Economists generally believe that inflation depends on the following, either in isolation or in combination.

Money supply: The amount of money in our national economy has an effect on its purchasing power. If there is too much money in the system (the Federal Reserve controls the flow of money) versus goods and services to purchase with that money, the value of dollars tends to decrease. When there are fewer dollars in the system, they become more valuable. The Federal Reserve seeks to increase the volume of money in the system at the same rate that the economy is growing.

Exchange rates: The strength of the dollar in world markets affects the profitability of international companies. Prices may be adjusted to compensate for the dollar's relative strength or weakness in the world market. As corporations' profits are weakened or eliminated in some markets owing to fluctuations in exchange rates, prices may be raised in other markets to compensate.

Cost–push: This cause of inflation develops as producers of goods and services "push" their increasing operating costs along to the customer through higher prices. These operating costs include fabrication/manufacturing, marketing, and sales.

Demand–pull: This cause is realized when consumers spend money freely on goods and services. As more and more people demand certain goods and services, the prices of those goods and services will rise (demand exceeding supply).

A further consideration in analyzing how inflation works is the usually different rates at which prices and wages rise. Do workers benefit if, as their wages increase, the prices of goods and services increase? To determine the net effect of differing rates of inflation, we must be able to make comparisons and understand costs and benefits from an equivalent perspective. In this chapter we will learn how to make such comparisons.

Definitions for Considering Inflation in Engineering Economy

The following definitions are used throughout this chapter to illustrate how inflation and price change affect two quantities: interest rates and cash flows.

Inflation rate (f): The inflation rate captures the effect of goods and services costing more—a decrease in the purchasing power of dollars. More money is required to buy a good or service whose price has inflated. The inflation rate is measured as the annual rate of increase in the number of dollars needed to pay for the same amount of goods and services.

Real interest rate (i'): This interest rate measures the "real" growth of our money excluding the effect of inflation. Because it does not include inflation, it is sometimes called the *inflation-free interest rate.*

Market interest rate (i): This is the rate of interest that one obtains in the general marketplace. For instance, the interest rates on passbook savings, checking plus, and certificates of deposit quoted by banks are all market rates. The lending interest rate for autos and boats is also a market rate. This rate is sometimes called the *combined interest* rate because it incorporates the effect of both real money growth **and** inflation. We can view i as follows:

Market interest rate	**has in it**	**"Real" growth of money**	**and**	**Effect of inflation**

The mathematical relationship between the inflation, real and market interest rates is given as:

$$i = i' + f + (i')(f) \qquad (14\text{-}1)$$

This is the first point where we have defined a real interest rate and a market or combined interest rate. Which naturally leads to the question of what meaning should be attached to the interest rate i, which is found throughout the text. In fact, both meanings have been used. In problems about savings accounts and loans, the interest rate is usually a market rate. In problems about engineering projects where costs and benefits are often estimated as $x per year, the interest rate is a real rate.

EXAMPLE 14-1

Suppose Tiger Woods wants to invest some recent golf winnings in his hometown bank for one year. Currently, the bank is paying a rate of 5.5% *compounded annually*. Assume inflation is expected to be 2% per year. Identify i, f, and i'. Repeat for inflation of 8% per year.

SOLUTION

If Inflation Is 2% per Year

The bank is paying a *market rate* (i). The *inflation rate* (f) is given. What then is the *real interest rate* (i')?

$$i = 5.5\% \qquad f = 2\% \qquad i' = ?$$

Solving for i' in Equation 14-1, we have

$$i = i' + f + (i')(f)$$
$$i - f = i'(1 + f)$$
$$i' = (i - f)/(1 + f)$$
$$= (0.055 - 0.02)/(1 + 0.02) = 0.034 \quad \text{or} \quad \textbf{3.4\% per year}$$

This means that Tiger Woods will have 3.4% **more** purchasing power than he had a year ago. At the end of the year he can buy 3.4% more goods and services than he could have at the beginning of the year. For example, assume he was buying golf balls that cost $5 each and that he had invested $1000.

At the *beginning* of the year he could buy:

$$\text{Number of balls purchased today} = \frac{\text{Dollars today available to buy balls}}{\text{Cost of balls today}}$$

$$= 1000/\$5 = 200 \text{ golf balls}$$

At the *end* of the year he could buy:

$$\text{Number of balls bought at end of year} = \frac{\text{Dollars available for purchase at end of year}}{\text{Cost per ball at end of year}}$$

$$= \frac{(\$1000)(F/P, 5.5\%, 1)}{(\$5)(1 + 0.02)^1} = \frac{\$1055}{\$5.10} = 207 \text{ golf balls}$$

Tiger Woods can, after one year, buy 3.4% more golf balls than he could before. With rounding, this is 207 balls.

If Inflation Is 8%

As for the lower inflation rate, we would solve for i':

$$i' = (i - f)/(1 + f)$$

$$= (0.055 - 0.08)/(1 + 0.08)$$

$$= -0.023 \quad \text{or} \quad \textbf{-2.3\% per year}$$

In this case the real growth in money has *decreased* by 2.3%, so that Tiger can now buy 2.3% fewer balls with the money he had invested. Even though he has more money year-end, it is worth less, so he can purchase less.

Regardless of how inflation behaves over the year, the bank will pay Tiger $1055 at the end of the year. However, as we have seen, inflation can greatly affect the "real" growth of dollars over time. In a presidential speech, inflation has been called "that thief" because it steals real purchasing power from our dollars.

Let us continue the discussion of inflation by focusing on cash flows. We define dollars of two types:

Actual dollars (A$): These are the dollars that we ordinarily think of when we think of money. These dollars circulate in our economy and are used for investments and payments. We can touch these dollars and often keep them in our purses and wallets—they are "actual" and exist physically. Sometimes they are called *inflated dollars* because they carry any inflation that has reduced their worth. These are also the dollars shown on paychecks, credit card receipts, and normal financial transactions.

Real dollars (R$): These dollars are a bit harder to define. They are always expressed in terms of some constant purchasing power "base" year, for example, 2008-based dollars. Real dollars are sometimes called *constant dollars* or *constant purchasing power dollars,* and because they do not carry the effects of inflation, they are also known as *inflation-free dollars*.

Having defined *market, inflation,* and *real interest rates* as well as *actual* and *real dollars,* let us describe how these quantities relate. Figure 14-1 illustrates the relationship between these quantities.

Figure 14-1 illustrates the following principles:

When dealing with actual dollars (A$), use a market interest rate (i), and when discounting A$ over time, also use i.

When dealing with real dollars (R$), use a real interest rate (i'), and when discounting R$ over time, also use i'.

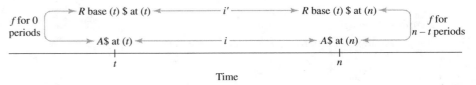

FIGURE 14-1 Relationship between i, f, i', $A\$$, and $R\$$.

Figure 14-1 shows the relationships between $A\$$ and $R\$$ that occur **at the same period of time.** Actual and real dollars are related by the *inflation rate,* in this case, over the period of years defined by $-t$. To translate between dollars of one type to dollars of the other ($A\$$ to $R\$$ or $R\$$ to $A\$$), use the inflation rate for the right number of periods. The following example illustrates many of these relationships.

EXAMPLE 14-2

When the university's stadium was completed in 1955, the total cost was $1.2 million. At that time a wealthy alumnus gifted the university with $1.2 million to be used for a future replacement. University administrators are now considering building the new facility in the year 2010. Assume that:

- Inflation is 6.0% per year from 1955 to 2010.
- In 1955 the university invested the gift at a market interest rate of 8.0% per year.

(a) Define i, i', f, $A\$$, and $R\$$.

(b) How many actual dollars in the year 2010 will the gift be worth?

(c) How much would the actual dollars in 2010 be in terms of 1955 *purchasing power?*

(d) How much better or worse should the new stadium be?

SOLUTION TO PART a

Since 6.0% is the inflation rate (f) and 8.0% is the market interest rate (i), we can write

$$i' = (0.08 - 0.06)/(1 + 0.06) = 0.01887, \quad \text{or} \quad 1.887\%$$

The building's cost in 1955 was $1,200,000, which were the actual dollars ($A\$$) spent in 1955.

SOLUTION TO PART b

From Figure 14-1 we are going from *actual dollars at t, in 1955,* to *actual dollars at n, in 2010.* To do so, we use the *market interest rate* and compound this amount forward 55 years, as illustrated in Figure 14-2.

$$\text{Actual dollars in 2010} = \text{Actual dollars in 1955} \ (F/P, i, 55 \text{ years})$$

$$= \$1,200,000(F/P, 8\%, 55)$$

$$= \$82,701,600$$

FIGURE 14-2 Compounding A$ in 1955 to A$ in 2010.

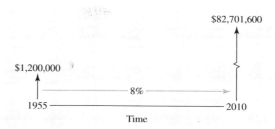

SOLUTION TO PART c

Now we want to determine the amount of *real 1955 dollars that occur in the year 2010,* which are equivalent to the $82.7 million from the solution to part **b**. Let us solve this problem two ways.

1. Translate *actual dollars in the year 2010 to real 1955 dollars in the year 2010.* From Figure 14-1 we can use the inflation rate to **strip 55 years of inflation** from the actual dollars. We do this by using the P/F factor for 55 years at the inflation rate. We are not physically moving the dollars in time; rather, we are simply removing inflation from these dollars one year at a time—the P/F factor does that for us. This is illustrated in the following equation and Figure 14-3.

$$\text{Real 1955 dollars in 2010} = (\text{Actual dollars in 2010})(P/F, f, 55)$$
$$= (\$82,701,600)(P/F, 6\%, 55)$$
$$= \$3,357,000$$

FIGURE 14-3 Translation of A$ in 2010 to R 1955-based dollars in 2010.

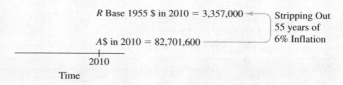

2. Translate real 1950 dollars in 1950 to real 1955 dollars in 2010. The $1.2 million can also be said to be *real 1955 dollars that circulated in 1955.* So, let us translate those real dollars from 1955 to the year 2010 (Figure 14-4). Since they are *real dollars,* we use the *real interest rate.*

$$\text{Real 1955 dollars in 2010} = (\text{Real 1955 dollars in 1955})(P/F, i', 55)$$
$$= (\$1,200,000)(F/P, 1.887\%, 55)$$
$$= \$3,355,000$$

FIGURE 14-4 Translation of R 1955 dollars in 1955 to R 1955 dollars in 2010.

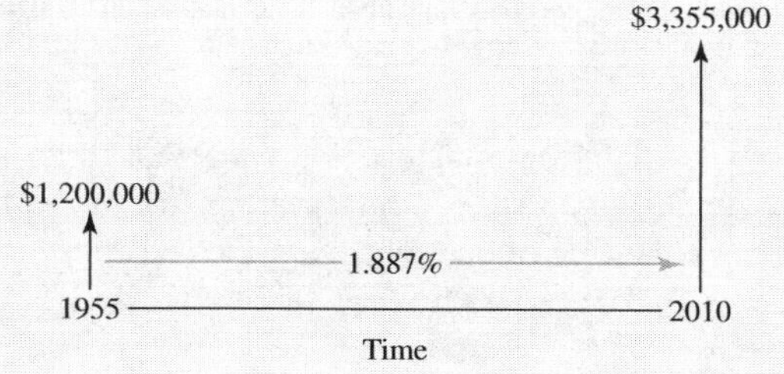

Note: The answers differ due to rounding the market interest rate off to 1.887% versus carrying it out to more significant digits. The difference due to this rounding is less than 0.1%. If i' and the factors have enough digits, the answers to the two parts would be identical.

SOLUTION TO PART d

Assuming that construction costs increased at the rate of 6% per year, then the amount available for the project *in terms of 1955 dollars* is almost $3.4 million. This means that the new stadium will be about 3.4/1.2 or approximately 2.8 times "better" than the original one using *real dollars*.

EXAMPLE 14-3

In 1924 Mr. O'Leary buried $1000 worth of quarters in his backyard. Over the years he had always thought that the money would be a nice nest egg to give to his first grandchild. His first granddaughter, Gabrielle, arrived in 1994. From 1924 to 1994, inflation averaged 4.5%, the stock market increased an average of 15% per year, and investments in guaranteed government bonds averaged 6.5% return per year. What was the relative purchasing power of the jar of quarters that Mr. O'Leary gave to his granddaughter Gabrielle at birth? What might have been a better choice for his "backyard investment"?

SOLUTION

Mr. O'Leary's $1000 are *actual dollars* in both 1924 **and** in 1994.

To obtain the *real 1924 dollar equivalent* of the $1000 that Gabrielle received in 1994, we would **strip 70 years of inflation out of those dollars.** As it turned out, Gabrielle's grandfather gave her $45.90 worth of 1924 purchasing power. Because inflation has "stolen" purchasing power from his stash of quarters during the 70-year period, Mr. O'Leary gave his grandaughter much less than the amount he first spaded underground. This loss of purchasing power caused by inflation can be calculated as follows:

$$\text{Real 1924 dollars in 1994} = (\text{Actual dollars in 1994})(P/F, f, 1994 - 1924)$$

$$= \$1000(P/F, 4.5\%, 70) = \$45.90$$

On the other hand, if Mr. O'Leary had put his $1000 in the stock market in 1924, he would have made baby Gabrielle an instant multimillionaire by giving her $17,735,000. We calculate this as follows:

$$\text{Actual dollars in 1994} = (\text{Actual dollars in 1924})(F/P, i, 1994 - 1924)$$

$$= \$1000(F/P, 15\%, 70) = \$17,735,000$$

At the time of Gabrielle's birth that $17.7 million translates to $814,069 in 1924 purchasing power. This is quite a bit different from the $45.90 in 1924 purchasing power calculated for the unearthed jar of quarters.

Real 1924 dollars in 1994 = $17,735,000(P/F, 4.5\%, 70) = \$814,069$

Mr. O'Leary was never a risk taker, so it is doubtful he would have chosen the stock market for his future grandchild's nest egg. If he had chosen guaranteed government bonds instead of his backyard, by 1994 the investment would have grown to $59,076 (actual dollars)—the equivalent of $2712 in 1924 purchasing power.

$$\text{Actual dollars in 1994} = (\text{Actual dollars in 1924})(F/P, i, 1994 - 1924)$$

$$= \$1000(F/P, 6\%, 70) = \$59,076$$

$$\text{Real 1924 dollars in 1994} = \$59,076(P/F, 4.5\%, 70) = \$2712$$

Obviously, either option would have been better than the choice Mr. O'Leary made. This example illustrates the effects of inflation and purchasing power, as well as the power of compound interest. However, in Mr. O'Leary's defense, if the country had experienced 70 years of *deflation* instead of *inflation,* he might have had the last laugh!

There are in general two ways to approach an economic analysis problem after the effects of inflation have been recognized. The first is to ignore these effects in conducting the analysis, as we've done so far in the text.

> *Ignoring inflation in the analysis:* Use **real dollars** and a **real interest rate** that does not reflect inflation.

The second approach is to systematically include the effects of inflation, as we study in this chapter.

> *Incorporating inflation in the analysis:* Use a **market interest rate** and **actual dollars** that include inflation.

Since inflation is so common, why do many economic analyses of engineering projects and most of this text choose *not* to explicitly address inflation? This question is best answered by referring to the many examples and problems that contained statements like "Operations and maintenance costs are expected to be $30,000 annually for the equipment's 20-year life."

Does such a statement mean that accounting records for the next 20 years will show constant costs? Obviously not. Instead, it means that in constant-dollar terms the O&M costs are not expected to increase. In real dollars, O&M costs are uniform. In actual or inflated dollars, we will pay more each year, but each of those dollars will be worth less.

Most costs and benefits in the real world and in this text have prices that increase at about the same rate of inflation as the economy as a whole. In most analyses these inflation increases are addressed by simply stating everything in real dollar terms and using a real interest rate.

There are specific items, such as computers and depreciation deductions, where inflation is clearly expected to differ from the general rate of inflation. It is for these cases, that this chapter is included in this text.

ANALYSIS IN CONSTANT DOLLARS VERSUS THEN-CURRENT DOLLARS

Performing an analysis requires that we distinguish cash flows as being either constant dollars (real dollars, expressed in terms of some purchasing power base) or then-current dollars (actual dollars that are then-current when they occur). As previously stated, constant (real) dollars require the use of a *real interest rate* for discounting, then-current dollars require a *market (or combined) interest rate*. We must not mix these two dollar types when performing an analysis. If both types are stated in the problem, one must be converted to the other, so that a consistent comparison can be made.

EXAMPLE 14-4

The Waygate Corporation is interested in evaluating a major new video display technology (VDT). Two competing computer innovation companies have approached Waygate to develop the technology. Waygate believes that both companies will be able to deliver equivalent products at the end of a 5-year period. From the yearly development costs of the VDT for each firm, determine which one Waygate should choose if the corporate MARR (investment market rate) is 25% and price inflation is assumed to be 3.5% per year over the next 5 years.

> *Company Alpha costs:* Development costs will be $150,000 the first year and will increase at a rate of 5% over the 5-year period.

> *Company Beta costs:* Development costs will be a constant $150,000 per year in terms of today's dollars over the 5-year period.

SOLUTION

The costs for each of the two alternatives are as follows:

Year	Then-Current Costs Stated by Alpha	Constant Dollar Costs Stated by Beta
1	$150,000 \times (1.05)^0 = \$150,000$	$150,000
2	$150,000 \times (1.05)^1 = \ 157,500$	150,000
3	$150,000 \times (1.05)^2 = \ 165,375$	150,000
4	$150,000 \times (1.05)^3 = \ 173,644$	150,000
5	$150,000 \times (1.05)^4 = \ 182,326$	150,000

We inflate (or escalate) the stated yearly cost given by Company Alpha by 5% per year to obtain the then-current (actual) dollars each year. Company Beta's costs are given in terms of today-based constant dollars.

Using a Constant Dollar Analysis

Here we must convert the then-current costs given by Company Alpha to constant today-based dollars. We do this by stripping the number of years of general inflation from each year's cost using $(P/F, f, n)$ or $(1 + f)^{-n}$.

Year	Constant Dollar Costs Stated by Alpha	Constant Dollar Costs Stated by Beta
1	$150{,}000 \times (1.035)^{-1} = \$144{,}928$	$150,000
2	$157{,}500 \times (1.035)^{-2} = 147{,}028$	150,000
3	$165{,}375 \times (1.035)^{-3} = 149{,}159$	150,000
4	$173{,}644 \times (1.035)^{-4} = 151{,}321$	150,000
5	$182{,}326 \times (1.035)^{-5} = 153{,}514$	150,000

We use the *real interest rate* (i') calculated from Equation 14-1 to calculate the present worth of costs for each alternative:

$$i' = (i - f)/(1 + f) = (0.25 - 0.035)/(1 + 0.035) = 0.208$$

$$\text{PW of cost (Alpha)} = \$144{,}928(P/F, 20.8\%, 1) + \$147{,}028(P/F, 20.8\%, 2)$$
$$+ \$149{,}159(P/F, 20.8\%, 3) + \$151{,}321(P/F, 20.8\%, 4)$$
$$+ \$153{,}514(P/F, 20.8\%, 5) = \$436{,}000$$

$$\text{PW of cost (Beta)} = \$150{,}000(P/A, 20.8\%, 5) = \$150{,}000(2.9387) = \$441{,}000$$

Using a Then-Current Dollar Analysis

Here we must convert the constant dollar costs of Company Beta to then-current dollars. We do this by using $(F/P, f, n)$ or $(1 + f)^n$ to "add in" the appropriate number of years of general inflation to each year's cost.

Year	Then-Current Costs Stated by Alpha	Then-Current Costs Stated by Beta
1	$150{,}000 \times (1.05)^{0} = \$150{,}000$	$150{,}000 \times (1.035)^{1} = \$155{,}250$
2	$150{,}000 \times (1.05)^{1} = 157{,}500$	$150{,}000 \times (1.035)^{2} = 160{,}684$
3	$150{,}000 \times (1.05)^{2} = 165{,}375$	$150{,}000 \times (1.035)^{3} = 166{,}308$
4	$150{,}000 \times (1.05)^{3} = 173{,}644$	$150{,}000 \times (1.035)^{4} = 172{,}128$
5	$150{,}000 \times (1.05)^{4} = 182{,}326$	$150{,}000 \times (1.035)^{5} = 178{,}153$

Calculate the present worth of costs for each alternative using the *market interest rate* (i).

$$\text{PW of cost (Alpha)} = \$150{,}000(P/F, 25\%, 1) + \$157{,}500(P/F, 25\%, 2)$$
$$+ \$165{,}375(P/F, 25\%, 3) + \$173{,}644(P/F, 25\%, 4)$$
$$+ \$182{,}326(P/F, 25\%, 5) = \$436{,}000$$

$$\text{PW of cost (Beta)} = \$155{,}250(P/F, 25\%, 1) + \$160{,}684(P/F, 25\%, 2)$$
$$+ \$166{,}308(P/F, 25\%, 3) + \$172{,}128(P/F, 25\%, 4)$$
$$+ \$178{,}153(P/F, 25\%, 5) = \$441{,}000$$

Using either a constant dollar or then-current dollar analysis, Waygate should chose Company Alpha's offer, which has the lower present worth of costs. There may, of course, be intangible elements in the decision that are more important than a 1% difference in the costs.

PRICE CHANGE WITH INDEXES

We have already described the effects that inflation can have on money over time. Also, several definitions and relationships regarding dollars and interest rates have been given. We have seen that it is not correct to compare the benefits of an investment in 2008-based dollars with costs in 2010-based dollars. This is like comparing apples and oranges. Such comparisons of benefits and costs can be meaningful only if a standard purchasing power base of money is used. Thus we ask, How do I know what inflation rate to use in my studies? and, How can we measure price changes over time?

What Is a Price Index?

Price indexes (introduced in Chapter 2) describe the relative price fluctuation of goods and services. They provide a *historical* record of prices over time. Price indexes are tracked for **specific commodities** as well as for **bundles (composites) of commodities.** As such, price indexes can be used to measure historical price changes for individual cost items (like labor and material costs) as well as general costs (like consumer products). We use **past** price fluctuations to predict **future** prices.

Table 14-1 lists the historic prices of sending a first-class letter in the U.S. from 1970 to 2007. The cost is given both in terms of dollars (cents) and as measured by a fictitious price index that we could call the letter cost index (LCI).

Notice two important aspects of the LCI. First, as with all cost or price indexes, there is a **base year,** which is assigned a value of 100. Our LCI has a base year of 1970—thus for 1970, LCI = 100. Values for subsequent years are stated in relation to the 1970 value. Second, the LCI changes only when the cost of first-class postage changes. In years when this quantity does not change, the LCI is not affected. These general observations apply to all price indexes.

In general, engineering economists are the "users" of cost indexes such as our hypothetical LCI. That is, cost indexes are calculated or tabulated by some other party, and our interest is in assessing what the index tells us about the historical prices and how these may affect our estimate of future costs. However, we should understand how the LCI in Table 14-1 was calculated.

In Table 14-1, the LCI is assigned a value of 100 because 1970 serves as our base year. In the following years the LCI is calculated on a year-to-year basis based on the annual percentage increase in first-class mail. Equation 14-2 illustrates the arithmetic used.

$$\text{LCI year, } n = \frac{\text{cost } (n)}{\text{cost 1970}} \times 100 \tag{14-2}$$

For example, consider the LCI for the year 1980. We calculate the LCI as follows.

$$\text{LCI year 1980} = \frac{0.15}{0.06} \times 100 = 250$$

As mentioned, engineering economists often use cost indexes to project future cash flows. As such, our first job is to use a cost index to **calculate** the *year-to-year* percentage increase (or *inflation*) of prices tracked by an index. We can use Equation 14-3:

$$\text{Annual percentage increase, } n = \frac{\text{Index}(n) - \text{Index}(n-1)}{\text{Index}(n-1)} \times 100\% \tag{14-3}$$

TABLE 14-1 Historic Prices of First-Class Mail, 1970–2003, and Letter Cost Index

Year, n	Cost of First-Class Mail	LCI	Annual Increase for n	Year, n	Cost of First-Class Mail	LCI	Annual Increase for n
1970	$0.06	100	0.00%	1989	0.25	417	0.00%
1971	0.08	133	33.33	1990	0.25	417	0.00
1972	0.08	133	0.00	1991	0.29	483	16.00
1973	0.08	133	0.00	1992	0.29	483	0.00
1974	0.10	166	25.00	1993	0.29	483	0.00
1975	0.13	216	30.00	1994	0.29	483	0.00
1976	0.13	216	0.00	1995	0.32	533	10.34
1977	0.13	216	0.00	1996	0.32	533	0.00
1978	0.15	250	15.74	1997	0.32	533	0.00
1979	0.15	250	0.00	1998	0.33	550	3.13
1980	0.15	250	0.00	1999	0.33	550	0.00
1981	0.20	333	33.33	2000	0.33	550	0.00
1982	0.20	333	0.00	2001	0.34	567	3.03
1983	0.20	333	0.00	2002	0.37	617	8.82
1984	0.20	333	0.00	2003	0.37	617	0.00
1985	0.22	367	10.00	2004	0.37	617	0.00
1986	0.22	367	0.00	2005	0.37	617	0.00
1987	0.22	367	0.00	2006	0.39	650	5.41
1988	0.25	417	13.64	2007	0.41	683	5.13

To illustrate, let us look at the percent change from 1977 to 1978 for the LCI.

$$\text{Annual percentage increase (1978)} = \frac{250 - 216}{216} \times 100\% = 15.74\%$$

For 1978 the price of mailing a first-class letter increased by 15.74% over the previous year. This is tabulated in Table 14-1.

An engineering economist often wants to know how a particular cost quantity changes over time. Often we are interested in calculating the *average* rate of price increases over a period of time. For instance, we might want to know the average yearly increase in postal prices from 1987 to 2007. If we generalize Equation 14-3 to calculate the percent change from 1987 to 2007, we obtain:

$$\% \text{ Increase (1987 to 2007)} = \frac{683 - 367}{367} \times 100\% = 86\%$$

How do we use this to obtain the **average** rate of increase over those 20 years? Should we divide 86% by 20 years (86/20 = 4.31%)? Of course not! Inflation, like interest, compounds. Such a simple division treats inflation like simple interest—without compounding. So the question remains: How do we calculate an *equivalent average rate of increase* in postage rates over a period of time? If we think of the index numbers as cash flows, we have:

$$P = 367 \qquad F = 683 \qquad n = 20 \text{ years} \qquad i = ?$$

Using $F = P(1 + i)^n$ $683 = 367(1 + i)^{20}$ $i = (683/367)^{1/20} - 1$ $i = 0.0315 = 3.2\%$

We can use a cost index to calculate the average rate of increase over any period of years, which should provide insight into how prices may behave in the future.

Composite Versus Commodity Indexes

Cost indexes come in two types: commodity-specific indexes and composite indexes. Commodity-specific indexes measure the historical change in price for specific items—such as construction labor or iron ore. Commodity indexes, like our letter cost index, are useful when an economic analysis includes individual cost items that are tracked by such indexes. For example, if we need to estimate the direct-labor cost portion of a construction project, we could use an index that tracks the inflation, or escalation, of labor costs. The U.S. Departments of Commerce and Labor track many cost quantities through the Department of Economic Analysis and Bureau of Labor Statistics. Example 14-5 uses data from a California government website (www.resd.dgs.ca.gov/CaliforniaConstructionCostIndexPage.htm) to demonstrate using a commodity index. This data is compiled from the *Engineering News-Record*.

EXAMPLE 14-5

In January 1997 bids were opened for a new building in Los Angeles. The low bid and the final construction cost were $1.30 million. Another building of the same size, quality, and purpose is planned with a bid opening in January 2010. Estimate the new building's low bid and cost.

SOLUTION

In January 2007 the California Construction Cost Index (CCCI) had a value of 4869 and in January 1997 the value was 3473. If we wanted a cost estimate for January 2007, we could simply use the ratio of these values and Equation 14-2. But we want a value for January 2010, which is outside our data set. (This is true for all future estimates.)

The solution is to estimate the average annual rate of increase, and then to apply this for the longer period.

$$F = 4869, P = 3473, n = 10, \text{ find } f$$

$$F = P(1 + f)^n$$

$$f = (4869/3473)^{1/10} - 1 = 3.44\% \text{ per year}$$

Now we can apply the inflation rate for $n = 13$ years to the building's cost in 1997.

$$F = \$1.3 \text{ million} \times (1.0344)^{13} = \$2.02 \text{ million}$$

TABLE 14-2 CPI Index Values and Yearly Percentage Increases, 1973–2006

Year	CPI Value*	CPI Increase	Year	CPI Value*	CPI Increase
1973	44.4	6.2%	1990	130.7	5.4%
1974	49.3	11.0	1991	136.2	4.2
1975	53.8	9.1	1992	140.3	3.0
1976	56.9	5.8	1993	144.5	3.0
1977	60.6	6.5	1994	148.2	2.6
1978	65.2	7.6	1995	152.4	2.8
1979	72.6	11.3	1996	156.9	2.9
1980	82.4	13.5	1997	160.5	2.3
1981	90.9	10.3	1998	163.0	1.6
1982	96.5	6.2	1999	166.6	2.2
1983	99.6	3.2	2000	172.2	3.4
1984	103.9	4.3	2001	177.1	2.8
1985	107.6	3.6	2002	179.9	1.1
1986	109.6	1.9	2003	184.0	2.7
1987	113.6	3.6	2004	188.9	2.7
1988	118.3	4.1	2005	195.3	3.4
1989	124.0	4.8	2006	201.6	3.2

*Reference base: 1982–1984 = 100.

Composite cost indexes do not track historical prices for individual classes of items. Instead, they measure the historical prices of *bundles* or *market baskets* of assets. Examples of composite indexes include the *Consumer Price Index* (CPI) and the *Producer Price Index* (PPI). The CPI measures prices for consumers in the U.S. marketplace, and each PPI measures prices for categories of producers in the U.S. economy.

The CPI, an index calculated by the Bureau of Labor Statistics, tracks the cost of a standard *bundle of consumer goods* from year to year. This "consumer bundle" or "market basket" includes housing, clothing, food, transportation, and entertainment. The CPI enjoys popular identification as the "inflation" indicator. Table 14-2 gives yearly index values and annual percent increases in the CPI. Figure 14-5 charts the CPI inflation rate for the same period.

Composite indexes are used the same way as commodity-specific indexes. That is, we can pick a single value from the table if we are interested in measuring the historic price for a single year, or we can calculate an *average inflation rate* or *average rate of price increase* as measured by the index over a time period extending several years.

How to Use Price Indexes in Engineering Economic Analysis

One may question the usefulness of *historical* data (as provided by price indexes) when engineering economic analysis deals with economic effects projected to occur in the *future*.

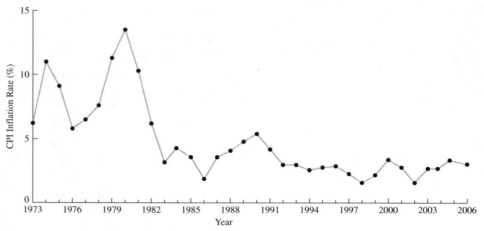

FIGURE 14-5 CPI inflation rate: 1973–2006.

However, historical index data are often better predictors of future prices than official government predictions, which may be influenced by political considerations. The engineering economist can use *average historical percentage increases (or decreases)* from commodity-specific and composite indexes, along with data from market analyses and other sources, to estimate future costs and benefits.

> When the estimated quantities are items that are tracked by commodity specific indexes, then those indexes should be used to calculate *average historical percentage increases (or decreases)*. If no commodity-specific indexes are kept, use an appropriate composite index to make this calculation.

For example, to estimate electric usage costs for a turret lathe over a 5-year period, you would first want to refer to a commodity-specific index for electric power in your area. If such an index does not exist, you might use a specific index for a very closely related commodity—perhaps an index of electric power costs nationally. In the absence of such substitute or related commodity indexes, you could use a composite index for national energy prices. The key point is that you should try to identify and use the price index that most closely relates to the quantity being estimated.

CASH FLOWS THAT INFLATE AT DIFFERENT RATES

Engineering economic analysis requires the estimation of various parameters. Over time, it is not uncommon for these parameters to *inflate* or *increase* (or even decrease) at different rates. For instance, one parameter might *increase* 5% per year and another 15% per year, and a third might *decrease* 3.5% per year. Since we are looking at the behavior of cash flows over time, we must have a way of handling this effect.

EXAMPLE 14-6

On your first assignment as an engineer, your boss asks you to develop the utility cost estimate for a new manufacturing facility. After some research you define the problem as finding the present worth of utility costs given the following data:

- Your company uses a minimum attractive rate of return (MARR) = 35% as i (not adjusted for inflation.)
- The project has a useful life of 25 years.
- Utilities to be estimated include electricity, water, and natural gas.
- The 35-year historical data reveal:

> Electricity costs increase at 8.5% per year
> Water costs increase at 5.5% per year
> Natural gas costs increase at 6.5% per year

- First-year estimates of the utility costs (in today's dollars) are as follows:

> Electricity will cost $55,000
> Water will cost $18,000
> Natural gas will cost $38,000

SOLUTION

For this problem we will take each of the utilities used in our manufacturing facility and inflate them independently at their respective historical annual rates. Once we have these actual dollar amounts (A\$), we can total them and then discount each year's total at 35% back to the present.

Year	Electricity		Water		Natural Gas		Total
1	$55,000(1.085)^0$ =	\$ 55,000	$18,000(1.055)^0$ =	\$18,000	$38,000(1.065)^0$ =	\$ 38,000	\$111,000
2	$55,000(1.085)^1$ =	59,675	$18,000(1.055)^1$ =	18,990	$38,000(1.065)^1$ =	40,470	119,135
3	$55,000(1.085)^2$ =	64,747	$18,000(1.055)^2$ =	20,034	$38,000(1.065)^2$ =	43,101	127,882
4	$55,000(1.085)^3$ =	70,251	$18,000(1.055)^3$ =	21,136	$38,000(1.065)^3$ =	45,902	137,289
5	$55,000(1.085)^4$ =	76,222	$18,000(1.055)^4$ =	22,299	$38,000(1.065)^4$ =	48,886	147,407
6	$55,000(1.085)^5$ =	82,701	$18,000(1.055)^5$ =	23,525	$38,000(1.065)^5$ =	52,063	158,290
7	$55,000(1.085)^6$ =	89,731	$18,000(1.055)^6$ =	24,819	$38,000(1.065)^6$ =	55,447	169,997
8	$55,000(1.085)^7$ =	97,358	$18,000(1.055)^7$ =	26,184	$38,000(1.065)^7$ =	59,051	182,594
.	.		.		.		.
.	.		.		.		.
.	.		.		.		.
24	$55,000(1.085)^{23}$ =	359,126	$18,000(1.055)^{23}$ =	61,671	$38,000(1.065)^{23}$ =	161,743	582,539
25	$55,000(1.085)^{24}$ =	389,652	$18,000(1.055)^{24}$ =	65,063	$38,000(1.065)^{24}$ =	172,256	626,970

The present worth of the total yearly utility costs is:

$$PW = \$111,000(P/F, 35\%, 1) + \$119,135(P/F, 35\%, 2) + \cdots + \$626,970(P/F, 35\%, 25)$$
$$= \$5,540,000$$

In Example 14-6 several commodity prices changed at different rates. By using the respective individual inflation rates, the **actual dollar** amounts for each commodity were obtained in each year. Then, we used a market interest rate to discount these actual dollar amounts.

DIFFERENT INFLATION RATES PER PERIOD

In this section we address the situation of inflation rates that are changing over the study period. Rather than different inflation rates for different cash flows, in Example 14-7 the *interest rate* for the same cash flow is changing over time. A method for handling this situation is much like that of the preceding section. We can simply apply the inflation rates in the years in which they are projected to occur. We would do this for each cash flow. Once we have all these actual dollar amounts, we can use the market interest rate to apply PW, EUAC, or other measures of merit.

EXAMPLE 14-7

While working as a clerk at Piggly Wiggly, Elvis has learned much about the cost of different vegetables. The kitchen manager at Heartbreak Hotel called recently, requesting Elvis to estimate the raw material cost over the next 5 years to introduce succotash (lima beans and corn) to the buffet line. To develop his estimate, Elvis has used his advanced knowledge of soil growing conditions, world demand, and government subsidy programs for these two crops. He has estimated the following data:

- Costs for lima beans will inflate at 3% per year for the next 3 years and then at 4% for the following 2 years.
- Costs for corn will inflate at 8% per year for the next 2 years and then will decrease 2% in the following 3 years.

The kitchen manager wants to know the equivalent annual cost of providing succotash on the buffet line over the 5-year period. His before-tax MARR is 20%. An average of 50 pounds each of beans and corn will be needed each day. The hotel kitchen operates 6 days per week, 52 weeks per year. Current costs are $0.35/lb for lima beans and $0.80/lb for corn.

SOLUTION

Today's cost for one year's supply of vegetables is:

Lima beans	0.35 $/lb × 50 lb/day × 6 day/wk × 52 wk/yr =	$ 5460/yr
Corn	0.80 $/lb × 50 lb/day × 6 day/wk × 52 wk/yr =	12,480/yr

Year	Lima Beans	Corn	Total
0	$5,460	$12,480	
1	5,460(1.03) = 5,624	12,480(1.08) = 13,478	$19,102
2	5,624(1.03) = 5,793	13,478(1.08) = 14,556	20,349
3	5,793(1.03) = 5,967	14,556(1.02)$^{-1}$ = 14,271	20,238
4	5,967(1.04) = 6,206	14,271(1.02)$^{-1}$ = 13,991	20,197
5	6,206(1.04) = 6,454	13,991(1.02)$^{-1}$ = 13,717	20,171

$$\text{EUAC} = [19{,}102(P/F, 20\%, 1) + 20{,}349(P/F, 20\%, 2) + 20{,}238(P/F, 20\%, 3)$$
$$+ 20{,}197(P/F, 20\%, 4) + 20{,}171(P/F, 20\%, 5)](A/P, 20\%, 5)$$
$$= \$19{,}900 \text{ per year}$$

In Example 14-7, both today's cost of each vegetable and the respective inflation rates were used to calculate the yearly costs of purchasing the desired quantities over the 5-year period. As in Example 14-6, we obtained a total marginal cost (in terms of actual dollars) by combining the two individual yearly costs. We then calculated the equivalent uniform annual cost (EUAC) using the given market interest rate.

Example 14-8 provides another example of how the effect of changes in inflation rates over time can affect an analysis.

EXAMPLE 14-8

If general price inflation is estimated to be 5% for the next 5 years, 7.5% for the 3 years after that, and 3% the following 5 years, at what market interest rate (i) would you have to invest your money to maintain a real purchasing power growth rate (i') of 10% during those years?

SOLUTION

In Years 1–5 you must invest at $0.10 + 0.050 + (0.10)(0.050) = 0.1150 = 11.50\%$ per year.

In Years 6–8 you must invest at $0.10 + 0.075 + (0.10)(0.075) = 0.1825 = 18.25\%$ per year.

In Years 9–13 you must invest at $0.10 + 0.030 + (0.10)(0.030) = 0.1330 = 13.30\%$ per year.

Note: Most interest-bearing investments have fixed, up-front rates that the investor well understands going in. On the other hand, inflation is not quantified, and its effect on real return is not measured until the end of the year. Therefore the real investment return (i') may not turn out to be what was originally required.

INFLATION EFFECT ON AFTER-TAX CALCULATIONS

Earlier we noted the impact of inflation on before-tax calculations. If the future benefits keep up with the rate of inflation, the rate of return will not be adversely affected by the inflation. Unfortunately, we are not so lucky when we consider a situation with income taxes, as illustrated by Example 14-9. The value of the depreciation deduction is diminished by inflation.

EXAMPLE 14-9

A $12,000 investment with no salvage value will return annual benefits for 6 years. Assume straight-line depreciation and a 46% income tax rate. Solve for both before- and after-tax rates of return for two situations:

1. *No inflation:* the annual benefits are constant at $2918 per year.
2. *Inflation equal to 5%:* the benefits from the investment increase at this same rate, so that they continue to be the equivalent of $2918 in Year-0 dollars.

The benefit schedules are as follows:

Year	Annual Benefit for Both Situations (Year-0 dollars)	No Inflation, Actual Dollars Received	5% Inflation Factor*	5% Inflation, Actual Dollars Received
1	$2918	$2918	$(1.05)^1$	$3064
2	2918	2918	$(1.05)^2$	3217
3	2918	2918	$(1.05)^3$	3378
4	2918	2918	$(1.05)^4$	3547
5	2918	2918	$(1.05)^5$	3724
6	2918	2918	$(1.05)^6$	3910

*May be read from the 5% compound interest table as $(F/P, 5\%, n)$.

SOLUTIONS

Before-Tax Rate of Return

Since both situations (no inflation and 5% inflation) have an annual benefit, stated in Year-0 dollars of $2918, they have the same before-tax rate of return.

$$\text{PW of cost} = \text{PW of benefit}$$

$$12,000 = 2918(P/A, i, 6) \qquad (P/A, i, 6) = \frac{12,000}{2918} = 4.11$$

From compound interest tables: before-tax rate of return equals 12%.

After-Tax Rate of Return, No Inflation

Year	Before-Tax Cash Flow	Straight-Line Depreciation	Taxable Income	46% Income Taxes	Actual Dollars, and Year-0 Dollars, After-Tax Cash Flow
0	−$12,000				−$12,000
1–6	+2,918	$2000	$918	−$422	+2,496

PW of cost = PW of benefit

$$12,000 = 2496(P/A, i, 6) \qquad (P/A, i, 6) = \frac{12,000}{2496} = 4.81$$

From compound interest tables: after-tax rate of return equals 6.7%.

After-Tax Rate of Return, 5% Inflation

Year	Before-Tax Cash Flow	Straight-Line Depreciation	Taxable Income	46% Income Taxes	Actual Dollars, After-Tax Cash Flow
0	−$12,000				−$12,000
1	+3,064	$2000	$1064	−$489	+2,575
2	+3,217	2000	1217	−560	+2,657
3	+3,378	2000	1378	−634	+2,744
4	+3,547	2000	1547	−712	+2,835
5	+3,724	2000	1724	−793	+2,931
6	+3,910	2000	1910	−879	+3,031

Converting to Year-0 Dollars and Solving for Rate of Return

Year	Actual Dollars, After-Tax Cash Flow	Conversion Factor	Year-0 Dollars, After-Tax Cash Flow	Present Worth at 4%	Present Worth at 5%
0	−$12,000		−$12,000	−$12,000	−$12,000
1	+2,575	$\times (1.05)^{-1} =$	+2,452	+2,358	+2,335
2	+2,657	$\times (1.05)^{-2} =$	+2,410	+2,228	+2,186
3	+2,744	$\times (1.05)^{-3} =$	+2,370	+2,107	+2,047
4	+2,835	$\times (1.05)^{-4} =$	+2,332	+1,993	+1,919
5	+2,931	$\times (1.05)^{-5} =$	+2,297	+1,888	+1,800
6	+3,031	$\times (1.05)^{-6} =$	+2,262	+1,788	+1,688
				+362	−25

Linear interpolation between 4 and 5%:

$$\text{After-tax rate of return} = 4\% + 1\%[362/(362 + 25)] = 4.9\%$$

From Example 14-9, we see that the before-tax rate of return for both situations (no inflation and 5% inflation) is the same. Equal before-tax rates of return are expected because the benefits in the inflation situation increased in proportion to the inflation. No special calculations are needed in before-tax calculations when future benefits are expected to respond to inflation or deflation rates.

The after-tax calculations illustrate that equal before-tax rates of return do not produce equal after-tax rates of return considering inflation.

	Rate of Return (%)	
Situation	**Before Taxes**	**After Taxes**
No inflation	12	6.7
5% inflation	12	4.9

Inflation reduces the after-tax rate of return, even though the benefits increase at the same rate as the inflation. A review of the cash flow table reveals that while benefits increase, the depreciation schedule does not. Thus, the inflation results in increased taxable income and, hence, larger income tax payments.

The result is that while the after-tax cash flow in actual dollars increases, the augmented amount is not high enough to offset *both* inflation and increased income taxes. The Year-0-dollar after-tax cash flow is smaller with inflation than the Year-0-dollar after-tax cash flow without inflation.

USING SPREADSHEETS FOR INFLATION CALCULATIONS

Spreadsheets are the perfect tool for incorporating consideration of inflation into analyses of economic problems. For example, next year's labor costs are likely to be estimated as equal to this year's costs times $(1 + f)$, where f is the inflation rate. Thus each year's value is different, so we can't use factors for uniform flows, A. Also the formulas that link different years are easy to write. The result is problems that are very tedious to do by hand, but easy by spreadsheet.

Example 14-10 illustrates two different ways to write the equation for inflating costs. Example 14-11 illustrates that inflation reduces the after-tax rate of return because inflation makes the depreciation deduction less valuable.

EXAMPLE 14-10

Two costs for construction of a small, remote mine are for labor and transportation. Labor costs are expected to be $350,000 the first year, with inflation of 6% annually. Unit transportation costs are expected to inflate at 5% annually, but the volume of material being moved changes each year. In Time-0 dollars, the transportation costs are estimated to be $40,000, $60,000, $50,000, and $30,000 in Years 1 through 4. The inflation rate for the value of the dollar is 3%. If the firm uses an i' of 7%, what is the equivalent annual cost for this 4-year project?

SOLUTION

The data for labor costs can be stated so that no inflation needs to be applied in Year 1: the cost is $350,000. In contrast, the transportation costs for Year 1 are determined by multiplying $40,000 by 1.05 $(= 1 + f)$.

Also in later years the labor $cost_t$ = labor $cost_{t-1}(1 + f)$, while each transportation cost must be computed as the time-0 value times $(1 + f)^t$. In Figure 14-6, the numbers in the Year 0 (or real) dollar column equal the values in the actual dollars column divided by $(1.03)^t$.

	A	B	C	D	E	F	G	H
1						7%	Inflation-Free Interest	
2	Inflation Rate	6%		5%		3%		
3			Transportation Costs		Total	Total		
4	Year	Labor Costs	Year 0 $s	Actual $s	Actual $s	Real $s		
5	1	120,000	40,000	42,000	162,000	157,282	= E5/(1+$F$2)^A5	
6	2	127,200	60,000	66,150	193,350	182,251		
7	3	134,832	50,000	57,881	192,713	176,360		
8	4	142,922	30,000	36,465	179,387	159,383		
9						$571,732	= NPV(F1,F5:F8)	
10					=B8+D8	$168,791	= −PMT(F1,4,F9)	
11	=B7*(1+$B$2)		=C8*(1+$D$2)^A8					

FIGURE 14-6 Spreadsheet for inflation.

The equivalent annual cost equals $168,791.

EXAMPLE 14-11

For the data of Example 14-9, calculate the IRR with and without inflation with MACRS depreciation. How are the results affected by inflation by comparison with the earlier results.

SOLUTION

Most of the formulas for this spreadsheet are given in rows 11 and 12 of Figure 14-6 for the data in Year 6. The benefits received are computed from the base value in cell B5. The depreciation is the MACRS percentage times the $120,000 spent in Year 0. This value is not influenced by inflation, so the depreciation deduction is less valuable as inflation increases. The tax paid equals the tax rate times the taxable income, which equals dollars received minus the depreciation charge. Then ATCF (after-tax cash flow) equals the before-tax cash flow minus the tax paid.

In Figure 14-7, notice that in Year 2 the depreciation charge is large enough to cause this project to pay "negative" tax. For a firm, this means that the deduction on this project will be used to offset income from other projects.

	A	B	C	D	E	F	G	H
1		0%	= Inflation Rate		46%	= Tax Rate		
2	Year	Actual $s Received	MACRS Deprec. %	Actual $s Deprec.	Actual $s Tax	Actual $s ATCF	Real $s ATCF	
3								
4	0	−12000				−12000	−12000	
5	1	2918	20.00%	2400	238	2680	2680	= F5/(1+$B$1)^A5
6	2	2918	32.00%	3840	−424	3342	3342	
7	3	2918	19.20%	2304	282	2636	2636	
8	4	2918	11.52%	1382	706	2212	2212	
9	5	2918	11.52%	1382	706	2212	2212	
10	6	2918	5.76%	691	1024	1894	1894	
11	Formulas		= −$B$4*C10		=B10−E10			
12	for Yr 6	=$B$5*(1+$B$1)^A10	=(B10−D10)*$E$1				7.29%	= IRR
13								
14		5%	= Inflation Rate		46%	= Tax Rate		
15	Year	Actual $s Received	MACRS Deprec. %	Actual $s Deprec.	Actual $s Tax	Actual $s ATCF	Real $s ATCF	
16								
17	0	−12000				−12000	−12000	
18	1	3064	20.00%	2400	305	2759	2627	
19	2	3217	32.00%	3840	−287	3504	3178	
20	3	3378	19.20%	2304	494	2884	2491	
21	4	3547	11.52%	1382	996	2551	2099	
22	5	3724	11.52%	1382	1077	2647	2074	
23	6	3910	5.76%	691	1481	2430	1813	
24							5.68%	= IRR

FIGURE 14-7 After-tax IRRs with MACRS and inflation.

The IRRs are higher in this example (7.29% without inflation vs. 6.7% with straight-line depreciation in Example 14-9, and 5.68% with inflation vs. 4.9%) because MACRS supports faster depreciation, so the depreciation deductions are more valuable. Also because the depreciation is faster, the results are affected somewhat less by inflation. Specifically, with MACRS 5% inflation lowers the IRR by 1.6% and with straight-line depreciation, 5% inflation lowers the IRR by 1.8%.

SUMMARY

Inflation is characterized by rising prices for goods and services, whereas deflation produces a fall in prices. An inflationary trend makes future dollars have less **purchasing power** than present dollars. Deflation has the opposite effect. If money is borrowed over a period of time in which deflation is occurring, then debt will be repaid with dollars that have **more** purchasing power than those originally borrowed. Inflation and deflation have opposite effects on the purchasing power of a monetary unit over time.

To distinguish and account for the effect of inflation in our engineering economic analysis, we define *inflation, real,* and *market* interest rates. These interest rates are related by the following expression:

$$i = i' + f + i'f$$

Each rate applies in a different circumstance, and it is important to apply the correct rate to the correct circumstance. Cash flows are expressed in terms of either *actual* or *real dollars*. The *market interest* rate should be used with *actual dollars* and the *real interest rate* should be used with *real dollars*.

The different cash flows in our analysis may inflate or change at different interest rates when we look over the life cycle of the investment. Also, a single cash flow may inflate or deflate at different rates over time. These two circumstances are handled easily by applying the correct inflation rates to each cash flow over the study period to obtain the actual dollar amounts occurring in each year. After the actual dollar quantities have been calculated, the analysis proceeds using the market interest rate to calculate the measure of merit of interest.

Historical price change for single commodities and bundles of commodities are tracked with price indexes. The Consumer Price Index (CPI) is an example of a composite index formed by a bundle of consumer goods. The CPI serves as a surrogate for general inflation in our economy. Indexes can be used to calculate the *average annual increase* (or decrease) of the costs and benefits in our analysis. The historical data provide valuable information about how economic quantities may behave in the future over the long run.

The effect of inflation on the computed rate of return for an investment depends on how future benefits respond to the inflation. Usually the costs and benefits increase at the same rate as inflation, so the before-tax rate of return will not be adversely affected by the inflation. This outcome is not found when an after-tax analysis is made because the allowable depreciation schedule does not increase. The result will be increased taxable income and income tax payments, which reduce the available after-tax benefits and, therefore, the after-tax rate of return. The important conclusion is that estimates of future inflation or deflation may be important in evaluating capital expenditure proposals.

PROBLEMS

Meaning and Effect

14-1 Define inflation in terms of the purchasing power of dollars.

14-2 Define and describe the relationships between the following: actual and real dollars, inflation, and real and market (combined) interest rates.

14-3 How does inflation happen? Describe a few circumstances that cause prices in an economy to increase.

14-4 Is it necessary to account for inflation in an engineering economy study? What are the two approaches for handling inflation in such analyses?

14-5 In Chapters 5 (Present Worth Analysis) and 6 (Annual Cash Flow Analysis) it is assumed that prices are stable and a machine purchased today for $5000 can be replaced for the same amount many years hence. In fact, prices have generally been rising, so the stable price assumption tends to be incorrect. Under what circumstances is it correct to use the "stable price" assumption when prices actually are changing?

14-6 An economist has predicted 7% inflation during the next 10 years. How much will an item that presently sells for $10 bring a decade hence? (*Answer:* $19.67)

14-7 A man bought a 5% tax-free municipal bond. It cost $1000 and will pay $50 interest each year for 20 years. At maturity the bond returns the original $1000. If there is 2% annual inflation, what real rate of return will the investor receive?

14-8 A man wishes to set aside some money for his daughter's college education. His goal is to have a bank savings account containing an amount equivalent to $20,000 in today's dollars at the girl's 18th birthday. The estimated inflation rate is 8%. If the bank pays 5% compounded annually, what lump sum should he deposit on the child's 4th birthday? (*Answer:* $29,670)

14-9 A newspaper reports that in the last 5 years, prices have increased a total of 50%. This is equivalent to what annual inflation rate, compounded annually? (*Answer:* 8.45%)

14-10 An economist has predicted that for the next 5 years, the U.S. will have an 8% annual inflation rate, followed by 5 years at a 6% inflation rate. This is equivalent to what average price change per year for the entire 10-year period?

14-11 An investor wants a real rate of return i' of 10% per year. If the expected annual inflation rate for the next several years is 6%, what interest rate i should be used in project analysis calculations?

14-12 A South American country has had a high rate of inflation. Recently, its exchange rate was 15 cruzados per dollar; that is, one dollar will buy 15 cruzados. It is likely that the country will continue to experience a 25% inflation rate and that the U.S. will continue at a 7% inflation rate. Assume that the exchange rate will vary the same as the inflation. In this situation, one dollar will buy how many cruzados 5 years from now? (*Answer:* 32.6)

14-13 An automaker has a car that gets 10 kilometers per liter of gasoline. Gas prices will increase 12% per year, compounded annually, for the next 8 years. The manufacturer believes that the fuel consumption for its new cars should decline as fuel prices increase to keep the fuel costs constant. To achieve this, what must be the fuel rating, in kilometers per liter, of the cars 8 years hence?

14-14 An economist has predicted that during the next 6 years, prices in the U.S. will increase 55%. He expects a further increase of 25% in the subsequent 4 years, so that prices at the end of 10 years will have increased to 180% of the present level. Compute the inflation rate, f, for the entire 10-year period.

14-15 Sally Johnson loaned a friend $10,000 at 15% interest, compounded annually. The loan will be paid in five equal end-of-year payments. Sally expects the inflation rate to be 12%. After taking inflation into account, what rate of return is Sally receiving on the loan? Compute your answer to the nearest 0.1%. (*Answer:* 2.7%)

14-16 You may pay $15,000 for an annuity that pays $2500 per year for the next 10 years. You want a real rate of return of 5%, and you estimate inflation will average 6% per year. Should you buy the annuity?

14-17 Inflation is a reality for the general economy of the U.S. for the foreseeable future. Given this assumption, calculate the number of years it will take for the purchasing power of today's dollars to equal *one-fifth* of their present value. Assume that inflation will average 6% per year.

14-18 A homebuilder's advertising has the caption, "Inflation to Continue for Many Years." The ad explains that if one buys a home now for $97,000, and inflation continues at 7%, the home will be worth $268,000 in 15 years. Thus, by buying a new home now, one can realize a profit of $171,000 in 15 years. Do you find this logic persuasive? Explain.

14-19 You were recently looking at the historical prices paid for homes in a neighborhood that interests you. Calculate on a year-to-year basis how home prices in this neighborhood have inflated (*a–e* in the table).

Year	Average Home Price	Inflation Rate for That Year
5 years ago	$165,000	(*a*)
4 years ago	167,000	(*b*)
3 years ago	172,000	(*c*)
2 years ago	180,000	(*d*)
Last year	183,000	(*e*)
This year	190,000	(*f*, see below)

(*f*) What is your estimate of the inflation rate for this year?

14-20 The average cost of a Model T Ford was $18,000 ten years ago. This year the average cost is $30,000.

(*a*) Calculate the average monthly inflation rate (f_m) for Model T cars?

(*b*) Given the monthly rate f_m, what is the effective annual rate, f, of inflation for Model T cars?

(*c*) Estimate what Model T cars will sell for 10 years from now, expressed in today's dollars.

Contributed by D. P. Loucks, Cornell University

14-21 Dale saw that the campus bookstore is having a special on pads of computation paper normally priced at $3 a pad, now on sale for $2.50 a pad. This sale is unusual and Dale assumes the paper will not be put on sale again. On the other hand, Dale expects that there will be no increase in the $3 regular price, even though the inflation rate is 2% every 3 months. Dale believes that competition in the paper industry will keep wholesale and retail prices constant. He uses a pad of computation paper every 3 months. Dale considers 19.25% a suitable minimum attractive rate of return. Dale will buy one pad of paper for his immediate needs. How many extra pads of computation paper should he buy? (*Answer:* 4)

Before-Tax Cases

14-22 Calculate the future equivalent in Year 15 of:

Use a market interest rate of 15% and an inflation rate of 8%.

(a) Dollars having today's purchasing power.

(b) Then-current purchasing power dollars, of $10,000 today.

14-23 The City of Columbia is trying to attract a new manufacturing business. It has offered to install and operate a water pumping plant to provide service to the proposed plant site. This would cost $50,000 now, plus $5000 per year in operating costs for the next 10 years, all measured in Year-0 dollars.

To reimburse the city, the new business must pay a fixed uniform annual fee, A, at the end of each year for 10 years. In addition, it is to pay the city $50,000 at the end of 10 years. It has been agreed that the city should receive a 3% rate of return, after taking an inflation rate, f, of 7% into account.

Determine the amount of the uniform annual fee. (*Answer:* $12,100)

14-24 A firm is having a large piece of equipment overhauled. It expects that the machine will be needed for the next 12 years. The firm has an 8% minimum attractive rate of return. The contractor has suggested three alternatives:

A. A complete overhaul for $6000 that should permit 12 years of operation.

B. A major overhaul for $4500 that can be expected to provide 8 years of service. At the end of 8 years, a minor overhaul would be needed.

C. A minor overhaul now. At the end of 4 and 8 years, additional minor overhauls would be needed.

If minor overhauls cost $2500, which alternative should the firm select? If minor overhauls, which now cost $2500, increase in cost at +5% per year, but other costs remain unchanged, which alternative should the firm select?   (*Answers:* Alt. *C*; Alt. *A*)

14-25 A group of students decided to lease and run a gasoline service station. The lease is for 10 years. Almost immediately the students were confronted with the need to alter the gasoline pumps to read in liters. The Dayton Company has a conversion kit available for $900 that may be expected to last 10 years. The firm also sells a $500 conversion kit that has a 5-year useful life. The students believe that any money not invested in the conversion kits may be invested elsewhere at a 10% interest rate. Income tax consequences are to be ignored in this problem.

(a) Assuming that future replacement kits cost the same as today, which alternative should be selected?

(b) If one assumes a 7% inflation rate, which alternative should be selected?

14-26 Pollution control equipment must be purchased to remove the suspended organic material from liquid being discharged from a vegetable packing plant. Two alternative pieces of equipment are available that would accomplish the task. A Filterco unit costs $7000 and has a 5-year useful life. A Duro unit, on the other hand, costs $10,000 but will have a 10-year useful life.

With inflation, equipment costs are rising at 8% per year, compounded annually, so when the Filterco unit needed to be replaced, the cost would be much more than $7000. Based on a 10-year analysis period, and a 20% minimum attractive rate of return, which pollution control equipment should be purchased?

14-27 Sam bought a house for $150,000 with some creative financing. The bank, which agreed to lend Sam $120,000 for 6 years at 15% interest, took a first mortgage on the house. The Joneses, who sold Sam the house, agreed to lend Sam the remaining $30,000 for 6 years at 12% interest. They received a second mortgage on the house. Thus Sam became the owner without putting up any cash. Sam pays $1500 a month on the first mortgage and $300 a month on the second mortgage. In both cases these are "interest-only" loans, and the principal is due at the end of the loan.

Sam rented the house to Justin and Shannon, but after paying the taxes, insurance, and so on, he had only $800 left, so he was forced to put up $1000 a month to make the monthly mortgage payments. At the end of 3 years, Sam sold the house for $205,000. After paying off the two loans and the real estate broker, he had $40,365 left. After taking an 8% inflation rate into account, what was his before-tax rate of return?

14-28 Ima Luckygirl recently found out that her grandfather has passed away and left her his Rocky Mountain Gold savings account. The only deposit was 50 years ago when Ima's grandfather deposited $2500. If the account has earned an average rate of 10% and inflation has been 4%, answer the following:

(a) How much money is now in the account in *actual dollars*?

(b) Express the answer to part (a) in terms of the purchasing power of dollars from 50 years ago.

14-29 Auntie Frannie wants to provide tuition for her twin nephews to attend a private school. She intends to send a check for $2000 at the end of each of the next 8 years.

(a) If general price inflation, as well as tuition price inflation, is expected to average 5% per year for those 8 years, calculate the present worth of the gifts. Assume that the real interest rate will be 3% per year.

(b) If Auntie Frannie wants her gifts to keep pace with inflation, what would be the present worth of her gifts? Again assume inflation is 5% and the real interest rate is 3%.

14-30 As a recent graduate, you are considering employment offers from three different companies. However, in an effort to confuse you and perhaps make their offers seem better, each company has used a different *purchasing power base* for expressing your annual salary over the next 5 years. If you expect inflation to be 6% for the next 5 years and your personal (real) MARR is 8%, which plan would you choose?

Company A: A constant $50,000 per year in terms of today's purchasing power.

Company B: $45,000 the first year, with increases of $2500 per year thereafter.

Company C: A constant $65,000 per year in terms of Year-5-based purchasing power.

Indexes

14-31 What is the Consumer Price Index (CPI)? What is the difference between commodity-specific and composite price indexes? Can each be used in engineering economic analysis?

14-32 A composite price index for the cost of vegetarian foods called *eggs, artichokes, and tofu* (EAT) was 330 ten years ago and has averaged an annual increase of 12% since. Calculate the current value of the index.

14-33 From the data in Table 14-1 in the text, calculate the *overall rate change* of first-class postage as measured by the LCI for the following decades:

(a) The 1970s (1970–1979)

(b) The 1980s (1980–1989)

(c) The 1990s (1990–1999)

14-34 From the data in Table 14-1 in the text, calculate the *average annual inflation rate* of first class postage as measured by the LCI for the following years:

(a) End of 1970 to end of 1979

(b) End of 1980 to end of 1989

(c) End of 1990 to end of 1999

14-35 From the data in Table 14-2 in the text, calculate the *average annual inflation rate* as measured by the CPI for the following years:

(a) End of 1973 to end of 1982

(b) End of 1980 to end of 1989

(c) End of 1985 to end of 2002

14-36 (a) Compute the equivalent annual inflation rate, based on the consumer price index, for the period from 1981 to 1986.

(b) Using the equivalent annual inflation rate computed in part (a), estimate the consumer price index in 1996, working from the 1987 Consumer Price Index.

14-37 Redo Problem 14-17, but estimate the annual inflation rate using the period from 1996 to 2006 and the CPI index values in Table 14-2.

14-38 Here is some information about a professor salary index (PSI).

Year	PSI	Change in PSI
1991	82	3.22%
1992	89	8.50
1993	100	*a*
1994	*b*	4.00
1995	107	*c*
1996	116	*d*
1997	*e*	5.17
1998	132	7.58

(a) Calculate the unknown quantities *a, b, c, d, e* in the table. Review Equation 14-3.

(b) What is the *base year* of the PSI? How did you determine it?

(c) Given the data for the PSI, calculate the *average annual price increase* in salaries paid to professors for between 1991 and 1995 and between 1992 and 1998.

14-39 Homeowner Henry is building a fireplace for his house. The fireplace will require 800 bricks.

(a) If the cost of a chimney brick in 1978 was $2.10, calculate the material cost of Henry's project in 1998. The chimney brick index (CBI) was 442 in 1978 and is expected to be 618 in 1998.

(b) Estimate the material cost of a similar fireplace to be built in the year 2008. What assumption did you make?

Different Rates

14-40 General price inflation is estimated to be 3% for the next 5 years, 5% the 5 years after that, and 8% the following 5 years. If you invest $10,000 at 10% for those 15 years, what is the future worth of your investment in actual dollars at that time and in Year-0-dollars at that time?

14-41 Due to cost structures, trade policies, and corporate changes three big automakers have different inflation rates for the purchase prices of their vehicles. Which car should Mary Clare buy at graduation 3 years from now, assuming everything but purchase price is equivalent?

Automaker	Current Price	Price Will Inflate $x\%$ per Year
X	$27,500	4 %
Y	30,000	1.5
Z	25,000	8

14-42 Granny Viola has been saving money in the Bread & Butter mutual fund for 15 years. She has been a steady depositor over those years and has a pattern of putting $100 into the account every 3 months. If her original investment 15 years ago was $500 and interest in the account has varied as shown, what is the current value of her savings?

Years	Interest Earned in the Account
1–5	12% compounded quarterly
6–10	16 compounded quarterly
10–15	8 compounded quarterly

14-43 Andrew just bought a new boat for $15,000 to use on the river near his home. He has taken delivery of the boat and agreed to the terms of the following loan: all principal and interest is due in 3 years (balloon loan), first year annual interest (on the purchase price) is set at 5%, this is to be adjusted up 1.5% per year for each of the following years of the loan.

(a) How much does Andrew owe to pay off the loan in 3 years?

(b) If inflation is 4%, what is the payment in Year-0 dollars?

14-44 Given the following data, calculate the present worth of the investment.

First cost = $60,000   Project life = 10 years

Salvage value = $15,000   MARR = 25%

General price inflation = 4% per year
Annual cost 1 = $4500 in Year 1 and
inflating at 2.5% per year
Annual cost 2 = $7000 in Year 1 and
inflating at 10.0% per year
Annual cost 3 = $10,000 in Year 1 and
inflating at 6.5% per year
Annual cost 4 = $8500 in Year 1 and
inflating at −2.5% per year

14-45 As the owner of Beanie Bob's Basement Brewery, you are interested in a construction project to increase production to offset competition from your crosstown rival, Bad Brad's Brewery and Poolhall. Construction cost percentage increases, as well as current cost estimates are given for a 3-year period. Use a market interest rate of 25%, and assume that general price inflation is 5% over the 3-year period.

Item	Cost if Incurred Today	Cost Percentage Increase		
		Year 1	Year 2	Year 3
Structural metal/concrete	$120,000	4.3%	3.2%	6.6%
Roofing materials	14,000	2.0	2.5	3.0
Heating/plumbing equipment/fixtures	35,000	1.6	2.1	3.6
Insulation material	9,000	5.8	6.0	7.5
Labor	85,000	5.0	4.5	4.5

(a) What would the costs be for labor in Years 1, 2, and 3?

(b) What is the *average percentage increase* of labor cost over the 3-year period?

(c) What is the present worth of the insulation cost of this project?

(d) Calculate the future worth of the labor and insulation material cost portion of the project.

(e) Calculate the present worth of the total construction project for Beanie Bob.

14-46 Philippe Marie wants to race in the Tour de France ten years from now. He wants to know what the cost of a custom-built racing bicycle will be ten years from today.

Item	Current Cost	Cost Will Inflate $x\%$ per Year
Frame	$800	2 %
Wheels	350	10
Gearing system	200	5
Braking system	150	3
Saddle	70	2.5
Finishes	125	8

After-Tax Cases

14-47 Sally Seashell bought a lot at the Salty Sea for $18,000 cash. She does not plan to build on the lot, but instead will hold it as an investment for 10 years. She wants a 10% after-tax rate of return after taking the 6% annual inflation rate into account. If income taxes amount to 15% of the capital gain, at what price must she sell the lot at the end of the 10 years? (*Answer:* $95,188)

14-48 The U.S. tax laws provide for the depreciation of equipment based on original cost. Yet owing to substantial inflation, the replacement cost of equipment is often much greater than the original cost. What effect, if any, does this have on a firm's ability to buy new equipment to replace old equipment?

14-49 Tom Ward put $10,000 in a 5-year certificate of deposit that pays 12% interest per year. At maturity he will receive his $10,000 back. Tom's marginal income tax rate is 42%. If the inflation rate is 7% per year, find his

(*a*) before-tax rate of return, ignoring inflation

(*b*) after-tax rate of return, ignoring inflation

(*c*) after-tax rate of return, after taking inflation into account

14-50 Dick DeWolf and his wife have a total taxable income of $60,000 this year and file a joint federal income tax return. If inflation continues for the next 20 years at a 7% annual rate, Dick wonders what their taxable income must be to provide the same purchasing power after taxes. Assuming the federal income tax rate table is unchanged, what must their taxable income be 20 years from now?

14-51 Assume that your private university's tuition is $28,000.
Contributed by D. P. Loucks, Cornell University

(*a*) If the inflation rate for tuition is 5% per year, calculate what the tuition will cost 20 years from now.

(*b*) If the general inflation rate for the economy is 3% per year, express that future tuition in today's dollars.

(*c*) Calculate the amount you would have to invest today to pay for tuition costs 20, 21, 22, and 23 years from now. Assume you can invest at 7% per year, your income tax rate is 40% per year, and the tuition has to be paid at the beginning of the year.

14-52 You must decide when to go on a vacation. One option is right after graduation. The other option is to wait and go after spending 2 years with the Peace Corps. Assume the vacation costs $2500 now, and your annual income tax rate is 20% now, and is expected to continue to be 20% during the next 2 years. Also assume the annual inflation rate for a week's trip to Hawaii (hotel included) is 4%.

(*a*) Calculate the additional money you could spend on your vacation, after taxes, by putting your vacation money ($2500) into a taxable investment at 6% per year (before taxes) and waiting 2 years until after you come out of the Peace Corps compared to taking your well-deserved vacation now.

(*b*) If your tax rate drops to 0% while you're in the Peace Corps, how much additional money will you have for your vacation?

Contributed by D. P. Loucks, Cornell University

14-53 Sam Johnson inherited $85,000 from his father. Sam is considering investing the money in a house, which he will then rent to tenants. The $85,000 cost of the property consists of $17,500 for the land, and $67,500 for the house. Sam believes he can rent the house and have $8000 a year net income left after paying the property taxes and other expenses. The house will be depreciated by straight-line depreciation using a 45-year depreciable life.

(*a*) If the property is sold at the end of 5 years for its book value at that time, what after-tax rate of return will Sam receive? Assume that his marginal personal income tax rate is 34% for federal and state taxes.

(*b*) Now assume there is 7% per year inflation, compounded annually. Sam will increase the rent 7% per year to match the inflation rate, so that after considering increased taxes and other expenses, the annual net income will go up 7% per year. Assume Sam's marginal income tax rate remains at 34% for all ordinary taxable income related to the property. The value of the property is now projected to increase from its present $85,000 at a rate of 10% per year, compounded annually.

If the property is sold after 5 years, compute the rate of return on the after-tax cash flow in actual dollars. Also compute the rate of return on the after-tax cash flow in Year-0 dollars.

14-54 A small research device is purchased for $10,000 and depreciated by MACRS depreciation. The net benefits from the device, before deducting depreciation, are $2000 at the end of the first year and increasing $1000 per year after that (second year equals $3000, third year equals $4000, etc.), until the device is hauled to the junkyard at the end of 7 years. During the 7-year period there is an inflation rate f of 7%.

This profitable corporation has a 40% combined federal and state income tax rate. If it requires a real 12% after-tax rate of return on its investment, should the device have been purchased?

14-55 A couple in Ruston, Louisiana, must decide whether it is more economical to buy a home or to continue to rent during an inflationary period. The couple rents a one-bedroom duplex for $450 a month plus $139 a month in basic utilities (heating and cooling). These costs have a projected inflation rate of 5%, so the couple's monthly costs per year over a 10-year planning horizon are:

$n =$	1	2	3	4	5	6	7	8	9	10
Rent	450	473	496	521	547	574	603	633	665	698
Utilities	139	146	153	161	169	177	186	196	205	216

The couple would like to buy a home that costs $75,000. A local mortgage company will provide a loan that requires a down payment of 5% plus estimated closing costs of 1% cash. The couple prefers a 30-year fixed-rate mortgage with an 8% interest rate. The couple falls in the 30% marginal income tax rate (federal plus state), and as such, buying a home will provide them some tax write-off. It is estimated that the basic utilities for the home inflating at 5% will cost $160 per month; insurance and maintenance also inflating at 5% will cost $50 per month. The home will appreciate in value about 6% per year. Assuming a nominal interest rate of 15.5%, which alternative should the couple select? Use a present worth analysis. (*Note:* Realtor's sales commission here is 5%.)

14-56 When there is little or no inflation, a homeowner can expect to rent an unfurnished home for 12% of its market value. About $^1/8$ of the rental income is paid out for property taxes, insurance, and other operating

expenses. Thus the net annual income to the owner is 10.5% of the market value. Since prices are relatively stable, the future selling price of the property often equals the original price paid by the owner.

For a $150,000 property (where the land is estimated at $46,500 of the $150,000), compute the after-tax rate of return, assuming the selling price 59 months later (in December) equals the original purchase price. Use modified accelerated cost recovery system depreciation beginning January 1. Also, assume a 35% income tax rate. (*Answer:* 6.84%)

14-57 (This is a continuation of Problem 14-56.) As inflation has increased throughout the world, the rental income of homes has decreased and a net annual rental income of 8% of the market value is common. On the other hand, the market value of homes tends to rise about 2% per year more than the inflation rate. As a result, both annual net rental income, and the resale value of the property rise faster than the inflation rate. Consider the following situation.

A $150,000 property (with the house valued at $103,500 and the land at $46,500) is purchased for cash in Year 0. The market value of the property increases at a 12% annual rate. The annual rental income is 8% of the beginning-of-year market value of the property. Thus the rental income also increases each year. The general inflation rate f is 10%.

The individual who purchased the property has an average income tax rate of 35%.

(*a*) Use MACRS depreciation, beginning January 1, to compute the actual dollar after-tax rate of return for the owner, assuming he sells the property 59 months later (in December).

(*b*) Similarly, compute the after-tax rate of return for the owner, after taking the general inflation rate into account, assuming he sells the property 59 months later.

14-58 Consider two mutually exclusive alternatives stated in Year-0 dollars. Both alternatives have a 3-year life with no salvage value. Assume the annual inflation rate is 5%, an income tax rate of 25%, and straight-line depreciation. The minimum attractive rate of return (MARR) is 7%. Use rate of return analysis to determine which alternative is preferable.

Year	A	B
0	−$420	−$300
1	+200	+150
2	+200	+150
3	+200	+150

SELECTION OF A MINIMUM ATTRACTIVE RATE OF RETURN

BP Goes to Russia

In the early 1990s, western investors flocked to Russia, hoping to reap a fortune as markets opened up following the fall of the Soviet Union. Many didn't stay long because contracts could be impossible to enforce and bribery was common. In 1998, when Russia devalued its currency and defaulted on debt obligations, most of the remaining investors fled in panic.

Despite this business outlook, British Petroleum (BP) announced in early 2003 that it was planning to pay $6.75 billion for a 50% interest in Tyumen Oil Company, Russia's fourth largest producer of oil. BP's deci-

sion is particularly striking in view of the company's own history in Russia: in 1997 it bought a share in a small Russian oil company, only to lose part of its investment a few years later after a bitter court battle. Moreover, Russia's state-owned pipeline infrastructure is outdated and inadequate—and the government has been slow to allow private companies to build and operate their own pipelines.

Given all these drawbacks, BP would seem to be taking a big gamble by investing in Tyumen.

1. Many of BP's older sources of oil are now reaching the end of their useful life. How might this have affected the firm's decision to invest in Tyumen Oil?
2. Outside of Tyumen, there are few other oil companies left in Russia for competitors to buy. How might this have affected BP's decision?
3. Where else are the world's largest available oil reserves located? How does the business climate in these areas compare to Russia's?
4. Most of the largest oil-producing nations are members of OPEC (the Organization of Petroleum Exporting Countries), but Russia is not. Is this good or bad for BP?
5. What are some ethical issues that arise when one is investing in foreign firms and countries?

After Completing This Chapter...

The student should be able to:

- Define various sources of capital and the costs of those funds to the firm.
- Discuss the impact of inflation and the cost of borrowed money.
- Select a firm's MARR based on the opportunity cost approach for analyzing investments.
- Adjust the firm's MARR to account for risk and uncertainty.
- Use spreadsheets to develop cumulative investments and the opportunity cost of capital.

Т he preceding chapters have said very little about what interest rate or minimum attractive rate of return is suitable for use in a particular situation. This problem is complex, and no single answer is always appropriate. A discussion of what interest rate to use must inevitably begin by examining the sources of capital, followed by looking at the prospective investment opportunities and risk. Only in this way can an interest rate or minimum attractive rate of return (MARR) be chosen intelligently.

SOURCES OF CAPITAL

In broad terms there are three sources of capital available to a firm: money generated from the firm's operation, borrowed money, and money from selling stock.

Money Generated from the Firm's Operations

A major source of capital investment money is retained profits from the firm's operation. Overall, industrial firms retain about half of their profits and pay out the rest to stockholders. In addition to profit, the firm generates money equal to the annual depreciation charges on existing capital assets. In other words, a profitable firm will generate money equal to its depreciation charges *plus* its retained profits. Even a firm that earns zero profit will still generate money from operations equal to its depreciation charges. (A firm with a loss, of course, will have still less funds.)

External Sources of Money

When a firm requires money for a few weeks or months, it typically borrows from banks. Longer-term unsecured loans (of, say, 1–4 years) may also be arranged through banks. While banks undoubtedly finance a lot of capital expenditures, regular bank loans cannot be considered a source of permanent financing.

Longer-term financing is done by selling bonds to banks, insurance firms, pension funds, and the public. A wide variety of bonds exist, but most are interest-only loans, where interest is paid every 6 months or once a year and the principal is due at the bond's maturity. Common maturities are 10 to 30 years, although some extend to 100 years and a few even longer. Often interest rates are explicitly stated, but not always; Chapter 7 includes examples of how to calculate the interest rates when these are not given.

A firm can also raise funds by issuing new stock (shares of ownership in the firm). Many firms have also repurchased their own stock in the past, which is called *treasury stock*. Another way firms can raise funds is to sell this treasury stock.

One of the finance questions each firm must address is maintaining an appropriate balance between debt (loans and bonds) and equity (stock and retained earnings). The debt has a maturity date, and there are legal obligations to repay it unless the firm declares bankruptcy. On the other hand, stockholders expect a higher rate of return to compensate them for the risks of ownership. Those who are interested in the models used to calculate the cost of equity capital are referred to *The Economic Analysis of Industrial Projects*, 3rd edition, by Eschenbach, Hartman, and Bussey, published by Oxford University Press.

Choice of Source of Funds

Choosing the source of funds for capital expenditures is a decision for the firm's top executives, and it may require approval of the board of directors. When internal operations generate adequate funds for the desired capital expenditures, external sources of money are not likely to be used. But when the internal sources are inadequate, external sources must be employed or the capital expenditures will have to be deferred or canceled.

COST OF FUNDS

Cost of Borrowed Money

A first step in deciding on a minimum attractive rate of return might be to determine the interest rate at which money can be borrowed. Longer-term loans or bonds may be obtained from banks, insurance companies, or the variety of places in which substantial amounts of money accumulates (for example, the oil-producing nations).

A large, profitable corporation might be able to borrow money at the **prime rate,** that is, the interest rate that banks charge their best and most sought-after customers. All other firms are charged an interest rate that is higher by one-half to several percentage points. In addition to the firm's financial strength and ability to repay the debt, the interest rate will depend on the debt's duration and on whether the debt has collateral or is unsecured.

Cost of Capital

Another relevant interest rate is the **cost of capital.** This is also called the weighted average cost of capital (WACC). The general assumption concerning the cost of capital is that all the money the firm uses for investments is drawn from all of the firm's overall capitalization. The mechanics for computing the cost of capital or WACC are given in Example 15-1.

EXAMPLE 15-1

For a particular firm, the purchasers of common stock require an 11% rate of return, bonds are sold at a 7% interest rate, and bank loans are available at 9%. Compute the cost of capital or WACC for the following capital structure:

		Rate of Return	Annual Amount
$ 20 million	Bank loan	9%	$1.8 million
20	Bonds	7	1.4
60	Common stock and retained earnings	11	6.6
$100 million			$9.8 million

SOLUTION

Interest payments on debt, like bank loans and bonds, are tax-deductible business expenses. Thus:

$$\text{After-tax interest cost} = (\text{Before-tax interest cost}) \times (1 - \text{Tax rate})$$

If we assume that the firm pays 40% income taxes, the computations become:

Bank loan	After-tax interest cost $= 9\%(1 - 0.40) = 5.4\%$
Bonds	After-tax interest cost $= 7\%(1 - 0.40) = 4.2\%$

Dividends paid on the ownership in the firm (common stock + retained earnings) are not tax deductible. Combining the three components, the after-tax interest cost for the $100 million of capital is:

$$\$20 \text{ million } (5.4\%) + \$20 \text{ million } (4.2\%) + \$60 \text{ million } (11\%) = \$8.52 \text{ million}$$

$$\text{Cost of capital} = \frac{\$8.52 \text{ million}}{\$100 \text{ million}} = 8.52\%$$

In practical situations, the cost of capital is often difficult to compute. The fluctuation in the price of common stock, for example, makes it difficult to pick a cost, and because of the fluctuating prospects of the firm, it is even more difficult to estimate the future benefits that purchasers of the stock might expect to receive. Given the fluctuating costs and prospects of future benefits, what rate of return do stockholders require? There is no precise answer, but we can obtain an approximate answer. As described in the next section, inflation complicates the task of finding the *real* interest rate.

Inflation and the Cost of Borrowed Money

As inflation varies, what is its effect on the cost of borrowed money? A widely held view has been that interest rates on long-term borrowing, like 20-year Treasury bonds, will be about 3% more than the inflation rate. For borrowers this is the real—that is, after-inflation—cost of money, and for lenders the real return on loans. If inflation rates were to increase, it would follow that borrowing rates would also increase. All this suggests a rational and orderly situation, about as we might expect.

Unfortunately, things have not worked out this way. Figure 15-1 shows that the real interest rate has not always been about 3% and, in fact, there have been long periods during which the real interest rate was negative. Can this be possible? Would anyone invest money at an interest rate several percentage points below the inflation rate? Well, consider this: when the U.S. inflation rate was 12%, savings banks were paying 5½% on regular passbook

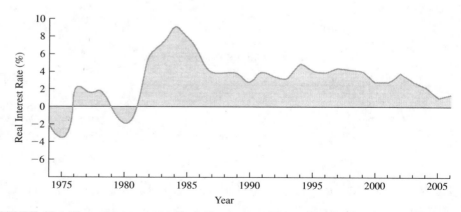

FIGURE 15-1 The real interest rate. The interest rate on 20-year Treasury bonds *minus* the inflation rate, f, as measured by changes in the Consumer Price index.

deposits. And there was a lot of money in those accounts. While there must be a relationship between interest rates and inflation, Figure 15-1 suggests that it is complex.

The relationship between the inflation rate and the rate of return on investments is quite important, because inflation reduces the real rate of return (as shown in Chapter 14). In addition, many interest rates are reported without adjusting for inflation. For example, you know the interest rate on your car loan, student loan, house loan, savings account, and so on—but all those rates are stated without adjusting for inflation.

INVESTMENT OPPORTUNITIES

An industrial firm can invest its money in many more places than are available to an individual. A firm has larger amounts of money, and this alone makes certain kinds of investment possible that are unavailable to individual investors, with their more limited investment funds. The U.S. government, for example, borrows money for short terms of 90 or 180 days by issuing certificates called Treasury bills that frequently yield a greater interest rate than savings accounts. The customary minimum purchase is $25,000.

More important, however, is the fact that a firm conducts a business, which itself offers many investment opportunities. While exceptions can be found, a good generalization is that the opportunities for investment of money within the firm are superior to the investment opportunities outside the firm. Consider the available investment opportunities for a partic-ular firm as outlined in Table 15-1. The cumulative investment required for all projects at or above a given rate of return is given in Figure 15-2.

Figure 15-2 illustrates that a firm may have a broad range of investment opportunities available at varying rates of return and with varying lives and uncertainties. It may take some study and searching to identify the better investment projects available to a firm. Typically, the good projects will almost certainly require more money than the firm budgets for capital investment projects.

Opportunity Cost

We see that there are two aspects of investing that are basically independent. One factor is the source and quantity of money available for capital investment projects. The other aspect is the firm's investment opportunities.

These two situations are typically out of balance, with investment opportunities exceed-ing the available money supply. Thus some investment opportunities can be selected and others must be rejected. Obviously, we want to ensure that *all the selected projects are better than the best rejected project.* To do this, we must know something about the rate of return on the best rejected project. The best rejected project is the best opportunity forgone, and this in turn is called the **opportunity cost.**

Opportunity cost = Cost of the best opportunity forgone

= Rate of return on the best rejected project

If one could predict the opportunity cost for some future period (like the next 12 months), this rate of return could be one way to judge whether to accept or reject any proposed capital expenditure. Examples 15-2 and 15-3 illustrate this.

TABLE 15-1 A Firm's Available Investment Opportunities

Project Number	Project	Cost ($\times 10^3$)	Estimated Rate of Return
	Investment Related to Current Operations		
1	New equipment to reduce labor costs	$150	30%
2	Other new equipment to reduce labor costs	50	45
3	Overhaul particular machine to reduce material costs	50	38
4	New test equipment to reduce defective products produced	100	40
	New Operations		
5	Manufacture parts that previously had been purchased	200	35
6	Further processing of products previously sold in semifinished form	100	28
7	Further processing of other products	200	18
	New Production Facilities		
8	Relocate production to new plant	250	25
	External Investments		
9	Investment in a different industry	300	20
10	Other investment in a different industry	300	10
11	Overseas investment	400	15
12	Purchase of Treasury bills	Unlimited	8

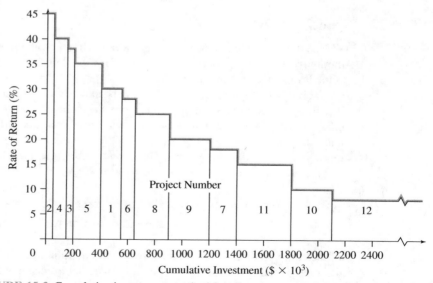

FIGURE 15-2 Cumulative investment required for all projects at or above a given rate of return.

EXAMPLE 15-2

Consider the situation represented by Table 15-1 and Figure 15-2. For a capital expenditure budget of $1.2 million ($1.2 × 10^6$), what is the opportunity cost?

SOLUTION

From Figure 15-2 we see that the eight projects with a rate of return of 20% or more require a cumulative investment of $1.2 ($×10^6$). We would take on these projects and reject the other four (7, 11, 10, and 12) with rates of return of 18% or less. The best rejected project is 7, and it has an 18% rate of return. Thus the opportunity cost is 18%.

EXAMPLE 15-3

Nine independent projects are being considered. Figure 15-3 may be prepared from the following data.

Project	Cost (thousands)	Uniform Annual Benefit (thousands)	Useful Life (years)	Salvage Value (thousands)	Computed Rate of Return
1	$100	$23.85	10	$0	20%
2	200	39.85	10	0	15
3	50	34.72	2	0	25
4	100	20.00	6	100	20
5	100	20.00	10	100	20
6	100	18.00	10	100	18
7	300	94.64	4	0	10
8	300	47.40	10	100	12
9	50	7.00	10	50	14

If a capital budget of $650,000 is available, what is the opportunity cost of capital? With this model, which projects should be selected?

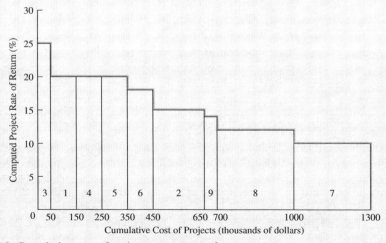

FIGURE 15-3 Cumulative cost of projects versus rate of return.

SOLUTION

Looking at the nine projects, we see that some are expected to produce a larger rate of return than others. It is natural that if we are to select from among them, we will pick those with a higher rate of return. When the projects are arrayed by rate of return, as in Figure 15-3, Project 2 is the last one funded. Thus, the opportunity cost of capital is 14% from Project 9, the highest ranked unfunded project. This model implies funding Projects 3, 1, 4, 5, 6, and 2.

SELECTING A MINIMUM ATTRACTIVE RATE OF RETURN

Focusing on the three concepts on the cost of money (the cost of borrowed money, the cost of capital, and opportunity cost), which, if any, of these values should be used as the minimum attractive rate of return (MARR) in economic analyses?

Fundamentally, we know that unless the benefits of a project exceed its cost, we cannot add to the profitability of the firm. A lower boundary for the minimum attractive rate of return must be the cost of the money invested in the project. It would be unwise, for example, to borrow money at 8% and invest it in a project yielding a 6% rate of return.

Further, we know that no firm has an unlimited ability to borrow money. Bankers— and others who evaluate the limits of a firm's ability to borrow money—look at both the profitability of the firm and the relationship between the components in the firm's capital structure. This means that continued borrowing of money will require that additional stock must be sold to maintain an acceptable ratio between **ownership** (equity) and **debt.** In other words, borrowing for a particular investment project is only a block of money from the overall capital structure of the firm. This suggests that the MARR should not be less than the cost of capital. Finally, we know that the MARR should not be less than the rate of return on the best opportunity forgone. Stated simply,

Minimum attractive rate of return should be equal to the largest of: cost of borrowed money, cost of capital, or opportunity cost.

ADJUSTING MARR TO ACCOUNT FOR RISK AND UNCERTAINTY

We know from our study of estimating the future that what actually occurs is often different from the estimate. When we are fortunate enough to be able to assign probabilities to a set of possible future outcomes, we call this a **risk** situation. We saw in Chapter 10 that techniques like expected value and simulation may be used when the probabilities are known.

Uncertainty is the term used to describe the condition when the probabilities are *not* known. Thus, if the probabilities of future outcomes are known, we have *risk*, and if they are unknown, we have *uncertainty*. In this case, adjustments for risk are more subjective.

In projects accompanied by normal business risk and uncertainty, the MARR is used without adjustment. For projects with greater than average risk or uncertainty, most firms increase the MARR. As reported in Block (2005), the percentage of firms using risk-adjusted rates varied from 66% in retail to 82% in health care. Some of the percentages for other industries are 70% for manufacturing, 73% for energy, and 78% for technology firms. Table 15-2 lists an example of risk-adjusted MARRs in manufacturing.

Some firms use the same rates for all divisions and groups. Other firms vary the rates by division for strategic reasons. There are even cases when a project-specific rate based on that project's financing may be justified. For example, a firm or joint venture may be founded to develop a specific mine, pipeline, or other resource development project.

TABLE 15-2 **Example Risk-Adjusted Interest Rates**

Rate (%)	Applies to:
6	Equipment replacement
8	New equipment
10	New product in normal market
12	New product in related market
16	New product in new market
20	New product in foreign market

However, as shown in Example 15-4, risk-adjusted rates may not work well. A preferable way deals explicitly with the probabilities using the techniques from Chapter 10. When the interest rate (MARR) used in economic analysis calculations is raised to adjust for risk or uncertainty, greater emphasis is placed on immediate or short-term results and less emphasis on longer-term results.

EXAMPLE 15-4

Consider the two following alternatives: the MARR of Alt. *B* has been raised from 10 to 15% to take into account the greater risk and uncertainty that Alt. *B*'s results may not be as favorable as indicated. What is the impact of this change of MARR on the decision?

Year	Alt. *A*	Alt. *B*
0	−$80	−$80
1–10	10	13.86
11–20	20	10

SOLUTION

Year	Alt.*A*	NPW At 14.05%	NPW At 10%	NPW At 15%
0	−$80	−$80.00	−$80.00	−$80.00
1–10	10	52.05	61.45	50.19
11–20	20	27.95	47.38	24.81
		0	+28.83	−5.00

Year	Alt. *B*	NPW At 15.48%	NPW At 10%	NPW At 15%
0	−$80	−$80.00	−$80.00	−$80.00
1–10	13.86	68.31	85.14	69.56
11–20	10	11.99	23.69	12.41
		0	+28.83	+1.97

Computations at MARR of 10% Ignoring Risk and Uncertainty

Both alternatives have the same positive NPW (+$28.83) at a MARR of 10%. Also, the differences in the benefits schedules (A − B) produce a 10% incremental rate of return. (The calculations are not shown here.) This must be true if NPW for the two alternatives is to remain constant at a MARR of 10%.

Considering Risk and Uncertainty with MARR of 10%

At 10%, both alternatives are equally desirable. Since Alt. B is believed to have greater risk and uncertainty, a logical conclusion is to select Alt. A rather than B.

Increase MARR to 15%

At a MARR of 15%, Alt. A has a negative NPW and Alt. B has a positive NPW. Alternative B is preferred under these circumstances.

Conclusion

Based on a business-risk MARR of 10%, the two alternatives are equivalent. Recognizing some greater risk of failure for Alt. B makes A the preferred alternative. If the MARR is increased to 15%, to add a margin of safety against risk and uncertainty, the computed decision is to select B. Since Alt. B has been shown to be less desirable than A, the decision, based on a MARR of 15%, may be an unfortunate one. The difficulty is that the same risk adjustment (increase the MARR by 5%) is applied to both alternatives even though they have different amounts of risk.

The conclusion to be drawn from Example 15-4 is that increasing the MARR to compensate for risk and uncertainty is only an approximate technique and may not always achieve the desired result. Nevertheless, it is common practice in industry to adjust the MARR upward to compensate for increased risk and uncertainty.

REPRESENTATIVE VALUES OF MARR USED IN INDUSTRY

We argued that the minimum attractive rate of return should be established at the highest one of the following: cost of borrowed money, cost of capital, or the opportunity cost.

The cost of borrowed money will vary from enterprise to enterprise, with the lowest rate being the prime interest rate. The prime rate may change several times in a year; it is widely reported in newspapers and business publications. As we pointed out, the interest rate for firms that do not qualify for the prime interest rate may be ½% to several percentage points higher.

The cost of capital of a firm is an elusive value. There is no widely accepted way to compute it; we know that as a *composite value* for the capital structure of the firm, it conventionally is higher than the cost of borrowed money. The cost of capital must consider the market valuation of the shares (common stock, etc.) of the firm, which may fluctuate widely, depending on future earnings prospects of the firm. We cannot generalize on representative costs of capital.

Somewhat related to cost of capital is the computation of the return on total capital (long-term debt, capital stock, and retained earnings) actually achieved by firms. *Fortune* magazine, among others, does an annual analysis of the rate of return on total capital. The after-tax rate of return on total capital for individual firms ranges from 0% to about 40% and averages 8%. *Business Week* does a periodic survey of corporate performance. This magazine reports an after-tax rate of return on common stock and retained earnings. We would expect the values to be higher than the rate of return on total capital, and this is the case. The after-tax return on common stock and retained earnings ranges from 0% to about 65% with an average of 14%.

Higher values for the MARR are used by firms that are short of capital, such as high-technology start-ups. They are also used in industries, such as petroleum and mining, where volatile prices increase the risk of poor returns for projects. Rates of 25 to 30% are relatively common, and even higher rates are sometimes used. For companies with more normal levels of risk, rates of 12 to 15% are more typical.

Note that the values of MARR given earlier are approximations. But the values quoted appear to be opportunity costs, rather than cost of borrowed money or cost of capital. This indicates that firms cannot or do not obtain money to fund projects whose anticipated rates of return are nearer to the cost of borrowed money or cost of capital. One reason that firms operate as they do is that they can focus limited resources of people, management, and time on a smaller number of good projects.

One cannot leave this section without noting that the MARR used by enterprises is much higher than can be obtained by individuals. (Where can you get a 30% after-tax rate of return without excessive risk?) The reason appears to be that businesses are not obliged to compete with the thousands of individuals in any region seeking a place to invest $2000 with safety, whereas the number of people who could or would want to invest $500,000 in a business is far smaller. This diminished competition, combined with a higher risk, appears to explain at least some of the difference.

CAPITAL BUDGETING OR SELECTING THE BEST PROJECTS

The opportunity cost of capital approach of ranking projects by their rate of return introduced a new type of problem. Up to that point we'd been analyzing mutually exclusive alternatives, where only one could be chosen. Engineering design problems are this type of problem, where younger engineers use engineering economy to choose the best alternative design.

At higher levels in the organization, engineering economy is applied to solve a different problem. For example, 30 projects have passed initial screening and are being proposed for funding. Every one of the 30 meets the MARR. The firm can afford to invest in only some of them. So, which ones should be chosen and how? This is called the *capital budgeting* problem.

Examples 15-2 and 15-3 applied the opportunity cost of capital approach to the capital budgeting problem. Firms often use this approach as a starting point to rank the projects from best to worst. In some cases the ranking by rate of return is used to make the decision.

More often, managers then meet and decide which projects will be funded by obtaining a consensus, or a decision by the highest-ranking manager, which will modify the rate of return ranking. At this meeting, business units argue for a larger share of the capital budget, as do plants in the same business, groups at the same plants, and individuals within the groups. Some considerations, such as strategy, necessity, and the availability and capability of particular resources and people are difficult to represent in the project's *numbers*, which are the subject of economic analysis.

Other firms rank projects using a benefit–cost ratio or present worth index. As shown in Example 15-5, the present worth index is the NPW divided by the cost's present value.

Anyone who has ever bought firecrackers probably used the practical ranking criterion of "biggest bang for the buck" in making a selection. This same criterion—stated more elegantly—is used by some firms to rank independent projects.

Rank independent projects according to their value of net present worth divided by the present worth of cost. The appropriate interest rate is MARR (as a reasonable estimate of the cutoff rate of return).

EXAMPLE 15-5

Rank the following nine independent projects in their order of desirability, based on a 14.5% minimum attractive rate of return.

Project	Cost (thousands)	Uniform Annual Benefit (thousands)	Useful Life (years)	Salvage Value (thousands)	Computed Rate of Return	Computed NPW at 14.5% (thousands)	Computed NPW/Cost (thousands)
1	$100	$23.85	10	$0	20%	$22.01	0.2201
2	200	39.85	10	0	15	3.87	0.0194
3	50	34.72	2	0	25	6.81	0.1362
4	100	20.00	6	100	20	21.10	0.2110
5	100	20.00	10	100	20	28.14	0.2814
6	100	18.00	10	100	18	17.91	0.1791
7	300	94.64	4	0	10	−27.05	−0.0902
8	300	47.40	10	100	12	−31.69	−0.1056
9	50	7.00	10	50	14	−1.28	−0.0256

SOLUTION

Ranked NPW/PW of cost, the projects are listed as follows:

Project	NPW/PW of Cost	Rate of Return
5	0.2814	20%
1	0.2201	20
4	0.2110	20
6	0.1791	18
3	0.1362	25
2	0.0194	15
9	−0.0256	14
7	−0.0902	10
8	−0.1056	12

With a 14.5% MARR, Projects 1 to 6 are recommended for funding and 7 to 9 are not. However, they are ranked in a different order by the present worth index and by the rate of return approaches. For example, Project 3 has the highest ranking for the rate of return and is fifth by the present worth index.

Some consider the present worth index to be a better measure, but this can be true only if PW is applied at the correct interest rate. It is more common for firms to simply rank on the rate of return. If independent projects can be ranked in their order of desirability, then the selection of projects to be included in a capital budget is a simple task. One may proceed down the list of ranked projects until the capital budget has been exhausted. The only difficulty with this scheme occurs, occasionally, when the capital budget is more than enough for n projects but too little for $n + 1$ projects.

In Example 15-5, suppose the capital budget is $550,000. This is more than enough for the top five projects (sum = $450,000) but not enough for the top six projects (sum = $650,000). When we have this situation, it may not be possible to say with certainty that the best use of a capital budget of $550,000 is to fund the top five projects. There may be some other set of projects that makes better use of the available $550,000. While some trial-and-error computations may indicate the proper set of projects, more elaborate techniques are needed to prove optimality.

As a practical matter, a capital budget probably has some flexibility. If in Example 15-5 the tentative capital budget is $550,000, then a careful examination of Project 2 will dictate whether to expand the capital budget to $650,000 (to be able to include Project 2) or to drop back to $450,000 (and leave Project 2 out of the capital budget). Or perhaps Project 2 can be started in this budget year and finished next year.

Spreadsheets, Cumulative Investments, and the Opportunity Cost of Capital

As shown in earlier chapters, spreadsheets make computing rates of return dramatically easier. In addition, spreadsheets can be used to sort the projects by rate of return and then calculate the cumulative first cost. This is accomplished through the following steps.

1. Enter or calculate each project's rate of return.
2. Select the data to be sorted. Do *not* include headings, but do include all information on the row that goes with each project.
3. Select the SORT tool (found in the menu under DATA), identify the rate of return column as the first key, and a sort order of descending. Also ensure that row sorting is selected. Sort.
4. Add a column for the cumulative first cost. This column is compared with the capital limit to identify the opportunity cost of capital and which projects should be funded.

Example 15-6 illustrates these steps.

EXAMPLE 15-6

A firm has a budget of $800,000 for projects this year. Which of the following projects should be accepted? What is the opportunity cost of capital?

Project	First Cost	Annual Benefit	Salvage Value	Life (years)
A	$200,000	$25,000	$50,000	15
B	250,000	47,000	−25,000	10
C	150,000	17,500	20,000	15
D	100,000	20,000	15,000	10
E	200,000	24,000	25,000	20
F	300,000	35,000	15,000	15
G	100,000	18,000	0	10
H	200,000	22,500	15,000	20
I	350,000	50,000	0	25

SOLUTION

The first step is to use the RATE function to find the rate of return for each project. The results of this step are shown in the top portion of Figure 15-4. Next the projects are sorted in descending order by their rates of return. Finally, the cumulative first cost is computed. Projects D, I, B, and G should be funded. The opportunity cost of capital is 10.6% the rate for the first project rejected.

	A	B	C	D	E	F	G	H
1	Project	First Cost	Annual Benefit	Salvage Value	Life	IRR		
2	A	200,000	25,000	50,000	15	10.2%	=RATE(E2,C2,−B2,D2)	
3	B	250,000	47,000	−25,000	10	12.8%		
4	C	150,000	17,000	20,000	15	8.6%		
5	D	100,000	20,000	15,000	10	16.0%		
6	E	200,000	24,000	25,000	20	10.6%		
7	F	300,000	35,000	15,000	15	8.2%		
8	G	100,000	18,000	0	10	12.4%		
9	H	200,000	22,500	15,000	20	9.6%		
10	I	350,000	50,000	0	25	13.7%		
11	Projects Sorted by IRR						Cumulative First Cost	
12	D	100,000	20,000	15,000	10	16.0%	100,000	
13	I	350,000	50,000	0	25	13.7%	450,000	
14	B	250,000	47,000	−25,000	10	12.8%	700,000	
15	G	100,000	18,000	0	10	12.4%	800,000	
16	E	200,000	24,000	25,000	20	10.6%	1,000,000	
17	A	200,000	25,000	50,000	15	10.2%	1,200,000	
18	H	200,000	22,500	15,000	20	9.6%	1,400,000	
19	C	150,000	17,500	20,000	15	8.6%	1,550,000	
20	F	300,000	35,000	15,000	15	8.2%	1,850,000	

FIGURE 15-4 Spreadsheet for finding opportunity cost of capital.

Example 15-7 outlines the more complicated case of independent projects with mutually exclusive alternatives.

EXAMPLE 15-7

A company is preparing its capital budget for next year. The amount has been set at $250,000 by the board of directors. Rank the following project proposals for the board's consideration and recommend which should be funded.

Project Proposals	Cost (thousands)	Uniform Annual Benefit (thousands)	Salvage Value (thousands)	Useful Life (years)
Proposal 1				
Alt. A	$100	$23.85	$0	10
Alt. B	150	32.20	0	10
Alt. C	200	39.85	0	10
Proposal 2	50	14.92	0	5
Proposal 3				
Alt. A	100	18.69	25	10
Alt. B	150	19.42	125	10

SOLUTION

For project proposals with two or more alternatives, incremental rate of return analysis is required.

Combination of Alternatives	Cost (thousands)	Uniform Annual Benefit (thousands)	Salvage Value (thousands)	Computed Rate of Return	Incremental Analysis			
					Cost (thousands)	Uniform Annual Benefit (thousands)	Salvage Value (thousands)	Computed Rate of Return
Proposal 1								
A	$100	$23.85	$0	20.0%				
B − A					$50	8.35	$0	10.6%
B	150	32.20	0	17.0				
C − B					50	7.65	0	8.6
C − A					100	16.00	0	9.6
C	200	39.85	0	15.0				
Proposal 2	50	14.92	0	15.0				
Proposal 3								
A	100	18.69	25	15.0				
B − A					50	0.73	100	8.3
B	150	19.42	125	12.0				

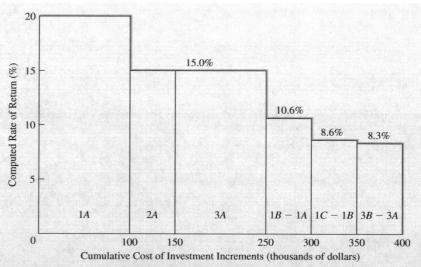

FIGURE 15-5 Cumulative cost versus incremental rate of return.

The various separable increments of investment may be ranked by the rate of return. They are plotted in a graph of cumulative cost versus rate of return in Figure 15-5. The ranking of projects by rate of return gives the following:

Project	
1A	20.0%
2	15.0%
3A	15.0%
1B in place of 1A	10.6%
1C in place of 1B	8.6%
3B in place of 3A	8.3%

For a budget of $250,000 the selected projects are 1A, 2, and 3A. Note that if a budget of $300,000 were available, 1B would replace 1A, making the proper set of projects 1B, 2, and 3A. At a budget of $400,000 1C would replace 1B; and 3B would replace 3A, making the selected projects 1C, 2, and 3B.

In Example 15-7, each of the more expensive mutually exclusive alternatives (1B, 1C, and 3B) had lower rates of return than the less expensive alternatives (1A and 3A). This is common because many projects exhibit decreasing returns to scale. As in Example 15-7, when it occurs, then it makes the ranking of increments easy to use. Sometimes more expensive mutually exclusive alternatives have higher rates of return, then several combinations or more advanced techniques must be tried.

SUMMARY

There are three general sources of capital available to a firm. The most important one is money generated from the firm's operations. This has two components: there is the portion of profit that is retained in the business; in addition, funds equal to its depreciation charges that are available for reinvestment.

The two other sources of capital are from outside the firm's operations.

Debt: borrowed as loans from banks, insurance companies, and so forth.

Longer-term borrowing: from selling bonds.

Equity: sale of equity securities like common or preferred stock.

Retained profits and cash equal to depreciation charges are the primary sources of investment capital for most firms, and the only sources for many enterprises.

In selecting a value of MARR, three values are frequently considered:

1. Cost of borrowed money.
2. Cost of capital. This is a composite cost of the components of the firm's overall capitalization.
3. Opportunity cost, which is the rate of return on the best investment project that is rejected.

The MARR should be equal to the highest one of these three values.

When there is a risk aspect to the problem (probabilities are known or reasonably estimated), this can be handled by techniques like expected value and simulation. Where there is uncertainty (probabilities of the various outcomes are not known), there are analytical techniques, but they are less satisfactory. A method commonly used to adjust for risk and uncertainty is to increase the MARR. This method can distort the time-value-of-money relationship. The effect is to discount longer-term consequences more heavily than short-term consequences, which may or may not be desirable. Prior to this chapter we had assumed that all worthwhile projects are approved and implemented. But industrial firms, like individuals and governments, are typically faced with more good projects than can be funded with the money available. The task is to select the best projects and reject, or at least delay, the rest.

Capital may be rationed among competing investment opportunities by either rate of return or present worth methods. The results may not always be the same for these two methods in many practical situations.

If projects are ranked by rate of return, a proper procedure is to go down the list until the capital budget has been exhausted. The rate of return at this point is the cutoff rate of return. This procedure gives the best group of projects, but does not necessarily have them in the proper priority order.

It has been shown in earlier chapters that the usual business objective is to maximize NPW, and this is not necessarily the same as maximizing rate of return. One suitable procedure is to use the ratio (NPW/PW of cost) to rank the projects, letting the MARR equal the cutoff rate of return (which is the opportunity cost of capital). This present worth ranking method will order the projects so that, for a limited capital budget, NPW will be maximized. The MARR must equal the cutoff rate of return for the rate of return and present worth methods to yield compatible results.

PROBLEMS

Cost of Funds

15-1 Examine the financial pages of your newspaper (or *The Wall St. Journal*) and determine the current interest rate on the following securities, and explain why the interest rates are different for these different bonds.

(a) U.S. Treasury bond due in 5 years.

(b) General obligation bond of a municipal district, city, or a state due in 20 years.

(c) Corporate debenture bond of a U.S. industrial firm due in 20 years.

15-2 A small engineering firm has borrowed $125,000 at 8%. The partners have invested another $75,000. If the partners require a 12% rate of return, what is the firm's cost of capital?   (*Answer:* 9.05%)

15-3 An engineering firm has borrowed $725,000 at 7%. The stockholders have invested another $600,000. The firm's retained earnings total $1.2M. The return on equity is estimated to be 11%. What is the firm's cost of capital?

15-4 A firm's stockholders expect a 15% rate of return, and there is $12M in common stock and retained earnings. The firm has $5M in loans at an average rate of 7%. The firm has raised $8M by selling bonds at an average rate of 6%. What is the firm's cost of capital?

15-5 A firm's stockholders expect an 18% rate of return, and there is $22M in common stock and retained earnings. The firm has $9M in loans at an average rate of 8%. The firm has raised $14M by selling bonds at an average rate of 4%. What is the firm's cost of capital?

15-6 Assume you have $2000 available for investment for a 5-year period. You wish to *invest* the money— not just spend it on fun things. There are obviously many alternatives available. You should be willing to assume a modest amount of risk of loss of some or all of the money if this is necessary, but not a great amount of risk (no investments in poker games or at horse races). How would you invest the money? What is your minimum attractive rate of return? Explain.

15-7 There are many venture capital syndicates that consist of a few (say, eight or ten) wealthy people who combine to make investments in small and (hopefully) growing businesses. Typically,

the investors hire a young investment manager (often an engineer with an MBA) who seeks and analyzes investment opportunities for the group. Would you estimate that the MARR sought by this group is more or less than 12%? Explain.

Inflation

15-8 What is the interest rate on a 2-year certificate of deposit at a bank or credit union in your area? What is the most recent value of the Consumer Price Index (CPI)? If inflation continues at that rate, what is the real rate of return on the 2-year CD? Include references for the sources of your data.

15-9 What is the interest rate on a 4- or 5-year new-car loan at a bank or credit union in your area? What is the most recent value of the Consumer Price Index (CPI)? If inflation continues at that rate, what is the real interest rate you would pay on the car loan? Include references for the sources of your data.

15-10 Over the last 10 years, what has been the inflation rate? Compare this with the rate of return on the "Dow" average over the same period. What has been the real rate of return for investing in this mix of stocks? Include references for the sources of your data.

15-11 Over the last 10 years, what has been the inflation rate? Compare this with the rate of return on the NASDAQ average over the same period. What has been the real rate of return for investing in this mix of stocks? Include references for the sources of your data.

Opportunity Cost of Capital

15-12 A factory has a $100,000 capital budget. Determine which project(s) should be funded and the opportunity cost of capital.

Project	First Cost	Annual Benefits	Life (years)	Salvage Value
A	$50,000	$13,500	5	$5000
B	50,000	9,000	10	0
C	50,000	13,250	5	1000
D	50,000	9,575	8	6000

15-13 Chips USA is considering the following projects to improve their production process. Chips have a short life, so a 3-year horizon is used in evaluation. Which projects should be done if the budget is $70,000? What is the opportunity cost of capital?

Project	First Cost	Benefit
1	$20,000	$11,000
2	30,000	14,000
3	10,000	6,000
4	5,000	2,400
5	25,000	13,000
6	15,000	7,000
7	40,000	21,000

15-14 The National Motors Rock Creek plant is considering the following projects to improve the company's production process. Which projects should be done if the budget is $500,000? What is the opportunity cost of capital?

Project	First Cost	Annual Benefit	Life (years)
1	$200,000	$50,000	15
2	300,000	70,000	10
3	100,000	40,000	5
4	50,000	12,500	10
5	250,000	75,000	5
6	150,000	32,000	20
7	400,000	125,000	5

15-15 The WhatZit Company has decided to fund six of nine project proposals for the coming budget year. Determine the next capital budget for WhatZit. What is the MARR?

Project	First Cost	Annual Benefits	Life (years)
A	$15,000	$ 4,429	4
B	20,000	6,173	4
C	30,000	9,878	4
D	25,000	6,261	5
E	40,000	11,933	5
F	50,000	11,550	5
G	35,000	6,794	8
H	60,000	12,692	8
I	75,000	14,058	8

15-16 Which projects should be done if the budget is $100,000? What is the opportunity cost of capital?

Project	Life (years)	First Cost	Annual Benefit	Salvage Value
1	20	$20,000	$4000	
2	20	20,000	3200	$20,000
3	30	20,000	3300	10,000
4	15	20,000	4500	
5	25	20,000	4500	−20,000
6	10	20,000	5800	
7	15	20,000	4000	10,000

Risk-Adjusted MARR

15-17 Use the example risk-adjusted interest rates for manufacturing projects in Table 15-2. Assume Project B in Problem 15-12 is a new product in a new market. What is the interest rate for evaluating this project? Should it be done?

15-18 Use the example risk-adjusted interest rates for manufacturing projects in Table 15-2. Assume Project E in Problem 15-15 is a new product in an existing market. What is the interest rate for evaluating this project? Should it be done?

15-19 Use the example risk-adjusted interest rates for manufacturing projects in Table 15-2. Assume Project 1 in Problem 15-16 is a new product in a foreign market. What is the interest rate for evaluating this project? Should it be done?

Capital Budgeting

15-20 Each of the following 10 independent projects has a 10-year life and no salvage value.

Project	Cost (thousands)	Uniform Annual Benefits (thousands)	Computed Rate of Return
1	$ 5	$1.03	16%
2	15	3.22	17
3	10	1.77	12
4	30	4.88	10
5	5	1.19	20
6	20	3.83	14
7	5	1.00	15
8	20	3.69	13
9	5	1.15	19
10	10	2.23	18

The projects have been proposed by the staff of the Ace Card Company. The MARR of Ace has been 12% for several years.

(a) If there is ample money available, what projects should Ace approve?

(b) Rank-order all the acceptable projects in according to desirability.

(c) If only $55,000 is available, which projects should be approved?

15-21 Ten capital spending proposals have been made to the budget committee as the members prepare the annual budget for their firm. Each independent project has a 5-year life and no salvage value.

Project	Initial Cost (thousands)	Uniform Annual Benefit (thousands)	Computed Rate of Return
A	$10	$2.98	15%
B	15	5.58	25
C	5	1.53	16
D	20	5.55	12
E	15	4.37	14
F	30	9.81	19
G	25	7.81	17
H	10	3.49	22
I	5	1.67	20
J	10	3.20	18

(a) Based on a MARR of 14%, which projects should be approved?

(b) Rank-order all the projects according to desirability.

(c) If only $85,000 is available, which projects should be approved?

15-22 At Miami Products, four project proposals (three with mutually exclusive alternatives) are being considered. All the alternatives have a 10-year useful life and no salvage value.

Project Proposal	Cost (thousands)	Uniform Annual Benefits (thousands)	Computed Rate of Return
Project 1			
Alt. A	$25	$4.61	13%
Alt. B	50	9.96	15
Alt. C	10	2.39	20
Project 2			
Alt. A	20	4.14	16
Alt. B	35	6.71	14
Project 3			
Alt. A	25	5.56	18
Alt. B	10	2.15	17
Project 4	10	1.70	11

(a) Use rate of return methods to determine which set of projects should be undertaken if the capital budget is limited to about $100,000.

(b) For a budget of about $100,000, what interest rate should be used in rationing capital by present worth methods? (Limit your answer to a value for which there is a compound interest table available in Appendix B).

(c) Using the interest rate determined in part (b), rank-order the eight different investment opportunities by means of the present worth method.

(d) For a budget of about $100,000 and the ranking in part (c), which of the investment opportunities should be selected?

15-23 Al Dale is planning his Christmas shopping for seven people. To quantify how much his various relatives would enjoy receiving items from a list of prospective gifts, Al has assigned appropriateness units (called "ohs") for each gift for each person (Table P15-23). A rating of 5 ohs represents a gift that the recipient would really like. A rating of 4 ohs indicates the recipient would like it four-fifths as much; 3 ohs, three-fifths as much, and so forth. A zero rating indicates an inappropriate gift that cannot be given to that person. Everyone must get a gift.

The objective is to maximize total ohs that can be obtained with the selected budget.

(a) How much will it cost to buy the seven gifts the people would like best, if there is ample money for Christmas shopping?

(b) If the Christmas shopping budget is set at $112, which gifts should be purchased, and what is their total appropriateness rating in ohs?

(c) If the Christmas shopping budget must be cut to $90, which gifts should be purchased, and what is their total appropriateness rating in ohs? (*Answer:* (a), $168)

15-24 A financier has a staff of three people whose job it is to examine possible business ventures for him. Periodically they present their findings concerning business opportunities. On a particular occasion, they presented the following investment opportunities:

Project A: This is a project for the use of commercial land the financier already owns. There are three mutually exclusive alternatives.

- *A1.* Sell the land for $500,000.
- *A2.* Lease the property for a car-washing business. An annual income, after all costs

TABLE P15-23 **Data**

| Prospective Gift | "Oh" Rating of Gift If Given to Various Family Members | | | | | | |
	Father	Mother	Sister	Brother	Aunt	Uncle	Cousin
1. $20 box of candy	4	4	2	1	5	2	3
2. $12 box of cigars	3	0	0	1	0	1	2
3. $16 necktie	2	0	0	3	0	3	2
4. $20 shirt or blouse	5	3	4	4	4	1	4
5. $24 sweater	3	4	5	4	3	4	2
6. $30 camera	1	5	2	5	1	2	0
7. $ 6 calendar	0	0	1	0	1	0	1
8. $16 magazine subscription	4	3	4	4	3	1	3
9. $18 book	3	4	2	3	4	0	3
10. $16 game	2	2	3	2	2	1	2

(property taxes, etc.) of $98,700 would be received at the end of each year for 20 years. At the end of the 20 years, it is believed that the property could be sold for $750,000.

A3. Construct an office building on the land. The building will cost $4.5 million to construct and will not produce any net income for the first 2 years. The probabilities of various levels of rental income, after all expenses, for the subsequent 18 years are as follows:

Annual Rental Income	Probability
$1,000,000	0.1
1,100,000	0.3
1,200,000	0.4
1,900,000	0.2

The property (building and land) probably can be sold for $3 million at the end of 20 years.

Project B: An insurance company is seeking to borrow money for 90 days at $13\,^3/4\%$ per annum, compounded continuously.

Project C: A financier owns a manufacturing company. The firm desires additional working capital to allow it to increase its inventories of raw materials and finished products. An investment of $2 million will allow the company to obtain sales that in the past the company had to forgo. The additional capital will increase company profits by $500,000 a year. The financier can recover this additional investment by ordering the company to reduce its inventories and to return the $2 million. For planning purposes, assume the additional investment will be returned at the end of 10 years.

Project D: The owners of *Sunrise* magazine are seeking a loan of $500,000 for 10 years at a 16% interest rate.

Project E: The Galveston Bank has indicated a willingness to accept a deposit of any sum of money over $100,000, for any desired duration, at a 14.06% interest rate, compounded monthly. It seems likely that this interest rate will be available from Galveston, or some other bank, for the next several years.

Project F: A car rental firm is seeking a loan of $2 million to expand its fleet. The firm offers to repay the loan by paying $1 million at the end of Year 1 and $1,604,800 at the end of Year 2.

* If there is $4 million available for investment now (or $4.5 million if the Project *A* land is sold), which projects should be selected? What is the MARR in this situation?

⦁ If there is $9 million available for investment now (or $9.5 million if the Project A land is sold), which projects should be selected?

15-25 The Raleigh Soap Company has been offered a 5-year contract to manufacture and package a leading brand of soap for Taker Bros. It is understood that the contract will not be extended past the 5 years because Taker Bros. plans to build its own plant nearby. The contract calls for 10,000 metric tons (one metric ton equals 1000 kg) of soap a year. Raleigh normally produces 12,000 metric tons of soap a year, so production for the 5-year period would be increased to 22,000 metric tons. Raleigh must decide what changes, if any, to make to accommodate this increased production. Five projects are under consideration.

Project 1: Increase liquid storage capacity. Raleigh has been forced to buy caustic soda in tank truck quantities owing to inadequate storage capacity. If another liquid caustic soda tank is installed to hold 1000 cubic meters, the caustic soda may be purchased in railroad tank car quantities at a more favorable price. The result would be a saving of 0.1¢ per kilogram of soap. The tank, which would cost $83,400, has no net salvage value.

Project 2: Acquire another sulfonation unit. The present capacity of the plant is limited by the sulfonation unit. The additional 12,000 metric tons of soap cannot be produced without an additional sulfonation unit. Another unit can be installed for $320,000.

Project 3: Expand the packaging department. With the new contract, the packaging department must either work two 8-hour shifts or have another packaging line installed. If the two-shift operation is used, a 20% wage premium must be paid for the second shift. This premium would amount to $35,000 a year. The second packaging line could be installed for $150,000. It would have a $42,000 salvage value at the end of 5 years.

Project 4: Build a new warehouse. The existing warehouse will be inadequate for the greater production. It is estimated that 400 square meters of additional warehouse is needed. A new warehouse can be built on a lot beside the existing warehouse for $225,000, including the land. The annual taxes, insurance, and other ownership costs would be $5000 a year. It is believed the warehouse could be sold at the end of 5 years for $200,000.

Project 5: Lease a warehouse. An alternative to building an additional warehouse would be to lease warehouse space. A suitable warehouse one mile away could be leased for $15,000 per year. The $15,000 includes taxes, insurance, and so forth. The annual cost of moving materials to this more remote warehouse would be $34,000 a year.

The contract offered by Taker Bros. is a favorable one, which Raleigh Soap plans to accept. Raleigh management has set a 15% before-tax minimum attractive rate of return as the criterion for any of the projects. Which projects should be undertaken?

15-26 Mike Moore's microbrewery is considering production of a new ale called Mike's Honey Harvest Brew. To produce this new offering he is considering two independent projects. Each of these projects has two mutually exclusive alternatives and each alternative has a useful life of 10 years and no salvage value. Mike's MARR is 8%. Information regarding the projects and alternatives are given in the following table:

Project/Alternative	Cost	Annual Benefit
Project 1. Purchase new fermenting tanks		
Alt. *A*: 5000-gallon tank	$ 5000	$1192
Alt. *B*: 15,000-gallon tank	10,000	1992
Project 2. Purchase bottle filler and capper		
Alt. *A*: 2500-bottle/hour machine	15,000	3337
Alt. *B*: 5000-bottle/hour machine	25,000	4425

Use incremental rate of return analysis to complete the following worksheet.

Proj./Alt.	Cost, P	Annual Benefit, A	A/P, i, 10	IRR
1A	$ 5,000	$1192	0.2385	20%
1B–1A	5,000	800	0.1601	
2A	15,000	3337		
2B–2A	10,000			

Use this information to determine:

(a) which projects should be funded if only $15,000 is available.

(b) the cutoff rate of return if only $15,000 is available.

(c) which projects should be funded if $25,000 is available.

CHAPTER 17

ACCOUNTING AND ENGINEERING ECONOMY

The Two Faces of ABB

In the late 1990s, ABB Ltd was flying high. The European conglomerate was an engineering giant with a global network of operations and forward-looking management. Unlike many of its competitors, ABB was also committed to modernizing its accounting system. ABB had followed the traditional practice of assigning overhead costs to its divisions on a roughly equal basis. But this practice tended to obscure the fact that some activities incurred far more costs than others.

So the company spent substantial time and resources switching over to an activity-based costing (ABC) system, which assigns costs to the activities that actually produce them. The results were quite positive, allowing ABB to zero in on areas where it could cut costs most effectively.

But in other respects, ABB's accounting practices were less effective. One of its most serious problems arose at Combustion Engineering, an American subsidiary that was exposed to numerous asbestos liability claims. For years, ABB had downplayed this potential liability, despite warnings from outside analysts. Finally, in late 2002, ABB admitted that its asbestos liability exceeded the subsidiary's total asset value.

But there was more bad news still. The company also issued a very poor third-quarter earnings report, despite having earlier assured investors that ABB was on target to improve its earnings and decrease its debt. When incredulous investors asked how this could have happened, ABB management blamed "poor internal reporting."

By this point, ABB's stock price had nose-dived, and credit rating agencies viewed the company's bonds as little better than junk. In 2003, Combustion Engineering went through bankruptcy and reached a settlement for the asbestos claims.

ABB has recovered, and by 2007 its stock price had climbed sevenfold over its low.

1. ABB's adoption of activity-based costing received widespread publicity and boosted the company's reputation for innovative management. How might this have affected investors' assumptions about the company's other accounting practices?
2. Outside analysts estimated that ABB lost over $690 million in 2001. Yet many investors were still stunned by its poor showing in late 2002. What does this say about the relationship between financial accounting and investor confidence?
3. ABB was not alone in its financial misery, of course. How did ABB's accounting problems compare with those of well-known American companies such as Enron and WorldCom?
4. In each of these well-publicized situations, were there ethical lapses? What were the lapses, and who was responsible?

After Completing This Chapter...

The student should be able to:

- Describe the links between engineering economy and accounting.
- Describe the objectives of general accounting, explain what financial transactions are, and show how they are important.
- Use a firm's balance sheet and associated financial ratios to evaluate the firm's health.
- Use a firm's income statement and associated financial ratios to evaluate the firm's performance.
- Use traditional absorption costing to calculate product costs.
- Understand the greater accuracy in product costs available with activity-based costing (ABC).

E ngineering economy focuses on the financial aspects of projects, while accounting focuses on the financial aspects of firms. Thus the application of engineering economy is much easier if one has some understanding of accounting principles. In fact, one important accounting topic, depreciation, was the subject of an earlier chapter.

THE ROLE OF ACCOUNTING

Accounting data are used to value capital equipment, to decide whether to make or buy a part, to determine costs and set prices, to set indirect cost rates, and to make product mix decisions. Accounting is used in private-sector firms and public sector agencies, but for simplicity this chapter uses "the firm" to designate both. Accountants track the costs of projects and products, which are the basis for estimating future costs and revenues.

The engineering economy, accounting, and managerial functions are interdependent. As shown in Figure 17-1, data and communications flow between them. Whether carried out by a single person in a small firm or by distinct divisions in a large firm, all are needed.

- Engineering economy analyzes the economic impact of design alternatives and projects over their life cycles.
- Accounting determines the dollar impact of past decisions, reports on the economic viability of a unit or firm, and evaluates potential funding sources.
- Management allocates available investment funds to projects, evaluates unit and firm performance, allocates resources, and selects and directs personnel.

Accounting for Business Transactions

A business transaction involves two parties and the exchange of dollars (or the promise of dollars) for a product or service. Each day, millions of transactions occur between firms and their customers, suppliers, vendors, and employees. Transactions are the lifeblood of the business world and are most often stated in monetary terms. The accounting function records, analyzes, and reports these exchanges.

Transactions can be as simple as payment for a water bill, or as complex as the international transfer of millions of dollars of buildings, land, equipment, inventory, and other

Accounting	Management	Engineering Economy
About past	About past and future	About future
Analyzing	Capital budgeting	Feasibility of alternatives
Summarizing	Decision making	Collect & analyze data
Reporting	Setting goals	Estimate
Financial indicators	Assessing impacts	Evaluate projects
Economic trends	Analyzing risk	Recommend
Cost acquisitions	Planning	Audit
	Controlling	Identify needs
	Record keeping	Trade-offs & constraints

Data and Communication ⟶ Data and Communication

Budgeting ⟵ ——— Data and Communication ——— ⟶ Estimating

FIGURE 17-1 The accounting, managerial, and engineering economy functions.

assets. Also, with transactions, one business event may lead to another—all of which need to be accounted for. Consider, for example, the process of selling a robot or bulldozer. This simple act involves several related transactions: (1) releasing equipment from inventory, (2) shipping equipment to the purchaser, (3) invoicing the purchaser, and finally (4) collecting from the purchaser.

Transaction accounting involves more than just reporting: it includes finding, synthesizing, summarizing, and analyzing data. For the engineering economist, historical data housed in the accounting function are the foundation for estimates of future costs and revenues.

Most accounting is done in nominal or *stable* dollars. Higher market values and costs due to inflation are less objective than cost data, and with a going concern, accountants have decided that objectivity should be maintained. Similarly, most assets are valued at their acquisition cost adjusted for depreciation and improvements. To be conservative, when market value is lower than this adjusted cost, the lower value is used. This restrains the interests of management in maximizing a firm's apparent value. If a firm must be liquidated, then current market value must be estimated.

The accounting function provides data for *general accounting* and *cost accounting.* This chapter's presentation begins with the balance sheet and income statement, which are the two key summaries of financial transactions for general accounting. This discussion includes some of the basic financial ratios used for short- and long-term evaluations. The chapter concludes with a key topic in cost accounting—allocating indirect expenses.

THE BALANCE SHEET

The primary accounting statements are the **balance sheet** and the **income statement.** The **balance sheet** describes the firm's financial condition at a specific time, while the income statement describes the firm's performance over a period of time—usually a year.

The balance sheet lists the firm's assets, liabilities, and equity on a specified date. This is a picture of the organization's financial health or a snapshot in time. Usually, balance sheets are taken at the end of the quarter and fiscal year. The balance sheet is based on the **fundamental accounting equation:**

$$\text{Assets} = \text{Liabilities} + \text{Equity} \qquad (17\text{-}1)$$

Figure 17-2 illustrates the basic format of the balance sheet. Notice in the balance sheet, as in Equation 17-1, that **assets** are listed on the left-hand side and **liabilities** and **equity** are on the right-hand side. The fact that the firm's resources are *balanced* by the sources of funds is the basis for the name of the balance sheet.

Assets

In Equation 17-1 and Figure 17-2, **assets** are owned by the firm and have monetary value. **Liabilities** are the dollar claims against the firm. **Equity** represents funding from the firm and its owners (the shareholders). In Equation 17-1, assets are always balanced by the sum of the liabilities and the equity. The value for retained earnings is set so that equity equals assets minus liabilities.

On a balance sheet, assets are listed in order of decreasing liquidity, that is, according to how quickly each one can be converted to cash. Thus, *current assets* are listed first, and within that category in order of decreasing liquidity are listed cash, receivables, securities,

Balance Sheet for Engineered Industries, December 31, 2007 (all amounts in $1000s)

Assets		Liabilities	
Current assets		Current liabilities	
Cash	$1940	Accounts payable	$1150
Accounts receivable	950	Notes payable	80
Securities	4100		
Inventories	1860	Accrued expense	950
(*minus*) Bad debt provision	−80	Total current liabilities	2180
Total current assets	8770		
		Long-term liabilities	1200
		Total liabilities	**3380**
Fixed assets			
Land	335		
Plant and equipment	6500		
(*minus*) Accumulated depr.	−2350		
Total fixed assets	4485	**Equity**	
		Preferred stock	110
Other assets		Common stock	650
Prepays/deferred charges	140	Capital surplus	930
Intangibles	420	Retained earnings	8745
Total other assets	560	Total equity	10,435
Total assets	**13,815**	**Total liabilities and equity**	**13,815**

FIGURE 17-2 Sample balance sheet.

and inventories. *Fixed assets,* or *property, plant, and equipment,* are used to produce and deliver goods and/or services, and they are not intended for sale. Items such as prepayments and intangibles such as patents are listed last.

The term "receivables" comes from the manner of handling billing and payment for most business sales. Rather than requesting immediate payment for every transaction by check or credit card, most businesses record each transaction and then once a month bill for all transactions. The total that has been billed less payments already received is called accounts receivable, or receivables.

Liabilities

On the balance sheet, liabilities are divided into two major classifications—short term and long term. The *short-term* or *current liabilities* are expenses, notes, and other payable accounts that are due within one year from the balance sheet date. *Long-term liabilities* include mortgages, bonds, and loans with later due dates. For Engineered Industries in Figure 17-2, total current and long-term liabilities are $2,180,000 and $1,200,000, respectively. Often in performing engineering economic analyses, the **working capital** for a project must be estimated. The total amount of working capital available may be calculated with Equation 17-2 as the difference between current assets and current liabilities.

$$\text{Working capital} = \text{Current assets} - \text{Current liabilities} \tag{17-2}$$

For Engineered Industries, there would be $8,770,000 - $2,180,000 = $6,590,000 available in working capital.

Equity

Equity is also called *owner's equity* or *net worth*. It includes the par value of the owners' stockholdings and the capital surplus, which are the excess dollars brought in over par value when the stock was issued. The capital surplus can also be called *additional paid-in capital*, or APIC. Retained earnings are dollars a firm chooses to retain rather than paying out as dividends to stockholders.

Retained earnings within the equity component is the dollar quantity that always brings the balance sheet, and thus the fundamental accounting equation, into balance. For Engineered Industries, *total equity* value is listed at $10,435,000. From Equation 17-1 and the assets, liabilities, and equity values in Figure 17-2, we can write the balance as follows:

$$Assets = Liabilities + Equity$$

$$Assets \text{ (current, fixed, other)} = Liabilities \text{ (current and long-term)} + Equity$$

$$8,770,000 + 4,485,000 + 560,000 = 2,180,000 + 1,200,000 + 10,435,000$$

$$\$13,815,000 = \$13,815,000$$

An example of owner's equity is ownership of a home. Most homes are purchased by means of a mortgage loan that is paid off at a certain interest rate over 15 to 30 years. At any point in time, the difference between what is owed to the bank (the remaining balance on the mortgage) and what the house is worth (its appraised market value) is the *owner's equity*. In this case, the loan balance is the *liability,* and the home's value is the *asset*—with *equity* being the difference. Over time, as the house loan is paid off, the owner's equity increases.

The balance sheet is a very useful tool that shows one view of the firm's financial condition at a particular point in time.

Financial Ratios Derived from Balance Sheet Data

One common way to evaluate the firm's health is through ratios of quantities on the balance sheet. Firms in a particular industry will typically have similar values, and exceptions will often indicate firms with better or worse performance. Two common ratios used to analyze the firm's current position are the current ratio and the acid-test ratio.

A firm's **current ratio** is the ratio of current assets to current liabilities, as in Equation 17-3.

$$Current \ Ratio = Current \ assets/Current \ liabilities \qquad (17\text{-}3)$$

This ratio provides insight into the firm's solvency over the short term by indicating its ability to cover current liabilities. Historically, firms aim to be at or above a ratio of 2.0; however, this depends heavily on the industry as well as the individual firm's management practices and philosophies. The current ratio for Engineered Industries in Figure 17-2 is above 2 $(8,770,000/2,180,000 = 4.02)$.

Both working capital and the current ratio indicate the firm's ability to meet currently maturing obligations. However, neither describes the type of assets owned. The **acid-test ratio** or **quick ratio** becomes important when one wishes to consider the firm's ability to pay debt "instantly." The acid-test ratio is computed by dividing a firm's **quick assets** (cash, receivables, and market securities) by total current liabilities, as in Equation 17-4.

$$\text{Acid-test ratio} = \text{Quick assets}/\text{Total current liabilities} \tag{17-4}$$

Current inventories are excluded from quick assets because of the time required to sell these inventories, collect the receivables, and subsequently have the cash on hand to reduce debt. For Engineered Industries in Figure 17-2, the calculated acid-test ratio is well above 1 [(1,940,000+ 950,000 + 4,100,000)/2,180,000 = 3.21].

Working capital, current ratio, and acid-test ratio are all indications of the firm's financial health (status). A thorough financial evaluation would consider all three, including comparisons with values from previous periods and with broad-based industry standards. When trends extend over multiple periods, the trends may be more important than the current values.

THE INCOME STATEMENT

The **income statement** or **profit and loss statement** summarizes the firm's revenues and expenses over a month, quarter, or year. Rather than being a snapshot like the balance sheet, the income statement encompasses a *period* of business activity. The income statement is used to evaluate revenue and expenses that occur in the interval *between* consecutive balance sheet statements. The income statement reports the firm's *net income (profit)* or *loss* by subtracting expenses from revenues. If revenues minus expenses is positive in Equation 17-5, there has been a profit, if negative a loss has occurred.

$$\text{Revenues} - \text{Expenses} = \text{Net profit (Loss)} \tag{17-5}$$

Revenue, as in Equation 17-5, serves to increase ownership in a firm, while expenses serve to decrease ownership. Figure 17-3 is an example income statement.

To aid in analyzing performance, the income statement in Figure 17-3 separates operating and nonoperating activities and shows revenues and expenses for each. Operating revenues are made up of sales revenues (minus returns and allowances), while nonoperating revenues come from rents and interest receipts.

Operating expenses produce the products and services that generate the firm's revenue stream of cash flows. Typical operating expenses include cost of goods sold, selling and promotion costs, depreciation, general and administrative costs, and lease payments. *Cost of goods sold (COGS)* includes the labor, materials, and indirect costs of production.

Engineers design production systems, and they are involved in labor loading, specifying materials, and make/buy decisions. All these items affect a firm's cost of goods sold. Good engineering design focuses not only on technical functionality but also on cost-effectiveness as the design *integrates* the entire production system. Also of interest to the engineering economist is *depreciation* (see Chapter 11)—which is the systematic "writing off" of a capital expense over a period of years. This noncash expense is important because it represents a decrease in value of the firm's capital assets.

Income Statement for Engineered Industries for End of Year 2008 (all amounts in $1000)

Operating revenues and expenses	
Operating revenues	
Sales	$ 18,900
(*minus*) Returns and allowances	−870
Total operating revenues	**18,030**
Operating expenses	
Cost of goods and services sold	
Labor	6140
Materials	4640
Indirect cost	2280
Selling and promotion	930
Depreciation	450
General and administrative	2160
Lease payments	510
Total operating expense	**17,110**
Total operating income	**920**
Nonoperating revenues and expenses	
Rents	20
Interest receipts	300
Interest payments	−120
Total nonoperating income	**200**
Net income before taxes	**1120**
Income taxes	−390
Net profit (loss) for 2008	**730**

FIGURE 17-3 Sample income statement.

The operating revenues and expenses are shown first, so that the firm's operating income from its products and services can be calculated. Also shown on the income statement are nonoperating expenses such as interest payments on debt in the form of loans or bonds.

From the data in Figure 17-3, Engineered Industries has total expenses (operating = $17,110,000 and nonoperating = $120,000) of $17,230,000. Total revenues are $18,350,000 (= $18,030,000 + $20,000 + $300,000). The net after-tax profit for year 2008 shown in Figure 17-3 as $730,000, but it can also be calculated using Equation 17-5 as:

$$\text{Net profits (Loss)} = \text{Revenues} - \text{Expenses [before taxes]}$$

$$\$1,120,000 = 18,350,000 - 17,230,000 \text{ [before taxes] and with}$$

$$\$390,000 \text{ taxes paid}$$

thus

$$\$730,000 = 1,120,000 - 390,000 \text{ [after taxes]}$$

Financial Ratios Derived from Income Statement Data

Interest coverage, as given in Equation 17-6, is calculated as the ratio of total income to interest payments—where *total income* is total revenues minus all expenses except interest payments.

$$\text{Interest coverage} = \text{Total income/Interest payments} \qquad (17\text{-}6)$$

The interest coverage ratio (which for industrial firms should be at least 3.0) indicates how much revenue must drop to affect the firm's ability to finance its debt. With an interest coverage ratio of 3.0, a firm's revenue would have to decrease by two-thirds (unlikely) before it became impossible to pay the interest on the debt. The larger the interest coverage ratio the better. Engineered Industries in Figure 17-3 has an interest coverage ratio of

$$(18,350,000 - 17,110,000)/120,000 = 10.3$$

Another important financial ratio based on the income statement is the **net profit ratio.** This ratio (Equation 17-7) equals net profits divided by net sales revenue. Net sales revenue equals sales minus returns and allowances.

$$\text{Net profit ratio} = \text{Net profit/Net sales revenue} \qquad (17\text{-}7)$$

This ratio provides insight into the cost efficiency of operations as well as a firm's ability to convert sales into profits. For Engineered Industries in Figure 17-3, the net profit ratio is $730,000/18,030,000 = 0.040 = 4.0\%$. Like other financial measures, the net profit ratio is best evaluated by comparisons with other time periods and industry benchmarks, and trends may be more significant than individual values.

Linking the Balance Sheet, Income Statement, and Capital Transactions

The balance sheet and the income statement are separate but linked documents. Understanding how the two are linked together helps clarify each. Accounting describes such links as the *articulation* between these reports.

The balance sheet shows a firm's assets, liabilities, and equity at a particular point in time, whereas the income statement summarizes revenues and expenses over a time interval. These tabulations can be visualized as a snapshot at the period's beginning (a balance sheet), a video summary over the period (the income statement), and a snapshot at the period's end (another balance sheet). The income statement and changes in the balance sheets summarize the business transactions that have occurred during that period.

There are many links between these statements and the cash flows that make up business transactions, but for engineering economic analysis the following are the most important.

1. Overall profit or loss (income statement) and the starting and ending equity (balance sheets).
2. Acquisition of capital assets.
3. Depreciation of capital assets.

The overall profit or loss during the year (shown on the income statement) is reflected in the change in retained earnings between the balance sheets at the beginning and end of the year. To find the change in retained earnings (RE), one must also subtract any dividends distributed to the owners and add the value of any new capital stock sold:

$$RE_{beg} + \text{Net income/Loss} + \text{New stock} - \text{Dividends} = RE_{end}$$

When capital equipment is purchased, the balance sheet changes, but the income statement does not. If cash is paid, then the cash asset account decrease equals the increase in the capital equipment account—there is no change in total assets. If a loan is used, then the capital equipment account increases, and so does the liability item for loans. In both cases the equity accounts and the income statement are unchanged.

The depreciation of capital equipment is shown as a line on the income statement. The depreciation for that year equals the change in accumulated depreciation between the beginning and the end of the year—after subtraction of the accumulated depreciation for any asset that is sold or disposed of during that year.

Example 17-1 applies these relationships to the data in Figures 17-1 and 17-2.

EXAMPLE 17-1

For simplicity, assume that Engineered Industries will not pay dividends in 2008 and did not sell any capital equipment. It did purchase $400,000 in capital equipment. What can be said about the values on the balance sheet at the end of 2008, using the linkages just described?

SOLUTION

First, the net profit of $730,000 will be added to the retained earnings from the end of 2007 to find the new retained earnings at the end of 2008:

$$RE_{12/31/2008} = \$730,000 + \$8,745,000 = \$9,475,000$$

Second, the fixed assets shown at the end of 2008 would increase from $6,500,000 to $6,900,000.

Third, the accumulated depreciation would increase by the $450,000 in depreciation shown in the 2008 income statement from the $2,350,000 posted in 2007. The new accumulated depreciation on the 2008 balance sheet would be $2,800,000. Combined with the change in the amount of capital equipment, the new fixed asset total for 2008 would equal:

$$\$335,000 + \$6,900,000 - \$2,800,000 = \$4,435,000$$

TRADITIONAL COST ACCOUNTING

A firm's *cost-accounting system* collects, analyzes, and reports operational performance data (costs, utilization rates, etc.). Cost-accounting data are used to develop product costs, to determine the mix of labor, materials, and other costs in a production setting, and to evaluate outsourcing and subcontracting possibilities.

Direct and Indirect Costs

Costs incurred to produce a product or service are traditionally classified as either *direct* or *indirect (overhead)*. Direct costs come from activities directly associated with the final product or service produced. Examples include material costs and labor costs for engineering design, component assembly, painting, and drilling.

Some organizational activities are difficult to link to specific projects, products, or services. For example, the receiving and shipping areas of a manufacturing plant are used by all incoming materials and all outgoing products. Materials and products differ in their weight, size, fragility, value, number of units, packaging, and so on, and the receiving and shipping costs depend on all these factors. Also, different materials arrive together and different products are shipped together, so these costs are intermingled and often cannot be tied directly to each product or material.

Other costs, such as the organization's management, sales, and administrative expenses, are difficult to link directly to individual products or services. These indirect or overhead expenses also include machine depreciation, engineering and technical support, and customer warranties.

Indirect Cost Allocation

To allocate indirect costs to different departments, products, and services, accountants use quantities such as direct-labor hours, direct-labor costs, material costs, and total direct cost. One of these is chosen to be the burden vehicle. The total of all indirect or overhead costs is divided by the total for the burden vehicle. For example, if direct-labor hours is the burden vehicle, then overhead will be allocated based on overhead dollar per direct-labor hour. Then each product, project, or department will *absorb* (or be allocated) overhead costs, based on the number of direct-labor hours each has.

This is the basis for calling traditional costing systems **absorption costing.** For decision making, the problem is that the absorbed costs represent average, not incremental, performance.

Four common ways of allocating overhead are direct-labor hours, direct-labor cost, direct-materials cost, and total direct cost. The first two differ significantly only if the cost per hour of labor differs for different products. Example 17-2 uses direct-labor and direct-materials cost to illustrate the different choices of burden vehicle.

EXAMPLE 17-2

Industrial Robots does not manufacture its own motors or computer chips. Its premium product differs from its standard product in having heavier-duty motors and more computer chips for greater flexibility.

As a result, Industrial Robots manufactures a higher fraction of the standard product's value itself, and it purchases a higher fraction of the premium product's value. Use the following data to allocate $850,000 in overhead on the basis of labor cost and materials cost.

	Standard	Premium
Number of units per year	750	400
Labor cost (each)	$400	$500
Materials cost (each)	$550	$900

SOLUTION

First, the labor and material costs for the standard product, the premium product, and in total are calculated.

	Standard	Premium	Total
Number of units per year	750	400	
Labor cost (each)	$ 400	$ 500	
Materials cost (each)	550	900	
Labor cost	300,000	200,000	$500,000
Materials cost	412,500	360,000	772,500

Then the allocated cost per labor dollar, $1.70, is found by dividing the $850,000 in overhead by the $500,000 in total labor cost. The allocated cost per material dollar, $1.100324, is found by dividing the $850,000 in overhead by the $772,500 in materials cost. Now, the $850,000 in allocated overhead is split between the two products using labor costs and material costs.

	Standard	Premium	Total
Labor cost	$300,000	$200,000	$500,000
Overhead/labor	1.70	1.70	
Allocation by labor	510,000	340,000	850,000
Material cost	412,500	360,000	0
Overhead/material	1.100324	1.100324	
Allocation by material	453,884	396,117	850,000

If labor cost is the burden vehicle, then 60% of the $850,000 in overhead is allocated to the standard product. If material cost is the burden vehicle, then 53.4% is allocated to the standard product. In both cases, the $850,000 has been split between the two products. Using total direct costs would produce another overhead allocation between these two values. However, for decision making about product mix and product prices, incremental overhead costs must be analyzed. All the allocation or burden vehicles are based on an average cost of overhead per unit of burden vehicle.

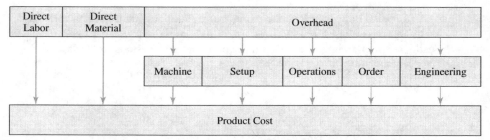

FIGURE 17-4 Activity-based costing versus traditional overhead allocation. (Based on an example by Kim LaScola Needy.)

Problems with Traditional Cost Accounting

Allocation of indirect costs can distort product costs and the decisions based on those costs. To be accurate, the analyst must determine which indirect or overhead expenses will be changed because of an engineering project. In other words, what are the incremental cash flows? For example, vacation and sick leave accrual may be part of overhead, but will they change if the labor content is changed? The changes in costs incurred must be estimated. Loadings, or allocations, of overhead expenses cannot be used.

This issue has become very important because in some firms, automation has reduced direct-labor content to less than 5% of the product's cost. Yet in some of these firms, the basis for allocating overhead is still direct-labor hours or cost.

Other firms are shifting to activity-based costing (ABC) where each activity is linked to specific cost drivers, and the number of dollars allocated as overhead is minimized (see Liggett, Trevino, and Lavelle, 1992). Figure 17-4 illustrates the difference between activity-based costing and traditional overhead allocations (see Tippet and Hoekstra, 1993).

Other Problems to Watch For

Project managers have often accused centralized accounting systems of being too slow or being "untimely." Because engineering economy is not concerned with the problem of daily project control, this is a less critical issue. However, if an organization establishes multiple files and systems so that project managers (and others) have the timely data they need, then the level of accuracy in one or all systems may be low. As a result, analysts making cost estimates will have to consider other internal data sources.

There are several cases in which data on equipment or inventory values may be questionable. When inventory is valued on a "last in, first out" basis, the remaining inventory may be valued too low. Similarly, land valued at its acquisition cost is likely to be significantly undervalued. Finally, capital equipment may be valued at either a low or a high value, depending on allowable depreciation techniques and company policy.

PROBLEMS

Accounting

17-1   Why is it important for engineers and managers to understand accounting principles? Name a few ways that they can do so.

17-2   Explain the accounting function within a firm. What does this function do, and why is it important? What types of data does it provide?

Balance Sheet

17-3   Develop short definitions for the following terms: balance sheet, income statement, and fundamental accounting equation.

17-4   Explain the difference between short-term and long-term liabilities.

17-5   Calculate the equity of the Gravel Construction Company if it has $1 million worth of assets. Gravel has $127,000 in current liabilities and $210,000 in long-term liabilities.

17-6   Matbach Industries has $870,000 in current assets and $430,000 in fixed assets less $180,000 in accumulated depreciation. The firm's current liabilities total $330,000, and the long-term liabilities $115,000.

   (a) What is the firm's equity?
   (b) If the firm's stock and capital surplus total $305,000, what is the value for retained earnings?

17-7   CalcTech has $930,000 in current assets and $320,000 in fixed assets less $108,000 in accumulated depreciation. The firm's current liabilities total $350,000, and the long-term liabilities $185,000.

   (a) What is the firm's equity?
   (b) If the firm's stock and capital surplus total $402,000, what is the value for retained earnings?

17-8   Mama L's Baby Monitor Company has current assets of $5 million and current liabilities of $2 million. Give the company's working capital and current ratio.   (*Answers:* $3 million; 2.50)

17-9   For Gee-Whiz Devices calculate the following: working capital, current ratio, and acid-test ratio.

Gee-Whiz Devices Balance Sheet Data

Cash	$100,000
Market securities	45,000
Net accounts and notes receivable	150,000
Retailers' inventories	200,000
Prepaid expenses	8,000
Accounts and notes payable (short term)	315,000
Accrued expenses	90,000

(*Answers:* $90,000; 1.22; 0.73)

17-10   From the following data, taken from the balance sheet of Petey's Widget Factory, determine the working capital, current ratio, and acid-test ratio.

Cash	$ 90,000
Net accounts and notes receivable	175,000
Retailers' inventories	210,000
Prepaid expenses	6,000
Accounts and notes payable (short term)	322,000
Accrued expenses	87,000

17-11   (a) For Evergreen Environmental Engineering (EEE) determine the working capital, current ratio, and acid-test ratio. Evaluate the company's economic situation with respect to its ability to pay off debt.

EEE Balance Sheet Data ($1000s)

Cash	$110,000
Securities	40,000
Accounts receivable	160,000
Inventories	250,000
Prepaid expenses	3,000
Accounts payable	351,000
Accrued expenses	89,000

   (b) The entries to complete EEE's balance sheet include:

More EEE Balance Sheet Data ($1000s)

Long-term liabilities	$ 220,000
Land	25,000
Plant and equipment	510,000
Accumulated depreciation	210,000
Stock	81,000
Capital surplus	15,000
Retained earnings	Value not given

Construct EEE's balance sheet.

(c) What are EEE's values for total assets, total liabilities, and retained earnings?

17-12 Turbo Start has current assets totaling $1.5 million (this includes $500,000 in current inventory) and current liabilities totaling $50,000. Find the current ratio and acid-test ratio. Are the ratios at desirable levels? Explain.

17-13 (a) For J&W Graphics Supply, compute the current ratio. Is this a financially healthy company? Explain.

J&W Graphics Supply Balance Sheet Data ($1000s)

Assets	
Cash	$1740
Accounts receivable	2500
Inventories	900
Bad debt provision	−75
Liabilities	
Accounts payable	1050
Notes payable	500
Accrued expenses	125

(b) The entries of complete J&W's balance sheet include:

More J&W Balance Sheet Data ($1000s)

Long-term liabilities	$950
Land	475
Plant and equipment	3100
Accumulated depreciation	1060
Stock	680
Capital surplus	45
Retained earnings	Value not given

Construct J&W's balance sheet.

(c) What J&W's values for total assets, total liabilities, and total earnings?

17-14 For Sutton Manufacturing, determine the current ratio and the acid-test ratio. Are these values acceptable? Why or why not?

Sutton Manufacturing Balance Sheet Data ($1000s)

Assets		Liabilities	
Current assets		Current liabilities	
Cash	$870	Notes payable	$500
Accounts receivable	450	Accounts payable	600
Inventory	1200	Accruals	200
Prepaid expenses	60	Taxes payable	30
		Current portion long-term debt	100
Total current assets	2670	Total current liabilities	1430
		Long-term debt	2000
		Officer debt (subordinated)	200
Net fixed assets			
Land	1200	Total liabilities	3630
Plant and equipment	3800	Equity	
(less accumulated depreciation)	−1000	Common stock	1670
		Capital surplus	400
Other assets		Retained earnings	1200
Notes receivable	200	Total equity	3270
Intangibles	120	Total liabilities and equity	6900
Total assets	6900		

17-15 If a firm has a current ratio less than 2.0 and an acid-test ratio less than 1.0, will the company eventually go bankrupt and out of business? Explain your answer.

17-16 What is the advantage of comparing financial statements across periods or against industry benchmarks over looking at statements associated with a single date or period?

Income Statement

17-17 List the two primary general accounting statements. What is each used for, and how do the two differ? Which is most important?

17-18 Scarmack's Paint Company has annual sales of $500,000 per year. If there is a profit of $1000 per day, 6 days per week operation, what is the total yearly business expense? All calculations are on a before-tax basis. (*Answer:* $188,000)

17-19 Find the net income of Turbo Start (Problem 17-12) given the following data from the balance sheet and income statement.

Turbo Start Data ($1000s)

Accounts payable	$ 1,000
Selling expense	5,000
Sales revenue	50,000
Owner's equity	4,500
Income taxes	2,000
Cost of goods sold	30,000
Accounts receivable	15,000

(*Answer:* $13,000,000)

17-20 Laila's Surveying Inc. had revenues of $100,000 in 2004. Expenses totaled $60,000. What was her net profit (or loss)?

17-21 The general ledger of the Fly-Buy-Nite (FBN) Engineering Company contained the following account balances. Construct an income statement. What is the net income before taxes and the net profit (or loss) after taxes? FBN has a tax rate of 27%.

	Amount ($1000s)
Administrative expenses	$ 2,750
Subcontracted services	18,000
Development expenses	900
Interest expense	200
Sales revenue	30,000
Selling expenses	4,500

17-22 For Magdalen Industries, compute the net income before taxes and net profit (or loss). Taxes for the year were $1 million.

(*a*) Calculate net profit for the year.

(*b*) Construct the income statement.

(*c*) Calculate the interest coverage and net profit ratio. Is the interest coverage acceptable? Explain why or why not.

Magdalen Industries Income Statement Data ($M)

Revenues	
Total operating revenue	$81
(including sales of $48 million)	
Total nonoperating revenue	5
Expenses	
Total operating expenses	70
Total nonoperating expenses	7
(interest payments)	

17-23 For Andrew's Electronic Instruments, calculate the interest coverage and net profit ratio. Is Andrew's business healthy?

Income Statement for Andrew's Electronics for End of Year 2008 ($1000s)

Revenues	
Operating revenues	
Sales	$395
(*minus*) Returns	−15
Total operating revenues	380
Nonoperating revenues	
Interest receipts	50
Stock revenues	25
Total nonoperating revenues	75
Total revenues, R	455
Expenses	
Operating expenses	
Cost of goods and services sold	
Labor	200
Materials	34
Indirect cost	68
Selling and promotion	20
Depreciation	30
General and administrative	10
Lease payments	10
Total operating expenses	372
Nonoperating expenses	
Interest payments	22
Total nonoperating expenses	22
Total expenses, E	394
Net income before taxes, R − E	61
Incomes taxes	30
Net profit (Loss) for the year 2008	31

Linking Balance Sheet and Income Statement

17-24 Sutton Manufacturing (balance sheet at the end of last year in Problem 17-14) had the following entries in this year's income statement.

Depreciation	$420,000
Profit	480,000

   In addition, we also know the firm purchased $800,000 of equipment with cash. The firm paid $200,000 in dividends this year.

   What are the entries in the balance sheet at the end of this year for:

(*a*) plant and equipment?

(*b*) accumulated depreciation?

(*c*) retained earnings?

17-25 Magdalen Industries (Problem 17-22) had the following entries in its balance sheet at the end of last year.

Plant and equipment	$15 million
(less accumulated depreciation)	8 million
Retained earnings	60 million

   In addition to the income statement data for this year in Problem 17-22, we also know that the firm purchased $3 million of equipment with cash and that depreciation expenses were $2 million of the $70 million in operating expenses listed in Problem 17-22. The firm paid no dividends this year.

   What are the entries in the balance sheet at the end of this year for:

(*a*) plant and equipment?

(*b*) accumulated depreciation?

(*c*) retained earnings?

Allocating Costs

17-26 Categorize each of the following costs as direct or indirect. Assume that a traditional costing system is in place.

Machine run costs	Cost to market the product
Machine depreciation	Cost of storage
Material handling costs	Insurance costs
Cost of materials	Cost of product sales force
Overtime expenses	Engineering drawings
Machine operator wages	Machine labor
Utility costs	Cost of tooling and fixtures
Support (administrative) staff salaries	

17-27 LeGaroutte Industries makes industrial pipe manufacturing equipment. Use direct-labor hours as the burden vehicle, and compute the total cost per unit for each model given in the table. Total manufacturing indirect costs are $15,892,000, and there are 100,000 units manufactured per year for Model *S*, 50,000 for Model *M*, and 82,250 for Model *G*.

Item	Model *S*	Model *M*	Model *G*
Direct-material costs	$3,800,000	$1,530,000	$2,105,000
Direct-labor costs	600,000	380,000	420,000
Direct-labor hours	64,000	20,000	32,000

(*Answers:* $132; $93; $84)

17-28 RLW-II Enterprises estimated that indirect manufacturing costs for the year would be $60 million and that 12,000 machine-hours would be used.

(*a*) Compute the predetermined indirect cost application rate using machine hours as the burden vehicle.

(*b*) Determine the total cost of production for a product with direct material costs of $1 million, direct-labor costs of $600,000, and 200 machine-hours.

(*Answers:* $5000; $2.6 million)

17-29 Par Golf Equipment Company produces two types of golf bag: the standard and deluxe models. The total indirect cost to be allocated to the two bags is $35,000. Determine the net revenue that Par Golf can expect from the sale of each bag.

(*a*) Use direct-labor cost to allocate indirect costs.

(*b*) Use direct-materials cost to allocate indirect costs.

Data Item	Standard	Deluxe
Direct-labor cost	$50,000	$65,000
Direct-material cost	35,000	47,500
Selling price	60	95
Units produced	1800	1400

Appendix A

Introduction to Spreadsheets

Computerized spreadsheets are available nearly everywhere, and they can be easily applied to economic analysis. In fact, spreadsheets were originally developed to analyze financial data, and they are often credited with initiating the explosive growth in demand for desktop computing.

A spreadsheet is a two-dimensional table, whose cells can contain numerical values, labels, or formulas. The software automatically updates the table when an entry is changed, and there are powerful tools for copying formulas, creating graphs, and formatting results.

THE ELEMENTS OF A SPREADSHEET

A spreadsheet is a two-dimensional table that labels the columns in alphabetical order A to Z, AA to AZ, BA to BZ, etc. The rows are numbered from 1 to 65,536 or higher. Thus a *cell* of the spreadsheet is specified by its column letter and row number. For example, A3 is the third row in column A and AA6 is the sixth row in the twenty-seventh column. Each cell can contain a label, a numerical value, or a formula.

A *label* is any cell where the contents should be treated as text. Arithmetic cannot be performed on labels. Labels are used for variable names, row and column headings, and explanatory notes. In Excel any cell that contains more than a simple number, such as 3.14159, is treated as a label, unless it begins with an =, which is the signal for a formula. Thus 2*3 and B1+B2 are labels. Meaningful labels can be wider than a normal column. One solution is to allow those cells to "wrap" text, which is one of the "alignment" options. The table heading row (row 8) in Example A-1 has turned this on by selecting row 8, right-clicking on the row, and selecting wrap text under the alignment tab.

A *numerical value* is any number. Acceptable formats for entry or display include percentages, currency, accounting, scientific, fractions, date, and time. In addition the number of decimal digits, the display of $ symbols, and commas for "thousands" separators can be adjusted. The format for cells can be changed by selecting a cell, a block of cells, a row, a column, or the entire spreadsheet. Then right-click on the selected area, and a menu that includes "format cells" will appear. Then number formats, alignment, borders, fonts, and patterns can be selected.

Formulas must begin with an $=$, such as $= 3*4\char`^2$ or $=B1+B2$. They can include many functions—financial, statistical, trigonometric, etc. (and others can be defined by the user). The formula for the "current" cell is displayed in the formula bar at the top of the spreadsheet. The value resulting from the formula is displayed in the cell in the spreadsheet.

Often the printed-out spreadsheet will be part of a report or a homework assignment and the formulas must be explained. Here is an easy way to place a copy of the formula in an adjacent or nearby cell. (1) Convert the cell with the formula to a label by inserting a space before the $=$ sign. (2) Copy that label to an adjacent cell by using cut and paste. Do not drag the cell to copy it, as any formula ending with a number (even an address like B4) will have the number automatically incremented. (3) Convert the original formula back into a formula by deleting the space.

DEFINING VARIABLES IN A DATA BLOCK

The cell A1, top left corner, is the HOME cell for a spreadsheet. Thus, the top left area is where the data block should be placed. This data block should have every variable in the spreadsheet with an adjacent label for each. This data block supports a basic principle of good spreadsheet modeling, which is to use variables in your models.

The data block in Example A-1 contains *entered data*—the loan amount (A1), the number of payments (A2), and the interest rate (A3), and *computed data*—the payment (A4). Then instead of using the loan amount of $5000 in a formula, the cell reference A1 is used. Even if a value is referenced only once, it is better to include it in the data block. By using one location to define each variable, you can change any value at one place in the spreadsheet and have the entire spreadsheet instantly recomputed.

Even for simple homework problems you should use a data block.

1. You may be able to use it for another problem.
2. Solutions to simple problems may grow into solutions for complex problems.
3. Good habits, like using data blocks, are easy to maintain once they are established.
4. It makes the assumptions clear if you've estimated a value or for grading.

In the real world, data blocks are even more important. Most problems are solved more than once, as more and more accurate values are estimated. Often the spreadsheet is revised to add other variables, time periods, locations, etc. Without data blocks, it is hard to change a spreadsheet and the likelihood of missing a required change skyrockets.

If you want your formulas to be easier to read, you can name your variables. *Note*: In Excel, the cell's location or name is displayed at the left of the formula bar. Variable names can be entered here. They will then automatically be applied if cell addresses are entered by the point and click method. If cell addresses are entered as A2, then A2 is what is displayed. To change a displayed A2 to the name of the cell (LoanAmount), the process is to click on Insert, click on Name, click on Apply, and then select the names to be applied.

COPY COMMAND

The copy command and relative/absolute addressing make spreadsheet models easy to build. If the range of cells to be copied contains only labels, numbers, and functions, then the copy command is easy to use and understand. For example, the formula =EXP(1.9) would be copied unchanged to a new location. However, cell addresses are usually part of the range being copied, and their absolute and relative addresses are treated differently.

An *absolute address* is denoted by adding $ signs before the column and/or row. For example in Figure A-1a, $A$4 is the absolute address for the interest rate. When an absolute address is copied, the column and/or row that is fixed is copied unchanged. Thus $A$4 is completely fixed, $A4 fixes the column, and A$4 fixes the row. One common use for absolute addresses is any data block entry, such as the interest rate. When entering or editing a formula, changing between A4, $A$4, A$4, $A4, and A4 is most easily done using the F4 key, which scrolls an address through the choices.

In contrast a *relative address* is best interpreted as directions from one cell to another. For example in Figure A-1a, the balance due in year t equals the balance due in year $t - 1$ minus the principal payment in Year t. Specifically for the balance due in Year 1, D10 contains =D9−C10. From cell D10, cell D9 is one row up and C10 is one column to the left, so the formula is really (contents of 1 up) minus (contents of 1 to the left). When a cell containing a relative address is copied to a new location, it is these directions that are copied to determine any new relative addresses. So if cell D10 is copied to cell F14, the formula is =F13−E14.

Thus to calculate a loan repayment schedule, as in Figure A-1, the row of formulas is created and then copied for the remaining years.

EXAMPLE A-1

Four repayment schedules for a loan of $5000 to be repaid over 5 years at an interest rate of 8% were shown in Table 3-1. Use a spreadsheet to calculate the amortization schedule for the constant principal payment option.

SOLUTION

The first step is to enter the loan amount, number of periods, and interest rate into a data block in the top left part of the spreadsheet. The next step is to calculate the constant principal payment amount, which was given as $1252.28 in Table 3-1. The factor approach to finding this value is given in Chapter 3 and the spreadsheet function is explained in Chapter 4.

The next step is to identify the columns for the amortization schedule. These are the year, interest owed, principal payment, and balance due. Because some of these labels are wider than a normal column, the cells are formatted so that the text wraps (row height increases automatically). The initial balance is shown in the Year-0 row.

Next, the formulas for the first year are written, as shown in Figure A-1a. The interest owed (cell B10) equals the interest rate ($A$4) times the balance due for Year 0 (D9). The principal payment (cell C10) equals the annual payment ($A$6) minus the interest owed and paid (B10). Finally, the balance due (cell D10) equals the balance due for the previous year (D9) minus the principal payment (C10). The results are shown in Figure A-1a.

Now cells A10 to D10 are selected for Year 1. By dragging down on the right corner of D10, the entire row can be copied for Years 2 through 5. Note that if you use cut and paste, then you must complete the year column separately (dragging increments the year, but cutting and pasting does not). The results are shown in Figure A-1b.

	A	B	C	D	E
1	Entered Data				
2	5000	Loan Amount			
3	5	Number of Payments			
4	8%	Interest Rate			
5	Computed Data				
6	$1,252.28	Loan Payment			
7					
8	Year	Interest Owed	Principal Payment	Balance Due	
9	0			5000.00	
10	1	400.00	852.28	4147.72	=D9−C10
11					
12		=$A$4*D9		=$A$6−B10	

(a)

	A	B	C	D	E
8	Year	Interest Owed	Principal Payment	Balance Due	
9	0			5000.00	
10	1	400.00	852.28	4147.72	
11	2	331.82	920.46	3227.25	
12	3	258.18	994.10	2233.15	
13	4	178.65	1073.63	1159.52	
14	5	92.76	1159.52	0.00	=D13−C14
15					
16		=$A$4*D13		=$A$6−B14	

(b)

FIGURE A-1 **(a)** Year 1 amortization schedule. **(b)** Completed amortization schedule.

This appendix has introduced the basics of spreadsheets. Chapter 2 uses spreadsheets and simple bar charts to draw cash flow diagrams. Chapters 4 to 15 each have spreadsheet sections. These are designed to develop spreadsheet modeling skills and to reinforce your understanding of engineering economy. As spreadsheet packages are built around using the computer mouse to click on cells and items in charts, there is usually an intuitive connection between what you would like to do and how to do it. The best way to learn how to use the spreadsheet package is to simply play around with it. In addition, as you look at the menu choices, you will find new commands that you hadn't thought of but will find useful.

Single Payment

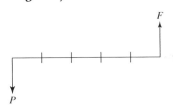

Compound Amount:

To Find F
Given P $(F/P, i, n)$ $F = P(1 + i)^n$

Present Worth:

To Find P
Given F $(P/F, i, n)$ $P = F(1 + i)^{-n}$

Uniform Series

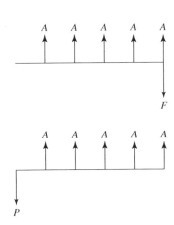

Series Compound Amount:

To Find F
Given A $(F/A, i, n)$ $F = A \left[\dfrac{(1 + i)^n - 1}{i} \right]$

Sinking Fund:

To Find A
Given F $(A/F, i, n)$ $A = F \left[\dfrac{i}{(1 + i)^n - 1} \right]$

Capital Recovery:

To Find A
Given P $(A/P, i, n)$ $A = P \left[\dfrac{i(1 + i)^n}{(1 + i)^n - 1} \right]$

Series Present Worth:

To Find P
Given A $(P/A, i, n)$ $P = A \left[\dfrac{(1 + i)^n - 1}{i(1 + i)^n} \right]$

Arithmetic Gradient

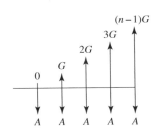

Arithmetic Gradient Uniform Series:

To Find A
Given G $(A/G, i, n)$ $A = G \left[\dfrac{(1 + i)^n - in - 1}{i(1 + i)^n - i} \right]$

        or $A = G \left[\dfrac{1}{i} - \dfrac{n}{(1 + i)^n - 1} \right]$

Arithmetic Gradient Present Worth:

To Find P
Given G $(P/G, i, n)$ $P = G \left[\dfrac{(1 + i)^n - in - 1}{i^2(1 + i)^n} \right]$

Geometric Gradient

Geometric Series Present Worth:

To Find P $(P/A, g, i, n)$
Given A_1, g When $i = g$ $P = A_1[n(1+i)^{-1}]$

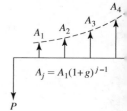

To Find P $(P/A, g, i, n)$
Given A_1, g When $i \neq g$ $P = A_1 \left[\dfrac{1 - (1+g)^n(1+i)^{-n}}{i-g} \right]$

$A_j = A_1(1+g)^{j-1}$

Continuous Compounding at Nominal Rate r

Single Payment: $F = P[e^{rn}]$ $P = F[e^{-rn}]$

Uniform Series: $A = F \left[\dfrac{e^r - 1}{e^{rn} - 1} \right]$ $A = P \left[\dfrac{e^{rn}(e^r - 1)}{e^{rn} - 1} \right]$

$F = A \left[\dfrac{e^{rn} - 1}{e^r - 1} \right]$ $P = A \left[\dfrac{e^{rn} - 1}{e^{rn}(e^r - 1)} \right]$

Compound Interest

i = Interest rate per interest period*.

n = Number of interest periods.

P = A present sum of money.

F = A future sum of money. The future sum F is an amount, n interest periods from the present, that is equivalent to P with interest rate i.

A = An end-of-period cash receipt or disbursement in a uniform series continuing for n periods, the entire series equivalent to P or F at interest rate i.

G = Uniform period-by-period increase or decrease in cash receipts or disbursements; the arithmetic gradient.

g = Uniform *rate* of cash flow increase or decrease from period to period; the geometric gradient.

r = Nominal interest rate per interest period*.

m = Number of compounding subperiods per period*.

---

*Normally the interest period is one year, but it could be something else.

To Find	Excel
P	$-PV(i, n, A, F, \text{Type})$
A	$-PMT(i, n, P, F, \text{Type})$
F	$-FV(i, n, A, P, \text{Type})$
n	$NPER(i, A, P, F, \text{Type})$
i	$RATE(n, A, P, F, \text{Type}, \text{guess})$
P	$NPV(i, CF_1 : CF_n)$
i	$IRR(CF_0 : CF_n)$

Economic Criteria

Method of Analysis	Fixed Input	Fixed Output	Neither Input Nor Output Fixed
PRESENT WORTH	Maximize PW of Benefits	Minimize PW of Costs	Maximize (PW of Benefits − PW of Costs), or Maximize Net Present Worth
ANNUAL CASH FLOW	Maximize Equivalent Uniform Annual Benefits (EUAB)	Minimize Equivalent Uniform Annual Cost (EUAC)	Maximize (EUAB − EUAC)
FUTURE WORTH	Maximize FW of Benefits	Minimize FW of Costs	Maximize (FW of Benefits − FW of Costs), or Maximize Net Future Worth
BENEFIT–COST RATIO	Maximize Benefit–Cost Ratio	Maximize Benefit–Cost Ratio	*Two Alternatives:* Compute the incremental Benefit–Cost ratio ($\Delta B/\Delta C$) on the increment of *investment* between the alternatives. If $\Delta B/\Delta C \geq 1$, choose higher-cost alternative; if not, choose lower-cost alternative. *Three or more Alternatives:* Incremental analysis is required (see Ch. 9).
RATE OF RETURN	*Two Alternatives:* Compute the incremental rate of return (ΔROR) on the increment of *investment* between the alternatives. If $\Delta ROR \geq$ minimum attractive rate of return, choose the higher-cost alternative; if not, choose lower-cost alternative. *Three or more Alternatives:* Incremental analysis is required (see Ch. 8).		

IEMS 326 Fall 2016 – Problem Set #1

Prof. T. Vander Veen

Due October 4, 4:00 pm

Please show all your work.
You should make sure to clearly state what concepts, formulas and parameter values you are using.
You may use Excel to carry out the actual calculations, in which case, print out clearly labeled
spreadsheets and attach them to your assignments, as well as upload the Excel file on Canvas.

Homework may be discussed with other students. However, every student must turn in their own, individually prepared assignment. As a student, you are not allowed to acquire, read, or otherwise utilize answers from the existent solutions of any kind. Preparing submissions independently means:

- Do not sit down with another person and work out the solution to a problem together.

- Do not collaborate on the preparation of a spreadsheet used in more than one person's submission.

- Do not copy or make use of another person's solutions or spreadsheets, and do not allow another person to copy or make use of yours.

All turned in work must be written in a legible and well organized manner. The problems need to be stapled together in the correct order. Instructor reserves the right not to give any credit for the problems that are not readable.

Spreadsheets should be submitted electronically on Canvas. The name of the attached Excel file should be "Lastname_Firstname." Please make your spreadsheets easy to understand. Make the spreadsheet self-contained by labeling and explaining things. Use formatting to make things easier to understand and to highlight the conclusions. Please do not hide columns or rows because the point of the spreadsheets is to explain. Use appropriate precision and formatting for the data (e.g., avoid scientific notation for cells displaying millions of dollars).

Read L. 1, 2.1-2.3, N. Appendix A

1. (15 points) Find the corresponding effective rates for:

    (a) 3% compounded monthly.

    (b) 18% compounded monthly.

    (c) 18% compounded quarterly.

2. (20 points) Find the value of q so that the present value of the cash flow stream in Figure 1 is equal to zero, assuming an interest rate of 12%.

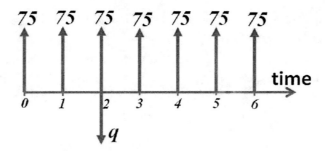

Figure 1: Problem 3

3. (20 points) Consider the following cash flow. At a 6% interest rate, what value of P at the end of Year 1 is equivalent to the benefits at the end of Years 2 through 7?

Year	1	2	3	4	5	6	7
Cash Flow	$-P$	$100	$200	$300	$400	$500	$600

4. (20 points) A young couple has made a non-refundable deposit of the first month's rent (equal to $1,000) on a 6-month apartment lease. The next day they find a different apartment that they like just as well, but its monthly rent is only $900. They plan to be in the apartment only 6 months. Should they switch to the new apartment? What if they plan to stay 1 year? Assume an interest rate of 12%, compounded monthly.

5. (25 points) By installing some elaborate inspection equipment on its assembly line, the Robot Corp. can avoid hiring an extra worker who would have earned $26,000 a year in wages and an additional $7,500 a year in employee benefits. The inspection equipment has a 6-year useful life and no salvage value. Use a nominal 18% interest rate in your calculations. How much can Robot afford to pay for the equipment if the wages and worker benefits would have been paid

   (a) at the end of each year
   (b) monthly

Explain why the answer in (b) is larger. Assume the compounding matches the way the wages and benefits would have been paid (that is, annually and monthly).